graphy

f

EA

Martin Thom and
Eileen Armstrong

Colourpoint
Educational

Rewarding Learning

A2 LEVEL

ISBN: 978 1 906578 11 4

First Edition
Third Impression, 2015

Layout and design: April Sky Design

Printed by: GPS Colour Graphics, Belfast

Colourpoint Educational
An imprint of Colourpoint Creative Ltd
Colourpoint House
Jubilee Business Park
21 Jubilee Road
Newtownards
County Down
Northern Ireland
BT23 4YH

Tel: 028 9182 6339
Fax: 028 9182 1900
E-mail: sales@colourpoint.co.uk
Web site: www.colourpoint.co.uk

The Authors

Martin Thom is a graduate of QUB and teaches Geography at Sullivan Upper School, Holywood. He has worked with CCEA for over 20 years and published a number of A-levels texts and articles.

The author wants to offer his sincere thanks to the following people without whose help, insight and patience this task would have proved too onerous: Dr Lindsey Finch, Louise Gildea, Prof Steve Royle, Dr Stephen Roulston, Clifford Thom, his colleagues at Sullivan Upper School, the staff at Colourpoint and especially ALEC@Clovathoms.

Eileen Armstrong has a B.A. (Hons) in Geography from QUB. She began her teaching career in St Dominic's Grammar School, Belfast and is currently teaching in Sullivan Upper School, Holywood. In addition she has widespread experience with CCEA as an examiner. She became Principal Examiner for A-level Human Geography in 1996 and was a co-writer of the current AS and A2 level specification.

The author is grateful for the help and support of her family during the writing of this book, especially to Gregory for the photographs of Cambridge. She also wishes to acknowledge the helpful discussions on Curitiba with Louise Gildea (St Louis' Grammar School, Ballymena) and the support and encouragement of her colleagues at Sullivan Upper School.

Picture credits

All photographs by the authors except for the following which are included with kind permission of the copyright holders:

Helen Adams and Michael Stanley: 206
CCEA, Chief Examiner, Geography: 74, 79
CCEA, Principal Examiner, Geography: 233
Owen Glenn: 230 (middle), 232
David Harlow: 265
Rachel Irwin: 115
iStockphoto: 5, 32, 51, 96, 259
Malcolm Johnston: 86
Norman Johnston: 89
Wesley Johnston: 87, 78, 260 (top)
Stephen Royle: 269 (top left)
David Rydevik: 272
US Department of the Interior, Bureau of Reclamation: 157
USAID: 123
USGS: 268, 269 (bottom), 271, 275, 277

Contents

A2 1: Human Geography

A2 2: Physical Geography

Examination Technique

Glossary

A2 1 HUMAN GEOGRAPHY

A1 NATURAL POPULATION CHANGE

Population characteristics – total number and structures – change all the time. These changes are the result of variations in fertility and mortality, as well as changes in migration rates. Natural population change deals only with variations in fertility and mortality. Fertility and mortality rates vary globally (patterns) and also over time (trends). There are a number of measures for assessing fertility and mortality.

Fertility measures

Crude Birth Rate (CBR): This measures the total number of live births per thousand of the population per year. This measure has several weaknesses largely because it takes no account of the age or gender composition of the population. However, it is a simple and widely used measure.

General Fertility Rate: This records the total number of live births per thousand women in the normal reproductive age groups (15–44 years) per year. As this measures deals only with the female population in a specific age group, it is a more reliable measure than the crude birth rate.

Total Fertility Rate (TFR): This records the average number of children a woman will have during her reproductive years, assuming she will live to the end of her reproductive life. Generally, TFR is lower in MEDCs than LEDCs and therefore this is a reliable measure of development.

Age Specific Fertility Rate: This is the number of live births per thousand women within specific age bands per year. In some LEDCs women have children at an early age and this makes the Age Specific Fertility Rate a reliable indicator of the status of women in society.

Net Reproduction Rate (NRR): This is the average number of daughters born per woman. An NNR of 1 means that a population is replacing itself.

Mortality measures

Crude Death Rate (CDR): This measures the total number of deaths per thousand of the population per year. This measure takes no account of the age of death as it relates to the total population. However, like the crude birth rate above, it is a simple and widely used measure.

Age Specific Mortality Rate: This is the number of deaths per thousand of the population within specific age bands per year. This measure is often used by insurance companies to calculate the risk of death to specific age groups. It is a good indicator of lifestyle deaths.

Infant Mortality Rate (IMR): This is the number of deaths per thousand children in the first year of life. This is a variation of the Age Specific Mortality Rate but only records the number of deaths of children who die within the first year of life. It excludes stillbirths. This is a useful indicator to use when comparing levels of development between countries.

Global Population Data **Resource 1**

	Births per/1000 CBR	Deaths per/1000 CDR	Total fertility rate	Infant deaths per/1000 IMR	Maternal mortality rate. 1 in:	Life expectancy years	Rate of natural increase %
World	21	8	2.6	49	92	68	1.3
LEDC	23	8	2.8	54	75	65	1.5
Least developed	36	13	4.7	85	22	55	2.3
MEDC	12	10	1.6	6	6,000	77	0.2
Sub-Saharan Africa	40	15	5.4	88	22	50	2.5
Sierra Leone	48	23	6.1	158	8	48	2.5
Burkina Faso	45	15	6.2	89	22	51	3.0
Zimbabwe	31	21	3.8	60	43	40	1.0
USA	14	8	2.1	6.6	4,800	78	0.6
Brazil	20	6	2.3	8.8	3,200	72	1.4
Mexico	20	5	2.3	19	670	75	1.5
Syria	28	4	3.5	19	210	73	2.4
Bangladesh	24	7	2.7	52	51	63	1.7
Taiwan	9	6	1.1	4.6	No data	78	0.3
Japan	9	9	1.3	2.8	11,600	82	0
India	24	8	2.8	57	70	65	1.6
China	12	7	1.6	23	1,300	73	0.5
Sweden	12	10	1.9	2.5	17,400	81	0.2
UK	13	9	1.9	4.9	8,200	79	0.4
Australia	14	7	1.9	4.7	13,300	81	0.7

Source: Data from 2008 world population data sheet, Population Reference Bureau, www.prb.org

Maternal Mortality Rates (MMR): This records the number of maternal deaths per hundred thousand live births and like IMR, it is a reliable indicator of development. The World Bank uses a refinement of this measure, where the average risks of women dying from chilbirth have been calculated and given as a ratio. In Sierra Leone the figure is 1:8 whereas in Sweden the figure is 1:17,400.

Life Expectancy: This is the number of years a person is expected to live, assuming that the current mortality levels are maintained. Mortality levels depend largely on health and welfare conditions and for this reason life expectancy is a useful measure of levels of development within a country. Globally, life expectancy has been increasing throughout the twentieth century. In MEDCs, average life expectancy is 77 years. In LEDCs, life expectancy ranges from 55 to 66 years. Generally, women have a longer life expectancy than men, by as much as seven years in MEDCs and by four years in LEDCs.

Natural change

This is the percentage net gain or loss to a population each year, based on the difference between the birth rate and the death rate. A natural increase occurs where the birth rate exceeds the death rate. A natural decrease occurs where the death rate is the greater figure. Two measures are often used when discussing rates of natural change, namely:

1. **Replacement rate:** This is the number of new births needed to maintain current numbers in a population, assuming there is no migration. A total fertility rate of 2.1 is the most commonly used figure. In other words, two children per women are needed. Countries with a TFR less than 2.1 will show a decrease in population.
2. **Doubling time:** This is the number of years that it will take a population to double if the current rates of natural increase are maintained.

Global contrasts in fertility and mortality

- Total global population in 1900 was 1.6 billion
- Total global population in 2000 was 6.1 billion
- Total global population in 2008 was 6.7 billion
- Total global population is predicted to reach 7 billion in 2012.

These changes are the result of variations in the two components of natural population change: fertility and mortality.

Resource 2 *Total fertility rates 2008*

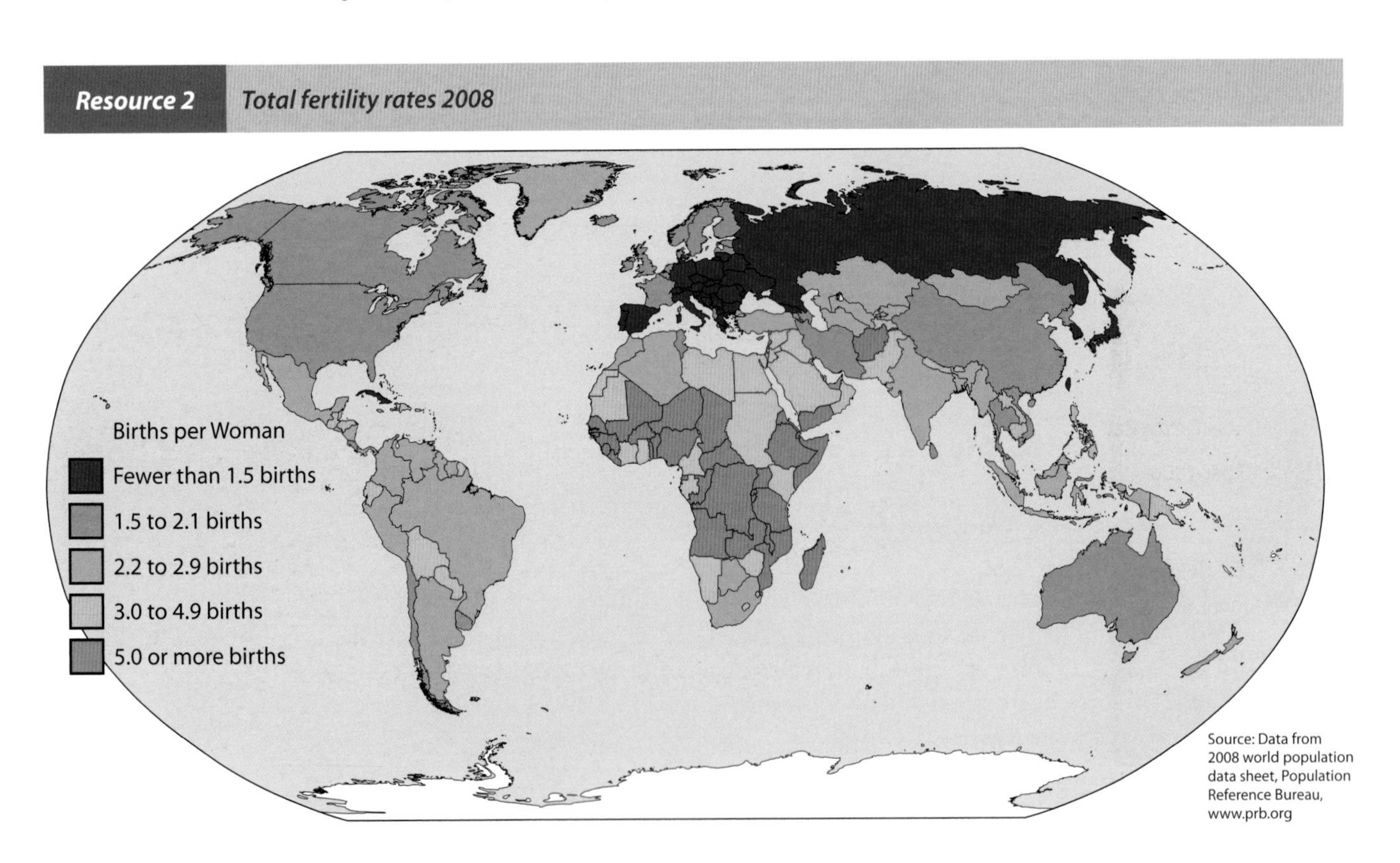

Global patterns in total fertility rates (TFR)

On a world scale, total fertility varies from 6.8 in Burundi and Angola to 1.3 in Germany. TFRs are generally higher in LEDCs than in MEDCs but there are marked variations within these two major world groups of countries. The map above shows that MEDCs have TFR levels close to or below replacement level. Much of South and Central America, along with India, Indonesia, South Africa and parts of central Asia have TFRs of 2.2 to 2.9. Africa has the highest total TFRs, with most Sub-Saharan Africa having values greater than 5. In the twentieth century there has been a dramatic decline in fertility rates in every major world region, but in some regions, the rate remains quite high.

Mortality rates

In terms of mortality patterns, the distinction between LEDCs and MEDCs is less clear than it was for fertility. In the MEDCs, death rates vary from 2–9 per thousand and are lowest in Australia. The slightly higher rates for North America and Western Europe are the result of ageing populations. The former communist countries in Eastern Europe and Russia have rates between 13–29 per thousand, reflecting the economic difficulties that those countries faced as they adjusted to a market economy. Mortality levels are low in most of South and Central America and in southern and eastern Asia. Africa, and Sub-Saharan Africa in particular, has the highest death rates. In most LEDCs the average life expectancy at birth was 66 years in 2007. The Middle East and North Africa region has experienced the largest increase in life expectancy since the late 1950s: from 43 years to 70 years.

Graph of decline in total fertility rates in selected countries1950–2008 **Resource 3**

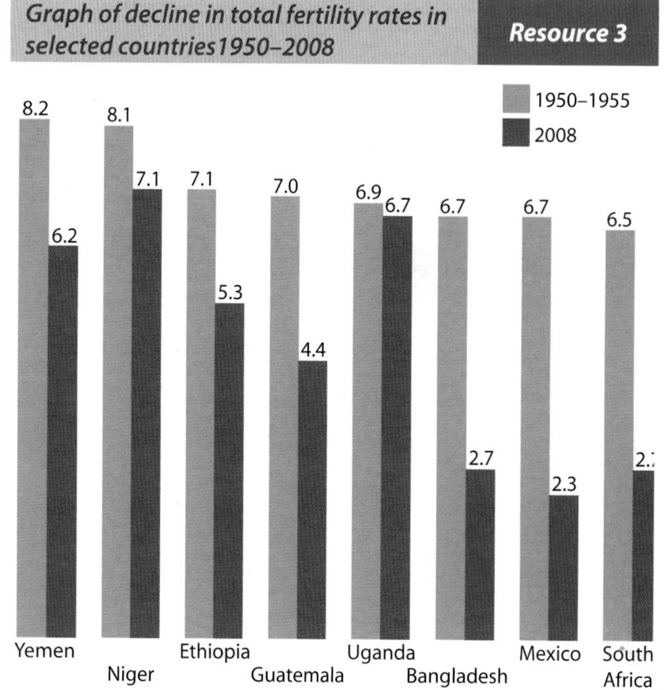

Source: Data from 2008 world population data sheet, Population Reference Bureau, www.prb.org

World mortality rates 2007 **Resource 4**

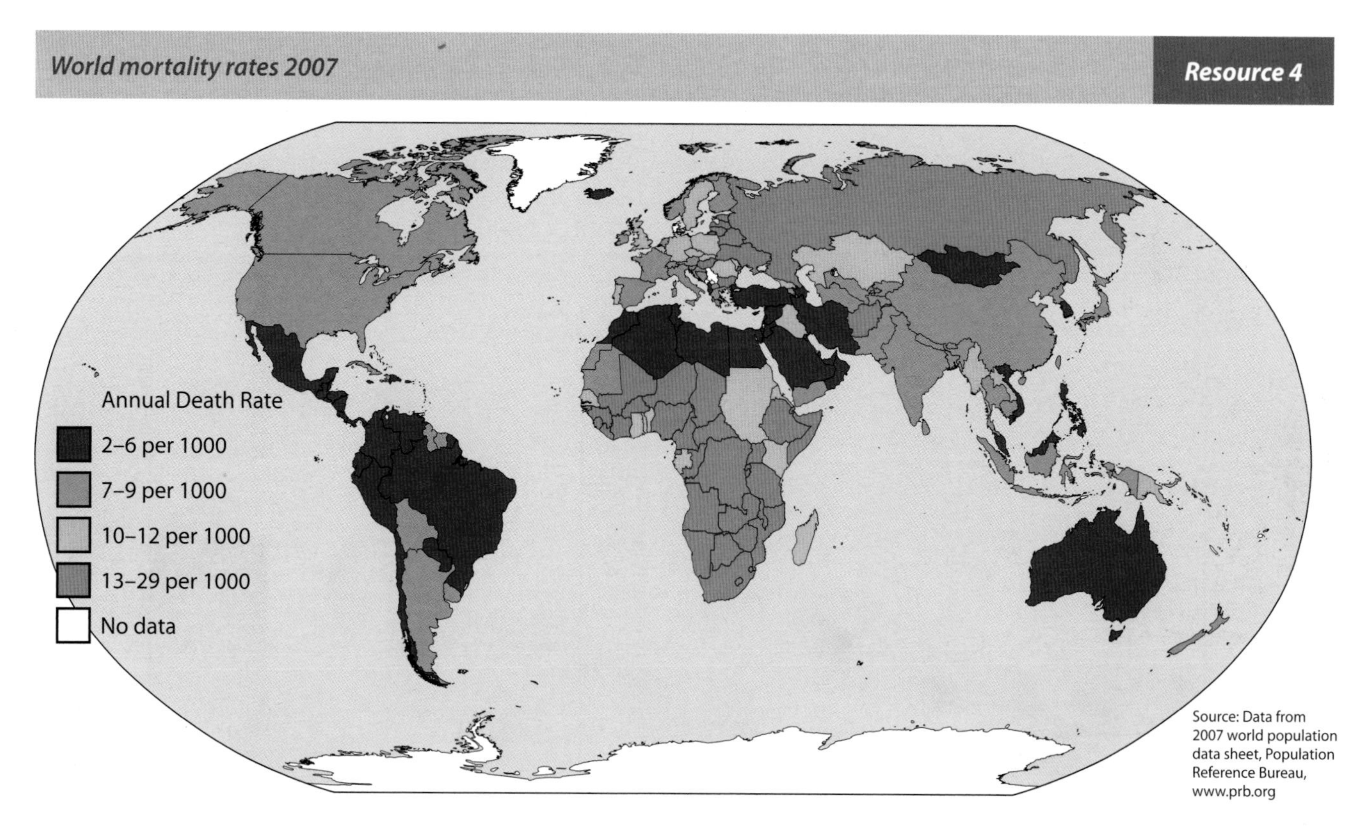

Source: Data from 2007 world population data sheet, Population Reference Bureau, www.prb.org

Exercise

1. ***Question adapted from CCEA January 2008***
   Study **Figure 1** below showing population change in the European Union 2004–2005. Explain the interaction between births, deaths and migration in causing population change. (5)

Figure 1

Source: adapted from J Rayner, 'Population change in the EU', *Geography Review*, 19.3, p2–5

2. ***Question from CCEA May 2008***
   Study **Figure 2A** and **2B** below showing population trends in Russia 1950–2035.

   (a) Describe the trends in Russia's population shown by the graphs. (2)

   (b) **Figures 2A** and **2B** use Net Reproduction Rate as a measure of fertility. Name one other fertility measure and indicate how it is calculated. (3)

Figure 2A

Figure 2B

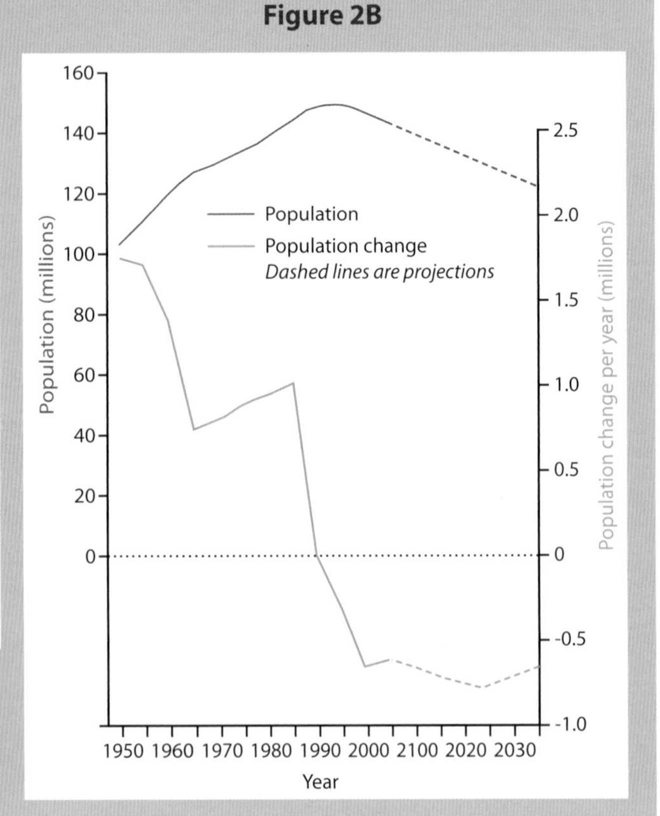

Exercise continued

3. Study the maps below, which use two different means of displaying spatial variations in fertility. Discuss the merits of each method.

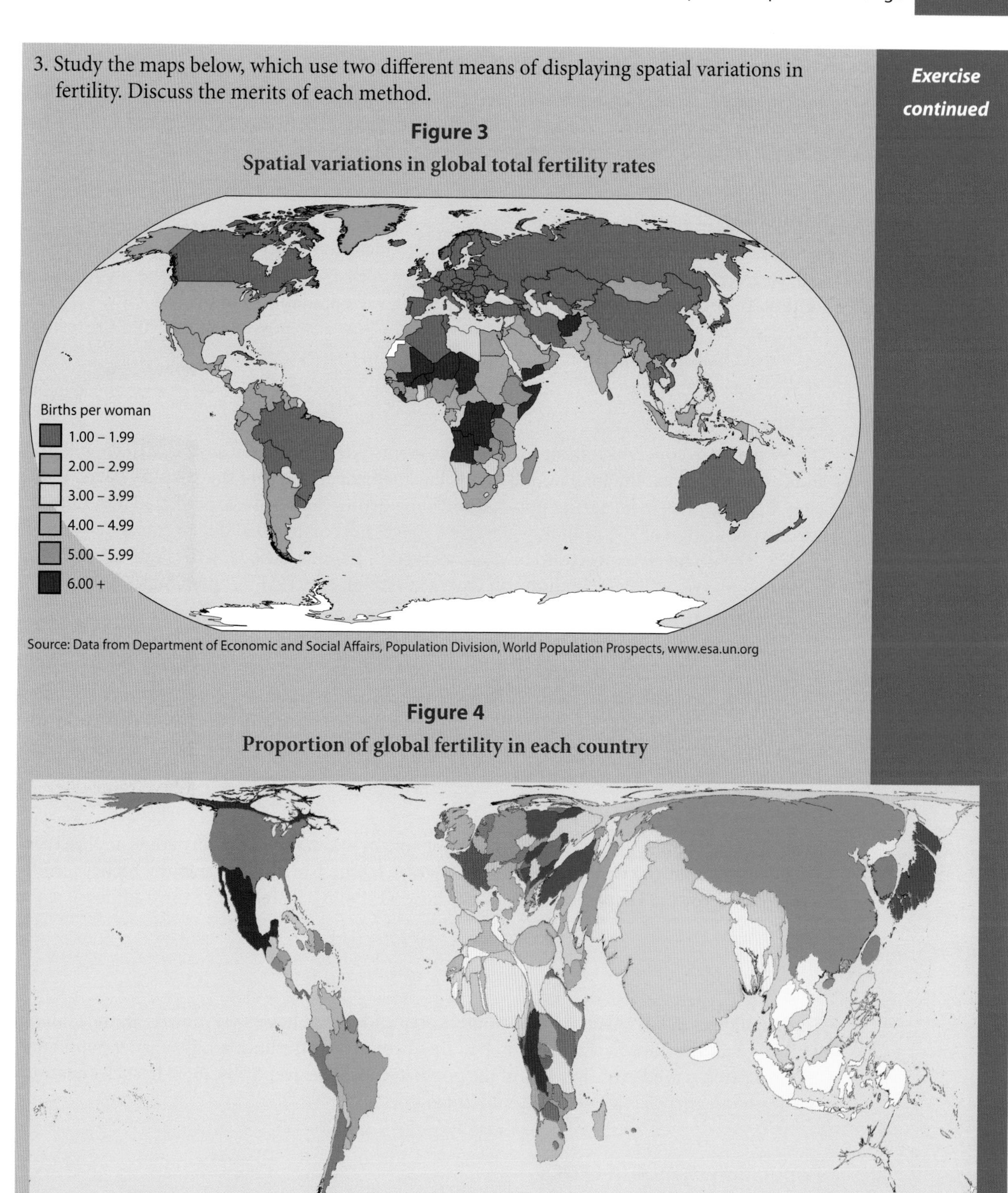

Figure 3

Spatial variations in global total fertility rates

Source: Data from Department of Economic and Social Affairs, Population Division, World Population Prospects, www.esa.un.org

Figure 4

Proportion of global fertility in each country

Source: Online Geography Resources, www.geographyalltheway.com, accessed 21 January 2009
Map from Worldmapper, www.worldmapper.org, © Copyright 2006 SASI Group (University of Sheffield) and Mark Newman (University of Michigan)

Global trends in population change

The patterns of fertility and mortality described above have important repercussions for future population change. There will still be a broad distinction between MEDCs and LEDCs but there are regional variations within each of these major groups.

Population change in MEDCs

In the MEDCs, improvements in health care have reduced mortality rates while general affluence and the increased numbers of women in the workforce have brought about huge reductions in fertility. The end result of this is a gradual ageing of the population and consequently very low, even negative, growth rates. As mortality levels are as low as is possible in the MEDCs, fertility is the main reason for variations in the growth rates of these countries.

Europe

One of the main concerns for European governments is the continued ageing of the population and the prospect that the total population will actually decrease over the next few years. Death rates inevitably rise in an ageing population. Some demographers have predicted that Europe's current population of 736 million will decline to 685 million by 2050 due to continued decline in TFR. The decline is expected to be most marked in Eastern Europe, where out-migration of the economically active population will have a knock-on effect on fertility levels.

In other parts of Europe, there are signs that government pro-natalist policies are having the desired effect. Sweden has seen modest increases in TFR from 1.6 to 1.9 (although still below replacement level) between 1999 and 2008. Similar increases have occurred in France, Finland, UK, Spain and Italy. In all of these countries there is some form of government-funded, financial incentive to help young families. Some of this increase in fertility is undoubtedly due to the influx of migrants in the reproductive age groups.

North America and Oceania

In all of these regions immigrants play a major role in maintaining fertility above replacement level. For example, the United Sates has a TFR of 2.1, which is partly due to the higher fertility levels of the growing Hispanic population, whose TFR of 3.0 is well above the traditional white American TFR of 1.9.

East Asia

Some countries in East Asia (Taiwan, South Korea and Japan) have a very low TFR. In Japan the TFR is 1.3 and in Taiwan the figure is 1.1. These countries also have a high ageing population and in Japan it is predicted that 40% of the population will be over 65 by 2050. In such situations the death rate increases (9 per thousand in Japan).

Population change in LEDCs

Within the LEDCs the trends in fertility and mortality show much greater variation than those seen in the MEDCs. As noted earlier, the overriding factor in the demography of the LEDCs has been the decline in the death rate.

Africa and the Middle East

Africa has the highest fertility levels and also the greatest potential for future growth as a result of its youthful age structure. In 2008, Africa's population was 967 million and is predicted to reach 1 billion in 2009. The TFR for the entire continent is 4.9 but for Sub-Saharan Africa the figure is 5.4. In addition, the region has the world's highest death rates at 15 per thousand. Africa's population is also youthful with 43% of Sub-Saharan Africa's population under 15. If, as is expected, mortality rates fall, there is huge potential for future growth, unless there is a comparable fall in fertility levels.

In North Africa and the Middle East, fertility levels have fallen due to delayed marriage and greater acceptance of family planning services.

Latin America and the Caribbean

Population will continue to grow in this region but at a much slower rate than was seen in Africa. In 2008 the total population was 577 million and was predicted to reach 778 million by 2050. TFR is currently just over replacement level at 2.5 and in some of the more developed countries, such as Brazil, TFR is expected to fall to replacement level in the near future. Death rates are low – currently about 6 per thousand.

Asia

Asia's population is currently 4 billion and this will increase by 1.4 billion between 2008 and 2050, even though many countries – including China – pursue rigorous anti-natalist policies. The main reasons for this sustained growth is the youthful population structure throughout the region and an average death rate of 7 per thousand. India, with an average TFR of 3.6, will surpass China (TFR of 1.6) in the next fifty years as the fastest growing population in the world. Some have predicted India's population could double in the next fifty years.

World map of natural increase 2007 **Resource 5**

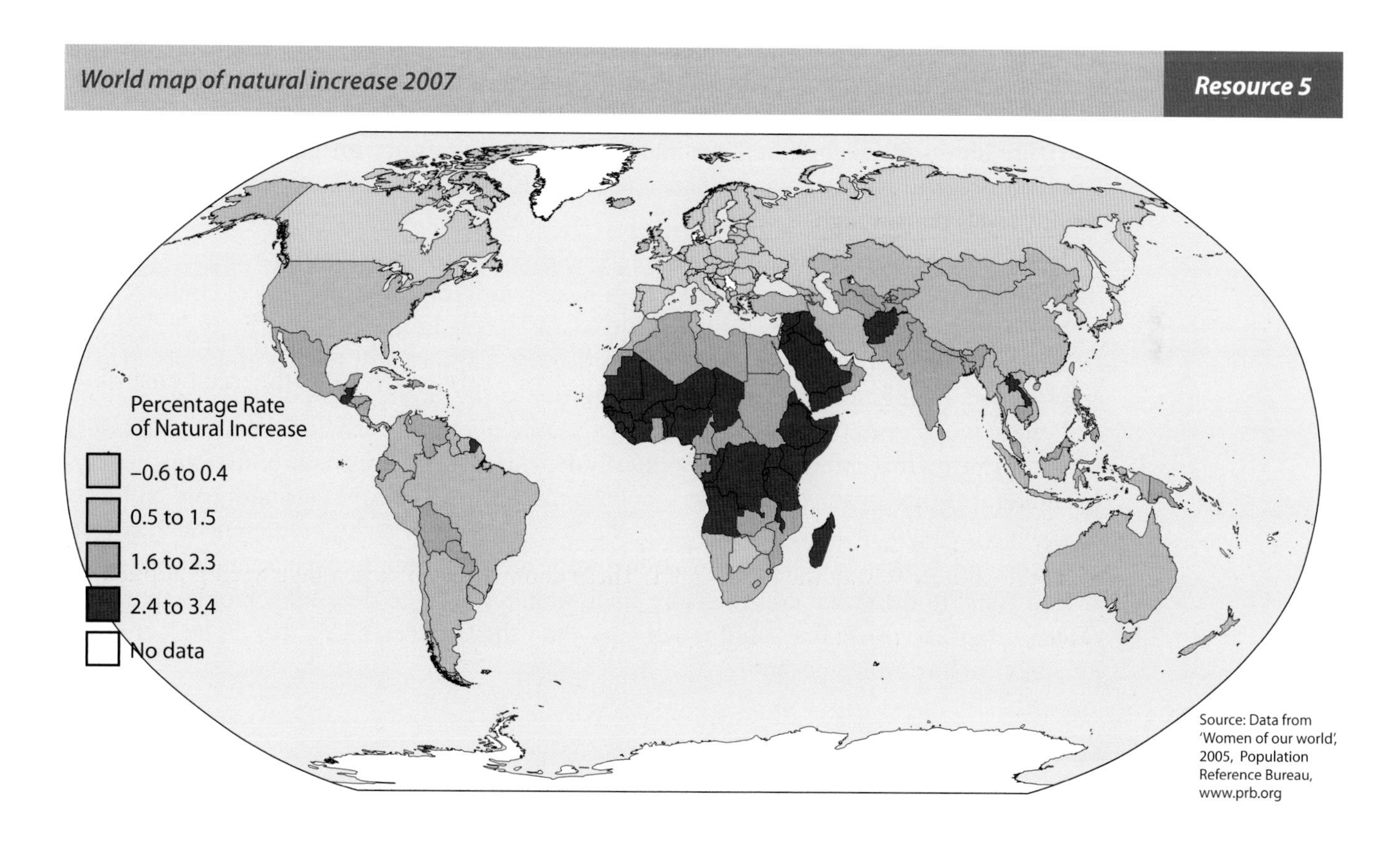

Source: Data from 'Women of our world', 2005, Population Reference Bureau, www.prb.org

Resource 5 shows the present pattern of natural increase falling into four major bands:

- Negative or very low rates of natural increase (-0.6–0.4) occur in Europe, Russia and Canada.
- Low rates (0.5–1.5) occur in much of South America, China, USA, South Africa and Oceania.
- Moderate rates (1.6–2.3) occur in Central America, North Africa, India and Pakistan.
- High rates (2.4 +) occur in sub-Saharan Africa and Saudi Arabia.

Additional references

http://www.prb.org/pdf08/63.3highlights.pdf

http://www.prb.org/pdf08/08WPDS_Eng.pdf

The most obvious pattern emerging from this map is the contrast between the LEDC and MEDCs. Figures produced by the Population Reference Bureau reveal that in the twentieth century 90% of population growth took place in the LEDCs and between 2008 and 2050 virtually all population growth will emanate from there. There are two sets of processes responsible for this. One relates to ageing and fertility decline in the MEDCs, the other relates to the unprecedented drop in mortality, along with higher TFRs in the LEDCs.

Factors influencing fertility and mortality

Patterns and trends in fertility and mortality are the result of a complex interaction of a number of factors. These factors, ranging from economic, social, political, cultural and environmental, all play a part but their relative importance varies both spatially and over time.

Factors influencing fertility

Economic

Generally, fertility levels are highest in the LEDCs. The stark contrasts in fertility between the LEDCs and MEDCs can be explained by the different economic perception of children in both regions. In LEDCs, children are seen as an addition to the workforce and potential breadwinners. In rural areas families often live as part of an extended family system and practise subsistence farming. Some of the children will work on the farms while others supplement the family income by finding employment in the growing urban areas. State pensions are rarely available in LEDCs and the duty of caring for elderly parents often falls on the children. Infant Mortality Rates, although falling, are still high, so it is necessary for parents to have a large family in order to ensure some will survive to adulthood. It is not surprising therefore that fertility levels remain high.

In MEDCs the situation is quite different. People have much more control over their lives and the economic requirements for children have been removed. The availability of contraception means that parents can decide when and how many children they will have. There are pension schemes and care facilities for the elderly and many families will have both adults in paid employment. Infant mortality rates are very low due to the development of healthcare systems and vaccinations, and it is a rare tragedy when a child does not reach adulthood. Compulsory education means that children are economically dependent on their parents until at least sixteen. In addition, as most women will be in employment, having a child necessitates paid childcare or giving up employment. In other words, the decision to have a child represents a major life changing and expensive event. Most parents want their children to have a standard of living at least equal to their own and therefore small families become the norm. Women pursuing careers often have their first child much later than their predecessors, thereby reducing the possibility of having a large family.

Social

Social factors are often the result of prevailing economic circumstances and the two factors are closely linked. In MEDCs, with low TFRs and an ageing population, the number of potential parents is reduced, leading to further reductions in the overall number of births. In poorer countries the opposite is the case. This explains why countries such as China continued to grow in absolute numbers, even when the one child policy was introduced. In MEDCs the developments in health care resulting in low infant mortality rates have already been discussed. Female education has been shown to be one of the most important social factors affecting fertility. In MEDCs, where women have equal access to education, the impact on fertility is well established. In LEDCs, where female education is far from universal, the contrasts in fertility are clearly seen. It has been shown that women with at least a secondary-level education eventually give birth to one-third to one-half as many children as women with no formal education. An Ethiopian woman with no education has 6.1 children on average, but an Ethiopian woman with secondary or higher education has 2.0 children on average. Better-educated women are generally able to exercise more control over their reproductive lives, including delaying marriage and childbearing. The availability and acceptance of contraception has had a dramatic impact on fertility in MEDCs. However, in LEDCs there are great variations between countries, both in the availability and use of contraception. Worldwide, use of contraception rose from less than 10 % of married women of childbearing age in the 1960s to 62% in 2007. In Africa, 28% of married women use contraception; in Latin America, the share is 71%.

Fertility levels and Education in LEDCs — **Resource 6**

Lifetime births per woman with

	no education	secondary education or above
Ethiopia (2005)	6.1	2.0
Senegal (2005)	6.0	2.9
Philippines (2003)	5.3	3.1
Honduras (2005)	4.9	2.2
Egypt (2005)	3.8	2.9

Source: Measure DHS STATComplier, www.measuredhs.com

Political

Governments exert influence on fertility in a number of ways and for a variety of reasons. As governments have access to information regarding total population and are in the business of planning for future years, they will be advised on what is considered to be the optimum population numbers. Where it is thought there are too few people to meet future needs, they may follow a pro-natalist policy. This can take the form of offering financial or other incentives to have larger families. This type of policy has taken place in France over the last 60 years. In the UK each newborn child is given a £500 bond, which will be invested until the child reaches eighteen. Government policy can have an influence on fertility, for example, by offering tax relief for children, a period of paid or unpaid maternity and paternity leave, flexible working arrangements for working mothers along with help with childcare costs. On other occasions governments have followed a more coercive policy such as in Romania under President Caucescau. If governments feel that the population is too large then they may instigate an anti-natalist policy. Probably the best-documented example of such a policy is the one-child policy in China. The underlying political situation can affect a couple's decision to have a child, although the exact nature of that effect is unclear. In times of economic hardship or political instability some may decide to postpone having a child but at other times economic prosperity can lead to smaller families. In Singapore the government used fertility policies as a form of social engineering. The better educated in society were targeted with financial incentives in the hope of encouraging them to have more children, while at the same time poorer educated families were encouraged to undergo sterilisation to reduce their fertility levels.

Cultural

Some cultural traditions or values promote higher fertility. The most obvious example is religion. The Catholic Church is opposed to the use of contraception and those countries with a large Catholic population will tend to show high fertility. However, Italy, which is predominantly Catholic, has the lowest fertility in Europe. It seems that the importance of this factor may be diminishing in the more affluent countries. Other religions attach great status to large families while some cultures favour male children. Male children are often required to perform funeral rights so parents with female children will continue having children in the hope of having a son. The status of women is vitally important in determining levels of fertility. Where women have equal rights with men in terms of access to education and careers, fertility will be low. In some Islamic countries women do not enjoy these rights and consequently fertility is higher. In some cultures a man may have several wives – a fact that should increase family size.

Environmental

The impact of environmental factors on fertility is closely tied in with the economic and social conditions in a particular place. In remote areas, where access to economic opportunities is limited, there will usually be out-migration from the economically active section of the community and this in turn will result in lower fertility. In contrast, where industry is modern and there are ample job opportunities, the age structure will be considerably more youthful and fertility will be higher. There are also claims that areas with high levels of environmental pollution reduce fertility levels. The nature of economic activity can also affect fertility. Where there is a demand for labour-intensive activity, such as in subsistence farming areas, family size will be considerably larger than in an industrial society.

Resource 7 *World life expectancy*

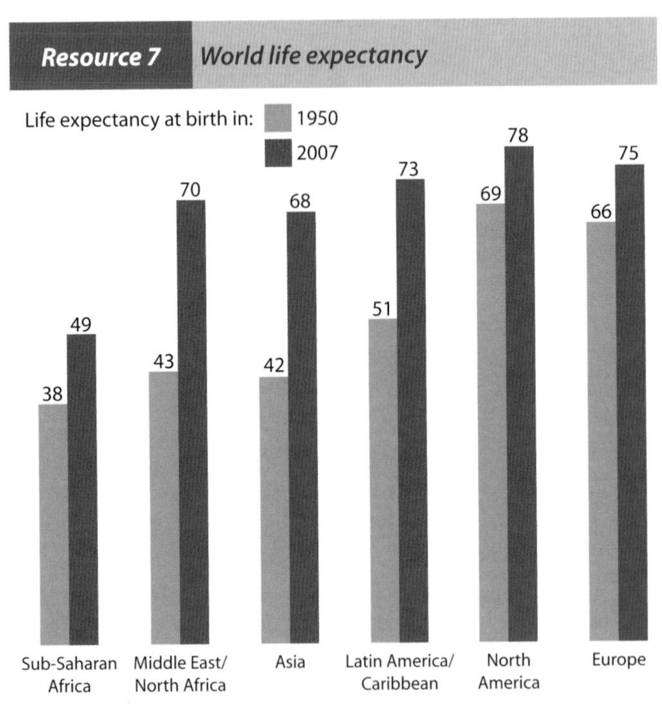

Source: United Nations, *World Population Prospects: The 2006 Revision*; and Haub, C, 2007 World Population

Factors influencing mortality

Economic

Mortality rates are affected directly and indirectly by economic conditions. On a global scale there is a great contrast in the death rates between the low and high-income countries. High-income countries are able to afford medical care, there is adequate food supply and sufficient nutrition, and there is provision to care for the unemployed and the elderly. Consequently, mortality levels are low and life expectancy for the MEDCs stands at 77 years in 2008.

In low-income countries many still die from malnutrition and famine. Medical care is inadequate and often depends on aid packages. Infant and child death is common and many could be prevented through vaccinations if more funds were available. However, there have been huge increases in life expectancy in many areas. For the LEDCs average life expectancy was 67 years ranging from 38 years in Zambia to 78 years in Chile.

Resource 8 *Age structure for MEDCs and LEDCs*

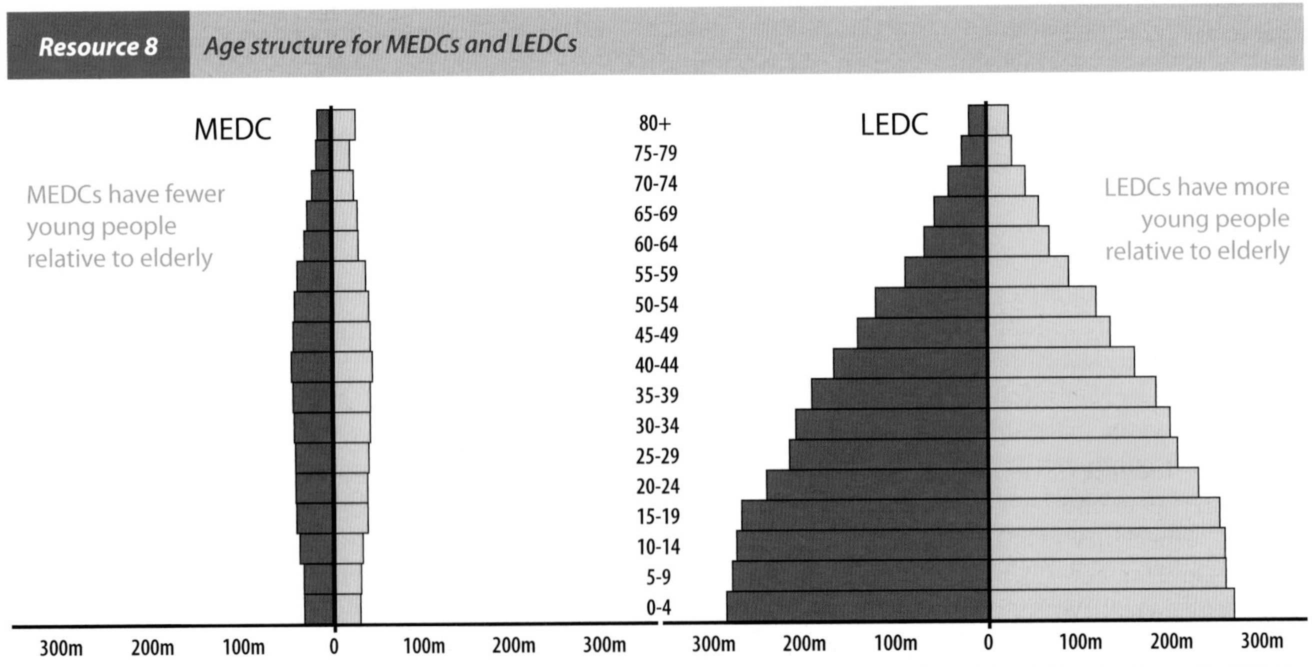

Source: United Nations, *World Population Prospects: The 2006 Revision*

Infant mortality rates **Resource 9**

Lowest

Country	Infant deaths per 1000 births
China (Hong Kong SAR)	1.6
Singapore	2.4
Sweden	2.5
Finland	2.7
Japan	2.8
Slovenia	3.1
Norway	3.1
Czech Republic	3.1
Republic of Ireland	3.1
Portugal	3.5
Israel	3.5

Excludes countries with fewer than 50 infant deaths per year.

Highest

Country	Infant deaths per 1000 births
Afghanistan	163
Sierra Leone	158
Liberia	133
Angola	132
Guinea-Bissau	117
Somalia	117
Guinea	113
Mozambique	108
Burundi	107
Chad	106

Source: Data from 2008 world population sheet, Population Reference Bureau, www.prb.org

Social

This is closely tied in with the underlying economic conditions. In LEDCs, where basic infrastructure is inadequate, many die because of a lack of clean water and basic sanitation (**Resource 9**). As stated above, infant and child mortality is common but so also is maternal mortality. **Resource 10** shows the incidence of maternal mortality in selected major world regions from 1990–2005. This graph highlights one important point regarding mortality in LEDCs. While mortality levels have fallen dramatically in LEDCs, there have only been minor improvements in maternal mortality. In MEDCs improvements in sanitation along with better understanding of hygiene and vaccination programmes means that many diseases have been wiped out. Age structure is an important variable in mortality levels. Some MEDCs are experiencing an increase in mortality due to ageing of their populations, while some LEDCs have seen a dramatic fall in mortality, especially amongst the younger members of their society.

Maternal mortality rates **Resource 10**

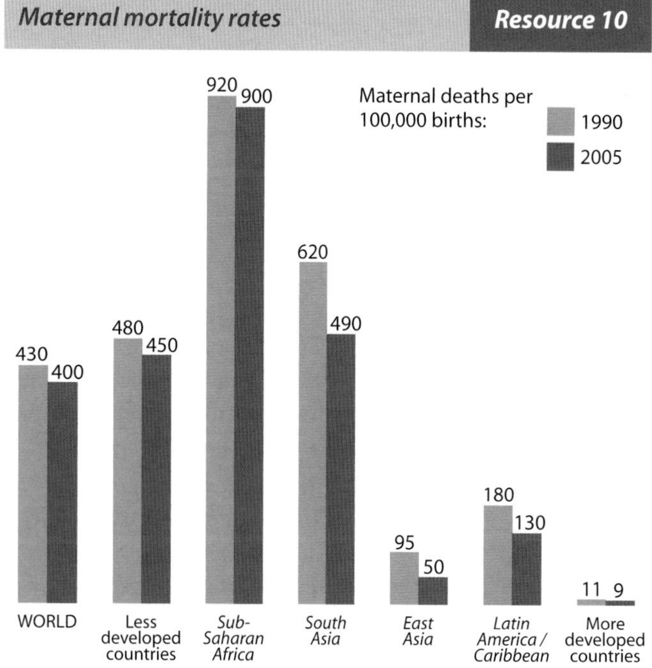

Source: Data from 2008 world population sheet, Population Reference Bureau, www.prb.org

Political

Governments can have a direct impact on mortality levels in their country. On occasions ill-advised government policies increase the death rate. In China, during the 1960s, the communist government followed a pro-natalist policy and made substantial changes to the organization of agriculture. The result was a failure and some 30 million people died during the famines that followed. At present the government of Zimbabwe has brought economic devastation to their country and life expectancy is now the lowest in the world, currently 35 years. Many LEDCs, especially in Africa, have experienced wars and conflict resulting in the deaths of many. The indirect effect of these wars on the death rate is difficult to calculate. However, if the money spent on wars were directed to the well-being of the people, then we might assume that life expectancy could be higher. In MEDCs mortality is also affected by government policy. Government-sponsored advertising on lifestyle habits such as smoking, obesity and unhealthy diets, have heightened awareness of the so-called lifestyle diseases of lung cancer, diabetes and heart attacks. In the UK there are screening programmes for various cancers and an annual vaccination for influenza for those over 65 years of age and other vulnerable persons. Governments also finance research into cures for cancer and other life-threatening diseases. All of these serve to increase life expectancy.

Cultural

Certain cultures put a higher value on male children than female children and this has led to higher mortality among female children. One of the most controversial claims against the one-child policy in China was the abandonment of female babies at birth. Parents anxious to have a son but allowed only one child were particularly disappointed at the birth of a female child. Some were said to have abandoned or even killed the child. It is claimed that such practices are common in other Asian countries such as India and Bangladesh, where families are required to provide a dowry for their daughters at marriage.

Environmental

It has been shown that where we live can have a direct influence on our life expectancy. In the industrialised world high incidences of death from respiratory causes have been recorded in coal mining areas. There are claims that living in close proximity to electricity pylons is a contributory factor in some childhood cancers. The effects of atmospheric pollution and ozone depletion are thought to be leading to an increase in skin cancers in many areas. One of the best-documented environmental influences on mortality comes from the Chernobyl nuclear explosion in the Ukraine in 1986. Apart from the immediate deaths of 60 people, there are thought to have been as many as 4,000 extra cancer cases and many others with serious genetic disorders as a result of the nuclear fallout.

In LEDCs, environmental factors play a very significant role in life expectancy and mortality. Many LEDCs are situated in tropical climates, where the spread of diseases like malaria can be rampant. Similarly, if there is unclean water and limited sanitation in these countries, a tropical climate increases the risk of cholera and typhoid. For those people in LEDCs living in areas prone to earthquakes and cyclones, the risk of death is much greater than in the MEDCs. Various transnational corporations have outsourced some of their production to low-income countries abroad. Often the health and safety regulations in these countries are less stringent than in the high-income countries. The example of the explosion at the American-owned, union carbide chemical factory in Bhopal in India illustrates this well. This factory was built close to an urban area and a fire in 1984 resulted in 7,000 deaths with up to 20,000 more in the years following the disaster.

In LEDCs, life expectancy is usually higher in cities because there are greater economic opportunities and more accessible medical care than in rural areas. In Kenya, the child mortality rate was 109 per thousand in rural areas and 88 per thousand in urban areas in 2000.

Exercise

1. *Question from CCEA May 2008*
   With reference to global contrasts, explain the factors that influence fertility and mortality trends across the world. (15)

2. *Question from CCEA January 2006*
   With reference to any two of the following factors, explain how they influence fertility: (8)
   - Economic
   - Social
   - Political
   - Cultural
   - Environmental

Exercise continued

3. (a) Study **Figure 1** showing demographic and economic data for a range of countries.
   (i) What evidence is there to suggest that fertility and mortality are influenced by economic factors?
   (ii) Draw a scatter graph to show the relationship between GNP per capita and birth rate. Describe the nature of the relationship observed.
   (iii) Use Spearman's Rank Correlation test to verify the strength of the relationship between fertility and GNP per capita.

Figure 1

Country	Birth rate per thousand	Death rate per thousand	GNP per capita US$
Egypt	27	6	5,400
Ethiopia	40	15	780
Chad	44	17	1,280
Peru	21	6	7,240
Venezuela	25	4	11,920
Canada	14	8	44,790
Denmark	12	10	36,740
Ireland	16	6	37,040
Norway	12	9	53,690
Singapore	11	5	48,520

Source: Data from 2008 world population data sheet, Population Reference Bureau, www.prb.org

HIV/AIDS

A major challenge for global health is the worldwide epidemic of AIDS/HIV. AIDS/HIV was first identified as a major concern in the 1980s because of its effects on specific population groups in countries across all levels of development. In the USA, HIV/AIDS was in the top fifteen causes of death between 1987 and 1997. In MEDCs, the number of AIDS/HIV related deaths has fallen, partly due to an extensive advertising programme on prevention measures and government investment in antiretroviral drugs. The deaths of some high profile celebrities from the disease brought the problem to the attention of the media. However, HIV/AIDS is now a major problem in LEDCs and in sub-Saharan Africa in particular. At the end of 2007, some 33 million people worldwide were infected and over two thirds of these were in sub-Saharan Africa. **Resources 11 and 12** show the global distribution of HIV/AIDS.

The impact of HIV/AIDS in the LEDCs will continue to be a major issue for years to come. For one thing the virus is much more widespread throughout the population. In MEDCs, HIV/AIDS is still largely associated with specific sub sets of the population. Sub-Saharan Africa has seen life expectancy decrease by several years as a result of this epidemic. In Swaziland life expectancy has decreased by 16 years, in Botswana by 20 years, and in Zambia and Lesotho by 13 years. Adults aged between 20–49 accounted for 16% of all AIDS deaths in 1990 and by 2010 that figure will have doubled. Such large scale losses of the usually economically active sectors of the population will have serious repercussions for the economy of those countries

People with HIV/AIDS (Millions) 2007 — *Resource 11*

Regions	Numbers
Latin America and Caribbean	1.9
North America	1.2
North Africa and Middle East	0.4
Sub-Saharan Africa	22.0
East Asia	0.7
South and Southeast Asia	4.2
Eastern Europe and Central Asia	1.5
Western and Central Europe	0.7
Oceania	0.1

Source: UNAIDS 2008 Report on the Global AIDS Epidemic

Resource 12 *World map of HIV infection 2007*

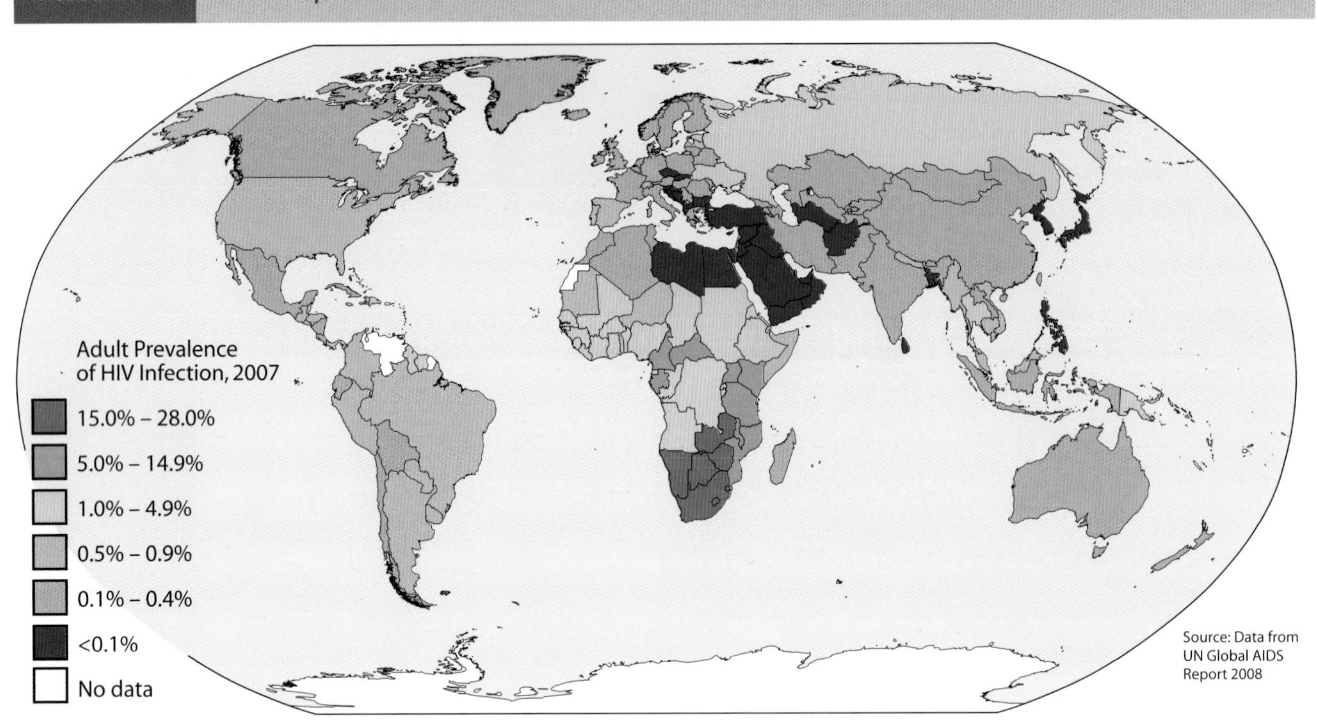

Resource 13 *Life expectancy at birth*

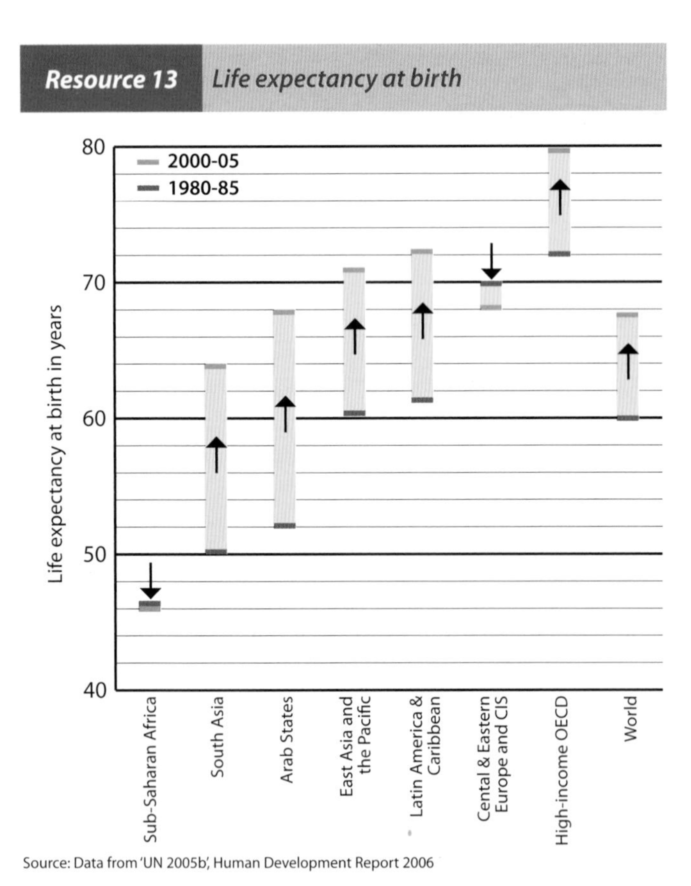

Source: Data from 'UN 2005b', Human Development Report 2006

worst affected. In South Africa (total population 48 million) the adult population is projected to decrease by 6 million by 2015 because of AIDS deaths.

Falling life expectancy is one aspect of this epidemic but another is the effect on women. In the worst affected areas, infection rates among women have been increasing more rapidly than for men. Over half of new infections are amongst women, and young African women are three times more likely to be infected than men. This is having a dramatic impact on the population structure of these areas. Women are more likely to die from the infection at a younger age and this is reducing the number of women in the older age groups quite significantly.

Women are more at risk because of their relative disadvantage in education and in decision making in a male-dominated society (**Resource 15**). Whatever the cause, the effect on the children born to infected mothers can be devastating. These children will become infected before birth and many will be orphaned at an early age. In sub-Saharan Africa there are thought to be approximately 12 million orphaned children due to AIDS between 1990 and 2007. In many families both parents are affected and unable to work. The task of bringing up the children falls on older siblings or increasingly on grandparents. In addition, Aids is having an impact on child mortality rates in the worst affected regions (**Resource 16a** and **16b**).

One of the Millennium Development Goals set a target to halt or reverse the spread of AIDS by 2015. There is clearly much to be done if this target is to be attained.

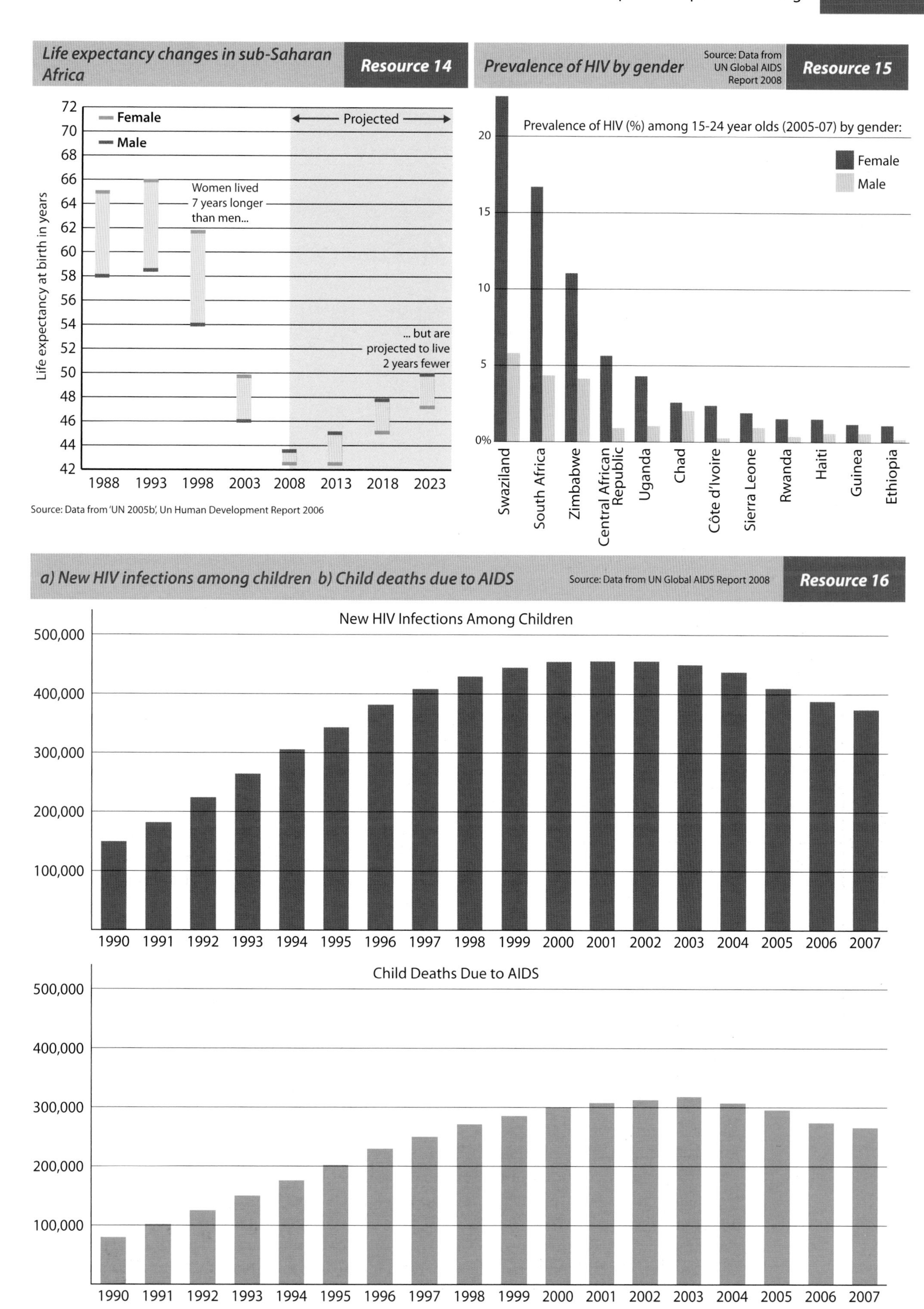
Life expectancy changes in sub-Saharan Africa
Resource 14
Female
Male
Projected
Women lived 7 years longer than men...
... but are projected to live 2 years fewer
Life expectancy at birth in years
72
70
68
66
64
62
60
58
56
54
52
50
48
46
44
42
1988
1993
1998
2003
2008
2013
2018
2023
Source: Data from 'UN 2005b', Un Human Development Report 2006
Prevalence of HIV by gender
Source: Data from UN Global AIDS Report 2008
Resource 15
Prevalence of HIV (%) among 15-24 year olds (2005-07) by gender:
Female
Male
20
15
10
5
0%
Swaziland
South Africa
Zimbabwe
Central African Republic
Uganda
Chad
Côte d'Ivoire
Sierra Leone
Rwanda
Haiti
Guinea
Ethiopia
a) New HIV infections among children b) Child deaths due to AIDS
Source: Data from UN Global AIDS Report 2008
Resource 16
New HIV Infections Among Children
500,000
400,000
300,000
200,000
100,000
1990
1991
1992
1993
1994
1995
1996
1997
1998
1999
2000
2001
2002
2003
2004
2005
2006
2007
Child Deaths Due to AIDS
500,000
400,000
300,000
200,000
100,000
1990
1991
1992
1993
1994
1995
1996
1997
1998
1999
2000
2001
2002
2003
2004
2005
2006
2007

Exercise

1. Study the population pyramids below for Ghana (which has not been affected by AIDS) and Lesotho, which has been badly affected.

   (a) Describe the impact of AIDS on the population structure of Lesotho.

   (b) Discuss the possible socio-economic impacts AIDS is likely to have on Lesotho.

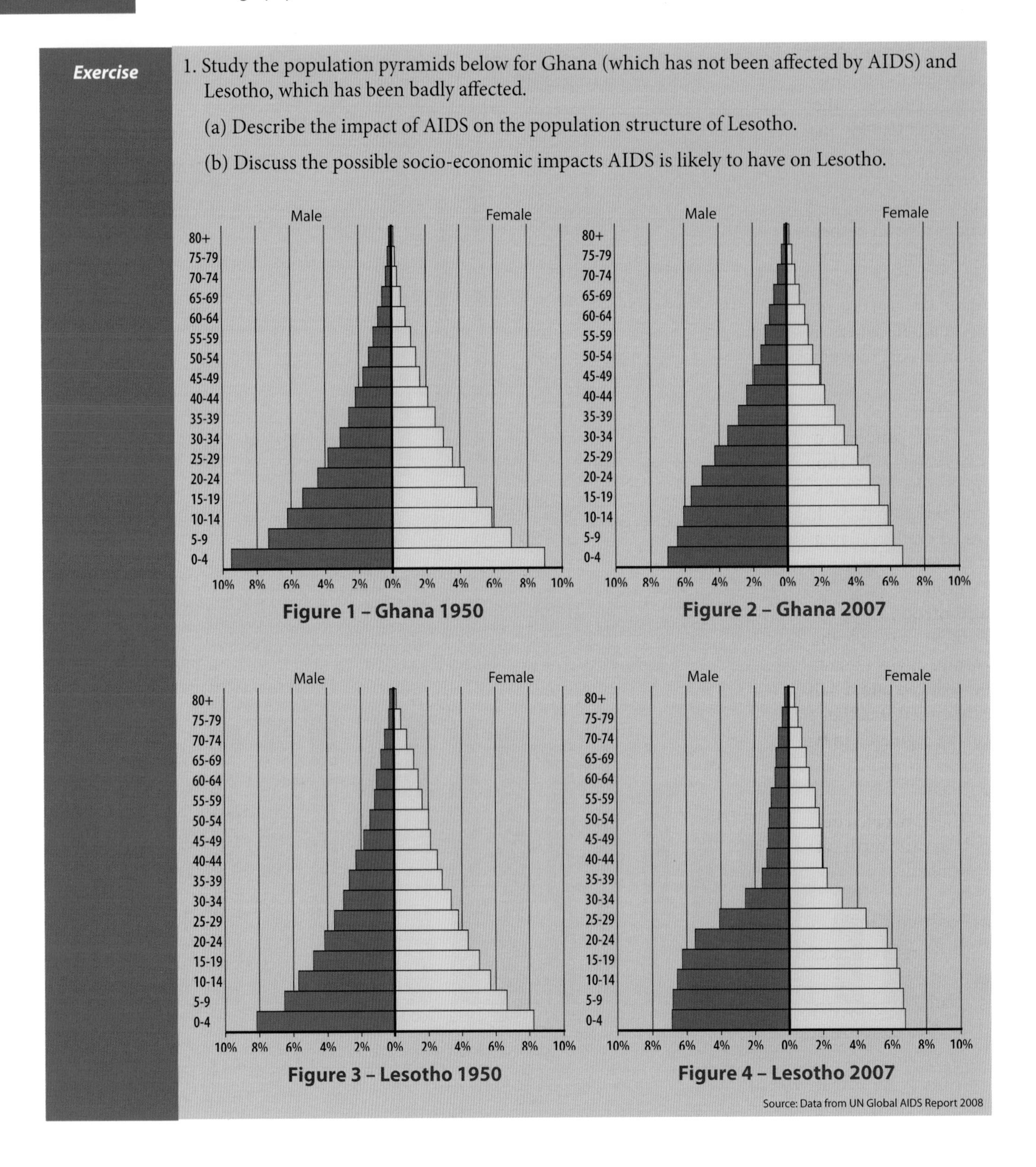

Figure 1 – Ghana 1950

Figure 2 – Ghana 2007

Figure 3 – Lesotho 1950

Figure 4 – Lesotho 2007

Source: Data from UN Global AIDS Report 2008

Theories and issues of population sustainability

At the beginning of the twenty-first century there were 6.1 billion people in the world and in June 2008 there were 6.7 billion. By 2012, the total population is predicted to reach 7 billion. The changes in total world population are dramatic but so too have been the developments in technology and affluence. Due to developments in transport, we now live in a global village. The large supermarket chains import food from all over the world; high street chains outsource routine manufacturing jobs to low-wage economies and sell the finished products at low prices. Until recently, air transport was relatively inexpensive and most people in richer countries still take holidays abroad.

In the twentieth century humans have achieved remarkable success in exploiting and developing new resources. The Green Revolution has opened the potential for increasing yields of crops in many poorer counties, and genetically modified (GM) crops seemed to offer almost limitless opportunities in food supplies generally. However, there are major issues underlying all of these developments, not least of which is the long-term impact on existing resources and the sustainability of our current situation. Studies of this topic are usually set in the framework of optimum population, where resources and population are in balance, or overpopulation and under population, where there is an imbalance between population and resources.

Optimum population graph **Resource 17**

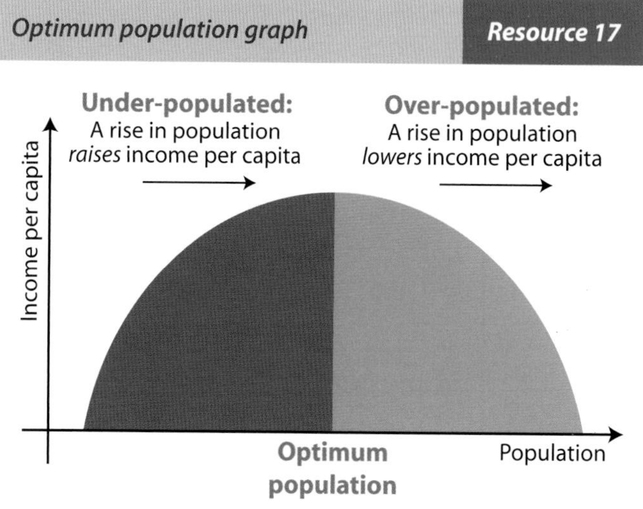

These concerns over resources and sustainability are not recent. Just over two hundred years ago (1798) **Thomas Malthus** produced his work on 'The Principle of Population Growth'. In this, he stated his concerns that population growth, if left unchecked, would outstrip the available resources. In this context, a resource referred to food supply. The basis of his theory rested on the differential rates of growth for population and resources. He claimed that human populations increased at a much faster geometric rate (1, 2, 4, 8, 16) and had the potential to double every twenty-five years. Food supplies on the other hand only increased at an arithmetic rate (1, 2, 3, and 4). Based on this belief, Malthus claimed that there was a finite number of people that a country could sustain and if population growth was not reduced then certain environmental checks would come into play. In this way, population numbers would be reduced and a balance between population numbers and available resources would be re-established. Malthus states that the balance between population numbers and food resources can be regulated in two main ways:

1. Preventative (negative) checks

These involved delayed age of marriage and abstinence from sex within marriage. This would lower the birth rate. It should be noted that Malthus was writing before contraception was available.

2. Positive checks

These referred to changes in the death rate. Malthus believed that when there was insufficient food available, disease, famine and war were likely outcomes, resulting in an increase in the death rate.

Two concepts are fundamental to Malthus' views. These are:

- Carrying capacity – which is the maximum capability of a region to support people with food.
- Population ceiling – which is the numerical limit for any given region.

In his writing, Malthus proposed three possible scenarios when population and resources were imbalanced (**Resource 18**).

In diagram A – The population grows unchecked until the carrying capacity is reached. When the carrying capacity is reached, population growth stops and remains at the carrying capacity level. There is no evidence that such an example has occurred.

Malthus' scenarios of population and resource imblance **Resource 18a**

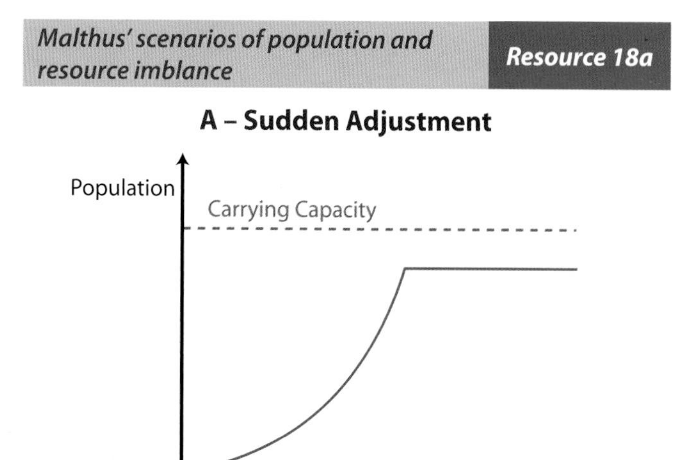

Resource 18b *Malthus' scenarios of population and resource imblance*

B – Progressive Adjustment ('S curve')

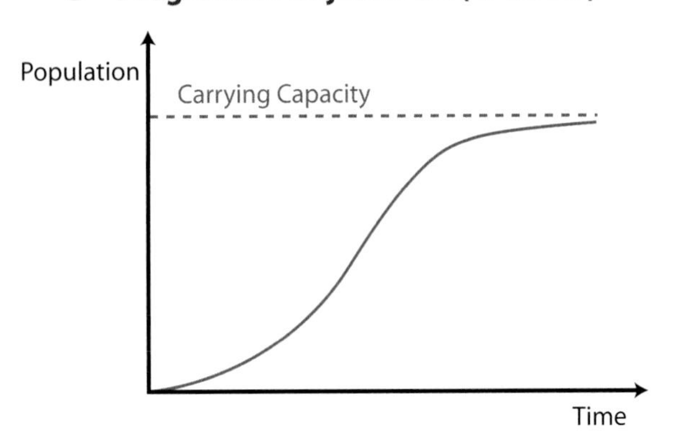

C – Progressive Approximation ('J curve')

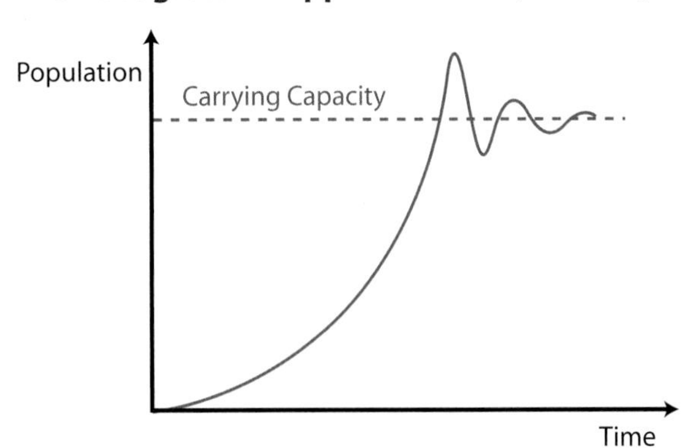

In diagram B – The population growth begins to slow down before the carrying capacity is reached and levels off close to the population ceiling. This is said to be typical of regions that are in control of their resources and appreciate the problems ahead, and so take decisive action beforehand. Population and resources are kept in balance by changes to the fertility levels – the so-called preventative checks.

In diagram C – The population growth rises beyond the carrying capacity of the region and then numbers are reduced either through the positive checks of famine, war and drought; or through the negative checks of birth control and delayed marriage. This process continues for a time before population levels off close to the carrying capacity.

Malthus' theories have been widely debated and as yet no agreement has been reached on the viability of his views in our world today. In 1965, many years after Malthus, **Esther Boserup** proposed a very different view concerning the balance between population and resources. Boserup claims that population growth is a necessary prerequisite for technological advances and innovation, and that society was held back by slow population growth. She believed that populations would continue to grow until they came close to the carrying capacity and at that point human inventiveness would find a way to avert the crisis and produce more food. This is an optimistic viewpoint but there is evidence to support it. Boserup claimed that population was increasing in Britain during the eighteenth century. At this time agricultural reform resulted in an increase in food production. Boserup argued that the increase in population was necessary for this reform to take place. From there, Britain's food production increased and the surplus was sufficient to feed the population working and living in the towns and cities that developed throughout the nineteenth century.

There are arguments for and against both of these theories.

In support of Malthus/against Boserup

- There are many examples of famine in Africa – Ethiopia in the 1980s or the potato famine in Ireland in the mid nineteenth century – that seem to have been caused by too many people in a given area.
- Desertification in the Sahel region in Africa is partly due to overgrazing on semi-arid land.
- In the Middle East, conflict between Israel, and Syria and Jordan is exacerbated by rival claims for scarce water resources from the river Jordan.
- Boserup believes population will always know how to get more food from their land but this is too simplistic.

Arguments against Malthus/support for Boserup

- There have been dramatic improvements in agriculture. By using modern methods such as chemical fertilizer, high yielding crops and genetically modified crops, we have increased food output.
- Countries can import food so there is no longer a need to be self-sufficient in food.
- More land has been brought into production and GM crops can be grown on land previously considered unsuitable.

- The Green Revolution in the 1950s produced new high-yielding cereal crops that have had considerable success in many Asian countries.
- Many Asian countries are able to grow two crops a year, thus doubling the output from their land.
- Increases in the distance that fishing boats can travel has led to more species being available.
- The use of irrigation means semi-arid lands can be made productive.
- Food mountains and food waste are used as evidence that there is adequate food available, and that scarcity of food is a problem of distribution not supply.
- In countries experiencing famine it is usually only the poorest people who suffer from lack of food.
- The problems of desertification are thought to be due to inappropriate farming techniques.
- Wars and corrupt governments often cause food shortages, either through destruction of crops or in some cases food is withheld from rival groups. During the long civil war in Ethiopia, the government was frequently accused of withholding food supplies from the rebel territories in Eritrea.

These are just some of the arguments for and against Malthus and Boserup. More recently a number of debates have taken place concerning this issue. The attention now seems to have moved away from the doomsday scenario of lack of food, although there are still areas where food supply is very inadequate, and focuses on the wider environmental implications of overconsumption of resources. Modern day protagonists of Malthusian views include Paul Erlich and the Club of Rome. They emphasise the environmental impacts of excessive population growth. The views of Ester Boserup are championed by Julian Simon. Regarding this debate the main points to consider include:

- Global warming
- Pollution of the atmosphere, the sea and land
- The risk to western style economies as oil reserves diminish
- The environmental effects of GM crops
- The health risks from over intensification of agriculture, for example, BSE

Study the following resources relating to problems associated with modern farming techniques.

Exercise

Figure 1

Cluster of BSE cows found on farm in Wales

A cluster of three BSE cases found in relatively young cows born on a farm in Wales is being studied by scientists. It is the first time for many years that three animals born at the same place within a short time of each other have been confirmed with the disease, which wreaked havoc on Britain's agriculture and forced safety controls for food, blood transfusions and operations as scores fell victim to BSE's fatal human form.

The cases on an unidentified farm in Dyfed are among the youngest in recent years, and came to light days after farmers were warned by the government not to be complacent over BSE, cases of which are falling at 50% a year…In all, there have been about 180,000 cases confirmed since 1986…Scientists are trying to assess whether all three cows…were infected by the same route, possibly contaminated feed imported after controls banning all ingredients from other mammals in cattle feed began in Britain in summer 1996… Some experts believe that containers carrying feed between countries were not always thoroughly cleaned between trips, allowing cross contamination.

Source: J Meikle, The Guardian, http://tinyurl.com/bsewales, accessed 20 August 2009

Exercise continued

Figure 2

River pollution

The single, biggest threat is from agriculture. This is perhaps unsurprising as agriculture covers over 70% of the land area of England and Wales and sources of diffuse pollution – including nutrients from fertilisers and manure – are integral parts of farming. Research suggests that agriculture, through leaching and run off, is responsible for 40–50% of phosphate pollution in our water systems.

Elevated levels of nutrients can result in toxic algal blooms and affect the natural aquatic ecosystems which in turn impact the food chain that supports fish, animals and birds.

Source: Agricultural Water Management Company LTD, http://tinyurl.com/rvrpolu, accessed 1 September 2009

Figure 3

EU under attack over plan to ease organic labelling

Environmental campaigners have hit out at EU plans to allow food contaminated with genetically modified material to be sold as organic. The draft regulation would permit products accidentally contaminated with up to 0.9% GM organisms to bear the EU organic logo.

[Peter] Melchett [The Soil Association's policy director] said he believed the European commission's position was legally wrong. Green groups agreed, saying current regulations do not allow organic products to contain GM substances "in any quantity". Helen Holder, of Friends of the Earth, said genetic contamination of organic food was unacceptable to consumers.

Source: D Adam, The Guardian, http://tinyurl.com/orglab, 6 January 2006

Figure 4

Crops giant retreats from Europe ahead of GM report

Monsanto, the huge American biotechnology company which has pioneered GM crops, is withdrawing from many of its European operations and laying off up to two thirds of its British workers.

The announcement came on the eve of the publication of the Government's GM crop trials today. Tony Blair is thought to be in favour of GM crops, stressing the need for Britain to be in the vanguard of new industries that could be worth billions of pounds. But ministers will be under pressure to limit, or scrap, further development of GM crops in the face of public opposition...Last month, a test of public opinion in Britain found that the majority of people did not want GM food in their supermarkets. In a series of questions that formed part of the "GM Nation" debate, 85% of respondents said they believed GM crops would benefit producers rather than consumers, 86% said they were unhappy with the idea of eating GM food, 91% said they thought GM crops had a potentially negative effect on the countryside and 93% said GM was being driven by profit rather than public interest.

[Following the publication of the Government's GM crop trial's Monsanto announced its decision to close its research centre in Cambrige, costing a further 80 British employees their jobs.]

Source: S Connor, The Independent, 16 October 2003, http://tinyurl.com/crpgiant, accessed 2 September 2009

Figures 1–4 adapted from resources for CCEA May 2008 and January 2005

Exercise continued

1. Use **Figures 1–4** to help you discuss the positive and negative outcomes that can result from modern farming techniques.
2. Recently there has been an increase in the amount of land used for the cultivation of biofuels and this is thought to have led to an increase in food prices. Research this topic further and discuss the extent to which you agree with the following statement:

   'The increase in biofuel production and the increase in food prices prove that Malthus' theory is just as relevant today as it was two hundred years ago.'
3. *Question from CCEA May 2008*
   To what extent does the argument of Ester Boserup regarding human inventiveness mean that the views of Thomas Malthus on population sustainability cannot be proved right, even in the long-term? (6)
4. Use **Figure 5** below to help you prepare an argument in support of Malthus.

Figure 5

Humanity gobbles a quarter of nature's resources

Almost a quarter of nature's resources are now being gobbled up by a single species – humans. People appropriate 24% of the Earth's production capacity that would otherwise have gone to nature, according to figures for the year 2000, the most recent available.

The analysis was performed by Helmut Haberl, of Klagenfurt University in Vienna, Austria, and colleagues using UN Food and Agriculture Organisation data on agricultural land use in 161 countries, covering 97.4% of the planet's land surface. The result is a gradual depletion of species and habitats as we take more of their resources for ourselves. And things could get even worse, they say, if we grow more plants like palm oil and rapeseed for biofuels to ease our reliance on fossil fuels.

Up in smoke

By comparing carbon consumption through human activity with the amount of carbon consumed overall, Haberl's team found that humans use 15.6 trillion kilograms of carbon annually. Half was soaked up by growing crops. 7% went up in smoke as fires lit by humans, and the rest was used up in a variety of other ways related to industrialisation, such as transport.

Haberl says that the Earth can just about cope if we meet future needs by producing food more efficiently. This could be done by intensifying production on the land used now. But we are asking for trouble, he says, if we expand production of biofuels, as the only fertile land available is tropical rainforests.

Dramatic implications

"If we want full-scale replacement of fossil fuels by biofuels, this would have dramatic implications for ecosystems," says Haberl. He warns that some projections foresee four or fivefold increases in biofuel production. This would mean clearing what remains of the world's rainforests in countries such as Brazil and Argentina.

As well as wiping out thousands of species, this would have devastating effects on the climate, he argues. Unlike farmland, forests help to seed rainfall because they have high evaporation rates. "The less evaporation there is, the less rainfall there is and the whole system dries up," Haberl says.

Source: A Coghlan, New Scientist, 2 July 2007, http://tinyurl.com/nscgb, accessed 2 September 2009

Additional References

The following websites have useful material on this topic:

www.geographyalltheway.com

www.populationsustainability.org

The Demographic Transition Model

The Demographic Transition Model (**Resource 19**) shows how the components of natural population change have operated through time. The model was based on the example of population change in England and Wales and has become one of the most widely used models in population Geography. The model is made up of four stages, although some have argued that a fifth stage is necessary to take account of recent trends in population change in MEDCs.

Resource 19 *The Demographic Transition Model*

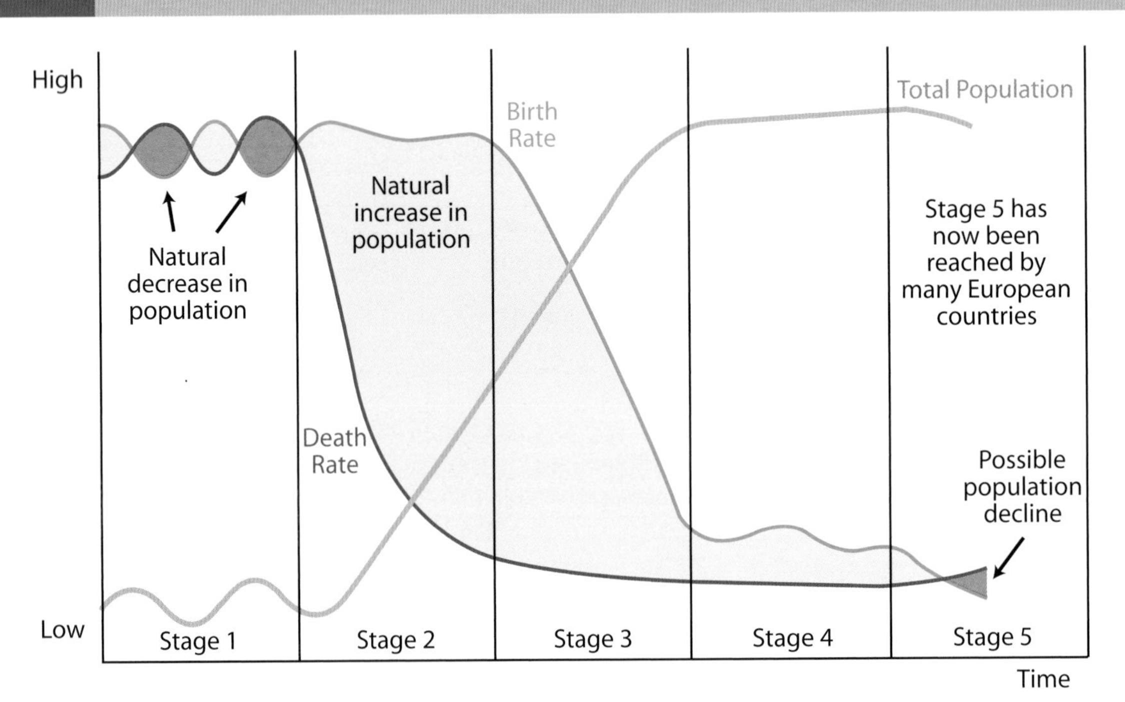

Stage 1 – High stationary

In this stage, birth rates and death rates are both high, typically between 35 and 40 per thousand. Infant mortality is high and life expectancy is low. This situation occurred in the UK before 1750. Medical care was limited and many died of infectious diseases and from frequent epidemics, resulting in occasional spikes in the death rate. Overall population growth was low and may even have decreased at times of epidemics. Today there are no countries reported at this stage.

Stage 2 – Early expanding

This is a period of continued high births but the death rate falls typically to about 20 to 25 per thousand. In the UK this occurred between 1750 and 1850, when the death rates fell as basic sanitation and health care improved. Medical advancements and the discovery of vaccinations against some of the most infectious diseases impacted greatly on death rates. However, the birth rates remained high and consequently total population numbers increased significantly. At present, LEDCs such as Afghanistan and Libya are thought to be at this stage.

Stage 3 – Late expanding

The fall in the death rate continues but gradually it stabilises between 15 and 10 per thousand as the population begins to age. The most significant development now is the fall in the birth rate to somewhere between 20 and 25 per thousand. The UK passed this stage by 1950. The decrease in the birth rate was due to changes in the perception of children as a source of labour supply, the improvements in the status of women, and greater access to contraception. In spite of the lower birth rate, overall population increased because the population structure was youthful, meaning there were large numbers of potential parents. Currently, the more affluent LEDCs such as Brazil and Argentina are in this stage.

Stage 4 – Low stationary

The trend of declining fertility continues at this stage to about 10 per thousand. The death rate remains stable. There are occasional spikes in the birth rate such as the post-war baby boom but the overall birth rate remains low and total population stabilises. In the UK this situation has been in place since 1950. Greater opportunities for women in work, increased access to contraception and abortion, along with increased materialism, have all contributed to the continued fall in the birth rate. Life expectancy has increased and degenerative illnesses are the most common causes of death. Only MEDCs are well established in his stage.

Stage 5 – Decline

Although not part of the original model, it is felt that some European countries have passed through the previous stage and are now in a situation where the death rate exceeds the birth rate. Increased affluence generally, and greater financial independence for women have resulted in significant lifestyle changes. Some women remain single, or at least do not have children because of career choices, while others delay the age at which they decide to have a child. As the population ages, there are fewer potential parents and consequently numbers decline overall. Italy and Germany are thought to have reached this stage. In the UK, although there are more people over 60 than there are under 15, the birth rate is still slightly higher than the death rate. This may be the result of a higher birth rate amongst some of the ethnic minorities and more recent migrants.

Even though the Demographic Transition Model is based on the changes that occurred in England and Wales, it is still useful when studying other MEDCs. However, it cannot be prescriptive for LEDCs. Many LEDCs have seen their death rates fall, largely due to medical advances and aid packages from outside. It is too optimistic to assume that they will automatically proceed eventually to stage 4 with low birth rates. The situation in the UK during the nineteenth century is significantly different from what is currently the case in the LEDCs. In the nineteenth century the UK was experiencing a social and economic advancement in industry, medicine and overseas expansion. The fall in the birth rate was due to increased materialism that resulted from these advancements. Most LEDCs are a long way behind the level of development required to bring about a fall in the birth rate.

Additional References

Thom, M and Armstrong, E, *AS Geography for CCEA*, pages 95–97

Exercise

1. Evaluate the Demographic Transition Model as a tool when studying population change in countries at different levels of development. You need to make reference to examples in your answer.

The Epidemiological Transition

Epidemiology is the study of disease and it has been suggested that an epidemiological transition occurs as countries proceed through development. This model focuses on the cause of death. However, as fertility rates are closely tied into patterns of mortality, this model has some similarities to the Demographic Transition Model. There are three stages:

Stage 1 – The pre-transition stage

At this stage, death rates are high and the common causes of death include infectious diseases such as small pox, measles, influenza. Many of these causes of mortality are directly related

Resource 20 *Health models*

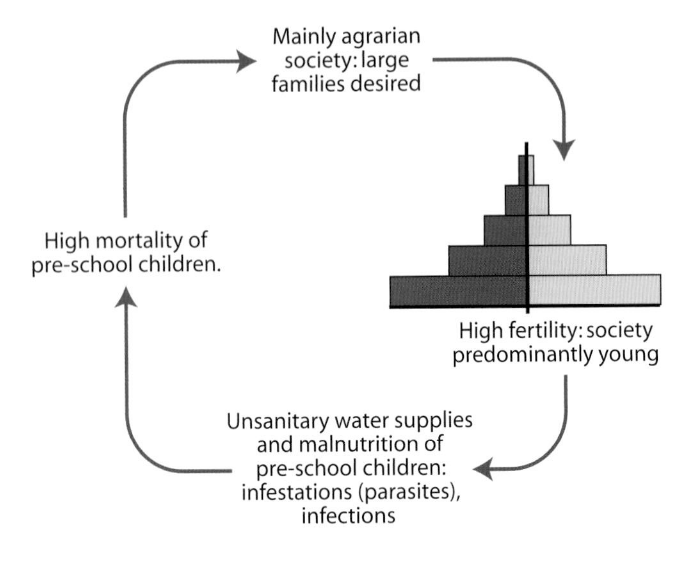

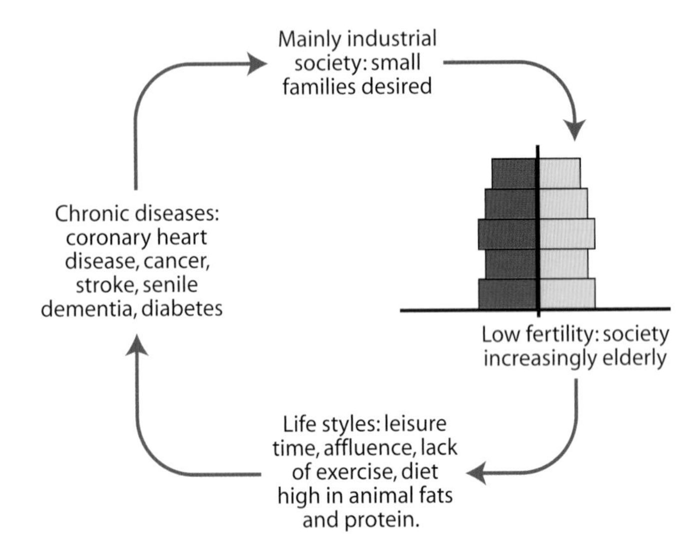

to environmental conditions, diet, hygiene and life style. Such causes of death are referred to as exogenetic, ie they are not related to genetics. At times these diseases reached epidemic or even pandemic status (the flu pandemic in 1919). Countries in this stage generally have inadequate nutrition, sanitation and hygiene. Medical facilities are inadequate and there are insufficient funds to develop these further. Britain passed through this stage before the mid-eighteenth century. Currently only those LEDCs in the lowest section of the development continuum are found here.

Stage 2 – The receding pandemic

Death rates fall rapidly during this stage as infectious diseases are controlled. In Britain this occurred from the nineteenth century onwards. During that time there were significant developments in nutrition and sanitation. Developments in medicine and vaccinations (as mentioned earlier) all played a vital role in this phase. There is greater understanding of how diseases are spread and governments take control to prevent the spread of communicable diseases across international boundaries. The outbreak of SARS (2003) and the measures taken to avoid the spread of Swine Flu (2009) are recent examples of this.

Stage 3 – The age of degenerative and man-made diseases

At this stage, people die from degenerative or endogenetic diseases of the elderly, such as Alzheimer's disease, as well as the so-called diseases of affluence, such as heart attacks, strokes and cancer.

Countries occupy different stages in this transition. In Europe, communicable diseases account for less than 10% of all deaths. However, in Africa, infectious diseases including HIV/AIDS, malaria and measles account for over 60% of deaths. The epidemiological transition also brings a shift in the ages when most deaths occur (the age-specific death rate). In countries at the beginning of the transition, most deaths occur in the youngest age groups because this group is the most vulnerable to infectious diseases. In the late 1990s, over 50% of deaths in LEDCs were under 20 and 40% were under 5. In MEDCs, only 2% of all deaths were under 20 and 68% were among the elderly. As countries pass through this transition, their age structure changes. For those in the early stages, life expectancy is low and birth rates are high. In the final stages the population begins to age and fertility rates fall.

Exercise

1. How effective is the epidemiological transition when explaining population change in countries at different levels of development?

A2 MIGRATION: CAUSES, STREAMS AND IMPACTS

Migration

Migration is defined as the permanent change in place of residence for at least one year. Migration is international when the movement involves crossing an international border or internal when the migrant moves from one region to another within his/her own country.

Unless the migration is forced where the individual has little or no choice, the decision process involved in migration is complex. For most, it is a life-changing experience and involves an assessment of those factors that promote the move and those which would discourage migration. These processes can be categorised into push factors and pull factors.

Push factors are those negative aspects of the potential migrant's current place of residence. It should be noted that these negative aspects are entirely subjective and are based on the migrant's perception. What one person regards as negative may have no influence on another person. Working in conjunction with the push factors are the pull factors. These are the perceived attractions of the new destination. These perceptions are based on information acquired from a number of sources, including previous migrants and advertising campaigns. Usually the migrants will make the decision to move to a particular destination because they believe that the deprivation they currently endure will be removed in this new location. In that sense, pull factors are the opposite of the push factors. Push and pull factors can be grouped into several categories.

Economic factors

These are often the most common factors in the decision making process. Lack of suitable jobs, low wages, uncertain future and lack of promotional opportunities are all possible push factors in the industrial sector. In rural areas, restructuring and mechanisation in farming have greatly reduced the number of job opportunities, prompting many younger people to consider moving elsewhere in search of work. Eastern European migration to the UK is an example of economic motivation for migration. When Poland became part of the European Union in 2005, the unemployment rate was 18%, while in rural areas it was as much as 40%. Unemployment in the UK is about 5%. The GDP per capita in Poland was less than half that in the UK. The 'brain drain' of highly trained individuals from LEDCs to the MEDCs in search of better opportunities is also an example of economic factors in operation.

An area that offers job opportunities and/or higher wages will attract in-migration. Some 50,000 Polish immigrants arrived in the UK in 2005, pulled by the prospect of improving their economic situation. Government investment in an area to bring new jobs can also act as a pull factor. The Urban Development Corporations set up by the Conservative government pursued this policy in the hope of encouraging people back into the inner cities.

Social factors

The desire to join family members who have already made a successful move is a very important social factor. Often men make the initial decision to migrate, usually for economic reasons, and after he becomes established, his family will decide to join him. The West Indian migration to the UK in the 1950s and 1960s followed this pattern. Many students move to the cities for third level education and it has been shown that this initial temporary move becomes a permanent one. As the student forms new social ties in the city, he/she is reluctant to leave these and return home on a permanent basis. In areas where the population is ageing, there are often inadequate medical, educational and recreational opportunities for younger families and this is often the catalyst for further out-migration. Remote rural areas in the UK provide many examples of this.

The dissemination of favourable information to the migrant's former home area can encourage others to migrate to that destination.

Cultural factors

Lack of religious, linguistic or cultural freedom will often promote migration. In Bosnia, even though the ethnic cleansing and war have ended in that country, Muslims still move away from Serbian areas out of fear. In some British cities where there are substantial ethnic minorities, some of the white population have moved to the suburbs where there are fewer ethnic minorities. Settling into a new country or city can be difficult and for many migrants the existence of clusters of people of similar culture or religion to themselves acts as a strong pull factor. This often leads to the development of a migration stream and the creation of enclaves of ethnic minorities. Many British cities have ethnic neighbourhoods as a result of migration.

Environmental factors

Desertification, such as is happening in the Sahel region in Africa, is causing large numbers of people to move in search of better farming land. Global warming is predicted to increase sea level in some of the most densely populated, low-lying areas of the world and this will undoubtedly promote considerable out-migration. Already some islands in the Pacific have been depopulated. Within the UK, remote upland areas and off-shore islands present harsh environmental conditions. People are pushed away from such regions and attracted to more accessible locations.

Barriers to migration

Having made the decision to migrate, a potential migrant must overcome a number of real and perceived obstacles before the move is made. These barriers and their assessment are crucial elements in the decision making process. One very important consideration is the cost of moving. Apart from the obvious transportation costs, a potential migrant may have a house to sell and need new accommodation in the new destination. Unless there is a guarantee of immediate employment, he/she will need to have sufficient funds to sustain him/her until a job is secured. Migration involves severing family and friendship ties and this hardship has to be weighed up against the potential rewards of the move. There is the added challenge of the new lifestyle, especially if the move involves going to an area where there are significant differences in culture or language. The laws regarding women's dress code and place in society in some Muslim countries can be a major obstacle for western women going to these countries and vice-versa. In the case of international migration, government policies can act either to encourage or discourage migrants. Often such policies are deliberately selective, so that the receiving country has control over the number and type of person who is permitted access. Following the enlargement of the European Union, the UK government initially allowed large numbers of East Europeans to migrate to Britain. In more recent times the numbers have been reduced. In the USA a migrant must have a work permit – the green card – before being allowed entry.

Woman wearing Hijab

Exercise

1. *Question from CCEA May 2005*
"The decision to migrate is complex, the potential migrant must consider push and pull factors and barriers to migration." Discuss this statement with reference to places for illustration. (15)

Typology of migration

Migration streams

Migration tends to involve groups of people moving from a common source region to a similar destination. This is known as a migration stream and it can be either internal or international. At present the movement of people from Eastern Europe to the UK is an example of an international stream. The movement of people from the Highlands of Scotland to the South East of England is an internal stream. Migration streams occur when the migrants have similar reasons for leaving in the first place and their choice of destination may have been influenced by a number of factors. The point made earlier concerning Britain's policy on migrants from the enlarged European Union is relevant here. It has been claimed that many of these migrants chose destinations served by the budget airlines from their home countries. Migrants from former colonies often move to their colonial rulers' country such as West Indians to Britain or Algerians to France.

Economic migrant

People who move to another country simply to obtain work and earn money are described as economic migrants. Such migrants frequently return home after they have earned the desired amount of money. Many of the East European migrants to Britain are said to fall into this category. Many are single men living in cheap accommodation and working long hours in jobs, often below their skills capability. According to figures issued by the government, many in this category have already returned to their home country.

Illegal migrants

Some people are unable to fulfil the legal requirements set down by their chosen destination country and are prepared to take the risk to enter illegally. These migrants travel undercover across Europe and then attempt to gain access to Britain via ferries concealed in the back of lorries. These people are willing to risk a lot to come to Britain and are prepared to take low wages in unregulated work places. On occasions some have died on the journey. In 2000, 58 illegal Chinese immigrants suffocated in the back of a container lorry on their way from Zeebrugge to Dover. In 1999, 2,500 illegal immigrants died attempting to gain access to Europe. Illegal migrants are a vulnerable group of people. Some will have paid huge sums of money to the illegal gangs who agree to smuggle them into their chosen country. Those who manage to gain entry often find themselves exploited by unscrupulous gang masters either through very low wages, or working in unsafe conditions. In 2004, 22 illegal migrants died in Morecambe Bay picking cockles in dangerous tidal conditions. Within weeks of the tragedy, more illegal migrants were apprehended in the same area.

Asylum seekers

These are people who have come to a new country without the required legal documentation to gain entry. They ask permission to remain on the basis that they will face torture or death if they return home. Such people will have fled persecution and there is an internationally agreed list of countries deemed likely to use torture. The number of asylum seekers has increased in recent times and although many applications are genuine, there are those who are seeking entry for purely economic reasons. Consequently, governments undertake rigorous checks to verify the asylum seeker's claims. It is a complicated procedure in Britain, involving the individual

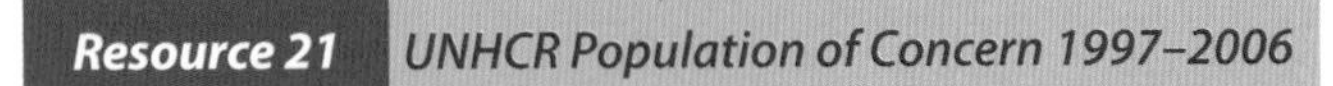

Resource 21 *UNHCR Population of Concern 1997–2006*

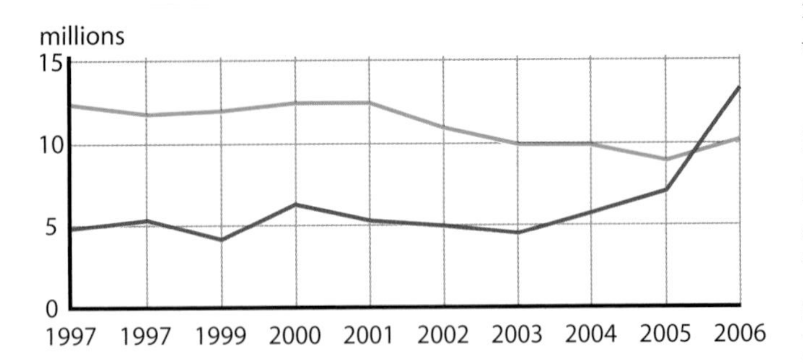

Refugees: chiefly people recognised under the 1951 UN Convention relating to the Status of Refugees and its 1967 protocol.

IDPs (Internally Displaced Persons) assisted/protected: people displaced by internal conflicts to which the UNHCR offers protection and/or assistance.

Source: Data from UNHCR, www.unhcr.org

being held in a holding centre until the application for asylum can be examined. This may take several weeks if not months. According to Home Office figures, there were close to 24,000 asylum applications made in 2007.

Refugees

Refugees are defined by the United Nations as "a group of people unable to live safely in their home country". These are people who have limited choice either in the decision to leave or in their ultimate destination. Natural disasters such as floods, volcanoes or famines all cause refugee movement. In Myanmar (Burma) many people are still living in refugee camps following the cyclone in May 2008. Wars, ethnic cleansing and any form of religious or political discrimination have all caused huge displacements of people. In Africa, at the time of writing, there are thousands of people in refugee camps in the Darfur region of Sudan. In August 2008 many thousands of people living in the former Soviet Republic of Georgia were forced to flee from the war that broke out between Russia and Georgia. **Resource 21** shows how the numbers of refugees and other groups at risk have increased recently. According to the United Nations, there are now approximately 10 million refugees and 13 million people displaced within their own country.

Exercise

1. *Question from CCEA May 2007*

   (a)What is an internal migration stream? Give an example in your answer. (3)

   (b) Explain how and why migration streams vary. (5)

2. *Question from CCEA January 2008*

   Why do migration streams rarely contain a representative cross-section of the population of their area of origin? (4)

Migrant characteristics

Much migration is work-related and therefore the majority of migrants will be from the economically active age groups. The Home Office in Britain issued the figures in Resource 22 for Eastern European workers in the UK in 2006.

Resource 22 *Eastern European workers in the UK 2006*

Age group	Numbers
18–24	183,000
25–34	168,000
35–44	44,710
45–54	26,000
55–64	3,400

A person's life stage is a prime consideration in the migration process. There are three main stages when an individual may decide to move. The first is associated with entry into the work place, perhaps to a large city. The second often follows marriage and the young family stage, perhaps close to schools or to a suburban location. A final stage comes at retirement, such as the coastal towns along the south coast of England.

Migration is often gender selective, especially in LEDCs where males are more likely to migrate than females. This is the result of the lower status of women in these countries, where women are expected to remain at home as wives and mothers. Such migrations are often the first stage in migration and once the male migrant is established his family will follow. In MEDCs the distinction between male and females in migration depends on the nature of employment opportunities in the area of destination. Certain types of occupation attract more male migrants such as manufacturing or mining areas. However, towns and cities with predominantly service industries will attract both genders.

New migrants will often locate in areas where their community has already been established. They do this to avail of services and places of worship but also for socio-economic reasons. In the case of Britain, the inner areas of cities provide the migrants with affordable housing and job opportunities as well as a social network with people of similar ethnic backgrounds. Many British cities have distinctive ethnic areas as a legacy of migration streams.

It used to be the case that migrants who were escaping from poverty, and therefore from the lower or deprived socio-economic status, came to perform the low paid and unskilled jobs. However, with increased mobility and greater opportunities to move, migrants can be of any socio-economic status. The 'brain drain' mentioned earlier is an example of highly qualified people, such as doctors and scientists, moving from LEDCs to Britain because of the greater opportunities and higher wages. However, the recent Eastern European migrants are mostly skilled and unskilled workers seeking employment in factories, hotels, food-processing plants and shops.

Main occupations of registered immigrants in the UK 2004–2006 **Resource 23**

Occupation	Total numbers
Factory worker	95,865
Cleaner, maid	33,925
Farm workers	29,705
Catering workers	28,975
Warehouse operative	25,215
Packer	24,130
Waiter/waitress	15,840
Care assistants	12,610
Food processing	11,325
Sales and retail	10,535
Building labourer	10,525
Drivers	6,315
Bar staff	6,030
Other unskilled	77,270
Total	**388,265**

Source: Home Office data published in *Geofile No 550*, September 2007

Exercise

1. Study the table above showing the main occupations of recent East European migrants to the UK.
   (a) Describe the composition of this migration stream.
   (b) What factors may have influenced their decision to come to the UK?

Implications of migration

Migration has significant impacts both on the area of out-migration and on the area of in-migration. Where substantial numbers of people relocate, often with their entire families, there are repercussions for service provision, economic activity and social stability.

Areas of in-migration

A sudden large influx of migrants puts immediate demands on services such as education, health and housing provision. However well intentioned, it will take a country/region some time to provide the extra capacity needed in schools and other areas of social need. In this way, existing services are put under pressure. The new migrants will eventually establish services for their own community. The presence of Chinese, Indian and other international restaurants are a product of in-migration. A number of services including shops and restaurants have recently opened in Belfast serving the Polish community. Similarly, migrant groups have established their own schools in some cities in England.

Polish supermarket on Belfast's Ormeau Road. An example of new services generated for and by Polish immigrants to Belfast.

Meanwhile, in LEDCs, migrants find it difficult to gain affordable housing in cities and so many end up living illegally in informal settlements. The problem is less serious in MEDCs but housing shortages often result in migrants living in overcrowded conditions in poor quality housing. Some of the worst problems are associated with refugees. In the Darfur region of Sudan, large numbers of refugees have fled to neighbouring Chad. Chad is one of the world's poorest countries and it cannot provide even the most basic of services to the refugees.

If the migrants are successful in gaining employment, they can add to the economic advancement of their new country. Turkish migrants played a vital role in rebuilding the German economy after World War II. In the UK, West Indian migrants performed a similar role. These groups were prepared to fill the low-wage, menial labour shortages that the local population were unwilling to do. By working for lower wages the migrants helped to keep wage inflation low. The migrants also spent money in their new country and paid tax to the government. According to some government figures, East European migrants have contributed £2.54 billion annually to the UK economy and contributed 1% of the UK's economic growth between 2005 and 2006. The Bank of England claims that without these migrants inflation and the cost of borrowing would have been higher.

Western Union Office on Belfast's Ormeau Road. Western Union facilitates the sending of remittances.

There are some negative implications in areas of in-migration. Many will send a large amount of their earnings back home and therefore there is limited consumer spending in their new country. This money (or remittances) is money that is actually lost to the host nation. Throughout the UK there are many Western Union offices where the remittances can be processed. Economies are dynamic and although migrants come in times of plentiful jobs, that situation can change. If there are job shortages, the migrants may have the advantage because they will accept lower wages. This situation can cause an increase in unemployment among the local people and cause resentment. Germany, for example, tried to repatriate their Turkish migrants when unemployment increased.

Social stability is the perception that a community has an identity based on a common culture and a balanced distribution of age and gender groups. Migrants change communities, especially if they are numerous, visibly different, do not speak the language of their adopted country or live in segregated groups. Sometimes the local community feel threatened or are unhappy with the changes, and this has resulted in the local people moving away. The migrants are often young with families and this can cause problems in schools, especially if the children have language difficulties. Each culture has its own accepted code of behaviour. What is acceptable in one culture is not accepted in another. Prejudice and racism often play a part in social stability and there have been attacks on migrants. In Northern Ireland some migrants have had their homes petrol bombed. The problems seem to be worse in areas that have not had much migration in the past or where the community is small in number.

Areas of out-migration

If the migrants leave because of overpopulation, the pressure on existing services will be removed and those remaining may enjoy increased access to services. However, this may be a short-term benefit because as more people move away, service provision usually deteriorates. In an area suffering out-migration of the economically active age groups, primary schools are one of the first services to be affected. Primary schools are usually neighbourhood or community-based, therefore if the young families leave, the school roll will fall. Falling rolls eventually lead to amalgamations and closures of the worst affected schools. For the families that remain this means their children have further to travel and this can promote further out-migration. This inevitably leads to an ageing of the population. Other services such as health centres, post offices, shops and public transport can all be similarly affected by out-migration.

Economic activity can enjoy short-term relief as out-migration will ease the demand for jobs. However, in many cases the area loses its qualified and skilled workers who, having been trained or educated in their home country, now take their services elsewhere. This constitutes a considerable loss for the home country, that will have invested in the education or training of the migrant. It is the receiving country that will gain from that education or training. Furthermore, as the area has lost its most able workforce, it is unlikely to attract much new industry. Some migrants do send some of their earnings back home, which will help the migrant's family in the first instance, but the money will eventually find its way into the overall economy of the home country. Remittances are a very important source of income, especially in LEDCs. Sometimes migrants return after they have earned sufficient money and often introduce new ideas, thereby contributing to the modernisation of their home country. Tourism, in the form of visiting friends and relatives, is another potential money earner. American tourists to Ireland illustrate this point well.

Distribution of population by age in the Western Isles and Scotland 1991–2001 (% of total population) — ***Resource 24***

Age group	Western Isles 1991	Western Isles 2001	Scotland 2001
0–4	6.1	4.9	5.5
5–19	20.8	18.1	18.7
20–44	32.3	30.2	35.5
45–64	22.4	27.1	24.5
65–84	16.2	17.1	14.2
85+	2.2	2.7	1.8

Source: Data adapted from Highlands and Islands Enterprise – Economic Update, October 2003

Components of Population Change in the Western Isles and Scotland 1991–2001 — ***Resource 25***

Area	Estimated change in numbers	Migration change	Estimated natural change
Western Isles	-2880	-1526 (-5.2%)	-1354 (-4.6%)
Scotland	-19 130	-12 785 (-0.3%)	-6345 (-0.1%)

Source: Data adapted from Highlands and Islands Enterprise – Economic Update, October 2003

Depopulation is a major concern for communities experiencing out-migration. It was mentioned earlier that once an area begins to lose people, services decline and that can lead to further out-migration. Soon the area can enter into a downward spiral of neglect with an ageing population and inadequate services. As the population ages the rate of natural increase also falls. This situation is very common in remote rural areas in the UK, and in the most extreme cases islands are totally depopulated. In Scotland the population of the Western Isles decreased by almost 10% between 1991 and 2001 (**Resources 24** and **25**).

Exercise

Figure 1

Filipino remittances hit $12.8 bn

Money sent home by Filipinos working overseas last year totalled a record $12.8 bn (£6.5 bn), the Philippines' central bank has said.

The remittances – a 20% rise on 2005 – account for about 10% of the country's economy, the bank added. Most of the eight million overseas workers are in the US or Middle East. According to the World Bank, the Philippines is the fifth-largest recipient of foreign remittances behind India, China, Mexico and France. It has forecast that Filipinos will send home about $14.1 bn this year. Their remittances play an increasingly significant role in boosting domestic consumption. In December 2006 alone, $1.3 bn was sent back to the Philippines, the highest amount sent in a single month of the year.

Source: 'Filipino remittances hit $12.8bn', BBC news, 15 February 2007, http://tinyurl.com/filirem, accessed 27 August 2009

Figure 2

Money sent home 'more than aid'

Migrant workers sending money home has become the biggest source of foreign income in some poor European countries, the World Bank has said. In a report on

Exercise continued

European and Central Asian (ECA) nations, the bank said that remittances sometimes beat foreign investment aid and exports in size. Officially recorded payments in the region – which includes former Soviet states – were over $19 bn (£9.67 bn). The largest amount of remittances, as a share of GDP, were sent to Moldova. The study, using data from 2004, indicated that money sent there by migrants was equivalent to 27% of GDP – an estimated $705 m...

Top 10 remittance receiving countries by percentage of GDP in 2004 *[Source: World Bank]*

1. Tonga
2. Haiti
3. Moldova
4. Lesotho
5. Lebanon
6. Bosnia & Herzegovina
7. Jamaica
8. El Salvador
9. Honduras
10. Albania

...The payments are a crucial part of the economy, have served as a "cushion" against the economic and political turbulence those countries have experienced, the Bank said. "For many of the poorest countries in the region [remittances] are the largest source of external financing," the report added. Some of the money is sent via official transfer services while others send money with friends...

In pure monetary value, the latest World Bank figures show that India was the largest recipient of remittances, with about $22 bn being sent home in 2005. China and Mexico were also at the top end of the table. In that year, total remittances globally topped $230 bn – of which developing countries received $167 bn, more than twice the level of development aid from all sources.

Source: 'Money sent home more than aid', BBC News, 16 January 2007, http://tinyurl.com/mtaid, accessed 19 July 2009

1. Study **Figure 1** and **2** above relating to remittances to the Philippines from migrants. Use this extract to help you discuss the economic impacts of out-migration.
2. *Question from CCEA May 2008*
   Study **Figure 3** and **4** below, which deal with the impact of remittances from migrants.
   (a) Explain why remittances become associated with the development of specific migration streams. (4)
   (b) Use the resources **to help you** explain how migration can have implications for service provision in the area of origin. (7)

Figure 3

Sending money home

Remittances are a portion of the earnings a migrant sends to relatives back home. Most migrant workers send home…20 to 30% of their earnings… At least US$232 billion will be sent back home globally by around 200 million migrants to their families in 2005, three times official development aid (US$78.6 billion dollars)…In most cases, these migrants receive low incomes working in the service or agricultural industry, for example as caterers, cleaners, or farmers. They respond to a demand for foreign labour in the host country…

Recipient families can only do so much with the money received; they are dependent upon whether their local economy can provide an effective supply of services and products…The average cost of sending money home is almost 10% of the total sent…[To promote development Government] Policies need to encourage a competitive environment, [minimise the costs of sending money home and ensure there is an adequate financial system so the money received can be saved and invested correctly]...Offering women access to financial institutions is particularly important as they are often excluded from credit and savings opportunities. [Also important is working with groups of migrants from the same community (known as hometown associations)]. For over 15 years Zacatecan migrants [(Zacatecas is an Mexican state)] have been using remittances to finance social infrastructure projects back home...[spending on] 1,500 community projects...

Exercise continued

In Central America approximately 90% of remittances are spent on basic family needs, including education and healthcare. The remaining 10% is saved or invested... research shows that migrants invest their savings in small businesses, real estate or other assets in their home country [because they intend to return one day]...In El Salvador, US$100 of remittance income lowers the probability of children leaving school by 54% in urban areas...Across Mexican rural municipalities, illiteracy among children aged 6 to 14 falls by 3% when the number of households receiving remittances rises by 1%...Studies in Mexico show that... Remittances may reduce infant mortality by improving housing conditions, allowing mothers to stay home and care for the newborn baby, or by improving access to public services such as drinking water...

'Sending money home', ind2 insights, http://tinyurl.com/sndmh, accessed 11 August 2009

Figure 3 adapted from resource for CCEA May 2008

Figure 4

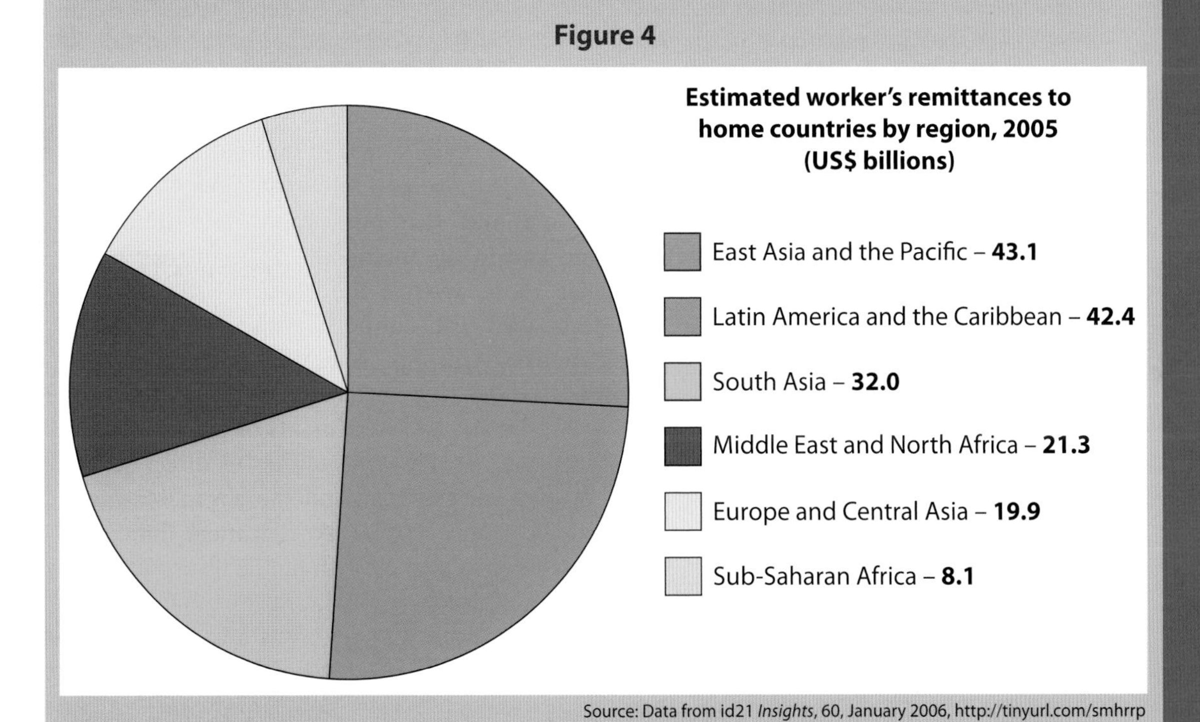

Source: Data from id21 *Insights*, 60, January 2006, http://tinyurl.com/smhrrp

3. Research the websites that follow, which have information on various impacts of migration. Use this material to help you discuss the following statement:
   "Migration has both positive and negative impacts for the area of origin and the area of destination."

Additional References

Impact of out-migration on Poland

http://www.ft.com/cms/s/0/432b5cfa-b007-11db-94ab-0000779e2340.html

http://www.guardian.co.uk/business/2007/jun/25/internationalnews

continued overleaf

Remittances

http://news.bbc.co.uk/1/hi/business/4442924.stm

Impact of in-migration to the UK

http://news.bbc.co.uk/1/hi/business/6766003.stm

http://www.guardian.co.uk/business/2007/feb/26/ukeconomy.economicpolicy

Problems of in-migration

http://news.bbc.co.uk/1/hi/uk/6654055.stm

http://news.bbc.co.uk/1/hi/uk/7001768.stm

http://property.timesonline.co.uk/tol/life_and_style/property/article1951400.ece

General article on Polish immigrants in Britain and the impact of out-migration on Poland

http://www.guardian.co.uk/world/2006/jul/21/eu.poland2

CASE STUDY: Small scale study of out-migration Barra and Vatersay Islands in Scotland

Barra and Vatersay are located on the Outer Hebrides, off the west coast of Scotland. In the 2001 census they had a combined total population of 1,172. Barra is the larger of the two islands. It has a mountainous centre and most settlements are found along the coast or in the glens. The main port and centre of population is at Castlebay on the south of the island. In the west and north of Barra there is a low-lying area with sand dunes. There are two small nucleated settlements here – Eoligarry and Ardmhor.

Resource 26 *Map of Barra and Vatersay*

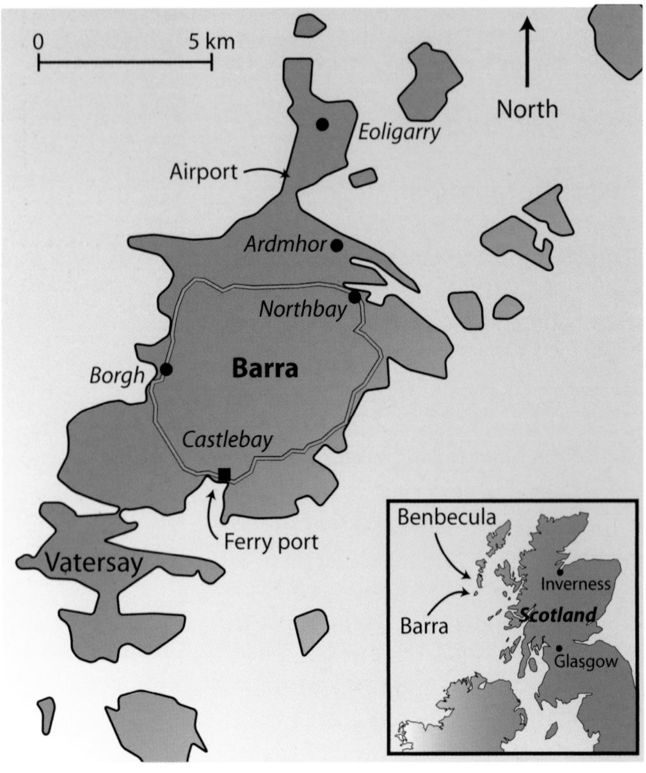

Transport and communications are difficult on the island and to the mainland. A main road follows a circular route around the coast. Castlebay is the main ferry port and connects with Oban, a journey of five hours. Ardmhor operates ferry crossings to the other islands. There are ongoing disputes with the ferry operators and the inhabitants of Barra. The ferry operators have reduced the number of direct services between Barra and the mainland, thereby increasing the length of the journey and making it more difficult for ferry passengers to link up with public transport on the mainland. There is an airport in the north of the island, where the beach serves as a runway and flight arrivals and departures are dependent on the tides. There are direct flight connections to Glasgow and indirect flights from Inverness, with stops at two other islands en route. The airport is also used by the Air Ambulance Service (there is no hospital on Barra).

Vatersay is a small narrow island south of Barra. A causeway joining it to Barra was completed in 1991 and this seems to have prevented the total depopulation of Vatersay. In 1988 its population had declined to just 65 but in the 2001 census the population had increased to 94.

Because of its small population, service provision is limited on Barra. Most services are low order and are concentrated in the island 'capital', Castlebay. Among the services in Castlebay are a primary school and a small secondary school, three small hotels (reflecting the importance of tourism), a convenience store, a petrol station and a post office. In 1981, faced with a declining population and dwindling services, local people successfully applied for government funding to establish the Barra Community Co-operative. The co-operative has set up a shop in Castlebay, which carries a wide range of goods including food, household and car accessories. In addition, the co-operative has set up a sub-post office in Northbay in the north of the island and a tea room at the airport. There are doctor and dental services on the island but all hospital services require a long journey to the Uist and Barra hospital on the island of Benbicula. There are few services in the remainder of the island apart from a few bed and breakfast facilities for tourists.

Barra offers few opportunities for those in the economically active age group. Some find work in the service industries in the main centres of population. Tourism generates some jobs but these are mostly seasonal. Traditional occupations such as crofting in the highland central of the island and fishing employ an ever decreasing number of workers. Some employment opportunities have arisen in the improvements to the island's infrastructure but these are temporary. Between January and June 2001 unemployment fell in Barra from 5% to 3.4%. This can be directly linked to the building of the Eriskay causeway but unemployment then rose again on its completion. In common with many island communities, long-term unemployment rates on Barra are above the national and regional average and wages are low. Gross weekly earnings are 12% lower than the Scottish average while the costs of fuel, food and transport can be up to 20% higher than mainland Scotland. The current high costs of fuel will only add to this situation on Barra. These facts are major reasons for the continued depopulation of the island.

Comparative unemployment rates **Resource 27**

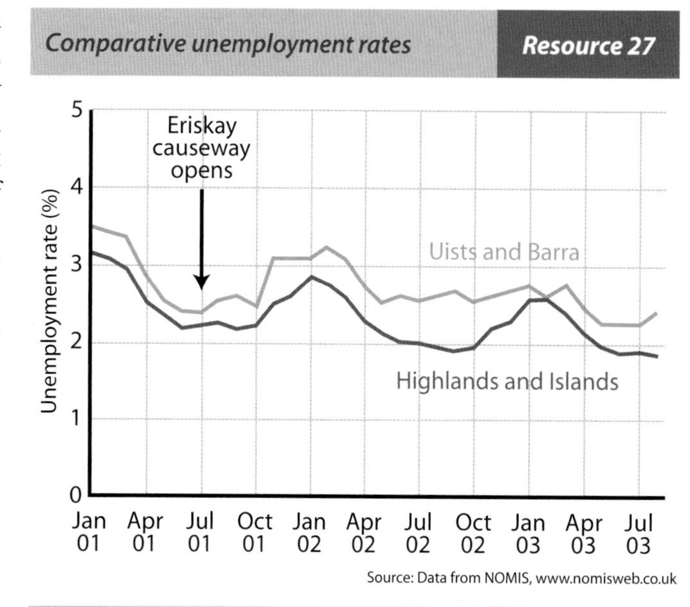

Source: Data from NOMIS, www.nomisweb.co.uk

Population pyramid for Barra **Resource 28**

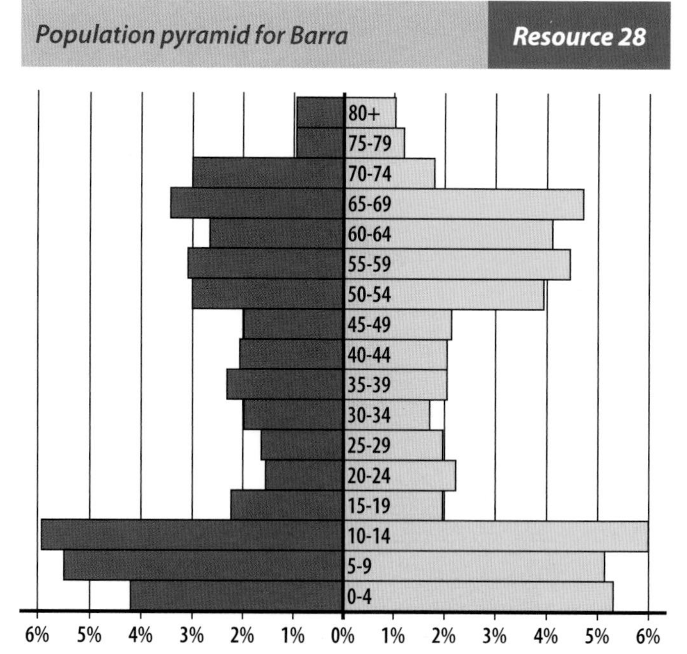

Population change on Barra and Vatersay 1951–2001 **Resource 29**

	1951	1961	1971	1981	1991	2001	% change '51–01	% change '91–01
Barra	1728	1369	1005	1232	1212	1078	-38	-11
Vatersay	151	95	77	108	70	94	-38	+34

The population pyramid (**Resource 28**) and table (**Resource 29**) for Barra highlight the island's future problems. The indent in the pyramid for the working population indicates the effect of out-migration. This will impact Barra in two ways. First, those who have left are unlikely to return with their families, so future growth in population is restricted. Secondly, it is likely that many inhabitants presently under fifteen will also leave when they reach working age. Statistical analysis by the European Commission has found that a critical population threshold of four to five thousand is required if an island population is to be sustained. Islands with populations below this level are likely to continue to experience net out-migration, ageing populations and inadequate provision of facilities.

Exercise

1. Discuss possible reasons for continued out-migration from Barra.
2. Explain the implications of sustained out-migration for service provision, economic activity and social stability on Barra.

Additional References

General information on Barra:

http://www.initiative-at-the-edge.org.uk/BarraVatersay.htm

http://www.scotland-inverness.co.uk/barra.htm

http://newsvote.bbc.co.uk/mpapps/pagetools/print/news.bbc.co.uk/l/hi/scotland

http://www.britinfo.net/cgi-bin/TLcats.cgi?s=D&cc=EAE&1=en

CASE STUDY: Small scale study of in-migration to Peterborough

Peterborough is a provincial city in the east of England that has had a long tradition of in-migration. The city, in Cambridgeshire, is located in one of Britain's most prosperous agricultural regions. The land is flat and fertile. The climate, with its low annual rainfall and sunshine hours above the national average, is ideally suited to arable farming. With excellent road and rail communications, it has become part of the hi-tech silicon fen region along the M11 corridor. Generations of seasonal workers have been employed in the many food-processing industries in the surrounding area. After World War II, large numbers of Italians arrived to work in the city's brick factories. In the 1970s and 1980s immigrants from Pakistan came to work as taxi drivers and as waiters in restaurants. More recently, there have been refugees from Iraq, Iran, Kurdistan and Albania as well as economic migrants from Portugal. All of these groups came in search of work in the surrounding farmlands. The population pyramid below, using data from the 2001 census, reveals that Peterborough has a youthful population structure, with a distinct bulge in the economically active age groups. Until a few years ago all of these migrants assimilated easily into the local community, but the most recent wave of migrants from Eastern Europe has increased local tensions in the area.

Resource 30 *Population pyramid for Peterborough*

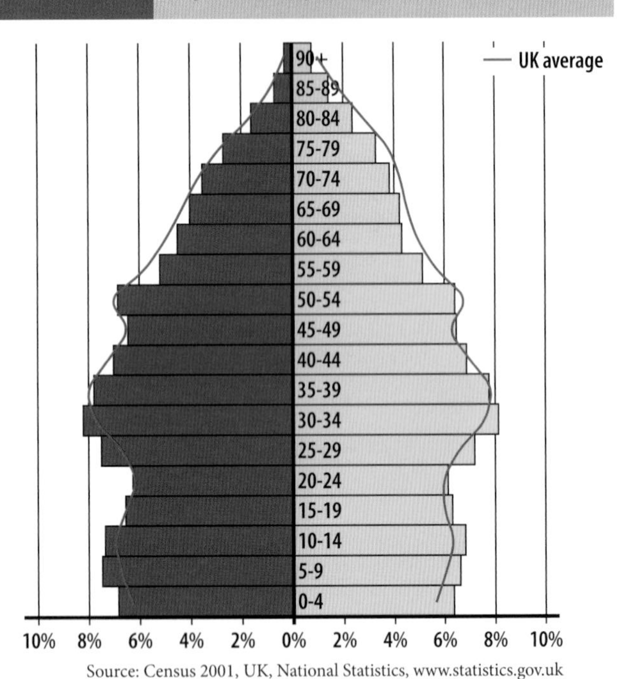

Source: Census 2001, UK, National Statistics, www.statistics.gov.uk

Since 2004 Peterborough has received a massive influx of East Europeans, who gained the right to live and work in Britain when the European Union was enlarged. The exact numbers are difficult to obtain (because of the suspected number of illegal migrants) but the official figure is about 20,000. This figure represents almost one in eight of the total population of 156,000 as recorded in the 2001 census. A police authority report estimated that new communities accounted for 64% of Peterborough's overall population growth.

There have been many repercussions of this massive increase in population in a period of just four years. The increased demand for housing, school places and medical care has severely impacted the existing level of services in these areas. Migrants are usually young and often have families (which may be quite large in number given the tradition for large families in the migrant's home country). This in turn exerts pressure on local primary schools, which have experienced a huge increase in pupil enrolment. One school enrolled sixty children from migrant families – about 10% of the total school role. In addition, many do not have English as their first language. The local council has had to employ large numbers of interpreters to help in those schools with large number of immigrant children. Health centres faced similar demands on scarce resources. The number of people registered with one GP in Peterborough has increased from 2,000 to 8,000 between 2004 and 2006. The problem is exacerbated because there has not been adequate funding from central government to keep pace with the increased demands. Cambridgeshire police spent over £800,000 on translators in 2005/2006. They employ 130 civilian workers to translate immigrant welcome packs into 15 languages. These welcome packs explain British laws, traffic regulations and give important contact numbers to the new migrant. Demand for social or council housing has increased dramatically. There are now almost 7,000 people on the council's waiting list for housing, and local people feel that their chances of being rehoused are disadvantaged by the influx of newcomers to the city. There is no evidence to prove or disprove these claims but the reality is that it is a perception held by the local people. Too often these perceptions influence people's attitudes towards the migrants and can fuel resentment.

The new migrants have made significant contributions to the local economy. Because most have come from low-income countries, they are prepared to accept lower wages than British workers, and in that way the profits of their employers are maximised. Furthermore, low wages mean that consumer prices are kept relatively low. The migrants also contribute to the local economy by filling the low skilled vacancies. However, it is often the negative economic impacts that are more apparent. Many of the recent immigrants who have families are eligible to claim welfare benefits under the British Government's tax credit and child benefit schemes. The increase in the number of migrants claiming benefits nationally has sparked fears that the government will increase taxation to meet this demand. Nationally, child support alone for new migrants costs £43 million a year.

One of the most controversial issues regarding the new migrants in Peterborough is the impact on society. Peterborough is a small city and therefore the impact on the local society is all the more evident. Local people feel that the character of their city has changed. There are now 55 different languages spoken in Peterborough and the migrants tend to live in the lower-priced housing in the inner parts of the city. There has been an increase in the number of houses in multiple occupation, with many properties housing ten or more people. The increased demand for housing has led to the rise in overcrowding, and some unscrupulous landlords charge exorbitant rents for very poor quality and unsafe accommodation. In one district of inner Peterborough, local residents complain of drunkenness and other anti-social behaviour in the streets occupied by the new migrants. In a minority of cases there have been ethnic or racial tensions amongst the new migrants, and in the summer of 2004 rival Pakistani residents clashed with Afghan and Iraqi asylum seekers. Part of the problem stems from the continuation of old rivalries from the migrants' home country and the adjustment process to new codes of behaviour that all migrants have to go through when they first arrive at a new destination. The local police claim that there has been an increase in crime following the latest wave of immigration to the city, but it is hoped that the information packs given to the new migrants may go some way towards reducing the conflicts.

Exercise

1. With reference to your small-scale case studies of both out-migration and in-migration, explain the impacts on service provision, economic activity and social stability.

Additional References

Impact on services in Peterborough:

http://www.dailymail.co.uk/news/article-482559/Police-force-spending

http://news.bbc.co.uk/1/hi/uk/6654055.stm

http://news.bbc.co.uk/1/hi/uk/7001768.stm

A3 POPULATION POLICIES

Population Policies

In situations where there are concerns about the future population resource imbalance, a government may decide to introduce a population policy to correct that imbalance. Population policies can either deal with fertility or migration.

Fertility policies

Anti-natalist policies

These policies aim to lower the fertility rates. They vary from the extremely coercive one-child policy in China to the more democratic approach adopted in Mauritius. In both of these cases the governments felt they were facing a Malthusian style crisis unless population growth was checked. The Chinese example was forced on the population but in Mauritius there were increased family planning facilities as well as restructuring of the economy. There was also an education programme, which informed people of the need to reduce family size.

Pro-natalist policies

These policies aim to increase the fertility rates in countries where it is felt there are insufficient people to fully utilize the available resources. As with the policies above, these vary from being coercive, such as those followed by the former Communist leader in Romania, to the financial reward schemes given to families who exceed a certain number of children in countries such as France and Sweden.

Migration policies

Migration policy is another method open to governments faced with an imbalance between population and resources. Migration policies can be employed to deal with over-population or under-population.

Out-migration policies

These are used to deal with the impending problems of overpopulation. One of the best-known examples is the trans-migration scheme in Indonesia. Indonesia is a large country made up of many islands. The population is unevenly distributed and concentrated in a few of the larger islands such as Java and Sumatra. There was clear evidence of population pressure in these islands and the Indonesian government embarked on a transmigration scheme moving large numbers of people from the overpopulated islands to the outlying and sparsely populated islands such as Iryan Jaya.

In-migration policies

Migration policies can also be used to encourage greater numbers of in-migrants. The United States of America, Canada and Australia are largely populated by migrants. Many countries have encouraged in-migrants to make up a labour shortfall in specific skills areas. In the 1960s and 70s Britain encouraged large numbers of migrants from the Commonwealth to work in the low paid jobs in the transport and service sector in cities. At present, Canada has introduced a scheme to fast track the immigration process for those potential immigrants with computer and medical qualifications.

Population policies are often controversial, especially when it appears that governments are interfering with family life decisions. If people feel that their freedom of choice is being diluted, they may withdraw their support from the ruling party at subsequent elections. For this reason governments do not take the decision to launch a population policy lightly. Only in communist countries such as China can the government introduce a deeply unpopular policy without fear of losing popular support. Usually population policies will be undertaken when a government considers that the current economic and social situation (health care and education) is unsustainable. There are, however, occasions when cultural and/or moral considerations underlie a population policy. In Singapore the government has encouraged higher birth rates amongst the better-educated Chinese population only and actively encouraged lower births amongst the less well educated Indian population. It could be argued that this is still an economic consideration but many observers have accused the Singaporean government of cultural discrimination against the Indian population. In the case of the Indonesian transmigration scheme, the government was accused of exporting Javan culture to the outer islands in an attempt to dilute opposition in these islands. Similar policies were followed by the former Soviet Union when Russians were moved to the semi-autonomous Soviet republics.

Governments in most democratic countries do respect the moral rights of individuals to decide on matters of family size. Communist countries give greater weight to the perceived needs of the state as a whole and consequently an individual's moral rights are often ignored.

CASE STUDY: National migration policy in Canada

Canada is a vast country, slightly larger than the United States of America, although much of it lies within the Arctic Circle. It has a population of 33 million (the UK has 60 million). Canada has a rich resource base for industry as well as plentiful power supplies and rich fertile soil. There are well-developed, modern industries, and the population is highly urbanised. Canada has had a long tradition of migration. About 75% of Canada's workforce growth comes from immigration and this is expected to reach 100% by 2010. Currently, one in five Canadian workers are foreign-born. Immigration has been a central component of nation building in Canada, establishing the pace of demographic and economic growth since the end of the nineteenth century. Throughout its history, Canada has always operated a highly selective migration system through the operation of various policies. These policies evolved over time in such a way that the numbers and types of migrants into the country were strictly controlled to meet the prevailing economic need. Several phases of the immigration policy can be identified.

Map of Canada **Resource 31**

The Open Door Policy 1870–1918

The main economic need at this stage was the development of communications and in particular, the building of the rail network across Canada. Canada is a huge country (**Resource 31**) and at this stage manufacturing industry was developing in the eastern provinces while the west and central provinces were largely agricultural. The building of the railways was deemed necessary to tie Canada into an integrated economy, with manufacturing strong in the east and agriculture in the west. The first Immigration Act encouraged farmers and female domestic workers to settle in the west. The policy was referred to as the Open Door Policy because there were no restrictions on numbers. However, the policy was very restrictive regarding the source of the migrants, who were sought almost exclusively from Britain, the United States of America and north Western Europe.

Immigration Act of 1910

May be excluded from immigrating to Canada:

1. "Those physically, mentally or morally unfit whose exclusion was provided for by Act of Parliament last session".
2. "Those belonging to nationalities unlikely to assimilate and who consequently prevent the building up of a united nation of people of similar customs and ideals".
3. "Those who from their mode of life and occupations are likely to crowd into urban centers and bring about a state of congestion which might result in unemployment and a lowering of the standard of our national life".

Source: Bélanger, C, Marianopolis College, 2006

This gave the Canadian government total control over the racial composition of the migrants. This policy was to continue up to 1960. The racial nature of the policy was underlined by the fact that the railway companies – who had not been able to attract sufficient migrants from the white countries – had to pay a head tax for each Chinese worker in their employment. People from warm countries were deemed unsuitable for immigration to Canada.

Preferred/non-preferred countries 1919–1929

During this phase immigration became much more selective. Prospective migrants had to pass a literacy test. The government separated prospective migrants into those from 'preferred' and those from 'non-preferred' countries. 'Preferred' countries included Britain, the USA, Australia, New Zealand and South Africa. Migrants from the preferred list were given financial assistance to aid their move and settlement in Canada. The Empire Settlement Act 1922 subsidised travel costs of British migrants willing to settle in farms in Western Canada. The 'non-preferred' list included Czechoslovakia, Poland, Romania and Russia. Immigrants from countries on the 'non-preferred' list were only admitted in times of need for the lowest paid jobs and they faced a variety of restrictions. Migrants from Western Europe were favoured to those from Eastern and Southern Europe. Immigrants from all other regions were admitted only if a relative already in Canada sponsored them. The 'non-referred' list also had a 'non-acceptable' category. These were people from 'visible minorities', such as the Chinese who had been brought to Canada by the railway companies. The Exclusion Act of 1923 prevented Chinese immigrants bringing family members with them. In addition, the government exercised tight control over the numbers of migrants gaining entry to the country. In times of labour shortage more were accepted and vice versa. The government also attempted to control the destination of the new migrants, again according to economic need.

Extract from The Exclusion Order 1923:

"It may be very right indeed to separate a man by law from his wife and family if he belongs to a race whose increase in the country would be disastrous to those already in occupation of it; especially if such intruding race be very prolific and very difficult to assimilate; and by reason of a more meagre standard of living capable of undoing the masses of those to whom such a country belongs. But aside from all that, the Chinese cannot rightly be said to be separated by any Canadian law from their wives and children in China. They are free to go back to their wives and children any time, and God speed them!"

Source: Bélanger, C, Marianopolis College, 2006

The Closed Door Policy 1930–1945

Canadian unemployment rose significantly at this time and the government stopped all migration apart from close relatives joining family already in Canada – the so-called 'family reunion' category. This category was restricted to those who were family dependents not wishing to enter the labour market and only from Britain and the United States.

1946–1962

At this stage the Canadian government sought to increase the number of immigrants but the selection process was to become even more stringent than before. A number of immigrants were admitted from Eastern Europe, particularly those fleeing or defecting from Communist regimes. However, it was still clearly stated that renewed immigration should not alter the population composition of Canada – a clear reference to the selective ethnic nature of Canadian immigration.

Immigration Act of 1952

The Act gave the Immigration Minister a great deal of discretionary powers. The following categories might be used to exclude some groups from entering Canada:

- "Nationality, citizenship, ethnic group, occupation, class or geographical area of origin".
- "Peculiar customs, habits, modes of life, or methods of holding property".
- "Unsuitability having regard to climatic, economic, social [conditions]".
- "Probable inability to become readily assimilated or to assume the duties or responsibilities of citizenship".

Source: Bélanger, C, Marianopolis College, 2006

1960–1986

This marked a turning point for Canada's immigration policy in two ways. First, the racist undertones of the policy were removed and secondly, attention now focussed on the skills level of the migrant rather than their source country. The preferred/non-preferred list was abandoned in favour of the points system. This system was meant to be a fairer method of selecting migrants, based on the economic requirements of Canada at that particular time. It provided an objective scale based on education, age, language, and skills, against which all migrants could be assessed. In addition, the family reunion category was widened to some extent. The points system could also be revised to meet changing economic conditions. Furthermore, migration numbers were tightly controlled to reflect job availability in the country, and during the recession of the 1980s immigration was greatly reduced.

Immigration Act from the 1970s

According to the Act, the objectives of immigration are:

a) "To enrich and strengthen the cultural and social fabric of Canada, taking into account the federal and bilingual character of Canada".

[...]

f) "To ensure that any person who seeks admission to Canada in either a permanent or temporary basis is subject to standards of admission that do not discriminate on grounds of race, national or ethnic origin, colour, religion or sex."

Source: Bélanger, C, Marianopolis College, 2006

1986–1993

This marked another major change in the direction of migration policy in Canada. In common with most MEDCs, the population of Canada is ageing and fertility levels had fallen close to replacement level by the mid 1980s. For the first time the Canadian government viewed migration not simply as a short-term solution to economic need but a long-term demographic necessity. Canada was at risk of under population and immigrants would bolster population growth and readjust the overall age structure of the population. To achieve these new aims, it was no longer necessary to have a pre-arranged job before entering Canada. The numbers gaining entry to Canada increased dramatically from 85,000 in 1985 to almost 250,000 in 1993. Selection did remain but greater emphasis was given to actual skills levels and to the self-employed and entrepreneurs.

1993–2008

The government has continued to view migration as an essential requirement for the demographic stability of the country. Potential migrants are still subjected to a points system but the scheme has been modified. Greater emphasis is now placed on technical and linguistic skills. The Canadian government has set an annual target of 320,000 immigrants. New categories of migrants have been introduced. Migration policies have continued to evolve over time in Canada and the last major overhaul of the policy occurred in 2002 with some revisions in 2005 and 2008.

Migration to Canada is a complicated procedure. There are three main categories of migrant and each one has its own visa regulations.

Temporary Immigration

These include visitors, students and short-term workers. Each person in these categories has to apply for a temporary visa which entitles the person to remain in Canada for a fixed term. The potential migrant has to justify his/her reason for coming to Canada and the Canadian Immigration Authority will carry out a criminal record check before a temporary visa or work permit is granted. At the end of the allocated time (two years in the case of a work permit) a temporary migrant can apply for an extension or renewal of the visa.

Asylum seekers and refugees

Canada has always accepted large numbers of refugees and asylum seekers who can justify their claims for refugee or asylum seeker status. However, the government gives preference to those considered most likely to become self-supporting. Most of Canada's refugees come from Eastern Europe and only 25% of those admitted are defined as refugees by the United Nations. Canada has its own system for selecting those refugees who are to gain entry. Some 80% of Canada's refugees are men, while on a global scale more than 75% of refugees are women and children. Such statistics have led many to suggest that Canada is applying economic criteria to the selection process. Furthermore, applications for asylum have to be made by the asylum seeker before he leaves his home country. The government does not want a large number of immigrants in Canada awaiting decisions on their asylum applications.

Resource 32 *Canadian points system*

Education	Maximum 25 points
Ability in English and/or French	Maximum 24 points
Experience	Maximum 21 points
Age	Maximum 10 points
Arranged employment in Canada	Maximum 10 points
Adaptability	Maximum 10 points
Total	Maximum 100 points
Pass mark	67 points

Source: Data from Citizen and Migration Canade, www.cic.gc.ca

Permanent Immigration

There are three ways to gain permanent immigration to Canada.

1. Independent class

This is the most common method and is used by the Canadian government to target skilled workers and professionals, which Canada deem necessary for the economic and/or cultural development of the country. A list of required skills and occupations, known as the National Occupation Classification has been produced. The Immigration Department of Canada uses this list to process all applications on the basis of the points system shown in **Resource 32**.

2. Entrepreneurial or self-employed class

To be considered under this category, an individual must have:

- Sufficient funds to set up a business in Canada (currently set at 300,000 Canadian dollars).
- Have one year of managerial experience to run and manage a business in Canada.
- Have a viable business plan that will employ at least one Canadian.

In addition, an investor prepared to invest 120,000 Canadian dollars for a period of five years is entitled to a visa at the end of the five year period. The initial investment is not returned.

3. Family class or sponsorship scheme

A Canadian citizen or permanent resident may make an application to sponsor a relative. Once the sponsorship is approved, the potential migrant must provide all the necessary documents to provide proof of identity and be called for interview. After security and medical clearance is provided, a visa allowing permanent residence is given.

In August 2008 a new category of migrant class was introduced. This was the '**Canadian Experience Class**'. Under this scheme certain temporary foreign workers and international student graduates with professional, managerial and skilled work experience in Canada could have their applications for permanent residence fast tracked. The scheme was widened in September 2008 to apply to any person with relevant experience who had worked in Canada but had left within the last year.

All of these categories allow a migrant to take up permanent residence in Canada but it does not give the migrant Canadian citizenship. Citizenship can only be applied for after the migrant has been resident in Canada for more than three years.

Evaluation of the policies

- 75% of growth in Canada's workforce is currently due to immigration. By 2010 the figure will be 100%.
- Since 1992 immigration has accounted for 50% of overall population growth and has reduced the aged dependency ratio.
- The national insurance contributions paid by the immigrants contributes to the state pension fund and health care for the elderly.
- Immigrants contribute to the domestic market demand for Canada's manufacturing industries.
- Migration has always been controlled to reflect perceived economic or demographic need.
- Earlier policies were racist but should be viewed along with prevailing policies elsewhere, such as the White Australia policy.
- More enlightened policies have been followed since 1967, with the introduction of the points system.
- Canada has become a more global society as a result of this change in policy.
- Migration has always been adjusted to the needs of Canada rather than the needs of the migrant.
- Attempts to direct the migrants to the less well-developed parts of the country have not succeeded and most migrants end up in one of the large cities.
- The establishment of the Family Reunion category allowed close family members to enter Canada, even during periods of economic recession.
- It has been suggested that Canada operates a selective immigration policy regarding refugees and asylum seekers.

- The recent increase in the numbers of migrants will increase the demand for services in the large cities.
- Some of the new migrants have been unable to find employment that matches their skills.
- The government is reducing the amount of financial help given to new migrants, due to the increase in numbers.
- A considerable amount of money is invested in Canada under the investor class.

Exercise

1. Discuss the relative importance of economic, social, cultural and moral considerations underlying Canada's migration policy.

Additional References

The following websites have up to date information regarding immigration to Canada:

http://www.canadaimmigrationvisa.com/morevisa.html

http://www.howtobooks.co.uk/abroad/canada/immigration.asp

http://www.migrationexpert.com/Canada/visa/canadian_immigration_news/2008/Jul/

http://www.workpermit.com/news/

http://www.cic.gc.ca/english/index.asp

CASE STUDY: National fertility policies in China

China is about the same size as the United States of America but has a population five times greater than that of the United States. China has vast resources but much of the land area of China is uninhabitable, meaning that population is concentrated in a relatively small area in the east and south-east of this vast country. It is estimated that about 90% of the population lives on less than 10% of the land area. Since becoming a Communist country in 1949, China has experienced very significant changes to the balance between population and resources. When the communists took control in 1949, total population was just over 500 million with many millions living in abject poverty, and life expectancy was just 40 years. Sixty years later, China is a modern industrial nation with a population of 1.2 billion and a life expectancy of 72.

The overriding aim of the new communist regime in 1949 was to improve the economic and military situation in the country. This was the era of the Cold War, when a new world order was established between newly emerging Communist countries and western styled democracies. China launched a series of reforms to utilise the resource-base more fully and to establish China as a major world power.

The Great Leap Forward – 1958 Pro-natalist policies

This was meant to be a period of increased agricultural and industrial production based on the Communist model. A large population was seen as necessary to provide the workers for

Resource 33 *Selected population measures in China 1950–2050 (projected)*

Year	Population (millions)	% urban	Life Expectancy (years)	Total Fertility Rate (children per woman)	Infant Mortality Rate /1000 live births
1950	565	13	40	6.2	195
2003	1,292	41	71	1.7	23
2050	1,394	No data	81	1.7	6

Source: Data from Population Reference Bureau, vol 59 no2, June 2004

these new developments, and the government encouraged large families. The total fertility rate averaged about six children per woman for most of the 1950s. The Great Leap Forward, with all its agricultural reform, resulted in one of the worst famines ever recorded. According to recent information, from 1958–61 the exact numbers of dead, originally thought to be 13 million, may be close to 30 million. Infant mortality soared as food production collapsed. Fertility levels dropped during the famine but within a few years they had risen to their pre-famine levels. In the aftermath of the famine, China set to improve health care provision with considerable success. Vaccinations were made available and even in the remoter rural areas the use of 'barefoot doctors' ensured that mortality levels dropped significantly in the late 1950s. This prompted the Chinese authorities to re-evaluate their pro-natalist fertility policies.

Early anti-natalist policies

In the 1960s and 70s the Chinese government sought to reduce fertility rates through a series of advertising and education programmes that highlighted the advantages of smaller families. Contraception and abortions were made more widely available. Later marriage was encouraged along with longer intervals between births. At this stage, the fertility policies were largely non-coercive and although there were some successes in the urban areas, the overall effect was negligible. Gradually throughout the 1970s, the policy was modified and where two children was seen as appropriate in the 1960s, by the late 1970s couples were discouraged from having more than one child.

The one-child policies

By the end of the 1970s the government felt the country was set for impending disaster. Mortality levels had fallen and although fertility had decreased, overall population growth continued. Policy makers had suggested that China had resources for 800 million but at the current level in the 1970s that figure was close to being exceeded. With increased economic development 1.2 billion could be sustained. However, given the youthful structure of the country's population, there was a realisation that even if fertility levels fell to replacement level, the population would continue to grow. This prompted the authorities to launch the well-documented one-child policy. The aim of the policy was to control population numbers to 1.2 billion by 2000. Earlier attempts at non-coercive policies had failed and it was against this background that the one-child policy was strictly enforced. The policy initially required that all couples have only one child and that they apply for official approval before conceiving a child. Compliance was encouraged through a system of rewards and punishments. Rewards included educational opportunities, healthcare, housing and job security. Punishments usually meant losing all of these rewards, as well as fines and forced abortions – even close to full term – and compulsory sterilisation. The policy has evolved and been modified over time. There are four distinct phases.

1979–1983

The policy was strictly enforced at this stage with no regard for individual circumstances. There were many reported cases of forced abortion and compulsory sterilisation. Under the communist regime all aspects of family life were monitored by local communist party officials. Local people were encouraged to pass on information about anyone not following the party rules.

Resource 34 *Population pryamid for China, 2000*

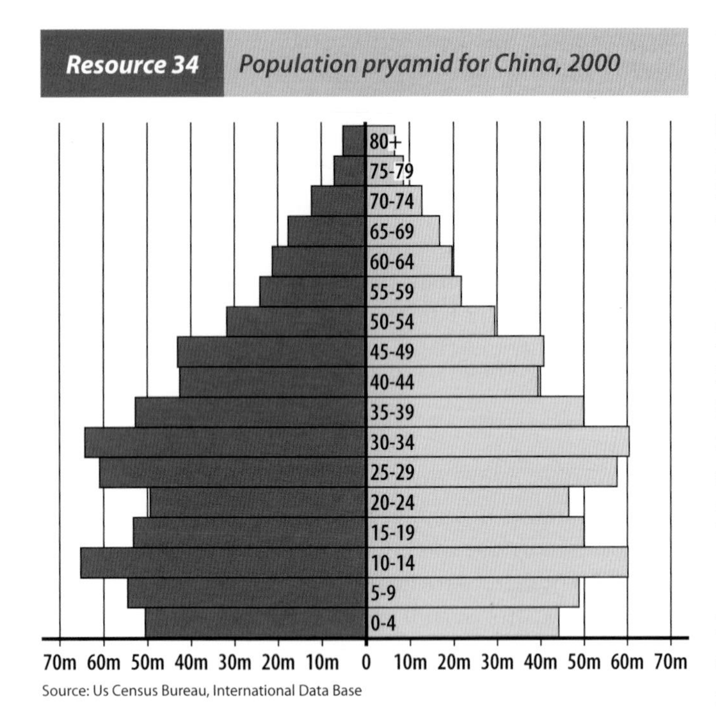

Source: Us Census Bureau, International Data Base

1984–1988

The success of the first few years prompted the government to relax the policy to some extent. In particular, local officials could allow some families in rural areas to have a second child so long as local quotas were maintained.

1989–1993

By the late 1980s fertility levels were beginning to increase again and this resulted in the tightening of regulations again. The administration of the policy remained at local level with a strengthening of the control of local party officials aided by the 'granny police'.

1994–present

In theory the policy is still in operation but less stringently enforced. In 2002 the New Population Law restated China's commitment to restricting family size but the emphasis is now more on informed choice. Other factors currently play a more important role. China has seen tremendous economic development in the last ten years and reduced fertility is synonymous with increased affluence, especially in the urban areas. Social changes are perhaps equally important. It appears that after almost 30 years of anti-natalist policies, the Chinese have lost the desire for large families.

Impacts of the one-child policy

- The methods employed throughout the duration of the policy showed complete disregard for human rights. However, we must not judge the Chinese authorities by our western standards. It is part of the Communist belief that the overall good of society overrides individual freedom. China was facing a serious problem in the late 1970s and they feared that without extreme measures population growth would not be reduced. There had been less extreme measures

Resource 35 *Projected population pryamids for China, 2025 and 2050*

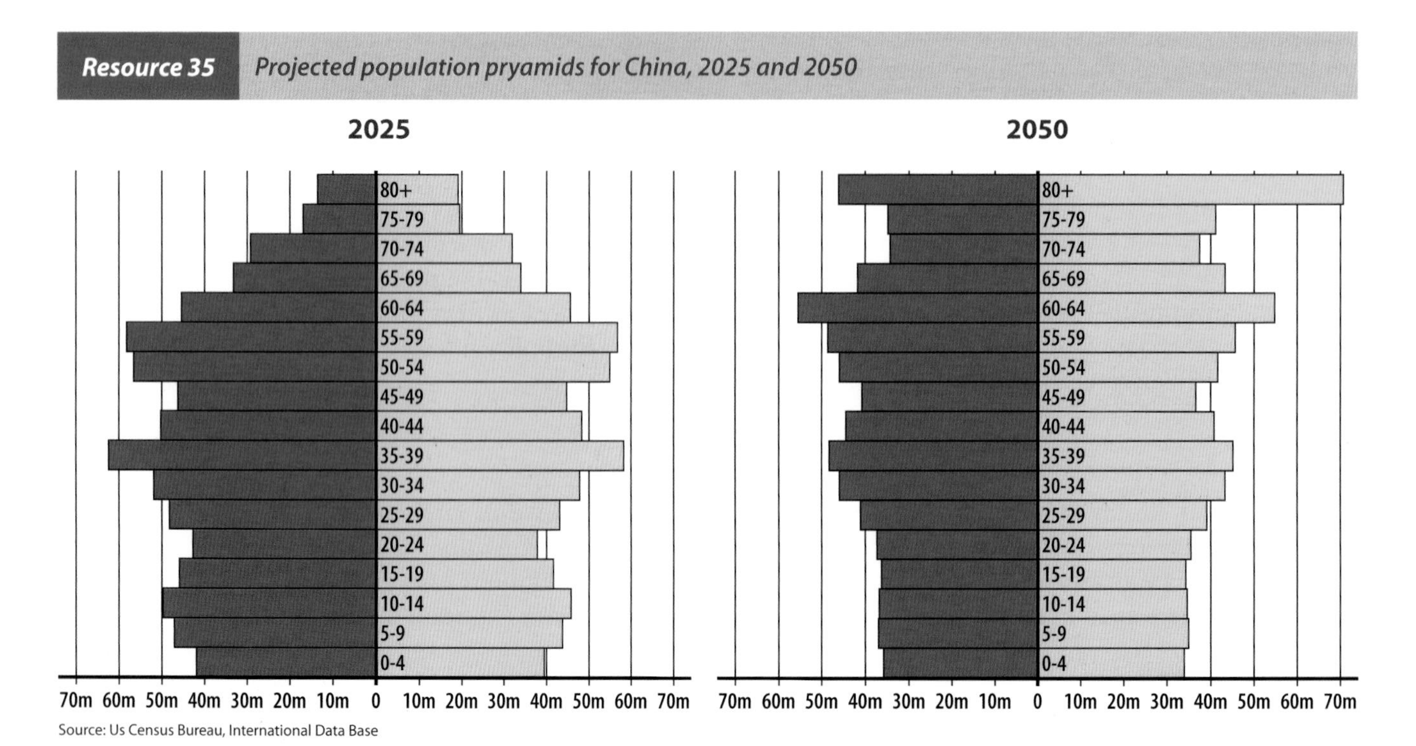

Source: Us Census Bureau, International Data Base

employed in the decade before the introduction of the one-child policy but with little effect.

- China has brought fertility levels down. Currently, the total fertility rate is down from 6 in 1960 to 1.7 in 2000. No other country has achieved such a dramatic reduction in 40 years. Total population has exceeded the 1.2 billion but the country is not facing overpopulation.
- Marriage continues to be nearly universal in China but the age of marriage has increased from 18 years in 1960 to 22 years in 2000.
- China has become economically well developed in the last decade and some of that success must be attributed to the anti-natalist policy.
- It has been claimed that the Chinese no longer want to have large families and that this change in attitude can be attributed to the one-child policy.
- The Chinese population is ageing and in the future there will be a reduced labour force. The proportion over 60 has increased from 7% in 1953 to 10% in 2000 and is predicted to reach 27% by 2050. Migration from the rural areas will overcome this problem in the cities in the short-term but this will be a challenge for the future.
- With fewer young people and more elderly as life expectancy increases, there are problems regarding care for the elderly. Traditionally, children take care of their parents in old age and this means that a newly married couple could, in theory, have to care for four sets of grandparents.
- State care for the elderly is not universal in China and it would be very expensive to provide adequately for the increasing numbers of older people.
- The Chinese authorities had claimed that the one-child policy would be beneficial to women. However, recent evidence shows that women were adversely affected. Late abortions and compulsory sterilisations carry serious risks for a woman's physical and mental health. There are also claims of women being beaten by husbands if their one child was female.
- The policy was always more successful in the urban areas where economic developments were taking place and the urban population was more aware of the economic benefits of smaller families. In the rural areas there was greater opposition from farmers, who relied on their children to work on the farms.
- Chinese culture places greater value on male children and there have been accusations of female infanticide, abandonment of female children or sex selective abortion. Whilst none of these practices were ever condoned by the authorities, there is clearly a gender imbalance in their population structure. The normal male/female ratio is 105 males for every 100 girls. In China the ratio in 2000 was 120 males for every 100 females.
- Normal family structures have changed drastically. Children have grown up without siblings and the next generation will have no aunts, uncles or cousins and it is claimed that the one and only child may grow up as over indulged – the so-called 'spoilt brat syndrome'.

Exercise

1. Discuss how China's fertility policy has been influenced by economic, social, cultural and moral considerations.
2. With reference to case study material, show how population policies attempt to balance population and resources.
3. With reference to your case studies of one migration policy and one fertility policy, evaluate the success of the policies.

Additional References

Population Reference Bureau, vol 59, no 2, 'China's Population: New Trends and Challenges', 2004

Geofile, 454, 'Population Policies', 2003

Geofile, 507, 'Demographic Change and Population Policy in China and India', 2005

B1 SUSTAINABLE DEVELOPMENT

The concept of sustainable development arose from the 1992 Earth Summit in Rio. It refers to development "that meets the needs of the present without compromising the ability of future generations to meet their needs|" (Bruntland Report 1987). At the Earth Summit in Rio it was agreed that all nations should adopt a sustainable development strategy for the twenty-first century. This became known as Agenda 21 (see page 65). The UK was one of the first countries to adopt these principles, publishing the *Sustainable Development Strategy* in 1994 and *A Better Quality of Life: A Strategy For Sustainable Development in the UK* in 1999.

The total world population currently stands at 6.7 billion, with more than 5.5 billion residing in LEDCs. Approximately 2.9 billion people or 47% of the world's population live in urban areas and especially in the very large cities.

The global economic situation is changing and countries like China and India, both with large populations, have made dramatic economic progress in the last decade. These recently industrialised nations will make demands on scarce resources and contribute to waste generation. Sustainable development is especially challenging in relation to settlements because they alter all components of the natural environment including drainage basins, forests and water resources. Economic activities in settlements have caused environmental damage to the atmosphere, resulting in global warming and acid rain; pollution of rivers and oceans; and generated large amounts of waste, much of which is non-biodegradable.

In MEDCs economic development was often based on the exploitation of finite reserves, mineral resources and fossil fuels, with little regard for the potential repercussions for the environment or the health of the local communities. When coal mining declined in Britain whole communities experienced social and economic difficulties associated with unemployment along with the environmental consequences of derelict buildings and waste tips. With limited alternative employment opportunities and lacking the skills required for modern industry, many people remained unemployed for long periods. Such unemployment has a knock on effect on other sectors of economic activity. A decrease in disposable income has a negative impact on those dealing in non-essential items. Gradually these areas become economic blackspots and can go into a downward spiral of decline. Research shows that personal morale diminishes in these circumstances and a raft of social problems often follows including family splits, poor educational attainment and vandalism. In other words these settlements, built and developed during the boom years of a single industry, such as coal mining or shipbuilding, were not sustainable.

Other settlement issues challenging sustainable development relate to urban sprawl where new residential, retail and industrial developments encroach onto the rural urban fringe, resulting in increased pollution from traffic and a reduction in biodiversity. Many inner city areas have become run down as developers seek more attractive Greenfield sites for development.

Exercise

Study **Figure 1**. Using the website sourced below the table, research this ward more fully. Discuss the evidence that shows that this ward was not developed in a sustainable way.

Figure 1

Social and economic data for Ballymacarret (inner city) and Belfast

Indicator	Ballymacarret	Belfast
% 16 year olds with 5 GCSE grade C	24	58
% Unemployed	9.3	5.4
Multiple Deprivation Rank*	9	n/a
Life expectancy	70	74
% Housing owner occupied	27	56

Source: http://www.ninis.nisra.gov.uk/mapxtreme/report.asp?DESC=FromGeneral&CurrentLevel=WARD&ID=95GG04&Name=Ballymacarrett

* Multiple Deprivation Rank – all 582 wards in Northern Ireland are ranked according to their level of deprivation. Rank 1 is the most deprived and rank 582 is the least deprived.

Figure 2

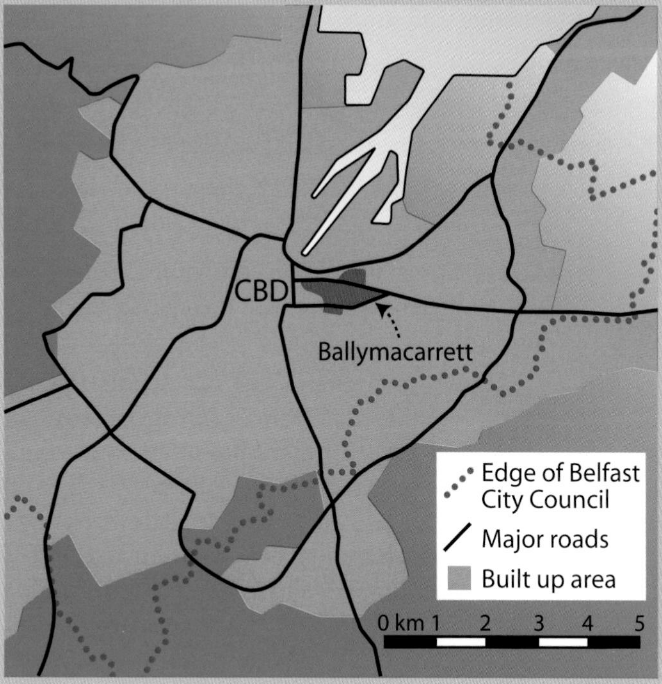

In the Sustainable Development Strategy in 1994 and again in 1999, the UK government set to deliver sustainability through three main areas: society, the economy and the environment. For each area a number of guidelines were published and much of the planning and delivery of the programmes for sustainable development was carried out by local government bodies.

Social considerations

In settlements a sustainable society should aim to incorporate the following guidelines in planning proposals:

- Provision of good quality housing, health and recreational facilities.
- Address poverty and social exclusion in the more deprived areas.

- Improve local surroundings, especially the areas of industrial decline.
- Ensure that the character of the countryside is maintained.
- Establish partnerships with local organisations to promote community involvement.

Economic considerations

In order to achieve sustainable economic development in settlements it is necessary to:

- make better use of existing resources;
- create a stable and competitive economy;
- develop a range of economic activities to prevent over reliance on one industry;
- develop a workforce with the appropriate skills that can adapt to change;
- aim to achieve increased efficiency in the production of goods and in the provision of services to the local community;
- encourage cooperation across all sections of the community.

Environmental considerations

Environmental concerns are perhaps the most challenging of all the targets for sustainable development. The key areas are:

- cutting greenhouse gas emissions and improving air quality;
- promoting the development and supply of renewable energy at competitive prices;
- improving waste management including recycling;
- safeguarding water resources;
- reversing the damaging trends that threaten landscapes and wildlife;
- working with other nations to tackle global challenges such as climate change.

In order to monitor progress on sustainable development the government have developed a number (150) of sustainability indicators in line with the principles of Agenda 21. **Resource 36** includes a sample of the indicators.

Resource 36 *Selected Sustainability Indicators*

- Level of crime
- Number of days when air pollution is moderate or high
- Number of rivers of good or fair quality
- Number of new homes built on previously developed land
- Percentage of waste that is recycled

Delivering sustainable practices requires financial input from central government. In the UK the government has attempted to raise money from taxes levied on key polluters, such as added tax for air travel and increasing vehicle licensing duty on cars with a high fuel consumption rate. A considerable amount of money has been invested in campaigns to raise public awareness of the issues concerned. A Sustainable Development Commission has been established to manage national and local sustainable development policies in the UK as well as promoting a global perspective on this issue.

Additional References

Sustainable Development Commission – http://www.sd-commission.org.uk/

Useful articles on this topic are available from the following website:
http://www.ace.mmu.ac.uk/Resources/Fact_Sheets/Key_Stage_4/Sustainable_Development/index.html

Urban ecological and carbon footprints

World population has increased dramatically in the twentieth century and so too has the demand on the Earth's resources. With increased affluence in MEDCs the demand for consumer goods has increased. In a global society it is possible to import from abroad and cheap airfares enables more international travel. Increasing amounts of waste are being produced and more finite resources used up. According to figures published by the United Nations it would take the equivalent of 1.3 planets to provide the resources we use in every day life and to absorb our waste for one year. This means that it takes the Earth one year and four months to produce what we use in one year. The UN also predicts that if current population and consumption trends continue, by 2030 we will need the equivalent of two Earths to support us! Turning resources into waste faster than waste can be turned back into resources threatens global ecosystems, and causes pollution, global climate change and food shortages. Many organisations, including the UN, have been proactive in formulating measures to ensure we live more sustainably. In particular, the environmental impacts of urban areas are of much concern because a growing proportion of the world's population lives in cities.

Ecological and carbon footprints are methods used to evaluate sustainability measures in an area and enable comparisons to be made between regions. The ecological footprint refers to the total number of hectares (global hectares) required to provide an area with all of its needs including farmland, fuel and water resources, as well as the amount of land required to absorb its carbon dioxide and other waste. This figure is then compared to the actual area of the region. The ecological footprint is really a measurement of the land area required to sustain a population of any size. Ecological footprints can be measured at any scale from individual level to global level. Because cities have high density populations, normally associated with industry and high levels of car ownership, the ecological footprint for a city is usually many times larger than the physical area of the city. In 2002 an organisation known as City Limits published the ecological footprint for London. Their results are summarised in **Resources 37** and **38**.

Resource use and waste generation in London 2000 — Source: Adapted from data published by www.citylimitslondon.com — **Resource 37**

- The population of Greater London in 2000 was 7.4 million.
- Londoners consumed 154,400 GigaWatt hours (GWh) of energy (or 13,276,000 tonnes of oil equivalent), which produced 41 million tonnes of CO_2.
- Londoners consumed 49 million tonnes of materials. On a per capita basis, this represents 6.7 tonnes.
- 27.8 million tonnes of materials were used by the construction sector.
- 26 million tonnes of waste were generated.
- 6.9 million tonnes of food was consumed, of which 81% was imported from outside the UK.
- Londoners travelled 64 billion passenger kilometres (pass–km), of which 69% was by car.
- Water consumption reached 876,000,000,000 litres, of which 28% was leakage.

Based on this consumption of resources it is possible to calculate the area or global hectares of land required to provide Londoners with these resources. This area is then compared to the biocapacity or resource production in London. The individual ecological footprint is calculated by dividing the total population of London by the total global hectares.

Ecological Footprint for London 2000 — Source: Adapted from data published by www.citylimitslondon.com — **Resource 38**

- The ecological footprint of Londoners was 49 million global hectares (gha), which was 42 times its biocapacity and 293 times its geographical area. This is twice the size of the UK, and roughly the same size as Spain.
- The ecological footprint per London resident was 6.63 gha. This compares with the UK average ecological footprint of 6.3 gha, and exceeds the global average of 2.18 gha.
- The ecological footprint of London tourists was estimated at 2.4 million gha, which equates to an additional 0.32 gha per Londoner.
- The proposed global average for 2050 is targeted at 1.44 gha per capita. For Londoners to be ecologically sustainable by 2050, a 35% reduction by 2020 and an 80% reduction by 2050, of their ecological footprint will be needed.

Resource 39 *National ecological footprints as a proportion of the global footprint*

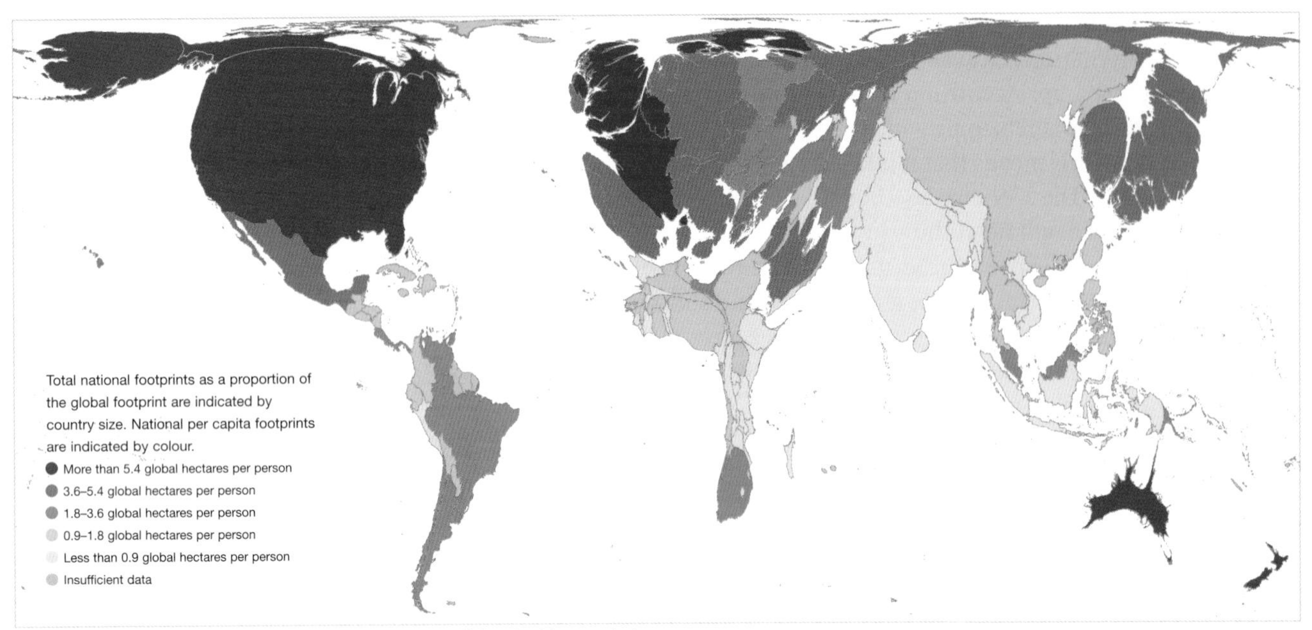

Source: Living Planet Report 2006, WWF International. Used with permission.

Exercise

1. Northern Ireland's ecological footprint is 5.63 gha. What does this figure mean?
2. Study the information relating to Ecological Footprints in the USA and Chad in **Figures 1–4**.
   (a) Describe the relationship between resource demand (ecological footprint) and resource supply (biocapacity) in both countries.
   (b) Contrast the ecological footprints of Chad and the USA.

Figure 1

Resource demand (ecological footprint) per person and resource supply (biocapacity) in Chad 1961–2005

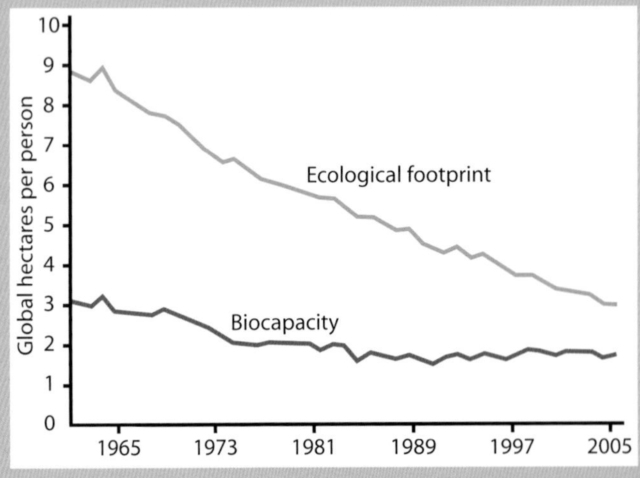

* Biocapacity varies each year with ecosystem management, agricultural practices (such as fertilizer use and irrigation), ecosystem degradation and weather.

Exercise continued

Figure 2

Components of the ecological footprint per person in Chad 1961–2005

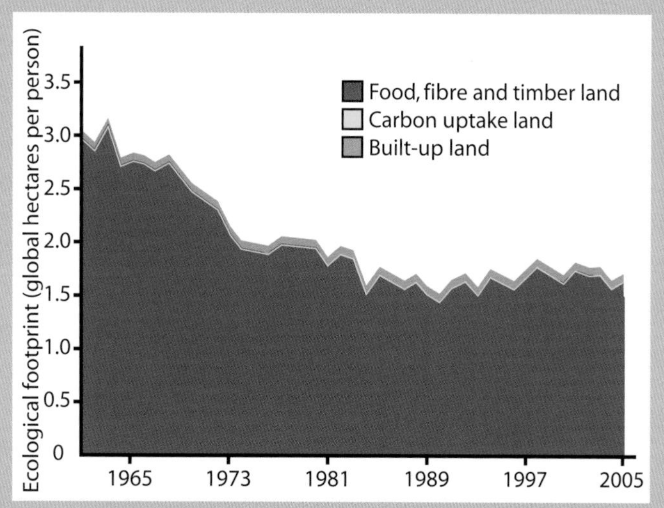

Figure 3

Resource demand (ecological footprint) per person and resource supply (biocapacity) in USA 1961–2005.

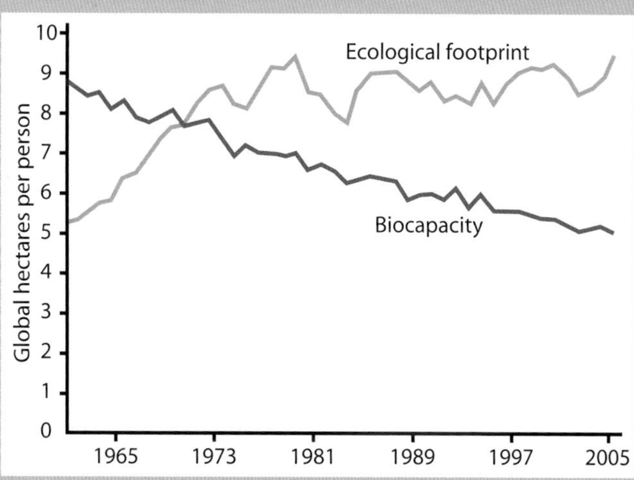

Figure 4

Components of the ecological footprint per person in USA 1961–2005

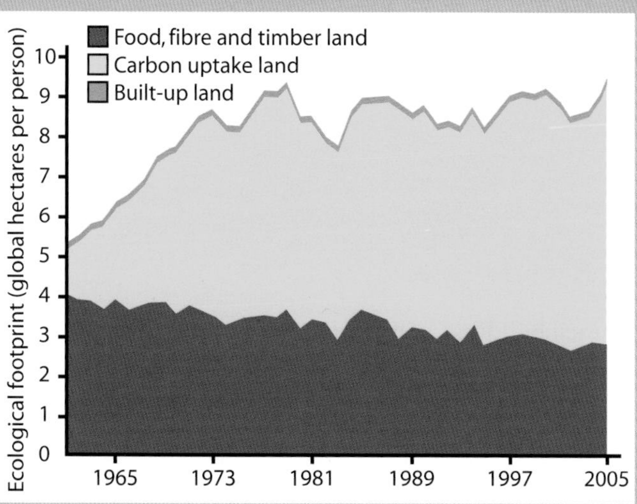

Carbon footprint

A carbon footprint is a sub set of the ecological footprint. It measures the total amount of carbon dioxide emissions that enters the atmosphere as a result of the electricity and fuel we use in everyday life as well as the amount of CO_2 emissions generated in making the products we buy. There are two types of emissions. Direct emissions result from heating and car use. Indirect emissions occur from the generation of electricity; the production of goods and services; and the amount of transport required to bring them to the point of sale. It is measured in tonnes of CO_2. Carbon footprints have been produced at various scales from national to local down to individual levels. The carbon footprint per capita in the UK was reported as 9.8 tonnes in 2004.

Resource 40 *Personal carbon footprint in the developed world*

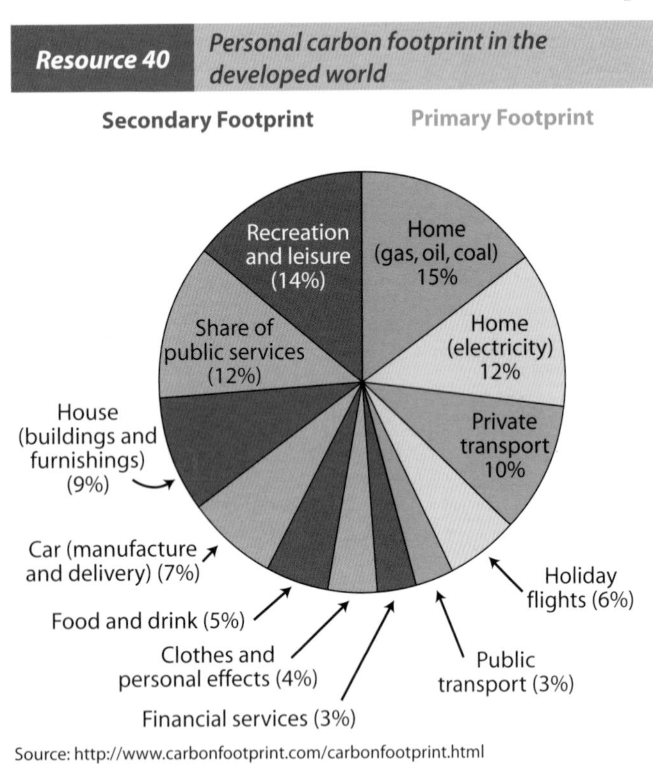

Source: http://www.carbonfootprint.com/carbonfootprint.html

The pie chart in **Resource 40** shows the main elements which make up the total of a typical person's carbon footprint in the developed world.

1. The **primary footprint** (in orange) is a measure of our direct emissions of CO_2 from the burning of fossil fuels, including domestic energy consumption and transportation (eg car and plane).
2. The **secondary footprint** (**in purple**) is a measure of the indirect CO_2 emissions from the whole lifecycle of products we use (those associated with their manufacture and eventual breakdown).

Local councils incorporate both ecological and carbon footprint analysis into the planning of new developments. Increasingly, government and public sector businesses will carry out carbon footprint analysis. Belfast City Council's website (www.belfast.gov.uk) has information on carbon footprints and how they can be reduced as well as a carbon footprint calculator.

CASE STUDY: Sustainable Development Practices in the UK: Leicester, Newcastle and Eco-towns

Leicester

Leicester, population 280,000, is the largest city in the East Midlands. Ethnic minorities constitute about a third of the total population, many of whom are involved in the commercial life of the city. Manufacturing industry accounts for 24% of all employment. In 1996, Leicester was the first city in the UK to receive a European Sustainable City Award. Leicester City Council has invested several million pounds implementing policies in line with sustainable development. Among the strategies introduced were:

An energy efficiency strategy

Leicester City Council aims to reduce the city's energy use by 50% by 2025 through the following policies:

1. 20% of all council buildings will use renewable energy by 2020.
2. Local people will be encouraged to rent solar panels to heat water. The rental scheme overcomes the financial obstacle of the high cost of solar heating systems. In some low income areas free solar panels have been given.
3. Home energy saving advice and information packs have been made available to all households free of charge.

Waste management strategy

The Council aims to recycle 40% of all household waste by 2025 through:

1. a weekly collection of household waste and a separate weekly collection of paper, glass and plastics.
2. a number of local community based recycling centres for bottles, paper and textiles. In addition, there is a recycling centre for the extraction of steel and aluminium and an anaerobic digester composts the city's organic waste. An energy recovery scheme from the composting site produces methane, which is converted to electricity providing power to 1,500 homes.
3. a public awareness campaign promoting waste management has been in operation for a number of years.
4. sending all the remaining waste to a landfill site.

Location map of Newcastle and Leicester **Resource 41**

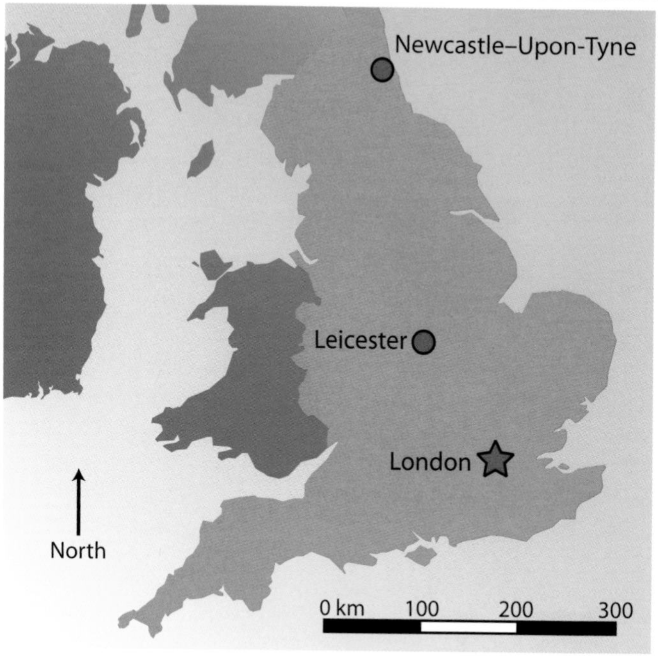

Improving air quality

In order to improve air quality Leicester City Council aims to achieve a 4% reduction in car trips to the city and a 25% reduction in individual family school run car trips through:

1. the appointment of A School's Travel Plan Officer to coordinate 'walk to school' or 'cycle to school' projects.
2. random testing of vehicle emissions. Fines are imposed on those car owners who fail the roadside emissions tests.

Sustainable transport programme

1. The provision of over 100 kms of cycle routes and bike parks across the city. The largest bike park also provides changing facilities for cyclists as well as storage areas and bicycle repair centres.
2. Improved bus services across the city.

Newcastle

Newcastle–upon–Tyne, population 285,000, is the largest city in the north-east of England. It was a major manufacturing city associated with shipbuilding and heavy engineering but in the mid-twentieth century the city suffered economic decline and deindustrialisation. In 2000 unemployment in Newcastle was 6.8% compared with a national average of 3.7%. This led to social and economic deprivation. A restructuring programme was undertaken by the local council to address these issues and a number of strategies were introduced. One of these included the 'Competitive Newcastle' strategy. This policy encouraged the growth of new service based industries in the redeveloped offices in the city centre. The council aimed to minimise the carbon footprint of all of these new developments. £40 million have been invested in a major redevelopment scheme in one of the derelict shipbuilding yards, providing high quality development space including industrial and commercial premises; riverside walks; a boat club; leisure facilities; and a riverside conservation area. This brownfield site has created 5,000 new jobs and attracted outside investment. Several other former ship building yards have also been redeveloped and are now a centre for modern marine and offshore technology.

Resource 42 *Map of the proposed Eco-towns*

Eco-towns

In 2007 the Prime Minister, Gordon Brown, unveiled a programme to build fifteen eco-towns in central and southern England. This was a radical proposal and marked the first new town development since the 1960s. Although designed for twenty-first century living, the eco-towns will draw on the experience of Ebenezer Howard's Garden City plan in the early twentieth century. A garden city planned to combine residential, employment, leisure and recreational facilities for all of the citizens of the city. The eco-towns will incorporate many of the principles of sustainability. They will be low-energy, carbon-neutral developments, built from recycled materials, with highly efficient waste management strategies. Renewable energy systems will be used in all public buildings and eventually in many homes. The largest will provide between 15,000 and 20,000 new homes and each development will have between 30% and 40% affordable housing aimed at first time buyers.

The new developments will have their own distinct identities, with good links to surrounding towns and cities. They will have a good range of facilities, including a secondary school, shopping and leisure conveniences. High quality public transport will be developed to reduce the number and frequency of car journeys. By locating all public services close together it is hoped to reduce the number of journeys required. Each eco-town will develop a plan to encourage community involvement in the new development. Furthermore, each town will have a clear economic strategy for its inhabitants. Work from home schemes will be encouraged through the provision of wireless and other IT networks. **Resource 42** shows the location of the proposed eco-towns. Developers of the new towns will have to comply with strict planning controls with regard to "sustainability, creativity and affordability" (Caroline Flint, Housing Minister 2007). The new towns will be largely car free and a speed limit of 15 mph will be enforced on those roads where traffic is permitted.

The government's intention behind these new developments is an attempt to address the housing shortage while at the same time addressing sustainability issues. However, opponents of the plan have raised the issue of the proposed location of the eco-towns, all of which are on Greenfield sites.

Exercise

Questions

1. With reference to the examples in this section explain how sustainable development is related to social, economic and environmental considerations.

2. Discuss how urban ecological and carbon footprint analysis has been incorporated into urban planning. You need to make reference to places.

3. Study **Figures 1, 2** and **3** opposite and overleaf and comment on the patterns shown.

4. Research the eco-towns more fully and prepare an argument for and against their development.

Exercise continued

Figure 1

Country	CO_2 emissions per capita ($t\ CO_2$) 2004	Equivalent global CO_2 emissions[(a)] ($Gt\ CO_2$) 2004	Equivalent number of sustainable carbon budgets[(b)]
World[(c)]	4.5	29	2
Australia	16.2	104	7
Canada	20.0	129	9
France	6.0	39	3
Germany	9.8	63	4
Italy	7.8	50	3
Japan	9.9	63	4
Netherlands	8.7	56	4
Spain	7.6	49	2
United Kingdom	9.8	63	4
United States	20.6	132	9

(a) Refers to global emissions if every country in the world emitted at the same per capita level as the specified country

(b) Based on a sustainable emissions pathway of 14.5 GT CO_2 per year

(c) Current global carbon footprint

Source: United Nations Development Programme, 'Human Development Report 2007/08'

Figure 2

Global variation in Co_2 emissions 2004

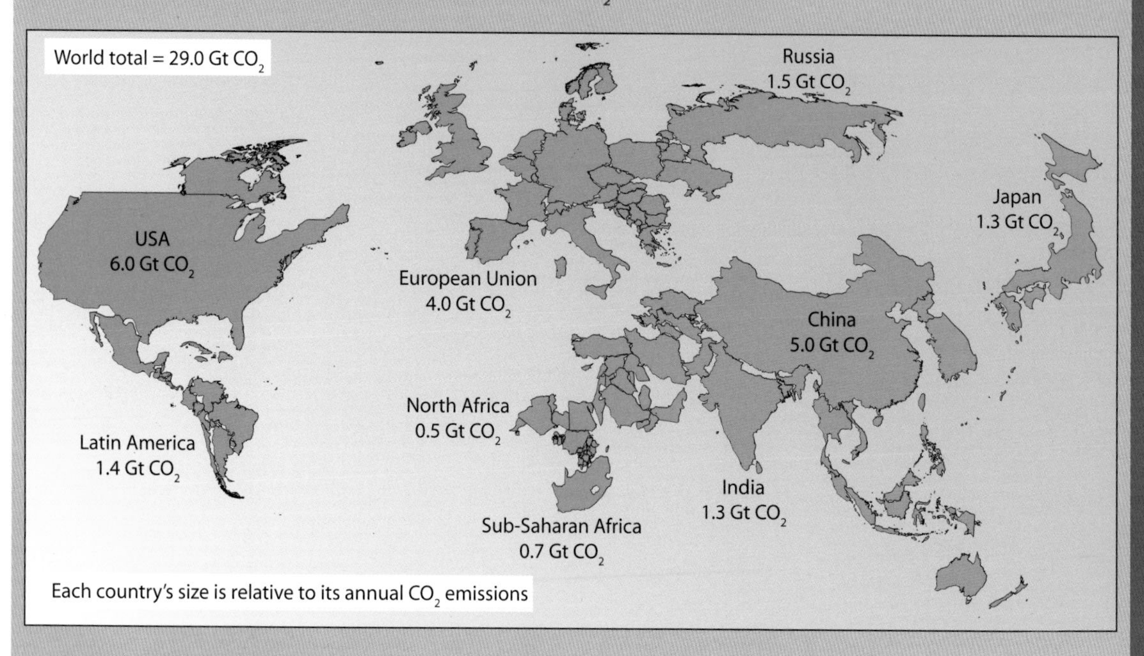

Figure 3

Tonnes of CO_2 emissions for selected countries 1990 and 2004

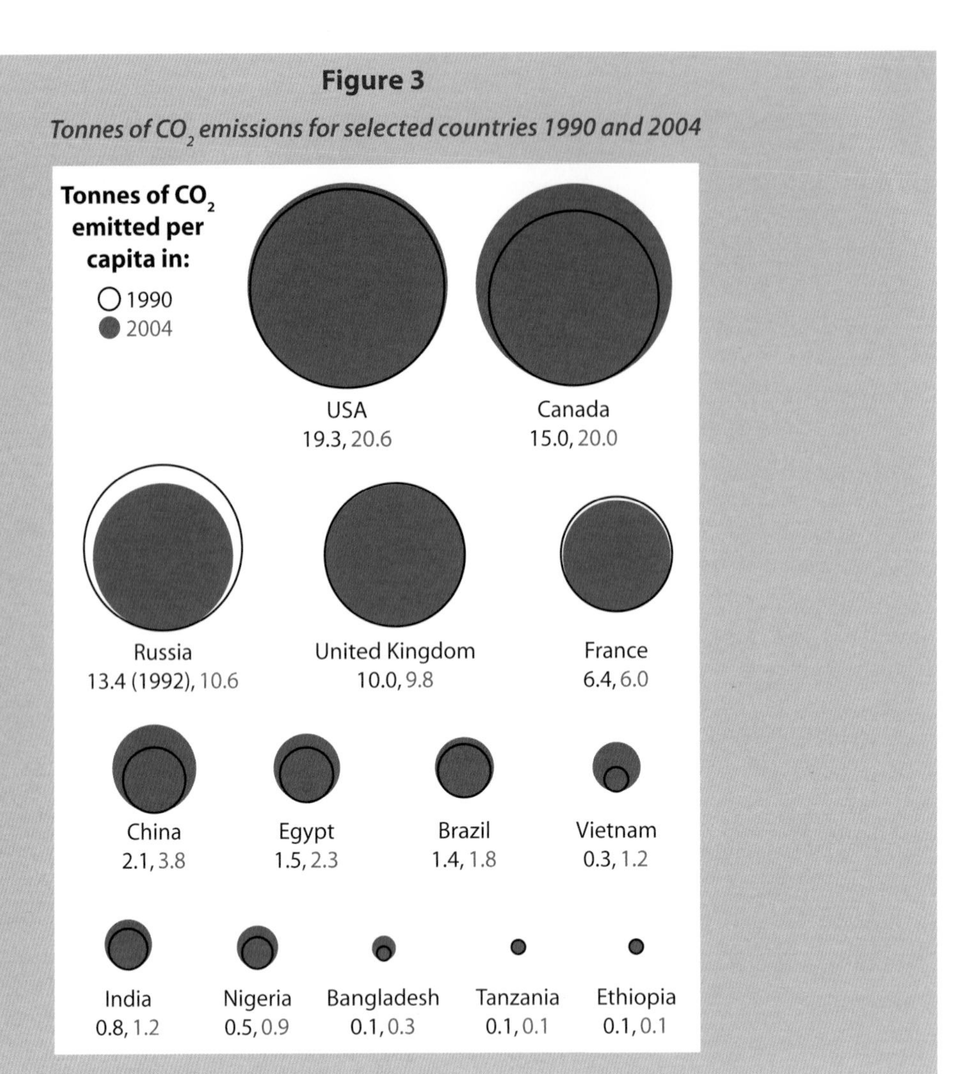

Additional References

Sustainability – http://www.ace.mmu.ac.uk

'Belfast – a sustainable city?' – http://www.geographyinaction.co.uk

'Is Northern Ireland putting its best foot forward?' – http://www.sd-commission.org.uk/communitiessummit/show_case_study.php/00181.html

Belfast City Council (a number of articles available) – www.belfastcity.gov.uk

World Footprint, 'Living Planet Report 2008' – http://www.footprint.org

Information on ecological footprints in Britain – http://www.wwf.org.uk/what_we_do/changing_the_way_we_live/cities/ecological_footprint_of_60_british_cities.cfm

Agenda 21

As stated earlier, concerns about global climate change, depletion of finite resources, population growth, waste management, pollution and disparities in wealth throughout the world led to the United Nations setting up an Earth Summit in Rio de Janeiro, in 1992. At this summit, attended by 179 nations from MEDCs and LEDCs, a set of guidelines was developed. These guidelines were designed to form the blueprint for sustainable development in the twenty-first century. The guidelines aimed to promote development along the lines of the Bruntland Report 1987 (see page 54). The agreed guidelines became known as Agenda 21. In essence, Agenda 21 provided a framework to tackle social and environmental problems including air pollution, deforestation, loss of biodiversity, poverty, energy consumption, waste production and transport issues. Many of the ideas in Agenda 21 were not new, even in 1992, but this was the first time that the issue of sustainable development attracted global attention. Agenda 21 was an international commitment by 179 nations to follow sustainable development practices. Those nations who pledged to adopt these practices were to be monitored by the International Commission of Sustainable Development and were encouraged to promote sustainable practices at local and regional levels within their own country. There was general agreement that sustainable development had to begin at the local level and with this in mind local Authorities were encouraged to formulate their own sustainability strategies, which became known as Local Agenda 21. Local Agenda 21 essentially followed the same principles of sustainable development at a local level. Where in the past decisions were made for short-term gain, now the potential long-term impacts of any new developments would be considered. For this reason, Local Agenda 21 strategies emphasised the need for widespread consultation and partnership with other community groups. Decisions made to deliver sustainable development work best if all members of the community are involved.

The main ideas behind Local Agenda 21 are:

- Protecting the environment for future generations, while improving life for present day communities.
- Thinking globally, acting locally. By making changes to the way we live locally we can benefit the wider community.
- Working together. By working together, organisations and individuals can make a significant contribution to sustainable development, locally and globally.
- Recognising the interdependence of the local economy, society and environment.

Evaluation

Since 1992 over 1,800 local councils in 64 countries have agreed to develop Local Agenda 21 policies. In Europe over 80 local authorities committed themselves to the principles of sustainable development by signing the Aalborg Charter in 1996. Many local councils set up public awareness campaigns to highlight the issues involved and to encourage greater participation and involvement in the policies. Local Agenda 21 strategies were not intended to be stand alone projects, rather they were to be incorporated into all aspects of the local council's development programmes.

Most councils agreed with the principles behind the Local Agenda 21 policy but it was not legally binding and some local councils failed to adopt a strategy. According to some estimates by 1997 only 36% of all local authorities in the UK had actually produced a strategy. When the Labour Government took office in the UK, in 1997, the Prime Minister said, "I want all local authorities in the UK to adopt Local Agenda 21 Strategies by the year 2000." However, in the late 1990s a number of amendments were made to Local Agenda 21 by the European Union and since 2000 many Local Agenda 21 strategies have been subsumed into more specific target areas, such as the European Sustainable Cities and Towns Campaign. In the UK, a Sustainable Development Commission was set up to implement the Sustainable Development

Strategy outlined in the Local Government Act 2000. This required local authorities to prepare a Community Strategy for their area, in partnership with other community groups. Local authorities were encouraged to set up Local Strategic Partnerships (LSP), to develop this long-term vision. A LSP brings together at a local level the different parts of the public, private, community and voluntary sectors.

By 2001 over 90% of local authorities were actively following Sustainable Development Policies. In 2005 the government revised their sustainable development policy, 'Securing Our Future', and in 2007 the Local Government and Public Involvement in Health Act extended Sustainable Community Strategies to other public sector organisations including Health Care Trusts, the Police Authority and the Fire and Rescue Services.

CASE STUDY: Local Agenda 21 in Dover

Resource 43 *Location map of Dover*

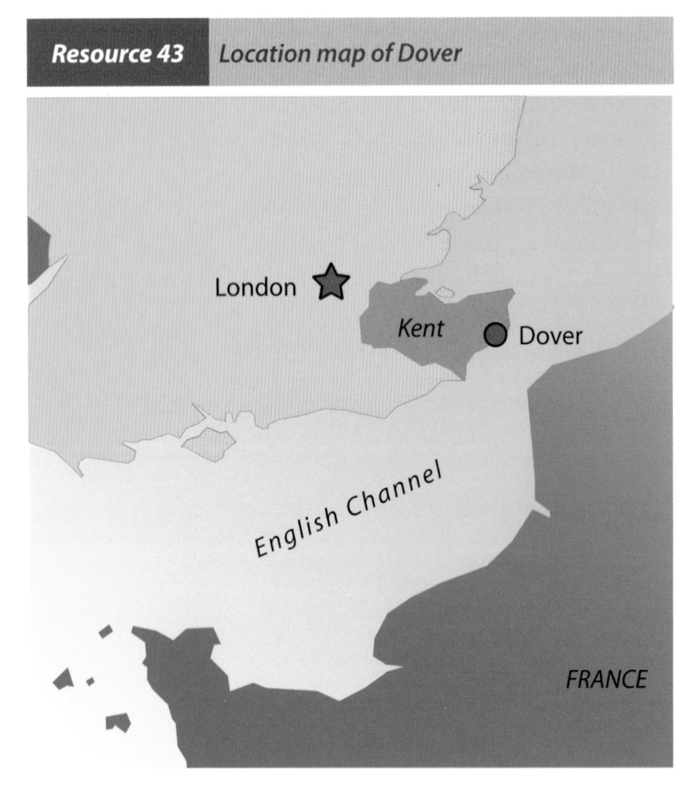

Background

Dover is a major ferry port in Kent in South-East England. The port guards the narrowest part of the English Channel beween England and France. Services related to the Port of Dover provide a great deal of the town's employment and there is also a well developed local tourist industry. Dover was one of the Councils that actively developed a Local Agenda 21 Strategy.

Dover District's Plan

Dover District's Local Agenda 21 Plan incorporated strategies that emerged from consultations with a number of organisations working at local and community level. A number of strategies were proposed:

Involvement:

1. Actively involve local people and organisations in Local Agenda 21 work.
2. Raise awareness of Local Agenda 21 issues across the whole community.

Community and health:

3. Improve the sense of community locally, especially for those who feel excluded, and celebrate cultural diversity.
4. Improve access for all local people to good quality health, leisure and cultural facilities.
5. Reduce the fear of crime.

Local economy:

6. Ensure that employment and training opportunities are available to meet everyone's needs.
7. Work with local and potential businesses to support sustainable practices.
8. Encourage communities to support their local businesses and services.

Natural environment:

9. Protect and improve the landscapes and biodiversity of the district's coast, countryside and villages.

10. Improve sustainable access to the countryside where this will not have adverse effects on biodiversity, agriculture or other countryside users.
11. Improve the sustainability of local food production and distribution.
12. Minimise the local use of products that jeopardise global biodiversity.

Built environment and resource use:

13. Improve the efficiency of energy use and increase use of renewable energy forms.
14. Protect water resources and reduce water consumption.
15. Reduce the amount of waste generated and increase the proportion that is reused and recycled.
16. Promote high environmental standards within new developments and refurbishments.
17. Conserve valued buildings and improve public access to them.
18. Bring previously used buildings back into active use where viable and appropriate.

Transport:

19. Improve the integration of transport in the district.
20. Work with public transport users and providers to make public transport a viable alternative to car use in most areas.
21. Improve facilities for walking and cycling throughout the district and promote these low impact forms of transport.
22. Promote more responsible and efficient car use.

Source: http://www.dover.gov.uk/la21/

What has been achieved in Dover?

Since April 2008, The Dover District is now part of an East Kent Local Strategic Partnership. The partnership brings together a number of public bodies, businesses, and voluntary and community sectors, in a voluntary partnership to work towards a prosperous and caring community.

Common priority areas **Resource 44**

A range of common priority areas for East Kent have been identified including:

Sustainable communities
Transport and infrastructure
Skills transformation
Health and well-being
Economic development and regeneration
Culture and tourism
Housing
Planning and local development framework
Inward investment
Community safety
Environment

Source: www.eastkentlsp.org.uk

Achievements to date include:

- The interests of local communities are considered in the formulation of any development programmes.
- Degree of community cohesion is assessed against government produced targets.
- Measures have been put in place to reduce crime levels.
- A number of coastal protection schemes have been implemented.
- A public awareness campaign is in operation regarding energy conservation and fact sheets have been produced with information on renewable energy schemes.

- 10,000 new homes will be built in the Dover area over the next thirty years. These will include some social housing.
- Kent Waste Partnership manages a successful waste management scheme. In 2007/08 Dover recycled 38% of all waste, the target is 40% by 2011. At the same time there has been a 16% decrease in the amount of waste going to landfill sites.
- Conservation areas and listed buildings are regularly monitored.
- A comprehensive transport plan has been produced with the aim of improving existing local networks and promoting greater use of public transport.

Additional References

Dover city council – http://www.dover.gov.uk/

East Kent Local Strategic Partnership – www.eastkentlsp.org.uk

Kent Waste Partnership – http://www.kent.gov.uk/environment/recycling-rubbish-and-waste/kent-waste-partnership/

Leicester – http://www.leics.gov.uk/local_agenda_21.htm

Stafford – http://www.staffordbc.gov.uk/static/page909.htm

Hammersmith and Fulham – http://www.lbhf.gov.uk/external/la21/index.htm

Sustainable communities – http://www.communities.gov.uk/communities/sustainablecommunities/sustainablecommunities/

Information on recent government proposals – www.sustainable.gov.uk

Question

Exercise

Using one of the above websites, prepare a presentation on:

"An evaluation of the impact of LA21 on planning for sustainability"

B2 URBAN LAND USE AND PLANNING IN RELATION TO SUSTAINABILITY

Urban land use and planning in relation to sustainability

Sustainable development, where planners do not simply focus on short-term gain but consider the long-term social, economic and environmental impacts of any developments, can be easily applied to settlements. Increasingly local councils, under government direction, have been attempting to incorporate sustainability concepts into their planning and management policies. In the UK there is a Sustainable Settlements Organisation. A sustainable settlement should aim to focus on many of the following strategies:

- The provision of efficient and affordable public transport systems that will reduce dependence on car journeys.
- Explore renewable energy sources and seek ways to reduce dependence on fossil fuels.
- Limit urban sprawl and prevent over use of Greenfield sites.
- Maximise the potential of all available land within a settlement boundary, including the redevelopment or regeneration of brownfield sites.
- Follow a recycling and waste management strategy.
- Provide a clean, healthy and safe environment for all of its inhabitants.
- Follow an effective social inclusion policy whereby all the inhabitants feel part of the community.
- Provide adequate employment opportunities and a skilled workforce so that the settlement has commercial and economic viability.
- Provide a range of recreational and leisure activities.
- Develop policies in relation to urban conservation and regeneration.

It is unlikely that all of these ideals will be realised everywhere but they are increasingly forming the basis of urban land use planning.

The management of residential areas

Within many western cities residential areas are segregated, albeit voluntarily, on an income basis. The better off members of society are able to choose where they will live and a person's address is often an indication of personal wealth. The less well off live where they find suitable accommodation that they can afford. In western cities this has often led to a segregated society, with the wealthy in the more prestigious suburban locations with the urban poor confined to the run down inner city areas. The Burgess model of urban land use was based on the idea that as people became better off they moved on to the next best residential district and their former neighbourhood became the home of more recent and poorer urban dwellers. The less well off areas were characterised by high levels of unemployment and associated socio-economic problems (**Figure 1, page 55**).

Urban planners in the 1960s sought to address this housing issue by building modern high rise flats in the inner city or in the suburbs. The idea was to house as many people as possible in their original neighbourhoods and high rise flats offered an affordable solution to this issue. However, many of these developments became 'sink estates', with high levels of unemployment, low educational attainments and crime. In the UK there was often an ethnic divide adding to the difficulties. It was clear that the urban planners had made fundamental miscalculations about the workings of communities.

In the USA a study of two housing developments in St Louis (Missouri) in the 1960s provided some interested findings for urban planners. Both housing developments were occupied by people from the same socio-economic grouping, with low income and high levels of unemployment. However, one development was blighted by crime and vandalism while the other was relatively free of crime. This apparent difference in behaviour in the two housing developments prompted planners to question the influence of residential styles on behaviour.

1. The crime free development consisted of terraced housing, each housing unit occupied by one family. There was a clear demarcation of the territory owned or rented by each family. The houses were of uniform design but individual families were able to paint the exterior according to their choice.
2. The development blighted by crime consisted of a series of 11 storey identical apartment blocks. Each apartment block had a communal first floor. Every third floor contained a communal laundry and other utilities, such as waste disposal chutes. A river flanked by trees flowed under the complex.

Resource 45 *Location of crime in the apartment block development in St Louis*

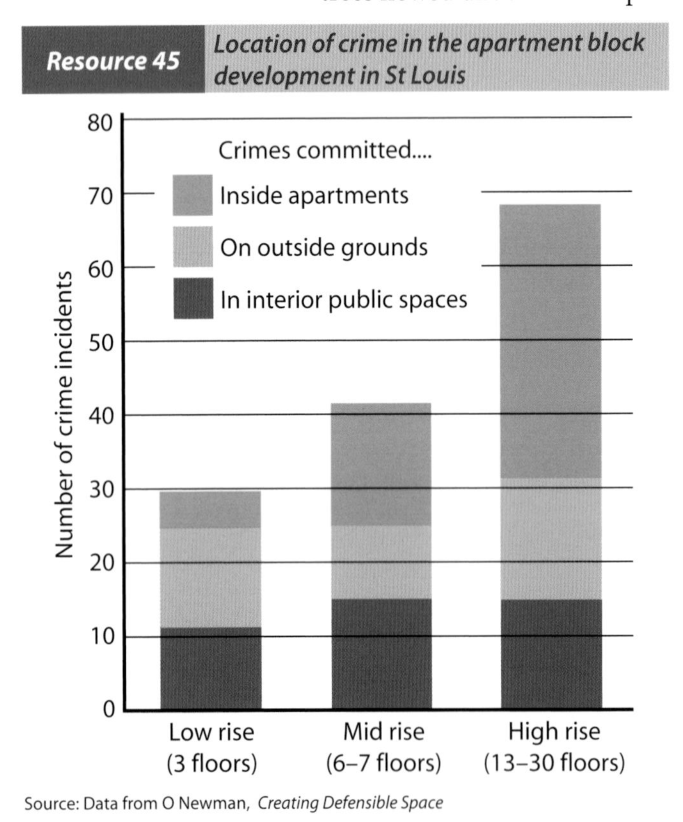

Source: Data from O Newman, *Creating Defensible Space*

Within a short period of time the high rise development showed evidence of vandalism and crime. The river was contaminated with litter, the communal areas were vandalised and the corridors, halls and staircases were covered with graffiti and became dangerous areas to walk alone. Women had to get together in groups to escort children to school or go shopping. The level of vandalism increased in the areas of most intense use. On closer inspection it was found that irrespective of the amount of vandalism, the interiors of the apartments were generally well maintained. Only 60% of the apartments were ever occupied and eventually the entire complex was demolished. The older terraced housing development remained fully occupied and trouble free.

Oscar Newman explained these observations through the concept of **defensible space**. At its simplest, defensible space displays the ideas behind a medieval castle. In other words, individuals will claim ownership of and take responsibility for territory that can be clearly demarcated by a physical boundary such as a wall, hedge or fence. The two main principles behind defensible space are:

- A family's claim to a territory diminishes as the number of families sharing that space increases.
- The larger the number of people sharing a communal area the more difficult it is for people to identify with it or to control the activity taking place within it.

Newman stated that, based on these two principles, land surrounding a dwelling could be classified as private, semi-private, public or semi-public depending on its degree of privacy and accessibility. In the case of a detached house the back of the house is private if it can only be accessed from within the house or via a gate. The front garden also belongs to the house owner but as it is accessible from the street it is only semi-private. In the case of a high rise apartment block there are areas within and outside the building that are communal and therefore the only private area is the interior of each apartment. The corridors, landings and staircases are at best semi-public and the areas outside the complex are all public. In other words, as the density of

High rise flats – The only private space is the interior of each flat; all other space is public space.

Private detached house in a gated cul de sac – Private space includes the interior of the house, the rear garden and the garage. The house is protected by a burglar alarm. The front garden and driveway are semi-private and the street in front of the house is semi-public.

occupancy increases, the amount of defensible space decreases.

The importance of this concept of defensible space has been appreciated by some urban planners today. The British Crime Survey (BCS) has established that the spatial pattern of burglaries in some British cities is associated with particular types of built environment. An investigation into the incidence of crime in an inner London estate found that the lack of defensible space in the dimly lit and blind corners of the communal staircases often provided the breeding grounds for crime. The interlocking walkways linking various tower blocks provided free access to the perpetrators of crime to escape from their victims. In the early 1990s a policy initiative called Secured by Design (SBD) encouraged planners to incorporate the concepts of defensible space into their housing developments.

Coal Pit Mews – Batley

Batley in Yorkshire is an area of high unemployment as a result of the decline of the textile and manufacturing industries. In the 1990s a new housing programme sought to follow the guidelines of SBD in the planning of a new neighbourhood of twenty-eight houses known as Coal Pit Mews (**Resource 46**). The main characteristics are:

- Every dwelling entry is overlooked by at least one other property.
- Tall trees and under growth were removed. New trees were planted which would have no foliage below 2 metres when fully grown.
- Trees were not planted to obscure windows, doors or street lights.
- The surface of the roads and pavements in the estate are noticeably different from those beyond the limits of the estate. This marks the limits or territory of the neighbourhood.
- Coal Pit Mews is a cul-de-sac development so non-residents will not use this route as through route to other destinations.

Plan of Coal Pit Mews **Resource 46**

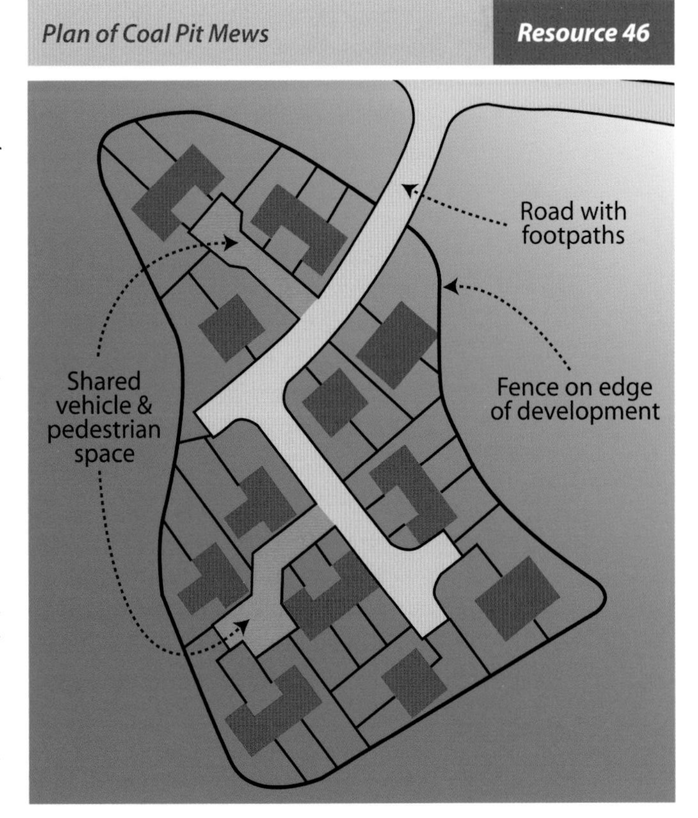

- The perimeter of the estate is bordered by a two metre high fence, providing an obvious physical barrier.
- All houses are clearly numbered and electricity and gas meters are in clear view at the front of each dwelling.
- Car parking space is provided at the front of each building enabling the owner to defend his/her property from inside the house.
- All houses have clearly identifiable security features, such as morticed locks, burglar alarms and security lighting.

In 2000 a survey showed that there were 26% fewer crime events per dwelling in a sample of 660 dwellings in a SBD development compared to those in a non SBD area.

Planners are also concerned with the building of neighbourhood units. Residential areas should be broken up into clearly identifiable neighbourhood units. A neighbourhood is defined as a subset of the wider community with some unifying characteristics. The size of these can vary but one method used the number of households required to populate a small primary school. The primary school would become the focal point in the neighbourhood and help engender a feeling of community. Children could walk to school thereby reducing the need for the 'school run' car journey. The absence of through traffic would make the area not only cleaner but also safer. Children could play on the streets close to their home under the supervision of their parents. A secondary school would serve several smaller neighbourhoods and in time other community services may follow (see **Figure 3**, page 74).

The re-use of industrial areas

The decline of inner city housing areas often followed from the decline in industry. Many cities in the UK grew rapidly during the industrial developments associated with heavy manufacturing in the late nineteenth and early twentieth century. At that time workers had to be housed close to their place of work, leading to the development of the high density low income terraced housing in the inner city. During the second half of the twentieth century, a combination of outdated production methods and competition from low waged economies abroad, resulted in the decline of much of the UK's heavy manufacturing industry. As stated earlier, many of these cities had grown around one major industry and its subsidiaries. When the main industry closed the subsidiaries also closed. Often entire families found employment in these neighbourhood industries. Belfast's lower Newtownards Road is an example where several generations had found employment in Harland and Wolff shipyards and associated industries. Abandoned factories, mines, collieries and shipyards all testify to this whole scale decline in industry or deindustrialisation. Redevelopment of the residential areas often involved building low income housing in suburban areas and new industries preferred the more accessible Greenfield sites on the edge of the city, where there were better and more efficient road links and cheaper land. The growth in car ownership and suburban sprawl in general meant that many inner city areas became run down and neglected. The sites of former industry were left derelict. Such sites are referred to as Brownfield sites. After years of neglect planners turned their attention towards these brownfield sites in the late 1980s. Most cities in the UK saw a comprehensive regeneration and redevelopment plans focussed on the inner cities by the Urban Development Corporations (UDCs), such as Laganside Development Corporation in Belfast and Merseyside Development Corporation in Liverpool.

Re-use of these brownfield sites has become a key element of urban land use planning in relation to sustainability. Such redevelopment/regeneration contributes to sustainability in a number of ways. Most of these schemes included a variety of land uses, including industrial, residential, recreational and transport. The juxtaposition of housing and place of work, together with improved public transport, should reduce the number of car journeys to work. The new buildings usually incorporate many of the principles of sustainability, such as carbon neutral developments, in their design. In addition, the re-use of these sites improves the overall environment of the region leading to a reduction in crime and at the same time the rural areas

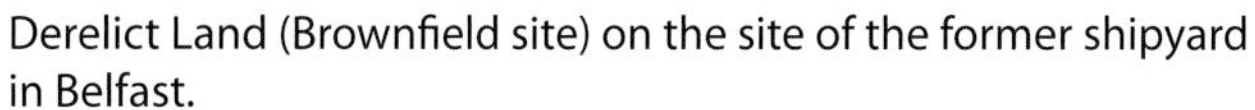
Derelict Land (Brownfield site) on the site of the former shipyard in Belfast.

Urban regeneration in Titanic Quarter: Computer software industry on part of the former shipyard.

at the edge of the city are protected from urban sprawl.

The former shipbuilding areas in Belfast are an example of a brownfield site currently in the process of regeneration. The extensive shipbuilding complex is being redesigned as the Titanic Quarter (recalling the most famous ship built there). When complete, the Titanic Quarter will have a number of modern hi-tech industrial units, a hotel and an apartment complex. The developers hope that the historical interest in the Titanic will attract a large number of tourists and a virtual reality Titanic centre is planned. Public transport will also be improved.

However, there are environmental issues regarding the re-use of some brownfield sites. Often the land has been contaminated through industrial use and a considerable amount of money is required to decontaminate such sites. Within Belfast, the Gasworks site has been successfully decontaminated and has been developed with a number of prestigious office complexes and a hotel. At the time of writing, work is in progress to decontaminate a former landfill site on the North Foreshore of Belfast Lough. This site operated as a landfill site for the dumping of waste until 2007. One of the issues associated with former landfill sites is the accumulation of methane as the waste decomposes. In this site a network of landfill gas wells and pipe work will collect the methane gas which will then be connected by cable to the national grid. It is estimated that this 'green' gas will be sufficient to provide power for up to 60,000 homes. In addition it is planned to build new facilities for waste management, including an Energy From Waste project. Part of the site will also be developed as an amenity area, with an open park, a visitor centre and discussions are taking place regarding a park and ride facility.

Exercise

1 .*Question from CCEA May 2005*
Figures 1 and **2** show cities that developed under socialism in Eastern Europe usually had neighbourhood units built on the 'microrayon' principle. Discuss the effectiveness of the principle in terms of sustainable development. (9)

Figure 1
Microrayon

The microrayon was a residential area that was intended to be self-sufficient. It housed people in high-rise apartment blocks and in addition to housing, each microrayon maintained nurseries for children, a primary school, a community centre or club, playgrounds and a neighbourhood park, all arranged at convient distances from the blocks of flats. Additionally industrial zones were spaced at regular intervals between microrayons in order to minimise distances to work.

Source: adapted from www.macalester.edu/geography/courses/geog261/ehoople/microrayan.htm, accessed June 2005

Exercise continued

Figure 2

Microrayon illustrations

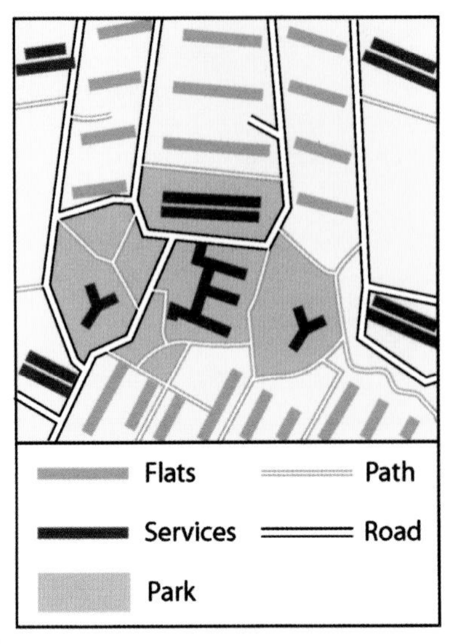

Microrayon model

Former East Berlin

Two views of Ujpest district Budapest, Hungary

Source: CCEA, Chief Examiner, Geography

Figures 1 and 2 from CCEA May 2005

2. Question from CCEA May 2005
Define 'brownfield development'. (3)

3. Study the information on The Eldonian Village in **Figure 3**. Discuss how the principles of sustainability have been incorporated into this development.

Figure 3

The Eldonian Village – a sustainable brownfield development in Liverpool

In 1976, Liverpool City Council had identified 57 slum clearance areas across the city, including most of the 1930s tenements from the south end to the city centre through to the docklands area in the north. Areas marked for demolition included the tenements around the Burlington and Eldon Streets in the Vauxhall area, affecting some 1,500 people. These plans were not based on any consultation with those who lived in the community.

This would mean breaking up the existing community, with the residents being offered re-housing across the city, usually in high-rise blocks on the outskirts. Most of the people living in the Vauxhall area of Liverpool had already survived bombing during the war, the loss of industry from the docks and the building of the new Mersey Tunnel. They were now witnessing the loss of most of the nearby neighbourhoods where the people went along with the Council's plans.

Exercise continued

The vast majority of the residents wished to remain in their community, but in new houses. In response to this, residents formed the Eldonian Community Association, invited professionals to work with them to plan new housing neighbourhoods and provide training for new jobs.

The new Eldonian estate

To enable these plans, the Eldonians formed a housing cooperative to build over 100 new houses for local families on the site of the Tate & Lyle sugar refinery that shut down in 1981.

The first phase of the Eldonian Village was completed by 1989. Having achieved their first objective, they then created a second phase of the Village, including 'build for sale', a village hall, sports facilities, offices, elderly accommodation, a nursery, and their own social enterprise that owns and manages the Village. The Eldonian Community based Housing Association manages 523 properties and employs 30 staff. The Eldonian Group (Development Trust) owns and manages the facilities on site and offers consultancy services. It employs over 50 people.

Retail Change: competition between out-of-town shopping and town centres

Shopping is one of just a few universal activities. We all shop at some stage but where and how often we shop has changed dramatically over the last forty years. Fifty years ago shopping was done locally and frequently. A number of social and economic changes have occurred since then, including the increased number of women in the work force, increased car ownership, increased disposable income, improved food storage facilities and globalisation. The retail industry has adapted to these changes in a number of ways.

One of the most significant changes has been the development of large chain stores, often part of a multi national company. The retail industry has greatly expanded the range and quality of the items for sale. In a global market competition between rival retailers is intense. The emphasis is on advertising and encouraging shoppers to spend ever increasing amounts of money. The retail outlets aim to make their premises attractive to a wide range of customers and many are attracted to out-of-town shopping centres, which have increased in number from the late 1960s onwards.

The earliest out-of-town shopping centres provided supermarket facilities for the ever growing population in the suburbs. As more and more housing developments were built at the edge of the city, the range of shops in the out-of-town shopping centres increased. By the mid 1980s the largest out-of-town shopping centres had at least one major non-food retailer. In the 1990s some very large shopping centres had developed. The Bluewater retail centre in Kent has over 300 shopping units as well as a number of recreational and leisure facilities.

There are many reasons for the development of these large retail centres:

- Land is cheaper at the edge of the city.
- Greenfield sites are easier to develop than brownfield sites in the inner city.
- The cheaper land facilitates the building of large shopping malls and car parks.
- Improvements in road transport attract customers from the surrounding area.
- Free and adequate car parking attracts shoppers with cars.
- An attractive environment where customers can visit a variety of shops.

As these developments were taking place the traditional high street retail areas were losing custom. Customers increasingly used the out-of-town shopping areas to avoid the congestion and high cost of parking in town centres. A number of British cities experienced a downturn in sales, with some of the major chain stores leaving town centres altogether. Traditional department stores and family owned shops were unable to compete with the more modern chain stores in the out-of-town shopping centres. Belfast suffered especially as the situation there was compounded by the civil unrest and bombings in Northern Ireland at that time. However, the change in retailing had more than an economic impact. Although most of the new retail centres were served to some extent by public transport, they were built with car owners in mind. As the pace of urbanisation and counterurbanisation continued in the latter part of the twentieth century, inner cities were populated by lower income groups and the elderly. As both of these groups have low levels of car ownership they became even more marginalised. Many town centres were already suffering from general decline associated with deindustrialisation and this change in retailing added to those problems. A lack of investment in any new developments led to increased unemployment and associated social problems.

The changing pattern of retail also had significant environmental consequences for the town centres and the edge of town locations. The continued use of Greenfield sites was a major issue of concern for a number of reasons. Whilst all of these centres do undertake landscaping they are to many observers a visual eyesore in what was formerly a rural area. There was much opposition to the effects of the increase in traffic and new road developments associated with these centres. All of these shopping areas have long opening hours, especially at weekends and residents close to them were concerned about the loss of privacy and the possible negative impact on the value of their properties. There is also the loss of biodiversity and increased pollution from the emissions of delivery lorries and litter.

In recent times, there has been a change of policy in relation to retail. Increasingly town centres are being reenergised and a number of new retailing developments have taken place in inner cities. In Belfast a new retailing centre opened at Victoria Square in the city centre, in March 2008. Covering a 1.8 hectare site, the development includes 68,000 sqm of retail space (including a 20,000 sqm House of Fraser anchor store), 106 apartments, 1,000 car park spaces and an eight screen Odeon cinema.

Exercise

1. *Question from January 2009*
(a) What has been the impact of out-of-town shopping on sustainable development? (4)

Leisure areas: sports facilities, open space and urban parks

If urban areas are to be sustainable they need to provide opportunities for all aspects of life including leisure and sporting activities. Local councils in most British towns and cities provide leisure centres and sports facilities with a range of leisure activities for all age groups. The Odyssey complex in Belfast is an example of a purpose built leisure and recreational facility provided by the city council. In addition, councils provide a range of outdoor sports facilities. These facilities encourage the development of local sporting activities and can help develop a community spirit.

As well as these functional leisure areas, City councils also need to provide a variety of open space. Open space can have many forms, including formal parks and gardens, wilderness areas and play areas for children. Some urban parks are laid out in a formal pattern while others are left more or less in a natural state. In Belfast there are over 40 parks and the city council has recently invested £8 million in improvement schemes. Most of Belfast's parks are landscaped, such as Botanic Gardens or Lady Dixon Park. The urban parks play a vital role in leisure and recreation in the city. Increasingly, many urban dwellers live in apartments with no gardens and these parks are their only access to green spaces. Open air music concerts have been held in Botanic Gardens and an international rose festival takes place annually in Lady Dixon Park. The parks also protect listed buildings such as the Victorian Palm House in Botanic Gardens. There are also a number of environmental benefits. The trees and other plants filter out some of the atmospheric pollutants and in hot climates they offer welcome shade. In some cases air temperatures in parks are two degrees lower than the surroundings. Green spaces also support wildlife and contribute to local biodiversity. Parkland can be used as an environmentally sensitive means of flood defence, where flood waters can be diverted onto parkland to prevent flooding commercial and residential areas. Some parks also provide sites for the composting of organic waste.

The UK Government set up the Urban Green Spaces Taskforce in 2001 to examine the provision, design, management and maintenance of green spaces and urban parks. It was agreed that good quality, well-designed parks and green spaces make a critical contribution to our neighbourhoods, towns and cities, and to people's quality of life playing an important role in creating a sense of place. Quality green spaces have been shown to:

- support the local economy, making neighbourhoods more desirable;
- enhance physical and mental health;
- benefit children and young people;
- reduce crime and fear of crime;
- support social cohesion;
- aid movement between other spaces;
- protect biodiversity and enhance the environment.

The principles and practice of urban conservation: redevelopment, regeneration and restoration

Decisions about how the older parts of towns and cities should be used and maintained are key considerations for urban planners. Most towns and city centres will have areas or buildings of at least local historic or architectural value. These buildings often reflect the former wealth or importance of the town. From a sustainable development point of view there is much merit in the continued use of older buildings in the urban area. However, buildings have to be functional and provide suitable facilities for current needs. This means that planners have to constantly review the existing provision of facilities in light of changing demands.

There are a number of different policy options for planners regarding the older parts of urban areas. Local councils compile lists of buildings with historic or architectural value. These are known as listed buildings and planning permission is required for even a minor alteration. The original character of the building can not be altered but it may be restored to its original state. This practice is known as **restoration**. Sometimes it is necessary to protect the area around the buildings in order to preserve the original character. The area is then made a conservation area. There are rules and regulations regarding the use of the conservation area. In Northern Ireland there are over 8,600 listed buildings and 40 conservation areas.

Some urban areas, particularly the inner areas, have suffered deindustrialisation and require some intervention to improve their social and economic outlook. There are two options available to planners in these areas. Urban **regeneration** refers to the practice of upgrading the area. In its simplest form, this might mean providing grants to householders to carry out modernisation of their homes or planting trees to improve the physical environment. Urban regeneration has also been carried out in many UK cities by the Urban Development Corporations in the 1980s using Government and private investment. In Belfast the recent developments in the Cathedral Quarter and the Titanic Quarter are examples of regeneration. Urban regeneration programmes may combine restoration practices as well as providing new developments. Within the Cathedral Quarter in Belfast, the Merchant Hotel occupies a former bank. The building

Resource 47 *Illustrations of urban conservation*

Restoration – The Merchant Hotel, Belfast

Redevelopment – Much of Belfast's Westlink is built on land occupied by housing until the 1960s.

has been restored but its use has changed. The Titanic Quarter also has some listed buildings such as Harland and Wolff Drawing Office. These buildings have been restored but their function will change.

On other occasions an entire area is demolished and redesigned. This is **redevelopment**. The whole scale demolition of terraced housing in many inner cities in the UK during the 1960s is an example of this. The terraced houses were replaced with blocks of high rise flats and new roads and motorways were built to improve the urban infrastructure. In Belfast, the Westlink dual carriageway is built on former residential land.

Urban restoration and regeneration contribute to sustainability by:

- reducing the need for new buildings;
- reducing energy use and relieving pressure on greenfield sites;
- preserving the best of the past and giving a sense of place;
- providing a tourist attraction;
- providing jobs and housing in the inner city and reducing the need for car journeys to work.

Redevelopment which results in the total demolition and rebuilding of an area would appear to be less sustainable than either restoration or regeneration. However, redeveloped areas can contribute to sustainability by incorporating energy efficiency and other environmentally friendly practices.

Exercise

1. ***Question from January 2007***
   Explain the principles that lie behind the establishment of urban conservation policies. (6)

2. ***Question from Summer 2005***
   How do leisure areas (open space/urban parks) contribute to planning policies promoting sustainable development? (6)

3. ***Questions from January 2009***
   (a) Study **Figures 1–4** on Dubrovnik, Croatia. This historic walled city has been restored following extensive damage in the early 1990s caused by the war that took place when Croatia broke away from Yugoslavia.

   (i) The Figures show that there is little open space and few urban parks within Dubrovnik. Explain the problems this might have for sustainable development. (4)

   (ii) Dubrovnik's post-war authorities chose a policy of restoration rather than redevelopment in dealing with their damaged city. Why do you think this choice would have been made? (4)

   (iii) Much of the space within the walls of Dubrovnik is occupied by high density residential areas. What are the benefits for sustainable development of such high density living? (8)

Exercise continued

Figure 1

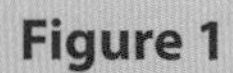

The cover of a book: V Gotovac, SP Noval, et al B Violic, *Dubrovnik in War*, published by Matica Hrvatska, 2000, ISBN: 978-9536316168

Figure 2

A typical street within the walled area of Dubrovnik.

Figure 3

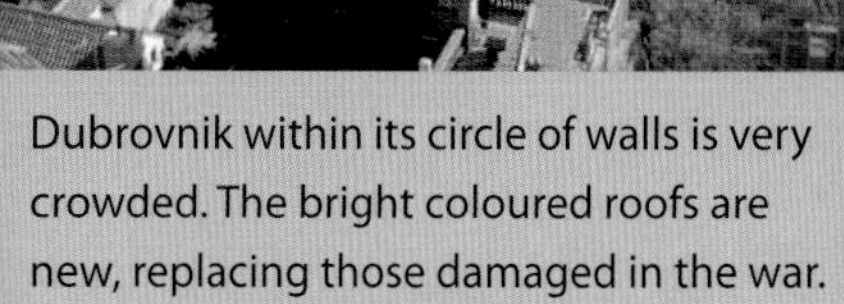

Dubrovnik within its circle of walls is very crowded. The bright coloured roofs are new, replacing those damaged in the war.

Figure 4

Tourists in Stradun, the main street in the centre of Dubrovnik.

Source: CCEA, Chief Examiner, Geography

Figures 1–4 from CCEA January 2009

Additional References

Titanic Quarter – www.titanicquarter.com/

Gasworks Belfast – www.belfastcity.gov.uk/parksandopenspaces/parksdetails.asp?id=101

Parks and open spaces in Belfast – www.belfastcity.gov.uk/parksandopenspaces/index.asp

Bluewater Shopping Centre –
www.greenwichmeantime.com/time-zone/europe/uk/england/county/kent/greenhithe/bluewater-shopping-centre

Further information on urban conservation and restoration practices is available on the following websites:
www.gotobelfast.com/downloads/Historic%20Belfast%20Leaflet.pdf
www.ni-environment.gov.uk/technical_note_58..pdf

CASE STUDY: Urban land use and planning in relation to sustainability, Curitiba

Curitiba is the capital of the State of Parana, a largely agricultural sate in Southern Brazil. During the 1970s and 1980s, Brazil experienced rapid economic growth and Curitiba became a major industrial and commercial centre. Population growth was equally rapid and the population doubled from 1970 to 1.8 million in 2008. Initially, the planners followed a policy of decentralisation, with new developments located at the edge of the existing city contributing to urban sprawl. However, there was a significant policy change, with a greater emphasis on sustainability largely due to the direction of the city's mayor and chief architect, Jaime Lerner. Lerner was involved in drawing up the city's Master Plan, helped establish the Urban Planning Institute of Curitiba (IPPUC) and served three terms as mayor of Curitiba.

Curitiba is a well known example of a sustainable city and the transport system is one of the key elements of its success. From the outset the planners sought to integrate traffic management, transportation and land use planning. The land use planning included industrial and residential areas as well as leisure areas and parkland. The planners had a single transport management aim – to reduce the number of car journeys from the suburbs and the outlying region into the city centre, which would reduce congestion and pollution. Many cities have attempted to resolve this issue by building an underground system. However, the construction costs and the length of time involved in laying an underground system meant this was not an option in Curitiba. Instead, the planners focused on the use of buses but attempted to incorporate many of the features that are associated with an underground system. There are five major arterial routes linking the centre of Curitiba to the suburbs, three ring roads serving suburb to suburb travel, creating a web like road pattern. Each of the arterial routes has a two-way lane dedicated to express buses only, a local access lane for cars and a lane for mixed traffic use. There are five different types of buses in Curitiba:

Resource 48 *Concept plan for Curitiba's transport system*

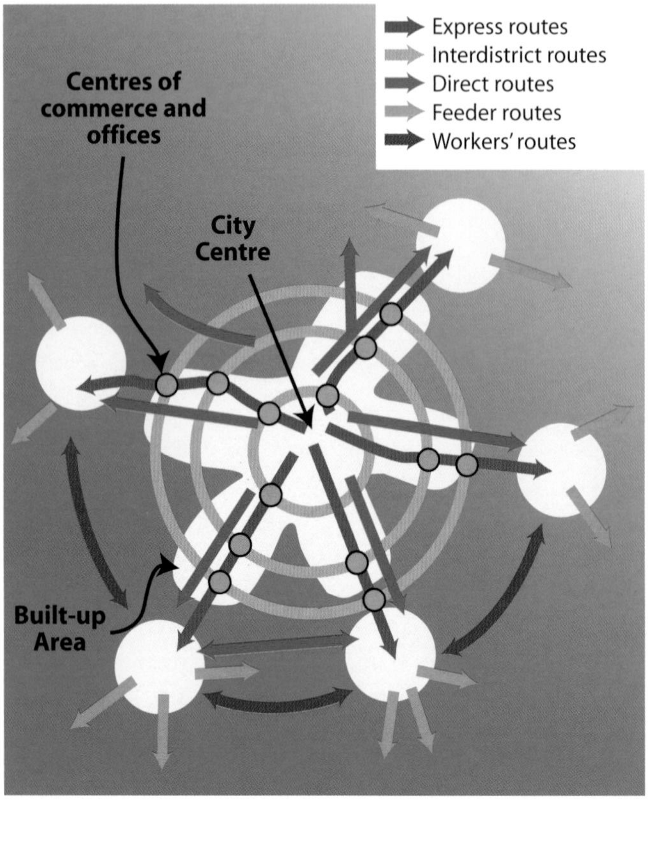

- Express buses operate on the dedicated bus lanes.
- A bi-articulated bus (a bus with additional carriages similar to train carriages) operates on the fast outer

lane of the dedicated bus routes. The bi-articulated buses in Curitiba are the largest in the world and carry 270 passengers. With a frequency of thirty seconds they can transport over 36,000 passengers every hour.

- 'Rapid' buses operate on all arteries and across the city's ring roads. These buses respond to level of demand.
- 'Inter district' buses bring passengers from the sectors between the arterial roads.
- Feeder buses bring passengers from outlying districts to transfer stations on the arterial routes.

Bi-articulated bus, *Luan Lenon*

In addition, all of the major bus routes have tube-shaped bus stations, with the door at the same level as the doors of the bus to facilitate rapid entry and a separate door to exit the bus. Passengers purchase their ticket prior to entering the bus. The buses are operated by private companies but tickets purchased from one company can be used anywhere on the network.

All of these measures reduce the amount of time the bus idles at the bus station and also reduces pollution. On major routes these schemes can save up to an hour a day for passengers and reduces costs by almost 20%. The fares are fixed for the entire journey, meaning that longer journeys by bus are relatively cheap and one fare can take a passenger 70 km. This benefits the urban poor, who are mostly located at the edge of the city.

All public utilities such as water services, electricity offices, police stations and hospitals are located close to the arterial routes in areas referred to as 'citizenship streets'. This means these services are accessible to everyone by public transport with no need for car journeys. Some services, including health centres, are available twenty-four hours daily. The density of buildings decreases with distance from these 'citizenship streets' and residential land use is more common. The residential areas have also been carefully planned to meet the needs of the local people. Residential areas are for the most part low rise and divided into neighbourhoods. Each neighbourhood has a multi-purpose community centre, which provides library and internet facilities, mostly for children. These centres or 'Lighthouses of Knowledge' work in collaboration with local schools and provide shelter for 'street children'. They are patrolled by policemen to add to the security of the neighbourhood.

The planners wanted to retain the commercial activity of the city centre while reducing car journeys. For this reason the centre of Curitiba has been pedestrianised. Initially, shop owners were concerned that this might lead to a decrease in customer numbers. However, this strategy has been very successful. The streets have been redesigned with new street lighting, trees and seating areas; and the historical buildings in the centre were restored. Some streets have twenty-four hour shopping.

An essential element of sustainable development in cities is the need to promote economic activity. Curitiba has a strict policy on industrial development. Only non-polluting industries are given planning permission. An industrial region referred to as Curitiba Industrial City (CIC) has been built some 10 km south-west of Curitiba. The industrial region is positioned here so that the prevailing south-easterly winds would blow the pollution away from the main city. The factories are closely linked to the public transport system, reducing the need for car journeys. By 2000 more than 200,000 new jobs had been created in this industrial city. Furthermore, CIC provides a highly diversified range of jobs, some of which are owned by multi-nationals but increasingly many are Brazilian owned. A diversified range of jobs is more sustainable than a highly specialised economic structure because the risks of mass unemployment and deindustrialisation are reduced in times of economic recession. The city council has also provided inexpensive courses to train workers in the necessary skills for modern industry. Old buses have often been used as mobile schools and offices in residential areas.

A park in Curitiba

Cutitiba is often referred to as the ecological capital of Brazil, with over 28 wooded areas and parks. These are important not just from a recreational perspective but they fulfil a vital environmental role by extracting CO_2 from the atmosphere. The World Health Organisation recommends 16 m^2 of green space per person. In Curitiba there are 52 square metres of green space per person. Builders are offered tax breaks if they incorporate green spaces and trees in their plans. These green spaces close to rivers also act as environmentally friendly flood defences, reducing the need for costly hard engineering flood projects. The trees reduce the amount of surface run off and lakes in the parks act as temporary storage basins for excess rainfall while the green spaces serve as environmentally friendly flood traps. Cuitiba actively pursues a policy for the re-use of brownfield sites as the following examples illustrate:

- A former landfill site has been reclaimed and developed as a botanical garden.
- A flooded disused quarry has been drained, landscaped and a Wire Opera House, using recycled telephone poles, mesh grating and metal tubing, has been built.

Curitiba has an impressive strategy regarding waste management. A 'garbage that's not garbage' programme has resulted in over 70% of the city's waste being recycled. In the UK the figure is about 20%. The waste for recycling is collected weekly from people's homes. The city's paper recycling saves the equivalent of 1,200 trees daily. Money raised from recycling materials is used to fund social programmes and the city employs the homeless and recovering alcoholics and drug addicts in the waste separation plants. A green exchange programme operates in the informal settlements that are inaccessible to the waste collection lorries. Under this scheme families bring their waste to a recycling centre where they can exchange their waste for bus tickets and food. This has resulted in less waste being dumped in rivers, less disease from polluted water and a better life for the under nourished poor.

Curitiba, like many large cities in LEDCs, attracts large numbers of rural migrants. Large scale rural to urban migration threatened to damage Curitiba's development strategies. Many of the migrants established informal settlements in the green spaces mentioned earlier and the shear numbers threatened to overwhelm the city's infrastructure. The authorities devised a two pronged approach to this problem. In the short-term, social workers intercept potential migrants at the main bus stations and attempt to persuade them to return home. In the long-term, the authorities have turned their attention to the surrounding rural areas and set in place a number of rural development programmes. These schemes aim to remove some of the rural push factors thereby preventing large scale migration to the urban area.

Evaluation

Overall, the strategies employed in Curitiba have been successful. Curitiba is a thriving industrial city where per capita income is significantly higher than in Brazil as a whole. This is all the more remarkable considering the achievements towards environmental sustainability. The example of Curitiba shows that the twin goals of economic prosperity and green policies are achievable. One of the key reasons for the successes in Curitiba relates to the planners policy of partnership and social inclusion. Curitiban authorities have always sought to include all of the city's inhabitants in the planning process. This has been achieved through consultations with local groups or planning for local areas. The location of essential services in close proximity to public transport not only reduced the need for car journeys but also made these services accessible to those who did not own a car. Indeed many of the policies relating to public transport, such as the single journey tariffs (see earlier section, page 81), give advantage to the poor. Attention has focused on creating the necessary skills for modern industry. The success of the transport strategy can be gauged from the fact that although Curitiba has the highest per capita car ownership in Brazil, it registers the lowest petrol consumption and pollution rates in the country. However, there are some causes for concern for the future of Curitiba. Population growth has been consistently high and has increased from just over 1 million in 1980 to 1.8 million in 2008. In addition, the recycling rates appear to have peaked and the only landfill site in the city was due to reach full capacity by the end of 2008. It would appear that the authorities will have to monitor the situation and adapt to changing demands if the achievements of the past thirty years are to be maintained.

Exercise

1. "Planning policies should be guided by an emphasis on sustainable development." Examine this statement with regard to your small-scale case study of an urban area.

B3 TRAFFIC AND TRANSPORT

Traffic and transport are two of the most important issues affecting the sustainability of modern settlements. Transport refers to the movement of goods and people while traffic refers to the volume of vehicles using a transport network at a given time. In MEDCs increased affluence has resulted in the decentralisation of people and industry as a result of suburbanisation and counterurbanisation. This has increased the number and distance of journeys to work. The National Traffic Survey figures for 1997–2000 showed the following changes from the 1980s:

- A 40% increase in the distance people travelled by car.
- Car travel accounted for over 80% of the total distance travelled on the roads.
- An increase of 16% in the number of children being driven to school.
- On average, people in Britain travelled about 7,000 miles annually, an increase of 28%.
- The average number of car journeys was 1046.

The unique flexibility of car transport, combined with the fact that cars have become for many an outward statement of success, are two of the main reasons for the increase in car journeys. In 1952 there were 2 million cars in Britain while in 2003 there were approximately 22 million. However, private car is one of the most unsustainable forms of transport. With ever increasing numbers of cars at peak times, congestion has become a major issue in many of our towns and cities. The problem stems from many inner city areas having a road layout designed in the nineteenth century, which is totally inadequate for twenty-first century transport. In central London, prior to the congestion charges, average speeds had dropped to 11 mph. Time lost spent in traffic jams is estimated to cost the British industry £15 billion annually. In addition, congestion causes increased fuel consumption and frustration to drivers and passengers. But it is the environmental impact on towns and cities caused by private car emissions that is of greatest concern at present. Approximately 18% of the UK's carbon dioxide emissions, as well as other greenhouse gases, including nitrogen oxides, carbon monoxide, hydrocarbons and lead, come from car exhausts. Congestion also damages the attractiveness of town centres and may deter new investors away, favouring Greenfield sites over the inner city. To avoid congested town centres motorists will often travel through residential areas causing problems for local residents such as parking space and safety issues for children.

Resource 49 *Map of the M25 motorway network*

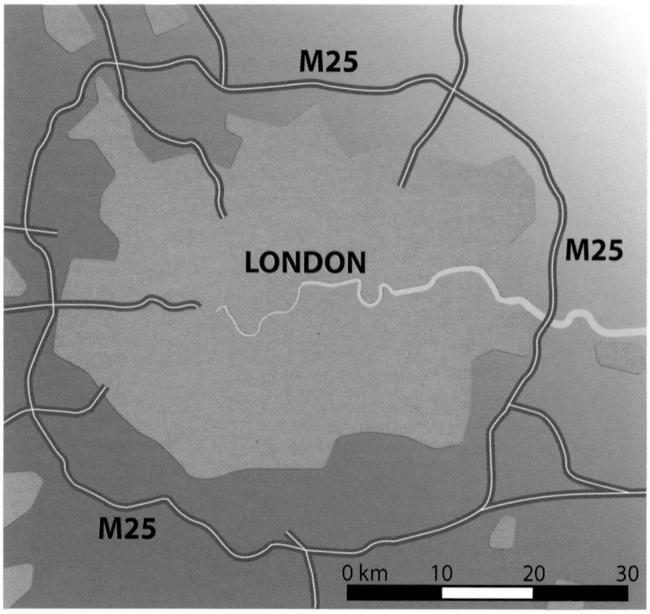

Road building was initially considered the main solution to traffic congestion but this has also raised many environmental issues. From the late 1960s onwards the British government embarked on a programme of road building that has transformed much of the countryside. Between 1980 and 2000

some 550 kms of motorway were added. Some of these schemes inevitably cut across rural land and others have encroached on protected land. The M25 orbital motorway is built entirely on London's greenbelt. In 2000 the Government announced a ten year transport plan with £29 billion earmarked for road widening and building bypasses. If these plans go ahead they will affect 28 Sites of Scientific Interest (SSIs), 8 Areas of Outstanding Natural Beauty (AONBs) and 5 National Parks. However, these may not all proceed as such proposals are subject to an environmental assessment procedure. This procedure is considered inadequate by some environmental groups but it does slow down the road building schemes.

Over time the size of commercial and industrial vehicles has increased and this has created major problems for town centres, especially in the oldest cities. The deindustrialisation process, which led to the development of modern industry in purpose built industrial/business parks in out-of-town areas, promoted increased road transport for commercial vehicles and workers.

Public transport networks, including trains and buses, have also suffered from increased demand in the last fifty years. Some countries appear to have responded to this increased demand more successfully than others.

The problem in the UK stems partly from the fact that the UK was one of the earliest nations to industrialise. The development of rail transport was associated with that industrialisation. London had the first underground system in 1863. The cost of railway infrastructure (rail track, stations, and trains) is immense and by being first to develop, the UK is now suffering from an ageing infrastructure. The railways in Britain were formerly nationalised (government controlled) but since the late twentieth century private companies have owned them. Some companies own the rail stock (trains) and others are in charge of the rail track etc. In 2002, the Strategic Rail Authority (SRA) unveiled a £56 billion plan to modernise the railways. The aim is to increase train passengers by 50% by 2010. This should contribute significantly to more sustainable transportation in the UK.

Traffic and transport statistics **Resource 50**

Rail traffic in Britain 1985–2000

Year	Passenger journeys (millions)	Passenger kms (millions)
1985	686	29,700
1990	809	33,200
1995	801	32,200
2000	957	39,200

Source: DETR 2000

Train reliability 2000

Country	% of all train journeys
France	90
Germany	95
UK	79

Source: Eurostat figures

Government spending on transport

Country	% of GDP spent on transport provision
Italy	1.25
Germany	1.15
UK	0.6

Source: Commission for Integrated Transport 1996

Traffic management strategies

In order to attain a sustainable transport policy, planners need to implement strategies that will make public transport more efficient and accessible, thereby reducing the popularity of private cars. There are a number of options available. Most governments operate a combination of the 'carrot and stick' approach, using disincentives for motorists and incentives for public transport users. Among the most common strategies used are:

Road pricing

This includes toll roads, where motorists have to pay to use a specific stretch of road and a congestion charge where motorists have to pay to enter the central part of the town or city. Toll roads are usually by-passes or ring roads/motorways that divert traffic along better quality and faster routes than the non-toll roads. Road pricing was first introduced in Singapore during peak travel periods in 1975. The scheme was deemed a success with over 60% of morning traffic switching to other forms of transport or travelling outside the peak period. In 2003 London city council introduced a congestion charge per vehicle using central London every weekday. London city council has issued the following information in relation to the scheme:

- Traffic entering the original charging zone remains 21% lower than pre-charge levels (70,000 fewer cars a day).
- Traffic entering the Western Extension has fallen by 14% (30,000 fewer cars a day).
- There has been a 6% increase in bus passengers during charging hours.
- There has been a 12% increase in cycle journeys into the Western Extension.
- £137 million being raised, in the financial year 2007/08, to invest back into improving transport in London.

Source: Transport for London: www.tfl.gov.uk/roadusers/congestioncharging/6723.aspx

A similar scheme has been introduced in Durham to alleviate congestion but also to protect the historic buildings in the town centre. The historic city of Cambridge has also considered implementing such a scheme (CASE STUDY: Traffic and transport in Cambridge, page 90).

Variable road tax

All motorists have to pay an annual road tax and the government has imposed a higher rate of tax on less efficient fuel consumption cars. The RAC claim that over 700,000 drivers have changed to a smaller car as a result of this policy.

Pedestrianisation

This strategy, effectively banning traffic from an area, is used to increase the attractiveness and safety of town centres for shoppers and to preserve historic buildings. In the centre of Belfast pedestrian areas include Cornmarket, Victoria Square and the Cathedral Quarter. The main shopping area of Donegal Square has limited access for buses only. In the past pedestrian only areas such as underpasses or footbridges were unsafe or unattractive. Now pedestrianised areas are designed with the emphasis on the needs of pedestrians. They are generally landscaped with ornamental plants and trees and seating areas. They are open, well lit areas, with no dark underpasses or steep staircases. The emphasis is on enhancing the environment in order to attract more shoppers to the town centres.

Pedestrianisation at Victoria Square Belfast

While such areas are undoubtedly attractive shopping environments, there is not universal approval of pedestrianisation. Opponents of pedestrianisation policies claim that shoppers can be deterred by having to carry bulky shopping on public transport. This may encourage shoppers to use the out-of-town shopping instead of town centres. Although, most pedestrianised areas will permit access for some delivery vehicles, the design of the streets is often not suitable for large container lorries. Furthermore, pedestrianisation can alleviate traffic congestion in one part of the town but may actually increase congestion in other areas. It can also lead to increased demand for parking spaces in the areas surrounding the pedestrianised zone.

Parking policies

A Park and Ride facility in Belfast

These operate in a number of ways. In town centres on-street parking is often not permitted in the busiest areas and controlled by the use of parking metres on less densely used streets. Multi-storey or underground car parks are located on the edge of the main commercial district. Variations in the cost of parking make the more centrally located car parks less attractive than those further away from the centre. In Belfast the most centrally located car parks in the main shopping arcades charge 50% more per hour than those in less accessible areas. In recent times 'Park and Ride' schemes have become increasingly popular. These are large car parks on the edge of the city which are served by public transport. They offer inexpensive car parking and low rates of public transport to the city centre. A number of such schemes are available in Belfast but some of the best known examples are found in the Cambridge area (CASE STUDY: Traffic and transport in Cambridge, page 90).

Traffic cells

Town centres are designed to be the most accessible in order to maximise the number of potential customers and all major route ways converge in the central business district. This accessibility has resulted in the centre of towns becoming the preferred route for through or cross-town traffic, leading to severe congestion at peak periods. This congestion presents three sets of problems for urban planners.

(i) It can reduce the commercial attractiveness of town centres prompting shoppers to use out-of-town shopping centres.

(ii) It causes air pollution.

(iii) To avoid this congestion, motorists often travel through nearby residential areas causing issues of safety and privacy for the residents.

Planners have sought to deal with these issues through the introduction of traffic cells. A traffic cell is a self contained zone within a town with limited entry and exit points. Through traffic must use distributor roads that surround the cells. The elimination of through traffic creates a safer and more attractive environment within the cell for pedestrians and residents. Traffic cells usually incorporate one-way streets and traffic calming measures, such as traffic humps, to deter through traffic.

Local residents usually welcome the use of traffic cells but opponents of the scheme raise many of the issues discussed with pedestrianisation schemes.

Public transport

A peak time bus lane the on Saintfield Road, Belfast

Traffic management strategies aim to reduce the popularity of private car journeys by improving the attractiveness of public transport. This can be achieved in a number of ways, including the provision of a more reliable and cost effective service and better quality buses and trains. A number of cities have introduced 'bus lanes' during peak periods to make public transport faster than car journeys. Bicycle lanes have also been introduced to make cycling safer and more attractive. Some larger cities have developed underground railways. London underground transports 28 million passengers over 1 billion journeys annually. In other cases, urban light rail systems (modern electrified trains) provide a reliable non-polluting form of transport across the main built up area. In Dublin, a tram system running on a dedicated track provides a similar service.

Integrated transport networks

Public transport can never offer the same flexibility as the private car. However, integrated transport networks do go some way towards increasing the flexibility and efficiency of public transport. An integrated transport network coordinates several forms of public transport in the one location. This means that passengers on one form of transport can connect with another transport mode without changing location. In London a ring of main railway stations surrounds central London. These also have underground stations and most have bus stations and bicycle parks. Victoria station in central London operates National Rail services to Gatwick airport and to all of the major cities in Britain. Victoria tube station (in the same building) provides underground rail services across London. Victoria bus station operates services within London and throughout England. Taxi ranks and secure parking for bicycles outside the station add to the flexibility of this system.

Integrated transport networks are also very important in industrial areas. Modern industry is often located at the edge of cities in purpose built industrial estates well away from the railway infrastructure. Such sites inevitably rely heavily on road transport. A combination of brownfield developments in inner cities and modernisation of transport networks could provide a more sustainable form of industrialisation.

Exercise

Question from CCEA January 2009

(a) Explain how integrating industrial areas with transport is beneficial in terms of sustainable development. (4)

(b) Study **Figures 1–3** which show transport policies in Dublin.

(i) Describe the way in which the concept of integrated transport networks has influenced transport policies and provision in Dublin. (6)

(ii) Use the resources to help you explain the significance of the role of public transport in traffic management strategies. (10)

Figure 1

- The main role of private transport will be to cater for inter-suburban trips and for trips in the outlying areas where no form of public transport is viable.
- The main role of public transport will be to provide for trips along radial routes to/ from the city centre
- Sustainable transport modes will be promoted
- Integrative measures will be encouraged including:
  - Park-and-Ride at key sites;
  - integrated ticketing;
  - provision of bicycle racks at public transport stops;
  - bus-rail connecting services

Source: J Killen, Trinity College Dublin

Exercise continued

Figure 2

Map of LUAS network

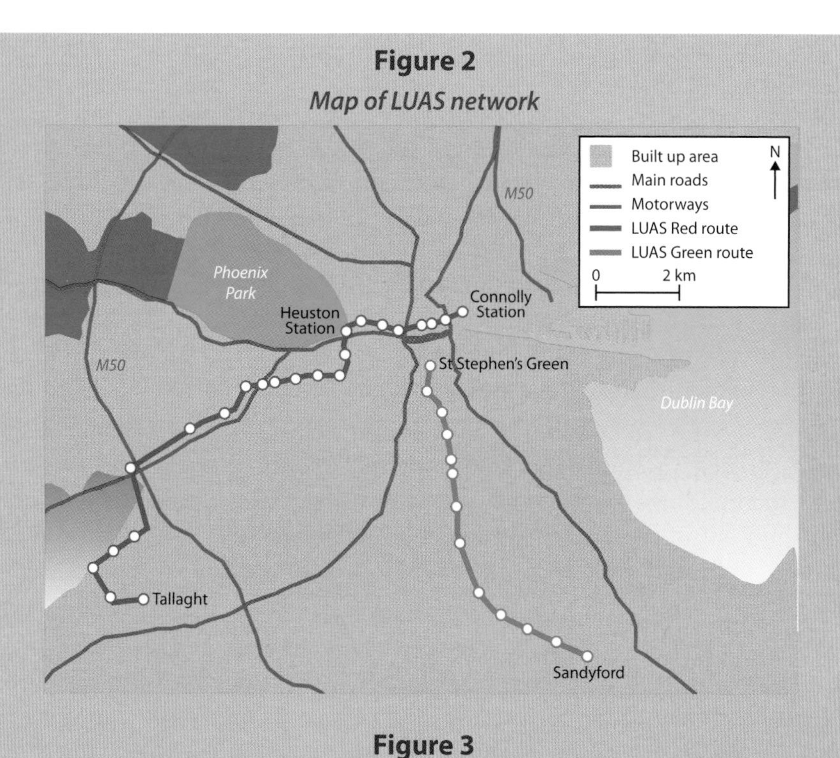

Figure 3

- Dublin's new tram system, LUAS, has two lines, Red (14 km) and Green (9km).
- LUAS occupies dedicated lanes in the road, which are not accessible by other vehicles.
- The Red Line from Connolly mainline station, to Tallaght in the southern suburbs stops at Heuston station, Dublin's other mainline terminal.
- The two lines connect with six Park-and-Ride car parks and bike racks are provided at most LUAS stops.
- Bicycles (other than folding bikes in bags) may not be taken aboard the trams
- 32 of the total of 36 stops also have a bus service
- Tickets valid on both LUAS and buses are available, but there is not fully integrated ticketing across all Dublin's transport modes.
- The two lines are not connected to eachother and there is no public transport link between them.
- 80,000 passengers are carried on average each day.
- 22 million passengers were carried in 2005; 26 million in 2006.

Source: Information from www.luas.ie

Additional References

Geofile, 515, 'Sustainable Cities', 2006

A number of short articles on various aspects of traffic and transport are available from the Commission for Integrated Transport website – www.cfit.gov.uk/links/index.htm

Transport for London – www.tfl.gov.uk/roadusers/congestioncharging/6723.aspx

CASE STUDY: Traffic and transport in Cambridge

Background

The historic city of Cambridge is a university town and the administrative centre of the county of Cambridgeshire. It occupies a crossing point on the Cam river and is approximately 80 km north of London. The city is best known for the University of Cambridge, one of the world's most prestigious universities. The oldest college that still exists, Peterhouse, was founded in 1284. The colleges that make up the university have considerable historic and architectural value and attract large numbers of tourists. Most are listed buildings. According to the 2001 United Kingdom census, the City's population was 108,863 (including 22,153 students), and the population of the urban area is estimated to be 130,000.

Cambridge and the surrounding area is sometimes referred to as Silicon Fen, because of the number of high-tech businesses that have developed on science parks around the city. Many of these parks and buildings are owned or leased by university colleges, and the companies often have been spun out of the university. Addenbrooke's hospital, located close to the ring road surrounding Cambridge, is a major centre for biomedical research.

The city is within an hour's journey from London either by the M11 motorway or railway. Throughout the 1960s and 1970s the size of the city was greatly increased by several large council estates planned to hold London overspill. Cambridge is also a thriving commercial centre with three modern shopping arcades and numerous high street shopping chain stores.

Transport modes in Cambridge

Cambridge is well served by public transport. There are rail links to East Anglia, Birmingham and London. A number of bus companies operate services between Cambridge and the major urban areas in the south and east; and there is a well developed bus network within the city. There is an excellent road network surrounding Cambridge but the approach roads to the city are often congested due to a number of factors:

- The M11 motorway from London terminates close to Cambridge, where it joins the A14. The A14 is a major east-west freight route connecting the port of Felixstowe on the east coast with the Midlands and the west of England. It is often congested.
- The ring road, the A1134, carries all through traffic as well as traffic destined for central Cambridge.

Resource 51 *Map of Cambridge*

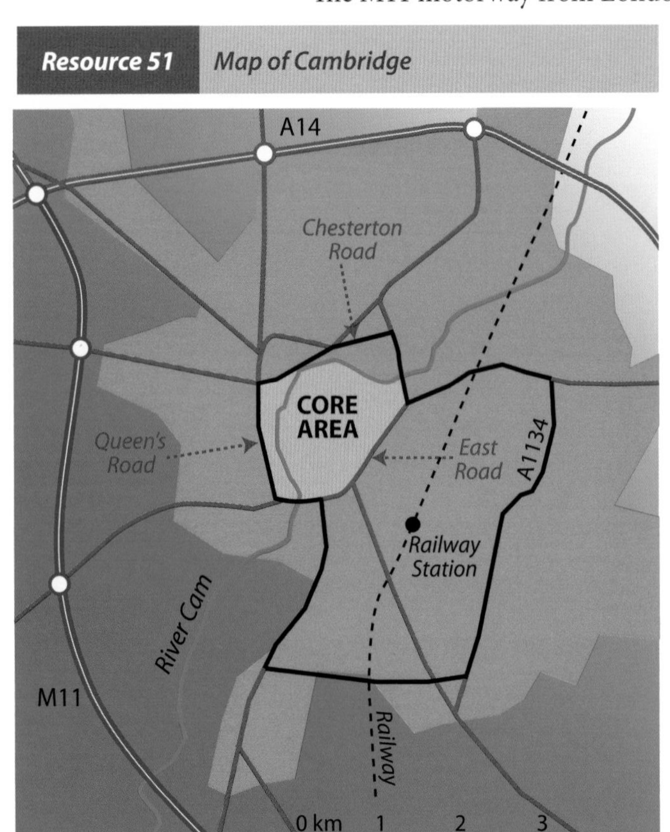

However, it is within the historic core of the city that the greatest problems arise. There are several reasons for this.

- The medieval streets of the historic core – narrow cobbled streets with sharp bends – were not built to cope with today's traffic.
- There are estimated to be about 85,000 car journeys into Cambridge daily. These traffic flows contribute to high levels of pollution in narrow streets where pollutants are difficult to disperse.

As part of an overall transport strategy for Cambridgeshire, the local council introduced a number of methods aimed at promoting a more sustainable way of accessing the city centre. The main aims of the Cambridge Transport Plan were to:

- encourage people to use cars less;
- promote other means of sustainable transport;
- improve the city centre environment for all users.

The Cambridge Transport Projects Team, who implemented the council's plan, used a 'carrot and stick' approach to traffic management by introducing a number of measures to improve public transport together with traffic restraint measures to dissuade the use of private car in the historic core. The traffic management scheme has been modified with time and currently the fourth stage of the scheme is being implemented.

Strategies for the historic core

1. Road Closures and Pedestrian zones

The historic core of Cambridge is the area bounded by Inner Ring Road and the River Cam (**Resource 51**). The area within the inner ring road, known as the Core Area, has been divided into eight traffic cells. Most have one main entry point from the inner ring road. Area name plates are provided at each entry point to facilitate drivers' selection of the appropriate cell. Automatic rising bollards operate on some routes in the central area to prevent through traffic movements (**Photographs 2** and **3**). They close the route to through traffic except for authorised buses and taxis, which are issued with electronic tags to lower the bollards. Traffic is further restricted within each cell by one-way systems to ease the flow of traffic through the narrow streets. A free shuttle bus transports passengers around the central area. Some parts of the historic core have been made pedestrian zones. In these areas parking is prohibited 24 hours a

Map of restrictions in Cambridge ***Resource 52***

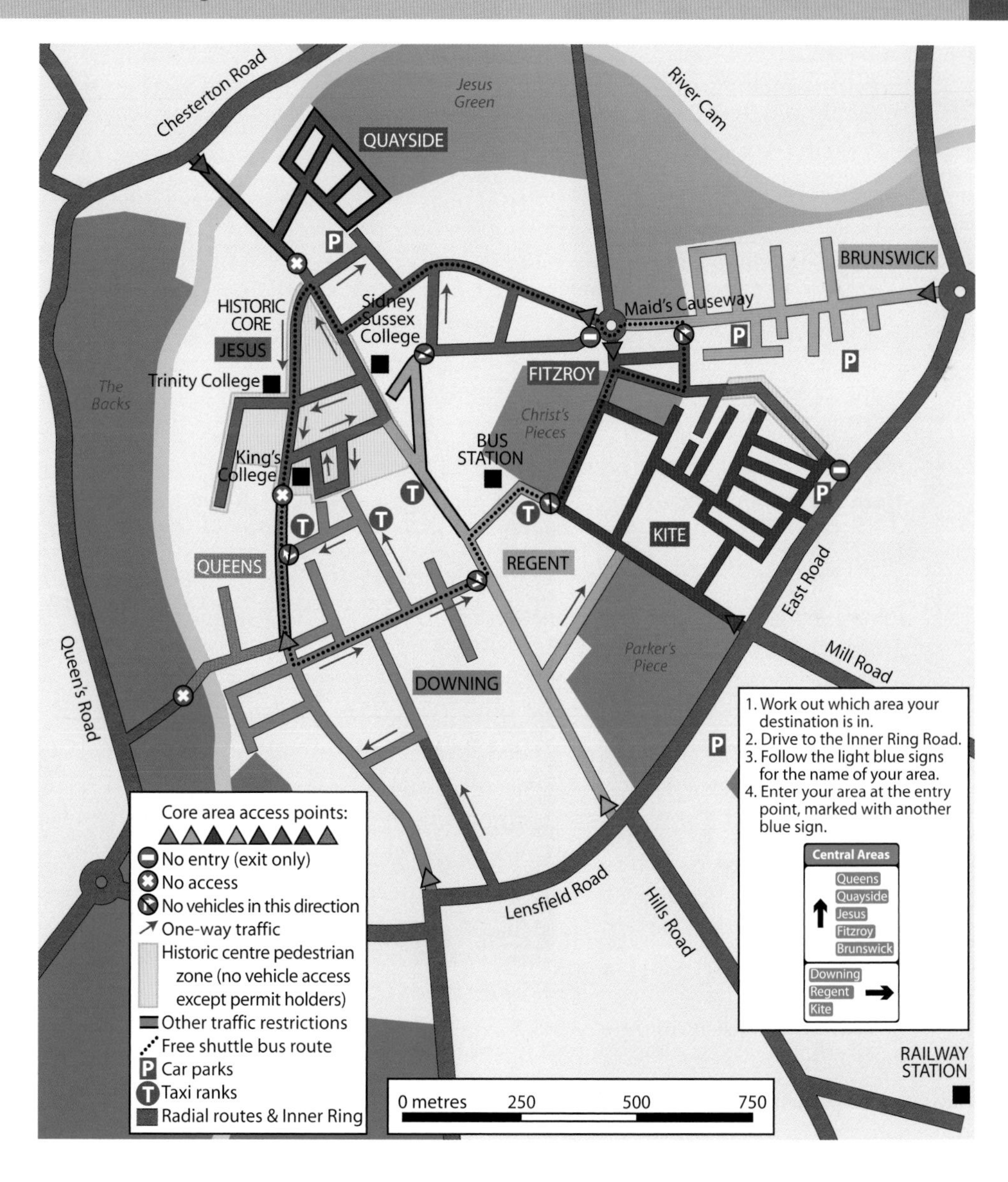

day, 7 days a week. Motor vehicles are not permitted access between 10am and 4pm, Monday to Saturday, except for special permit holders and disabled drivers. Cyclists are required to dismount and walk in some streets.

To allow for deliveries to be made and for other essential access, vehicles can enter and park to load and unload before 10am and after 4pm Monday to Saturday and all day on Sundays.

Photographs showing various views of the historic core of Cambridge

1. Pedestrianised street

2. Rising bollard

3. Traffic restrictions

4. Sidney Sussex College Cambridge

5. Pedestrianised street in the historic core of Cambridge – Note the narrow street, historic building and modern shops in close proximity.

As a university town, lying on fairly flat ground and with traffic congestion, Cambridge has a large number of cyclists. Many residents also prefer cycling to driving in the narrow, busy streets, giving the city the highest level of cycle use in the UK. According to the 2001 census, 25% of residents travelled to work by bicycle. A few roads within the city are adapted for cycling, including separate traffic lights for cycle lanes and cycle contraflows on streets which are otherwise one-way. Also, there are numerous bicycle parks throughout the city. However, within the city centre there are no separate cycle paths. Some streets are entirely pedestrianised (**Photographs 1 and 5**), with improved environments where possible, including widened footpaths.

The restriction on vehicular traffic in the centre has resulted in increased pressure on the ring road and the approach roads just beyond the restricted area. Many of these streets, including Maids Causeway in the north-east and Lensfield Road to the south, are residential and the increased traffic has created problems for the residents. Currently there are speed restrictions in operation and proposals to restrict the weight of vehicles using Maids Causeway, where there are a large number of residential areas.

2. Parking

Parking is prohibited throughout the historic core. Exceptions are made for disabled drivers in some streets and for emergency services. These restrictions and road closures have resulted in increased demand for parking in the area surrounding the historic core. Some of these streets only allow parking for residents. To ease this situation the Council has provided five car parks close to the centre providing over 3,000 spaces. However, pressure for car parking space remains an issue, particularly at peak times. The cost of a two hour stay in these car parks is more expensive than a return ticket on a Park and Ride bus.

3. Public Transport

In 1999, Cambridge Ciy Council set a target to achieve a 70% increase in the number of people using buses by 2011. The Council realised that in order to achieve this target there would need to be substantial improvements to the entire bus sytem. Cambridge buses are operated by a number of private companies and the Council provides the bus stations and bus stops. All bus operators are obliged to sign up to a Quality Bus Partnership (QBP) with the Council, which will deliver the following improvements:

- Improved bus shelters, with raised kerbs for easier passenger access and real time bus information. Real time bus information gives passengers up to date information about the bus service.
- Improved ticketing facilities to speed up boarding times.
- Reducing bus emissions to improve air quality. The central area is now a Low Emission Zone (LEZ) for buses.
- Relocating some bus stops to avoid congested areas.
- Improving the reliability of bus services.

Resource 53 *Map of Park-and-Ride sites*

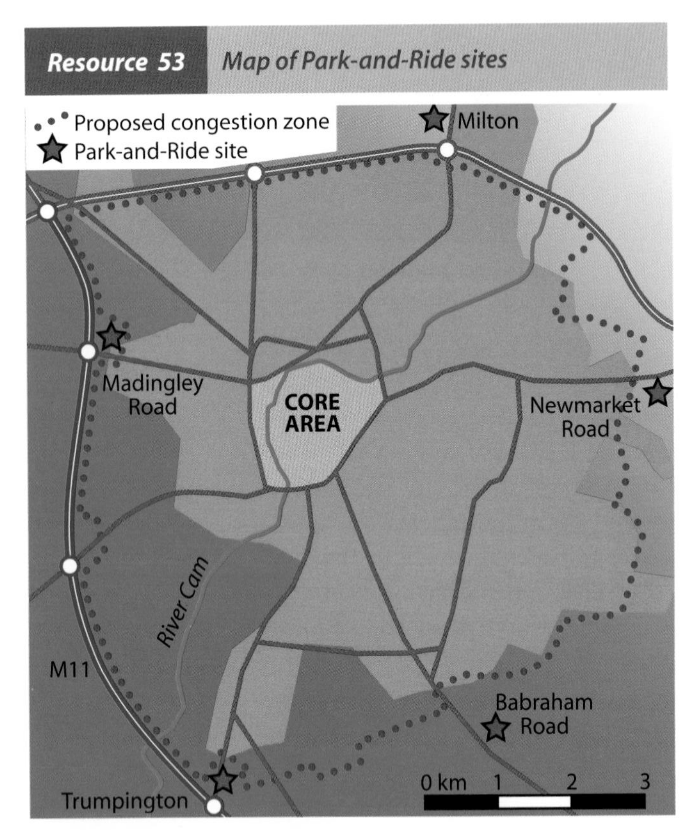

4. Park and Ride

Park and Ride provides direct travel into Cambridge and is used by over four million commuters, shoppers and visitors each year. Customers can park for free in one of five Park and Ride sites which provide 4,500 spaces. Each of the five sites is located on one of the main arterial roads leading to Cambridge. Each site provides waiting rooms with snack and drinks machines and information stands. The five sites operate between 7am and 8pm Monday to Friday; and between 8am and 8pm on Saturday. All sites are staffed during opening hours and are secured with barriers after the last bus. These barriers rise to allow traffic to leave after hours.

5. Rail transport

Cambridge railway station is located south-east of the city centre. The station has a direct bus link to the centre, bicycle parks, a car park and taxi rank. However, the journey from the city centre is subject to congestion. There are plans to build a more direct bus only road to the station. This new road would also have dedicated cycle lanes.

Cambridge Railway station. Note the large number of bicycles, bus stop and taxi rank, showing part of an integrated transport network.

6. Guided bus

A new guided busway is currently being developed in Cambridgeshire to ease pressure on the roads surrounding Cambridge. A guided busway is a dedicated track for buses only. This will run for part of its journey along a disused railway line. It will link directly with Cambridge railway station, Addenbrooke's Hospital and Trumpington Park and Ride. Where the busway travels on normal roads the buses will have new bus lanes and bus priority traffic signals. The busway is constructed with shredded car tyres, which is cheaper than tarmac and makes effective use of waste material. The scheme has been awarded a national waste management award for its innovative use of waste. The buses will produce 80% less carbon emission than standard buses. Some of the buses will run exclusively on bio-diesel. The busway was scheduled to open in early 2009 but has been beset by delays and is unlikely to open before the middle of 2009, and even then only in parts.

7. Current strategies

Research seems to suggest that improvements to public transport, cycling and walking facilities on their own may not be enough to address the congestion problem in Cambridge. The Council have therefore proposed a congestion charge (**Resource 53**) using the following strategies;

- A congestion charge would operate for two hours in the morning rush hour, Monday to Friday.
- The cost would need to be between £3 and £5 a day.
- Cars travelling into, out of or within the congestion zone would be charged once a day.

The council claim that congestion charging would deliver the following benefits:

- Delays at junctions would decrease by 30%.
- There would be a 20% decrease in overall travel time spent on the roads in Cambridge.
- CO_2 emissions would decrease by 16%.

As the time of writing no final decision has been made on whether the scheme should proceed.

Exercise

To what extent have Cambridge urban planners incorporated the principles of sustainability in their traffic management policy?

Additional References

Traffic management in Cambridge – http://www.cambridgeshire.gov.uk/transport/strategies

Geofile, 449, 'UK Transport Planning in the twenty-first Century', 2003

C1 THE DEFINITION OF ETHNICITY

The definition of ethnicity

The term ethnic group is usually limited to minority groups within society. There are many ways of defining an ethnic group but most commonly members of an ethnic group share cultural traditions, values, national identity, patterns of behaviour and language. Individual members recognise themselves as part of a separate group and are so recognised by others. Ethnic groups frequently have their own political party. In the UK the definition of an ethnic group was formally defined in UK law as:

> "a group of people with a long shared history and a distinct culture sharing some of the following characteristics: a common geographic origin or descent, a common language or literature, a common religion and being a minority within a larger community".

Orthodox Jew in New York

In the 2001 census people were asked to identify their ethnic group from a predetermined list.

Ethnicity refers to the outward manifestation of belonging to an ethnic group. This can be anything visible from skin colour and language to dress code. Male Orthodox Jews are recognised by their beards, black hats and long black coats. Muslim women are identified by their dress code and headscarves (hijab).

While the definition of an ethnic group is complex there are a number of factors that can be used to make broad classifications. These are:

- **Primary factors** – race, nationality, language, religion and perceived ethnic identity.
- **Secondary factors** – social status, residential concentration, age, gender and caste.

Primary factors

Race

Race is probably the most controversial factor used to define an ethnic group. Race classifies people according to the colour of their skin, visible facial features or hair type. Traditionally there are four major races: Caucasian (white or European), Mongoloid (Asian or Chinese), Negroid (black or African) and Australoid (Aboriginals). Early studies of these divisions assumed that there was some biological difference between the groups. However, modern studies have proved this to be false. About 99% of the genetic make up of the human population is common to all ethnic groups. The obvious physical difference in each group's appearance is related to adaptations to specific physical environments, such as climate. Nevertheless race has been the most divisive factor for centuries. White European colonialists assumed domination over black Africans, taking millions as slaves to the USA and elsewhere. Military superiority translated to racial superiority. Nineteenth century writers claimed that people from temperate climates had a superior work ethic. People living in tropical climates were deemed inferior and in need of civilising by their white superiors. Slavery and racial discrimination has had a profound impact on the history of the USA. Government law leading to the abolition of slavery was one of the main causes of the American civil war. In 2008 America elected its first black African President. There are still many black Americans who remember the struggle against segregation and for civil rights in the 1960s. Racial divisions are a very visible sign of ethnic division but movements of people and intermarriage means that there is no such thing as a 'pure' race anymore. In America anyone with any African characteristics is regarded as 'black' when they are a mix of black and white. For example, Tiger Woods, the current leading world golfer, is classified as black but he has ancestors from Africa, Europe and Thailand. Barack Obama is also classed as black but is not a descendent of the slave population.

Nationality

A strong unifying element for large numbers of people is the country of origin or ancestral home, with all the trappings of national flags and national anthems. Nationality is at once unifying and divisive. Nationality is a personal and mobile form of ethnicity even when the group are away from their home country. The examples of the Irish Americans or Hispanic Americans illustrate this point well. Members of an ethnic group identified by nationality present a group image of their national identity to the outside world. The group, although made up of individuals, proclaims its national unity to those who are different and excluded from their group. In the case of Northern Ireland, the Catholic population are often referred to as nationalist. Nationalist in this context refers to this group's allegiance to Ireland as opposed to the UK. In Northern Ireland there are laws regarding when and where flags may be displayed, the routes of marches and the playing of the national anthem. Nationalism has increased in Europe since the 1990s. The break up of the former Soviet Union has resulted in the emergence of a number of independent nations, each with their own identity. The aspirations of an ethnic group, defined by national identity, to break away from their current political rulers have often led to bitter conflict. The disintegration of the former Yugoslavia into ethnic national units followed bitter conflict and civil wars.

Language

Language unites and divides groups of people. Worldwide there are approximately 5–6,000 different languages. English is the most widely spoken language, reflecting past colonialism. English is spoken by somewhere between a quarter and a third of the global population. Language is often regarded as an outward expression of ethnicity. In Northern Ireland, members of Sinn Fein frequently deliver speeches in the Stormont Assembly in Irish. This is their attempt to stamp their ethnicity on political proceedings. Government documents are produced in Irish and Ulster Scots. There are Irish Medium schools and street names in predominantly republican parts of Belfast are written in Irish. In Sri Lanka, Sinhala (the language of the majority Sinhalese population) was made the official state language forcing all groups to learn it. This was seen as a discriminatory act against the Tamil minority population. In Canada, the province of Quebec maintains its separate identity from the rest of the country by speaking French. In Belgium, the individuality of the two provinces of Flanders (Dutch speaking) and Wallonia (French speaking) is emphasised by the linguistic differences between them. It has been shown that people who are unable to communicate because of language differences are more likely to maintain other differences as well and vice-versa. Some languages are dying out and about half of the world's languages are not spoken by children. Economic factors and globalisation which promote other languages are thought to be the main reasons for this.

Religion

Religion often provides a code of behaviour that makes its followers instantly recognisable. Reference has already been made to Orthodox Jews and Islam. On a global scale there are six major world religions, with numerous sub divisions (**Resource 54**). Some religions maintain

Resource 54 *Religions of the world*

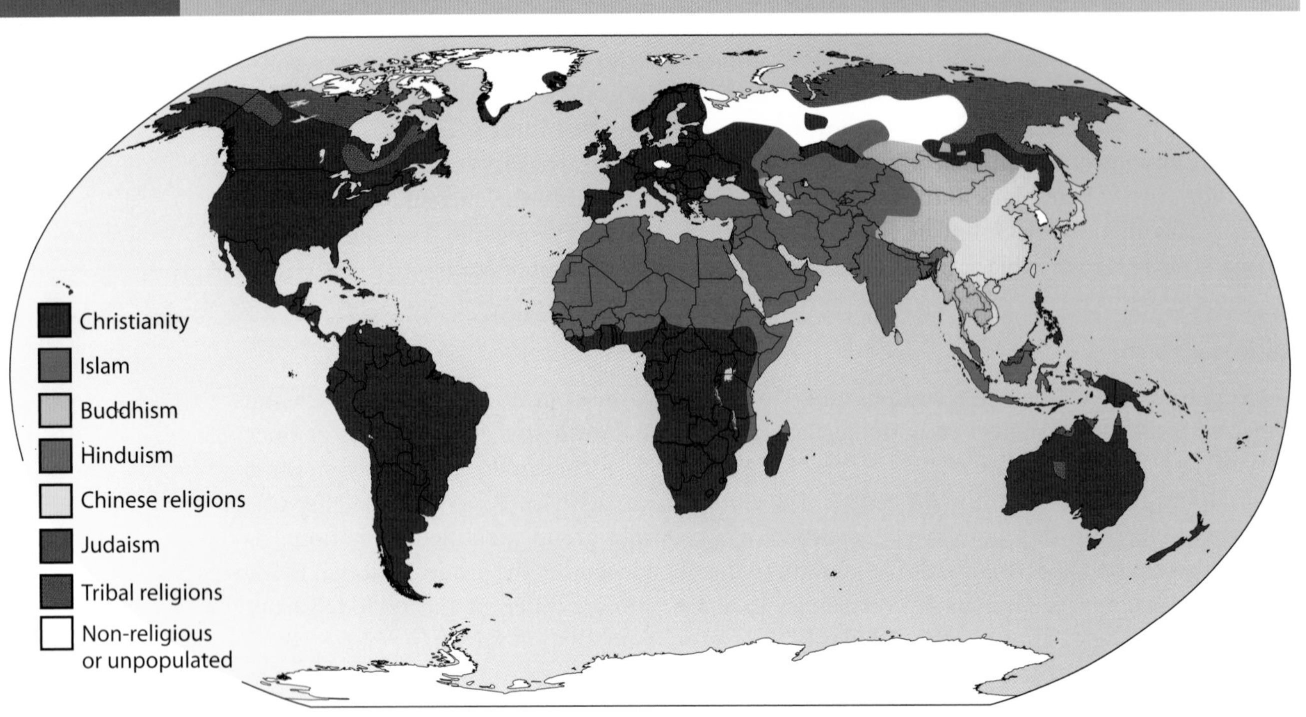

a degree of segregation from other members of society through Faith schools and sport. Some minority religions have taken this segregation to extremes and live in totally segregated communities, such as the Amish in USA. The important point is not so much the differences in belief but the convenient labels attached to the group. Some of the worst ethnic conflicts in recent times have had a religious label. The Holocaust, which resulted in the deaths of six million Jews under Nazi rule during World War II; the on going conflict in the Middle East between (Jewish) Israel and her Muslim neighbours; and the global conflict between Islamic extremists and the western world are all examples of this.

Perceived ethnic identity

It is rare for any of these factors to operate in isolation and most ethnic groups will have several of the above in common. Often it is the perception of a group that is most important to outsiders in society. In the USA, African Americans have frequently been portrayed in a negative and inferior way. In the nineteenth century Irish Americans were portrayed as stupid, alcoholic and violent. These stereotypes influenced decisions regarding these groups of people. From an individual's point of view, perceived ethnic identity is also important.

Exercise

Figure 1

Pakistanis living in Scotland feel more at home north of the border than the 400,000 English who live there

Pakistani immigrants feel more at home in Scotland than the English people that live there. Research into why Pakistanis, the largest non-white ethnic-minority group in Scotland, find it easier to adapt to the Scottish culture than the neighbouring [English] reveals that it is all down to English notions of identity.

A survey by the University of Glasgow discovered English perceptions of identity were primarily influenced by birthplace but Pakistanis defined themselves by religion. The study...found that almost half of English people living north of the border felt that to be "truly Scottish" it was essential to be born in Scotland but less than a quarter of Pakistanis believed birthplace matters. Current estimates suggest there are up to 400,000 English in Scotland, and there are now 21,000 Pakistanis –

Exercise continued

most of them in Glasgow...

While English people in Scotland were still more sympathetic than Pakistanis towards Scottish symbols...or towards the teaching of Scottish history in schools, such attitudes did not make them more comfortable living among Scots.

"English people in Scotland have a more rigid, territorial identity than people in the Scottish Pakistani community," Professor Miller [one of the authors of the study] said. "They are self-consciously aware they are not living in their birthplace, making it difficult for them to feel Scottish even though they respect and sympathise with Scotland." Professor Miller said that because the Scottish Pakistani community considered its identity was based on religion rather than birthplace, they did not struggle to choose allegiance between two territories. "Their identity is portable. Being Muslim first and Scottish second does not conflict," Professor Miller said...By contrast, English people tended to believe their identity was "tied to the soil".

While religion was the main influence behind Pakistani identity, with 60% of participants saying they were Muslim rather than Pakistani, British or Scottish, only 2% of English subjects chose a religious identity. Nearly six out of ten saw themselves as British opposed to English, Scottish, Catholic, Episcopalian or Protestant...

Source: P kelbie, The Independent, 30 October 2003, http://tinyurl.com/scotimm, accessed 21 August 2009

1. *Question from CCEA May 2006*
   "In terms of defining ethnicity, perceived ethnic identity is often more important than any other primary factor." Use the article above **to help you**, discuss the extent to which you agree with this statement. (9)
2. The article claims that most of the Pakistani and English people living in Scotland are to be found in Glasgow. How would values of the Location Quotient verify this claim? (3)

Secondary factors

These operate as an additional filter within society often in conjunction with one or more of the primary factors above.

Social status

All countries display some form of social division. Minority ethnic groups often fit into specific social niches from which it is very difficult to escape. The example of black Americans illustrates this point well. Most black Americans were descended from slaves and even after their emancipation they remained a disadvantaged group within American society. They were condemned by poverty and discrimination to the lowest paid jobs, which offered little opportunity for social mobility. It was only in the second half of the twentieth century that the black American population achieved basic civil rights but many still remain a disadvantaged group within American society. In South Africa the apartheid system divided society rigidly along racial lines. The division permeated all aspects of life including place of residence. The white population were the most favoured sections of society. They controlled the government, occupied the best jobs and were free to live and move around as they wished. At the other end of the social scale were the black population. They were forced to live apart from the white population either in townships, which were effectively slums at the edge of the city, or in the Homelands, which were areas given over for black communities, well away from white areas. Black South Africans needed to have a pass to access white areas of the towns and cities, and many areas were off limits for them. The Apartheid system has been abandoned and South Africa has had Black majority rule since 1990. The apartheid system was the most extreme example of social division and ethnicity but ethnic groups are often socially or economically disadvantaged. In the UK, the Afro-Caribbean population were associated with low paid jobs in the inner cities. When Northern Ireland was first set up, the Catholic population were a disadvantaged group.

Residential concentration

Ethnic minorities often live in clusters with people of similar ethnicity. This is partly for social and cultural reasons, so that they can avail of places of worship, shops and services, as well as the desire to socialise with those from similar backgrounds. Clusters of ethnic minorities in British cities often reflect the economic ability of the groups to purchase cheap accommodation or to access housing suitable for multiple occupation. The sense of security that comes from living in an ethnically homogeneous area is another major reason for ethnic clustering. Whatever the reason for the clustering, once established, this residential concentration develops, leading to ghettoes or enclaves. These clusters grow in two ways:

- These neighbourhoods are often hostile to those of different ethnicity. This can be achieved through visible displays such as flags and murals. During the 'troubles' Belfast developed clearly defined republican and loyalist areas. People of different ethnicity feel threatened and move away.
- The ethnic neighbourhoods attract more people of similar ethnicity.

Age

In some societies the elderly population are afforded preferential treatment. This is especially the case in some tribal societies, where the tribal or village leader will be an aged person whose lifetime experience is valued. In the case of immigrant populations, the elderly are more likely to hold on to the ethnicity of their ancestral homeland than their children. In MEDCs, increases in life expectancy have meant that the elderly are now a sizeable sector of society. Recently the UK government has appointed the veteran broadcaster Joan Bakewell as a spokesperson for the concerns of the elderly.

Gender

Women remain an under privileged group in many societies. In Saudi Arabia women cannot vote. In Afghanistan, under Taliban rule women had to adhere to a very strict dress code, the burkha. They were not allowed to be educated and their freedom of movement was greatly curtailed. In Somalia a teenage girl was sentenced to death by stoning when a local court rejected her claim that she had been raped. Arranged marriages in some societies have resulted in violence against women. In Britain there has been an increase in the number of the so-called 'honour killings'. These involve women, usually from an Islamic family, who have infringed some Islamic law regarding morality. The murders are all the more horrific because they are usually carried out by a family member in order to preserve the family honour – hence the term 'honour killing'. These are extreme examples but even western society women needed government laws to enable them to vote and more recently to ensure that they have equal pay with men. Even still there are social prejudices against women in certain occupations.

Caste

The Caste system is an extreme form of social stratification that occurs in India. There are four main castes or varna, each one containing many sub-divisions:

- Priestly or Brahman
- Warriors and rulers
- Landowners and merchants
- Craftsmen, labourers and servants

Below all of these and not assigned any caste status are the untouchables or Dalits. The caste system has no legal standing but it was none the less very strictly adhered to, particularly in the rural areas. A person's caste was determined by birth and there was no social mobility. The caste dictated the potential job opportunities. Prestigious jobs could only be performed by those of the higher and superior castes while other tasks were so menial that only the untouchables could perform them. Association and inter-marriage with members of a lower caste was not permitted.

Over the past fifty years the caste system has been weakened by western influences and by the Indian government. However, in traditional rural areas it is still in existence.

Exercise

Figure 1

Revival of multi-culturalism in Europe

The terrorist bomb attacks in London (July 2005) and Madrid (March 2004), some of which were carried out by Muslims born and living in Europe, have prompted many to discuss the issue of multi-culturalism. As these discussions are going on, a new debate is taking place. This debate is not about assimilating the diverse cultures of new immigrants to Europe – like those who have arrived from Asia or North Africa – but rather it concerns the preservation of Europe's oldest minority cultures.

Europe has seen many dramatic political changes in the later part of the twentieth century. The fall of communism in Eastern Europe has allowed those minorities that were suppressed under communist rule a new freedom to express their cultural identity. There has been a similar resurgence in Western Europe, albeit for different reasons. The enlargement of the European Union (EU) will facilitate greater freedom of movement of people. Many fear that these migrations along with globalisation and mass tourism will smooth out ethnic and regional differences.

Recently some of Europe's national minority groups have begun to reassert themselves and are demanding their rights to express their cultures. Some have already had some success. The Sami a reindeer herding community, who live across Northern Europe, have their own parliaments in Finland, Norway and Sweden to deal with linguistic and cultural matters. Some minority languages are also making a comeback. In the state of Schleswig-Holstein in Germany, 20% of the 50,000 people who consider themselves North Frisians – descendants of tribal migrants who settled in this region 2,000 years ago, still speak their own Frisian dialect.

Some argue there may be economic reasons underpinning this cultural revival. In fact having a distinctive culture is a competitive economic advantage. Tourists want precisely those experiences – folk dances, hand made crafts etc – which they cannot get at home and they will pay money for these experiences. It should also be noted that the idea of a nation state is fairly recent in Europe. It was not until the eighteenth and nineteenth centuries that many people, often by force rather than choice, began primarily identifying themselves by nationality. Prior to that people identified themselves by local ethnic group. Many believe that the time may be right for revival. The EU often encourages cultural diversity. In Cornwall for example part of the EU's current seven year aid package is devoted to harnessing the benefits from minority cultural groups. In Northern Ireland many official government documents are published in Irish and in Ulster Scots. Some politicians believe that a strong regional identity is an advantage when looking for EU funding.

Source: CCEA Principal Examiner, Geography

1. ***Question from CCEA May 2007***

   Study the **Figure 1** above relating to minority groups in Europe.

   (i) Use the **Resource above** to **help you** discuss the complexity of defining an ethnic group. (8)

   (ii) What economic and social reasons might explain the recent increase in the outward expression of ethnic diversity in Europe? (4)

C2 THE PROCESSES WHICH CREATE AND MAINTAIN ETHNIC DIVERSITY

For centuries powerful nations have sought to increase their power by overseas expansion, a process known as colonialism. When addressing the impact on ethnic diversity, attention is focused on the colonial expansion that occurred in the MEDCs from the sixteenth century onwards. There is a distinction between colonialism (see above) and colonisation. Colonisation involves setting up settlements in the new colony. This process resulted in the migration of people from the ruling country to the new colony. These people came as administrators and they usually established an enclave in a port which ultimately became a leading city, often the capital city. The colonialists needed military personnel to effect control over their new acquired territory and to fend off rival claims from other aspiring colonial powers. Much of Africa was colonised. The rival European powers subdivided the continent according to the agreement set out in the Berlin Conference in 1884–1885 (**Resource 55**). An examination of a map of Africa reveals very regular boundaries between countries, reflecting the arbitrary and almost geometric nature of the subdivision of land. This led to the creation of ethnic diversity in three ways:

- It established a European layer to the population. The Europeans were distinctive in Africa and Asia by their skin colour, language, nationality, religion, social status, residential concentration and they were mostly male. They usually established the European way of life in the colony. Everything from language and sport to architecture reflected the colonial rulers' home country. Even in post colonial days, relics of this Europeanisation remains. West Indian cricket is one example.
- The subdivision of territory, particularly in Africa, often cut across tribal homelands, leaving formerly united groups in rival countries. The post colonial period in Africa and in the Indian sub-continent has had many ethnic conflicts as a result of this.
- On occasions, the colonial rulers brought labour from other parts of the Empire to work on specific types of project. They were not slaves but were under contract to work for a given period in the new country – so called indentured labour. In this way Uganda in east Africa had Indian workers brought to work on the tea plantations and in a similar move Indian Tamils were brought to Sri Lanka.

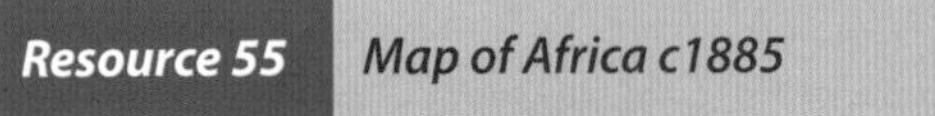
Resource 55 *Map of Africa c1885*

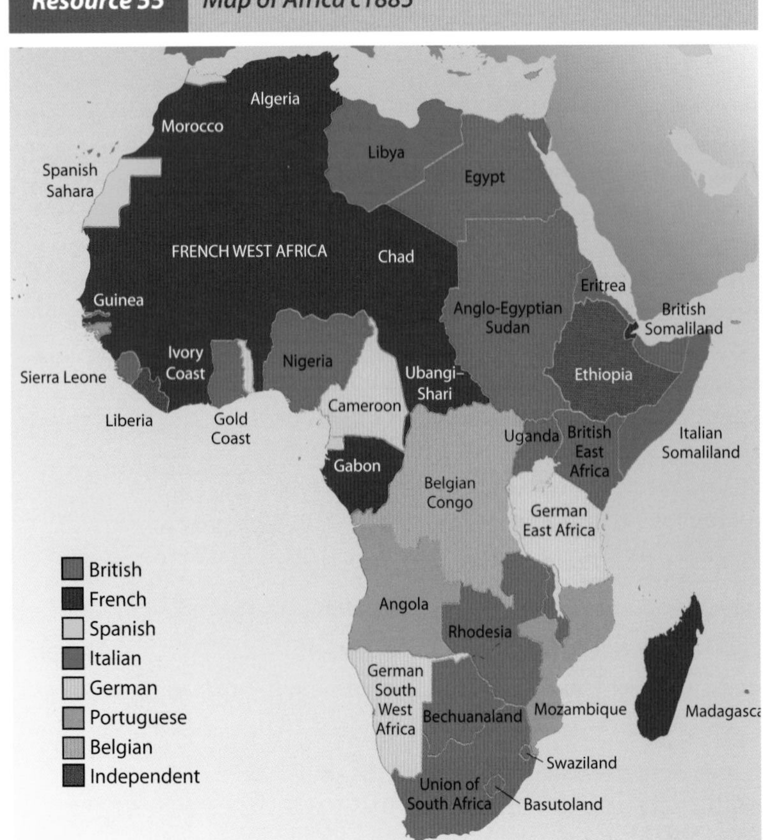

The colonies gained their independence at various times throughout the twentieth century but most have maintained links with their colonial rulers to some extent. The

British Commonwealth, a group of former colonies who still have the British Monarch as their titular Head of State, is an example. Following the end of World War II, European nations attracted migrants from their former colonies to fill the gap in the labour market. Many came to work in the low paid jobs in the inner cities. In Britain, immigrants from the West Indies, India and Pakistan added to the ethnic diversity of many cities. Like the colonialists, they were distinctive by many primary and secondary factors.

One lasting issue that both of these immigrants share concerns their second and subsequent generations. Should descendents of former British colonialists in Zimbabwe be regarded as Zimbabwean or British? Should descendents of West Indian immigrants to Britain be regarded as British or West Indian? In the Zimbabwean example, the president of that country has confiscated land belonging to white farmers, whom he regards as British even though they were born in Zimbabwe. In Britain, the census documents people who are black British. This is an attempt to accept that being British is not confined to a white population.

A second political process that can create increased ethnic diversity is Annexation. Annexation is taking political control of a neighbouring country. In 1990, Saddam Hussein annexed neighbouring Kuwait as the nineteenth province of Iraq. Indonesia, already in control over West Timor, annexed East Timor in 1975 (**Resource 56**). Germany annexed Czechoslovakia in 1939. The reason given for annexation is usually the unification of separated ethnic minorities but inevitably there will be those who do not wish to become an integral part of another country and most incidences of annexation result in conflict. Annexation creates ethnic diversity when the annexed region contains people of a different ethnic group from the invading country. The war in Georgia, in 2008, occurred when that country tried to annex the break away provinces of South Ossetia, in an attempt to reunite Georgians in South Ossetia under Georgian rule (**Resource 57**). The minority Russian population in South Ossetia were opposed to Georgia and were successfully supported by Russia. The majority of South Ossetians want to join their ethnic neighbours in North Ossetia, an autonomous republic within Russia. About one third of South Ossetians are Georgian. There are disputed claims about the origins of the conflict in August 2008 but Georgia did attempt to take South Ossetia under Georgian rule again renaming it the province of Tskhinvali.

Map of Indonesia and East Timor **Resource 56**

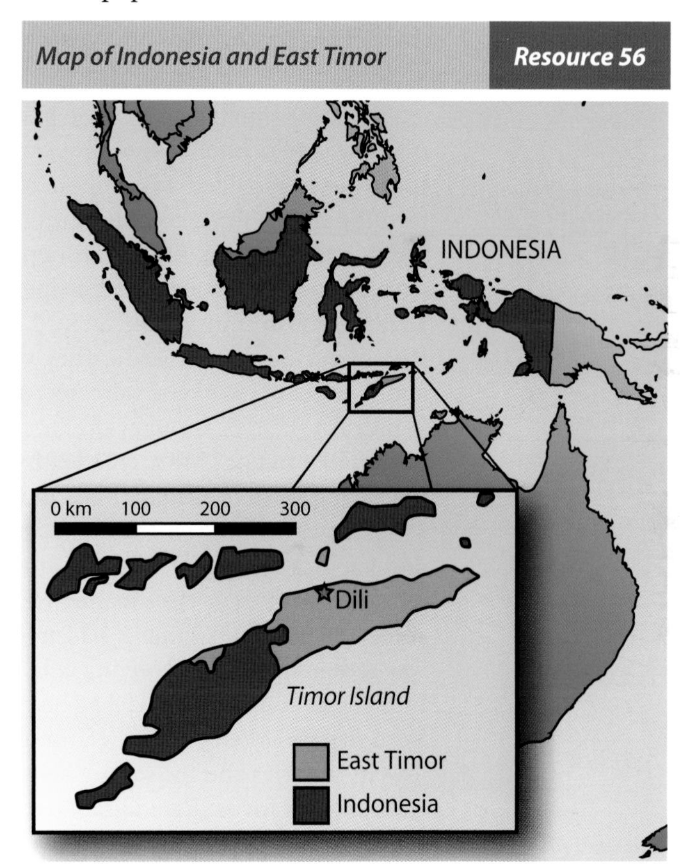

Map of the areas of conflict in Georgia **Resource 57**

International migration is perhaps the most widespread process creating ethnic diversity at the present time. The USA, Canada, Australia and New Zealand are populated almost entirely by migrants or their descendants. In Western Europe there has been unprecedented movement of economic migrants from the former communist countries that are now part of the enlarged European Union. Northern Ireland, which until recently was not a major destination country for international migrants, now receives large numbers of immigrants from Poland, Romania, Latvia, Lithuania and Estonia.

CASE STUDY: The processes that created ethnic diversity in Britain

The 2001 census included questions on ethnic identity and **Resource 58** shows the ethnic composition based on the data received from the census. There is no doubt that Britain has become an increasingly ethnically diverse country. Most large cities contain several ethnic groups, none more so than London, which has approximately 200 linguistic groups. The reasons for this ethnic diversity can be explained by looking at the combined effects of colonialism, annexation and international migration.

Britain has been colonised over the centuries by various groups from Roman times but these early colonists made limited impact on the present ethnic composition of the country. The British Isles came together as a political unit through various waves of annexation over a number of centuries culminating in Ireland. The first wave of immigrants to Britain came in the mid-nineteenth century when thousands of Irish fled from famine. They settled mainly in the port cities of Liverpool, Glasgow and London. While there are still some ties with Ireland in these cities, second and third generation Irish immigrants have blended seamlessly into British society.

The most significant increase in ethnic diversity in Britain started in the 1950s. During the two world wars hundreds of thousands of men from across the Empire had fought for Britain. India alone provided 1.3 million soldiers. In the interwar years many remained in Britain, forming small ethnic communities in the ports. A number of Jewish immigrants settled in the London area, fleeing from Nazi oppression in Europe. At the end of World War II there were work shortages throughout Europe and Britain began a recruitment drive abroad. Initially, 157,000 Polish immigrants arrived in Britain in search of work. They had formed ties with Britain during the war years. They were joined by Italians but there was still a labour shortage and eventually workers were recruited from the colonies. On 22 June 1948, The Empire Windrush (a ship) brought the first of many West Indian immigrants to Britain. The British Nationality Act of 1948 granted citizenship to people from the Commonwealth, enabling them to live and work in Britain. Mass immigration continued from the West Indies throughout the 1950s. In 1956, London Transport, struggling to find workers, advertised in Barbados, Trinidad and Jamaica for bus drivers and conductors. Within twelve years 4,000 Barbadians had been recruited with their fares loaned by London Transport and repaid from their wages. By 1958 some 125,000 West Indians had migrated to Britain in search of a better lifestyle and higher wages than they were receiving at home. In the 1960s they were joined by immigrants from the Indian sub-continent which had become India, West and East Pakistan, following independence from Britain. Mostly the new immigrants went to the London area, filling low paid, unskilled jobs in factories and the service sector. The car and engineering factories in the West Midlands were another focus. The migrants from India and Pakistan worked in the footwear and clothing factories in the East Midlands as well as in the transport and textile mills of the northern cities in Lancashire and Yorkshire. They frequently established clusters or neighbourhoods in the poorest areas in the inner cities – Toxteth in Liverpool, Brixton and Bethnal Green in London. In most cases the new immigrants eventually established their own places of worship and other ethnic services. These new immigrants were not welcomed easily into British society and there were protests at their arrival. The government reacted by amending the British Nationality Act to make it more difficult for non-white immigrants to bring their family members with them. In spite of this, the numbers of non-white residents continued to grow and by 1970 they numbered 1.5 million, one third of these were children born in Britain.

In 1972, 80,000 Ugandan Asians arrived in Britain. These were the descendents of indentured Asian workers brought to Uganda by Britain. The Ugandan dictator General Idi Amin expelled the entire Asian community in Uganda to Britain. Racial prejudice was quite widespread and there were racially motivated riots in the 1980s. Many ended up in areas of significant social deprivation as unemployment rose throughout the 80s. The riots were sparked by claims that ethnic minorities, especially black male youths, were being targeted by the police. Right wing politicians and political parties argued for at least curtailment of the numbers gaining entry. The numbers of new immigrants in the 1980s were much lower than at any time since

1948. However, as most of the immigrants were in the young economically active sector of the population there is a significant potential for future natural increase. In recent times, Britain has received another wave of migrants. This time the migrants are from Eastern Europe following the demise of communism and the entry of many former communist countries into the European Union in 2005. In addition, the growth of asylum seeker applications has contributed to increased ethnic diversity. Between 1998 and 2000 some 45,000 people arrived from Africa, 23,000 from India and 25,000 from various countries in Asia.

Exercise

Explain how the processes of colonisation, annexation and international migration have created ethnic diversity in any one country.

Processes maintaining ethnic diversity

In ethnically diverse societies there will usually be some degree of interaction between the various groups. While the first generation maintain their ethnic distinctiveness, subsequent generations may become more affiliated with the majority population, a process described as assimilation. This process is most readily observed where the original differences are less visible and where there is a willingness from both the majority and the minority populations for assimilation. There are, however, several processes operating in societies that prevent this 'melting pot' situation occurring.

The physical separation or segregation of ethnic groups maintains ethnic diversity because it minimises the opportunities for social interaction. In Nazi Germany, the Jews and Roma people were subjected to a very extreme form of segregation. During the 1930s and 1940s, Jews in Nazi-controlled states were made to wear yellow ribbons or stars of David. They were forced to live in ghettoes in tightly packed areas of cities and their movement outside of the ghetto was controlled by the Germans. The Warsaw ghetto was the largest containing about 400,000 people.

Another extreme case of segregation took place in the Apartheid era in South Africa. Under this scheme black South Africans were totally segregated from white South Africans. The segregation process was institutionalised by law and pervaded all aspects of life. Black South Africans were forced to live in homelands or townships and were excluded from all decision making and political life in white areas. In the USA segregation also occurred, especially in the southern states until the late 1960s. Sometimes segregation is re-enforced by social stratification, where each group occupies a particular position in society. After the emancipation of slavery in the USA, the white population often employed black Americans as servants. The black population were no longer slaves but their only contact with the white population was in this subservient role. These are extreme cases, where the segregation is enforced by law but residential segregation is widespread in many ethnically diverse societies (see the section on Residential Concentration, page 99). The net result is that the various groups live separate lives with little understanding of the cultural norms of other groups. In British cities there are enclaves of ethnic groups with their own services, schools, places of worship and recreation. In some cases there are linguistic and religious barriers which make social interaction with the majority population very difficult. In 2001, there were race riots in Bradford and Oldham between Asian and white youths. A government report on the riots referred to people "living parallel lives with no meaningful contact between the various groups". The segregation of the groups occurred partly because of social and economic reasons but also because many white people moved away from neighbourhoods populated by Asians. In Belfast Protestant and Catholic housing areas were

Security Gates separating Catholic housing areas in Short Strand from Protestants in East Belfast

Peace wall along Bryson Street separating Protestant and Catholic housing areas in East Belfast.

Loyalist mural at 'Freedom Corner' on Belfast's Lower Newtownards Road.

Resource 58 *Ethnic classification in Britain 2001 census*

	Total Numbers	Non-white Percentages
White	**54,153 898**	
Mixed	**677,117**	**14.6**
Asian/asian British	**2,331,423**	**50.2**
Indian		22.7
Pakistani		16.1
Bangladeshi		6.1
Other Asian		5.3
Black/black British	**1,148,738**	**24.8**
Black Caribbean		12.2
Black African		10.5
Black Other		2.1
Chinese	**247,403**	**5.3**
Other Ethnic Groups	**230,615**	**5.0**
Total Ethnic Population	**4,635,296**	**100**
Total Population	**58,789,194**	

Source: Data from the Office of National Statistics

separated by Peace walls for safety reasons. Murals and flags were used by both groups to delimit their territory and intimidate the opposing religious group. Attempts were made to establish mixed social housing areas in Belfast but these were abandoned as the numerically larger group in each case forced the rival group away.

Because of international migration and globalisation most countries have ethnic minorities. A country or society with several ethnic groupings is referred to as a pluralist society. The USA is one of the best examples of ethnic pluralism, being made up almost entirely of immigrant groups. The last census recorded ten major groups, with as many as 57 sub-divisions. In the UK most of the cities are ethnically plural. London has over 200 linguistic groups and almost 30% of its population are non-white, the largest proportion of non-white population in any European city. In Northern Ireland, the recent in-migration of East Europeans has added to the ethnic pluralism in many areas. Pluralism adds to ethnic diversity through ethnic services such as Chinese or Italian restaurants; places of worship; or festivals such as The Chinese New Year or the Notting Hill Carnival in London. The extent to which pluralism maintains ethnic diversity will depend on how readily various groups can or wish to assimilate. Due to improvements in communications many of the recent migrants maintain links with their home country and as many are temporary migrants they do not learn the language of their new country. This helps to maintain the ethnic diversity and slows down or prevents assimilation taking place. In Belgium, the two main ethnic groups rigidly defend their linguistic differences to give a very pluralistic country. **Resource 58**, showing the ethnic classification used in the 2001 census in the UK, illustrates a very pluralist society.

There has been much debate about how governments should respond to pluralist societies. There are those who argue for an integrationist approach. Under this scheme ethnic groups should not display outward manifestations of their ethnicity. In France the government have pursued this approach and banned the wearing of Muslim headdress, the Hijab, or Christian symbols such as crosses in schools. However, some countries, including Britain, have an official policy of multiculturalism aimed at recognising, celebrating and maintaining the different cultural identities within society. Indonesia is a country made up of many islands spread across a large archipelago and there are many different languages and dialects. Although predominantly Muslim the country also has large Christian and Hindu populations. Singapore recognises three languages, Mandarin Chinese, Tamil and English as its official languages, with Malay being the national language. Apart from languages, Singapore also celebrates festivals celebrated by these three ethnic communities.

Multiculturalism maintains ethnic diversity where an ethnic group has clearly defined outward manifestation of their culture, such as the Muslim dress code for women or the Sihk turban for men. A British government minister caused considerable controversy when he objected to Muslim women wearing the Hijab and veil. In Northern Ireland, the annual Protestant marches celebrating the defeat of the Catholic King James in the seventeenth century were a major cause of Catholic resentment and in the 1990s a Parades Commission was set up to divert some of these marches away from potential conflict zones.

Multiculturalism was adopted as official policy in most MEDCs from the 1960s onward and most large cities are increasingly made up of a mosaic of cultures.

Government multicultural policies include the following:

- Recognition of multiple citizenship. At one stage citizens of the British Commonwealth were entitled to British citizenship.
- Government support for minority languages.
- Support for minority festivals, holidays, and celebrations.
- Acceptance of traditional and religious dress in schools, the military, and society in general.
- Support for music and arts from minority cultures.
- Programmes to encourage minority representation in politics, education and the work force in general.

From the late 1990s multiculturalism became a contentious issue in some European countries including Britain. Some of the opposition came from extreme right wing groups such as the British National Party (BNP) but also from concern about the rise of Islamic fundamentalism in Europe.

In many ethnically diverse societies a minority group is actively discriminated against. This can take the form of unfair allocation of housing or jobs or the minority group may not enjoy the same freedom of religious, political or cultural expression as the ruling population. In some cases the underprivileged group is denied even the most basic human rights or killed, such as the genocide of Jews in Nazi Germany. At the time of writing, black Africans have been forced to flee to refugee camps in Darfur in Sudan because of discriminatory practices in Sudan. In Northern Ireland, the Civil Rights Movement in the late 1960s was set up to campaign against discrimination of the Catholic population in local government and in the allocation of council housing. A Fair Employment law is now in operation, passed to safeguard against religious discrimination in job allocations. Discrimination maintains ethnic diversity because it confines one sector of the population to an inferior niche in society and it also foments anger and hostility in the underprivileged group. This frustration can easily result in conflict, which the era of 'The Troubles' in Northern Ireland aptly demonstrates. One cause of the on-going crisis in the Middle East is the claim by the Palestinians of discrimination by Israel. Various terrorist organisations have fought against this discrimination for over half a century (see CASE STUDY: Processes maintaining ethnic diversity in Jerusalem, page 108).

Exercise

Figure 1

Ethnicity in British cities

'Too white' towns are labelled unhealthy

Professor Ted Cantle, who wrote the report on the 2001 riots in Bradford and Oldham, suggested people from ethnic minorities in some parts of the Midlands might not feel "safe and secure" living near predominantly white communities.

Cantle, who has chaired a panel advising ministers on implementing the recommendations of his report, made the remarks in an interview about multiculturalism with a local newspaper last week...

Cantle said he was concerned about the strength of support for the far-right British National party in some parts of the East Midlands...In February the BNP came second in a council by-election in Heanor. A few days later Channel Five dubbed it the "skinhead capital of Britain"...

In his 2001 report on the riots in Bradford, Burnley and Oldham, Cantle identified communities living "parallel lives" and highlighted the polarisation of communities with different schools, estates and social lives. He said schools should change their catchment areas to attract a broader mix.

At the time one in four primary schools in Bradford were more than 70% Asian while half were totally white. Cantle opposed single-faith and "monocultural" schools, but ministers ignored his advice.

[In 2005] Trevor Phillips, chairman of the Commission for Racial Equality, warned that unless steps were taken to promote deeper integration, segregation could reach the levels witnessed in New Orleans. He warned that Britain might be "sleepwalking to segregation".

Cantle's remarks go further by describing parts of the country as "unhealthily" white, a phrase that critics said this weekend appeared to place the blame for ethnic tensions on the white community.

Local people agree Heanor is predominantly white. But they deny they pose a threat to non-white communities. Brian Lucas, a Labour councillor for the nearby area of Cotmanhay, said: "I'm a big believer in people choosing where they live and not being pushed, guided or forced into an area."

Source: D Leppard and G Hinds, Times Online, 22 April 2006, http://tinyurl.com/2whitetwns, accessed 20 August 2009

Figure 1 adapted from resources for CCEA January 2008

1. *Question from CCEA January 2008*
Study **Figure 1** relating to ethnicity in British cities.

(i) **Figure 1** describes segregation in British cities. Use the Resource **to help you** explain how and why such segregation can come about. (10)

(ii) The Chairman of The Commission for Racial Equality claims that action is needed to promote deeper integration to preserve peace between the different racial groups. Discuss the extent to which you agree/disagree with this viewpoint. (4)

CASE STUDY: Processes maintaining ethnic diversity in Jerusalem

Jerusalem, with a population of over 740,000 (includes East Jerusalem), has been at the epicentre of the ethnic conflict in the Middle East since 1948. The population of Jerusalem is approximately 70% Jewish and the remaining 30% are largely Muslim but there is also a minority Christian population. The city holds a special place for the three western religions: Judaism, Islam and Christianity divided into several sects, including Roman Catholic Orthodox Armenians and

Coptic Christians from Ethiopia. Ethnic diversity is maintained in a number of ways in different parts of the city. The walled 'Old City' is a unique mosaic of areas of deep significance to each group. Ethnic pluralism is evidenced in the four-fold division of land:

- The Jewish Quarter
- The Muslim Quarter
- The Armenian Quarter
- The Christian Quarter

There is a high degree of segregation. Each quarter has its own unique places of worship, such as the Church of the Holy Sepulchre in the Christian quarter (reputed to contain the site of Christ's crucifixion, burial and resurrection), its own distinctive architecture, religious festivals and dress code.

One site, known as the Temple Mount, is of the utmost significance to the two main religious groups within Jerusalem – Judaism and Islam. The Temple Mount was the site of Jewish temples dating back to 960 BC. These temples have been destroyed, leaving only the Western or Wailing Wall, which has remained a sacred site for Jews throughout history. This Temple Mount is also significant to Muslims who believe it is the site from where Muhammad ascended to heaven. Two mosques – the Dome of the Rock, built on the site of the former Jewish temple and the nearby Al Aqsa mosque – mark Muslims' claim to this area. There is a strict territorial demarcation between each quarter on the walls surrounding this Old City (**Resource 61**).

Map of Israel showing the location of Jerusalem **Resource 59**

The Temple Mount, Jerusalem **Resource 60**

Photograph showing the Temple Mount, with the Dome of the Rock and Al Aqsa Mosque in the background and the Jewish Wailing wall in the foreground.

Map showing the religious segregation in the Old City of Jerusalem **Resource 61**

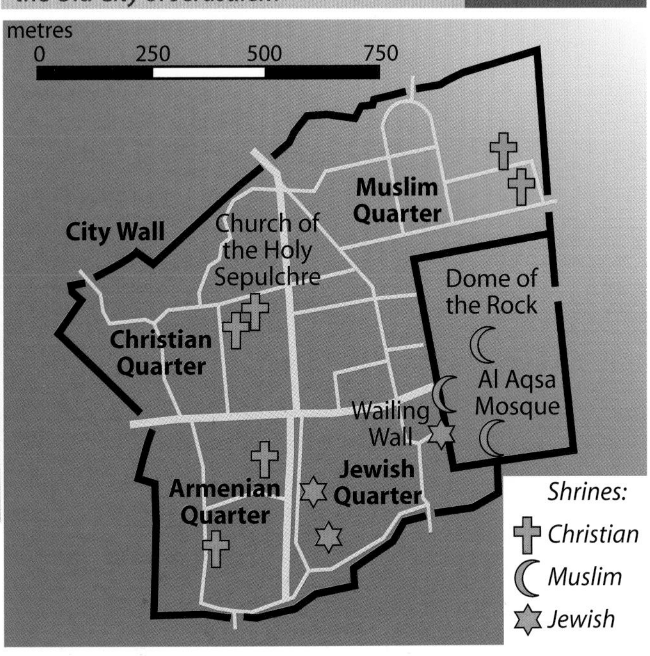

Resource 62 *Map of religious segregation in Jerusalem*

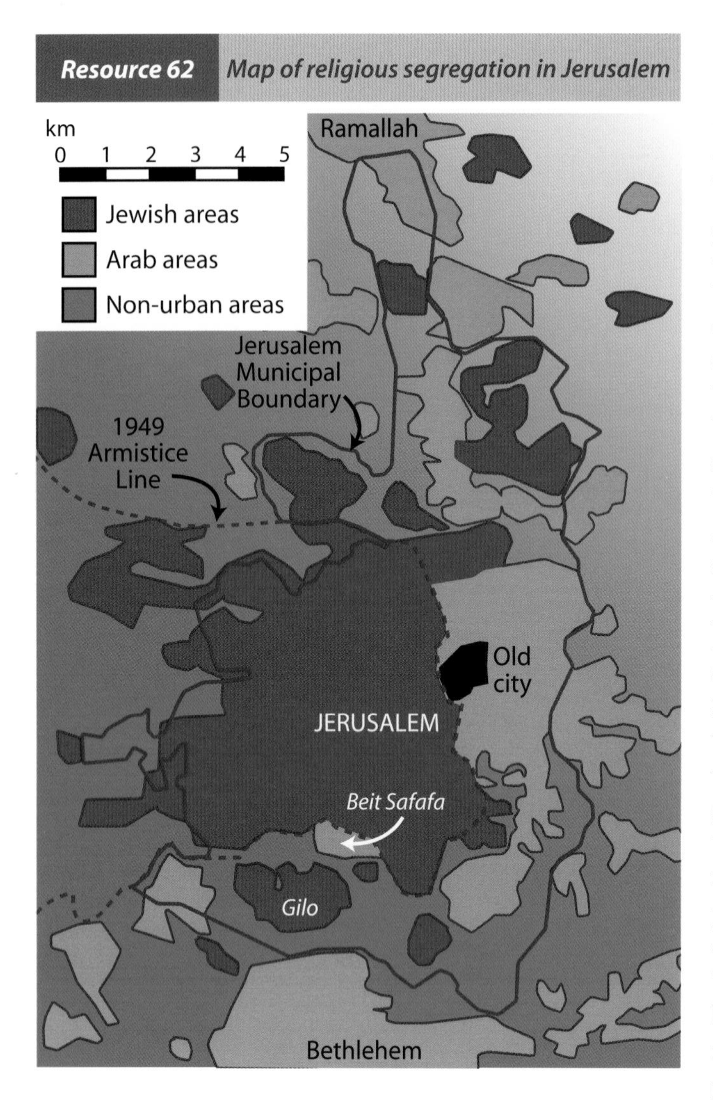

Within the residential areas of Jerusalem ethnic diversity is maintained by segregation on religious grounds. This segregation, although based on religion, is the end result of a number of processes operating within the wider area of Israel and the Middle East in general. The state of Israel was created by the United Nations from the partition of Palestine in 1948 into a western Jewish section – Israel and an Eastern Arab section – Jordan (**Resource 59**). The city of Jerusalem straddled the dividing line and under the initial plan, the city was to be a neutral area administered by the United Nations. The partition of Palestine was never acceptable to the Arab population in the region and when Israel claimed independence the neighbouring Arab nations declared war. The Arabs were defeated and part of the Peace Deal saw Jerusalem divided by the 'green line' into an Israeli western section and a Jordanian eastern section (**Resource 62**). The eastern section contained the Old City and separated Israelis from their most sacred religious sites as well as from the Hebrew University. At the end of the war Jews were in the majority in west Jerusalem and the new government set to develop this part of the city now under Israeli control but their stated aim was the reunification of Jerusalem. Ben Gurion, the first Israeli prime minister, claimed that "Jewish Jerusalem is an organic and inseparable part of the State of Israel". The 'green line' was a zone about 100 feet wide and included buildings and even whole streets. Many areas became no man's land, with concrete barriers constructed to protect Jews against sniper attacks. Jews were unable to access the Western or Wailing Wall. Relations between Israel and the surrounding Arab nations continued to deteriorate throughout the 1950s and 60s, culminating in the Six Day War in 1967. Israel annexed considerable amount of territory from Syria, Egypt and Jordan. Part of the territory annexed from Jordan included East Jerusalem, which still remains under Israeli rule although it is not ratified by international law. An entire Arab quarter close to the Western Wall was demolished and the boundaries of Jerusalem redrawn to exclude Palestinians living on the outskirts of the city. The Palestinians (about 240,000) remaining in Jerusalem were declared citizens of Israel.

When Israel annexed East Jerusalem the city was already segregated. Although the physical division has gone, the degree of segregation remains absolute and the city has been described as "groups of people living together separately". There are separate business districts, public transport systems and separate educational and medical facilities. Services administered across the city, such as police and emergency services, are not dispatched according to geographical proximity but according to their ethnic match to the neighbourhood requesting assistance. The two main ethnic groups, the Israelis and the Palestinians, are identified not just by their religion but also by social and economic factors. The Palestinians were a disadvantaged group before the Six Day War because Jordan had paid little attention to East Jerusalem, concentrating their efforts in their capital city of Amman. Under Israeli rule the Palestinians have become more marginalised. They have suffered discrimination in all aspects of life as Israel has sought to secure control over the city and the wider area. Israelis justify their actions in the annexed East Jerusalem, on the grounds of defence from attack from Palestinian militants and on the belief that this is their 'Promised Land' and that all Jews have a right to live there if that is their wish. Israel needed more land for settlement and following the annexation of East Jerusalem the government began building new neighbourhoods in East Jerusalem. Many of these new settlements surround the Palestinians or are built on hilly land to give the feeling of containing the Palestinians. Considerable amounts of land were expropriated from Palestinians. Some land had been abandoned by the Palestinians who fled to Jordan during the conflict and Israel expropriated this land. Other lands were taken from Palestinians still living in East Jerusalem. Palestinians do not recognise Israeli jurisdiction in East Jerusalem and they have operated a policy of non-cooperation with Israeli law. Part of this non-cooperation involved not applying for compensation for land expropriated by Israel. Palestinians from outside Jerusalem are largely excluded from East Jerusalem by a ring of roadblocks and Israeli military checkpoints.

Since 1967, Israeli political policies in Jerusalem have attempted to reunite the city so that future sub-division would be impossible. This has been achieved in East Jerusalem in several ways:

- Building more settlements for Jews. Jews at present make up 70% of the population of Jerusalem and the government wants this majority to be maintained so that, should the Palestinians ever rethink their non-cooperation in elections, there will always be an Israeli majority.
- Building roads across Palestinian areas that divide Palestinian settlements but unite Jewish settlements. In the Arab village of Beit Safafa (**Resource 62**) in southern Jerusalem, regional road building that connects the Jewish Gilo neighbourhood to west Jerusalem has divided the village into four pieces.
- Palestinian settlements have been subjected to a 'green areas' zoning plan. This zoning was to prevent urban sprawl and applied throughout the city. However, it was applied more strictly in Palestinian areas.
- Since 2000 Israel has constructed a massive wall separating some Palestinian suburbs from the centre of Jerusalem. The wall was built to protect Israelis from suicide bomb attacks from the Palestinians but some accused Israel of excluding Palestinians from Jerusalem.

As a result of these policies, Palestinians are denied planning permission to build new settlements on 80% of land in East Jerusalem. This has led to an increase in population density in existing settlements and overcrowding. It is estimated that additional housing for 20,000 is required but only 10,000 people have been rehoused since 1967. Over 30% of Palestinians live in housing with more than three people per room, as opposed to 2% of Jews. While Arabs make up about 30% of the city's population, 70% of substandard housing was in Arab neighbourhoods, many without inside toilets. Even in the areas where they can in theory build new housing, it is extremely difficult and expensive to get planning permission. Restrictions on the height of buildings and increasing the width of roads between settlements are just two examples of how planning regulations put obstacles in the way of building new houses for Palestinians. In the Arab village of Shuafat there was land available to build housing for 8,000 people. By the time all the planning procedures were completed only 7,000 were re-housed. In defence of this apparent discrepancy in housing and other service provision, Israel claims that the Palestinians do not pay their local taxes, which could be used to improve services. Whilst there is evidence of the non-payment of taxes in East Jerusalem, independent observers feel it does not fully explain the apparent discrimination in the Arab areas. Many Palestinians have had little alternative but to build neighbourhoods without planning permission and under these circumstances Israeli law permits the removal of illegal settlements. The Palestinians have a high rate of population growth while the Jewish population is ageing. To address this issue Israel has

Israeli restrictions on Palestinian growth in annexed East Jerusalem — **Resource 63a**

Method	% of land in annexed East Jerusalem
Expropriated	33
Green Area Zoning	40
Road construction	06
Land remaining for development	**21**
Palestinian built up areas	10
Vacant land for Palestinian growth	11

Source: Data from SA Bollens, *On Narrow Ground*

Resource 63b *Social problems in some Palestinian Neighbourhoods*

- One half of the fresh water supply network is in need of replacement.
- One half of neighbourhoods have no sewage system.
- Many of the older neighbourhoods have dirt roads with no proper lighting.
- Some neighbourhoods suffer from inadequate cleaning and refuse collection.

restricted the numbers of Palestinian migrants coming into Jerusalem from other parts of the Occupied Territories (the West Bank and Gaza). Many of the Palestinians who fled to Jordan during earlier conflict have not been allowed to return. Since 1991 non-Jerusalem Palestinians have been barred from entering the city without a permit issued by the Israeli Authorities. Further evidence of the inadequate provision of services for the Palestinian inhabitants in East Jerusalem can be observed in **Resources 63a and 63b**.

After twenty years of occupation by Israelis and several international wars, the Palestinians began an uprising throughout the Occupied territories, including Jerusalem. The first uprising or Intifada lasted from 1987–1993. A second Intifada originated in East Jerusalem following a controversial visit by a right wing Israeli politician Ariel Sharon to the Al Aqsa mosque in 2000. This mosque and its compound is a sacred site for both Jews and Muslims. Ariel Sharon described his visit as a message of peace but the Palestinians regarded the visit an act of provocation, coming at a time when discussions over the possible division of Jerusalem were taking place. Five years of violent unrest followed, including street riots, suicide bombings, and by swift and robust Israeli retaliation. Since then there have been many attempts to broker a peace deal between the opposing factions in Israel (see CASE STUDY: Ethnic conflict in Israel, page 124) and these will impact on Jerusalem, which remains a major stumbling block for any peace deal.

The economic, social and spatial outcomes of ethnic diversity

Ethnic diversity does not always result in conflict situations as in the case of Jerusalem. Pluralist or multicultural societies exist peacefully in many parts of the world, such as Australia, Canada and the USA, although the latter has had serious ethnic conflict in the past. Where there is harmony between the various groups the country will benefit economically and socially. In a society where there is no discrimination, economic advancement and social mobility are determined by ability rather than membership of the ruling elite. In the case of Jerusalem, ethnic diversity has resulted in serious and prolonged conflict that has had a detrimental effect on the city and its inhabitants. One of the most obvious is the human cost and the conflict in Jerusalem is no exception. Apart from this, the city of Jerusalem has suffered economically and not just from the cost of the security measures. Although Israel claims jurisdiction over all of Jerusalem the international community has refused to accept this claim. No foreign country has an embassy in Jerusalem. It is also one of Israel's poorest cities, ranked bottom in a survey of quality of life throughout Israel. Job shortages, economic stagnation and poor infrastructure are just some of the problems. With its historical sites Jerusalem has the potential to be a major tourist attraction but the violence over the years has seriously affected this lucrative industry, especially in the Old City. The situation in Arab East Jerusalem is even poorer than West Jerusalem. Since the tightening of controls on the numbers of Palestinians allowed to enter East Jerusalem from the West Bank, many Palestinian shopkeepers have lost business. Investment in all aspects of public services is lower in East Jerusalem.

Jerusalem has always been a city segregated into Jewish and Muslim areas and this is most apparent in the old city. The juxtaposition of the sites sacred to all the main groups in the old city has heightened tensions on many occasions. The Intifada mentioned earlier is the most serious example of this. Recently there have been minor skirmishes between the two main Christian groups over access to the claimed burial site of Christ. However, it is in the residential areas that the social outcomes of ethnic diversity are most apparent and these are largely the result of the economic discrimination of the Palestinians. In West Jerusalem a new segregation pattern has emerged within the Jewish population. Increasingly the city is being populated to the ultra orthodox Haredi Jews and the growth of this community is causing concern among the more secular Jews. This community has for more than a century been based in the Mea Shearim district outside the Old City. Haredi Jews now make up about one tenth of the Jewish population in Jerusalem and the previous mayor was from this community. They follow a strict moral code, including dress code for men and women. Haredi laws enforce strict observance of the Sabbath, forcing shops to close and banning the reading of newspapers or using cars. These measures have prompted many secular Jews to leave Jerusalem and go to the capital city of Tel Aviv. Currently, Jerusalem is showing a net-out migration of about 5,000 per year. In November 2008, a new mayor was elected from the secular Jewish community, giving many residents the hope that the city could see an economic revival. However, his claim that the division of Jerusalem is not a possibility remains a major stumbling block towards peace in the area.

The years of conflict have had an effect on the overall environment of the city. Apart from the decline in infrastructure mentioned above, the city is physically divided by walls and barriers built by the Israelis for security reasons and by murals and graffiti that delimit the territory of each of the major groups living there.

Exercise

1. *Question from CCEA May 2008*
   With reference to your case study of an ethnically diverse city:
   (a) explain the processes that have maintained its ethnic diversity;
   (b) discuss the social and economic consequences of these processes. (15)

Additional References

Israel's 'modesty buses' draw fire – news.bbc.co.uk/1/hi/world/middle_east/6584661.stm

Row over Jerusalem Muslim cemetery – news.bbc.co.uk/1/hi/world/middle_east/7715921.stm

Holy City facing splits and decline – news.bbc.co.uk/1/hi/world/middle_east/7719845.stm

Obstacles to peace: Jerusalem – news.bbc.co.uk/1/hi/world/middle_east/6668603.stm

C3 ETHNIC CONFLICT

The causes of ethnic conflict

Conflict is one of the most controversial outcomes of ethnic diversity. The conflict can be anything from a simple protest to a fully fledged war and ethnic conflict occurs across all levels of development. Some of the most serious conflicts in recent times have been ethnically based. At the time of writing there are major ethnic conflicts in several African countries, including Sudan and the Democratic Republic of Congo. The causes of these conflicts are complex and they are probably due to a combination of a number of factors.

Disputes over territory have been a major source of unrest and conflict in a number of major world regions. The continent of Africa was carved up amongst the European powers during their colonial days, with little attention given to either tribal or economic regions. Under colonial rule these 'artificial' countries were united against their colonial rulers but following independence old tribal loyalties have re-emerged. People separated from the remainder of their tribe or ethnic group by imposed international boundaries have engaged in territorial disputes with their neighbouring countries. Territorial disputes of this nature have occurred between Libya and Chad, with Libya annexing the Aozou Strip from Chad in 1973. The Aozou Strip is a long stretch of desolate land located in the middle of the Sahara Desert (**Resource 64**). Libya claims the Aozou Strip because of cultural, ethnic, and historical reasons. The area, like Libya, is populated with Berbers and Arabs that Libya wanted to protect from instability in Chad. The Strip was also part of Libya under colonial rule. Rumors of rich uranium deposits compelled Libya to invade and capture the Aozou region from Chad in 1973. It remained in Libyan hands until a Chadian offensive in the late 1980s. In 1990, the two countries finally agreed to take their dispute to the International Court of Justice, which ruled in early 1994 that the Aozou Strip belonged to Chad.

Resource 64 *Map of the Aozou strip*

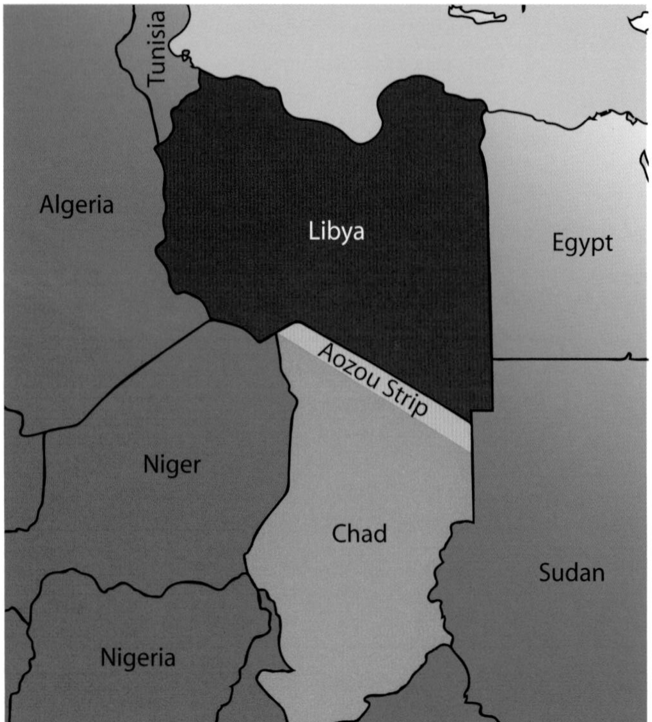

As stated earlier, territorial disputes between ethnic groups are sometimes based on some perceived economic or strategic value of the territory in question. The dispute between Israel and Syria over the Golan Heights is partly to do with the important water resources in that region. In August 2008 territorial disputes between Georgia and Russia over the breakaway provinces of South Ossetia and Arkhazia resulted in serious conflict. Closer to home, the conflict in Northern Ireland was really a territorial dispute between the Nationalist population many of whom wanted to unite Ireland and the Unionist population who wanted to maintain the division of Ireland and remain part of the United Kingdom.

Disputes between ethnic groups often last for generations and even after the conflict is over historical animosities keep the potential for future conflict very much to the fore. Each new generation grows up with information about past wrong doings of the other group in the country. Such situations are most likely to occur in segregated societies where there is little contact between the various groups. In these circumstances, where there is minimal social contact between the groups, mutual suspicions and animosities develop. Past grievances visited on one group by the other are kept very much alive through cultural differences in literature, music and political organisations. In Northern Ireland historical animosities between the Catholic and Protestant populations were expressed in the contrasting interpretations of the annual 12th of July Orange marches. For the Protestant population they were a sign of their British identity but for the Catholic population they were a sign of Protestant domination and division. Bitter riots followed some marches that came close to largely nationalist areas and now a Parades Commission decides the route of contentious marches.

Prejudice against one section of society either on racial grounds (racism) or on religious grounds (sectarianism) have been a significant cause of ethnic conflict throughout history. The Holocaust was based on Nazi doctrine of Aryan supremacy and the inferiority of the Jewish population. Under colonial rule, black Africans were regarded as inferior and therefore enslaving them was justified. In South Africa the apartheid system was a blatantly racist regime which condemned the non-white population to an underclass in society. At the time of writing the conflict in Sudan is the result of a racial conflict between black Africans and North African Arabs. Sectarian conflicts have occurred in Northern Ireland where the Catholic population were discriminated against in local government and in the allocation of jobs. In Israel the conflict is largely based on sectarianism.

Globalisation has facilitated the movement of people and ideas throughout the world. In theory, the mixing of ideas and cultures should be an enriching experience but in some cases cultural conflicts have resulted. Over the last thirty years some Middle Eastern Muslim nations have adopted a fundamentalist Islamic code. Iran was one of the first nations to have an Islamic revolution, which meant a total rejection of all western influences in the country. Following the First Gulf War in 1991, the USA maintained military bases in Saudi Arabia, the ancestral home of Islam. This enraged the growing number of fundamentalist Muslims who regarded western culture as immoral and anti-Muslim. Although from mixed backgrounds, a growing anti-western or anti-American movement has gathered momentum and unified the extremist Muslims. The attacks on New York in 2001 were carried out by Al Qaeda terrorists as part of a Holy War or Jihad against the west. The subsequent war on global terrorism (the name used in the west to describe the Islamic terrorism) gave rise to the American and British led invasions of Afghanistan and Iraq. This cultural conflict has not been confined to Middle Eastern Muslims. The London bombings in July 2005 were carried out by British born Muslims. Cultural conflicts can even occur within families. For many Asian people arranged marriages are part of traditional culture but many younger Asian women are now opposed to this practice, particularly those who have been born abroad. There have been several well documented cases of so-called 'honour killings' where young women have been killed by a family member because they had not complied with the cultural laws of their ethnic group.

In many cases, ethnic conflict arises from serious mistreatment of an ethnic group or mistreatment can follow an ethnic conflict. Collectively, these cases are referred to as human rights abuses. Human rights abuses can lead to ethnic conflict because it is essentially a form of extreme discrimination. The group of people targeted are likely to mount some form of protest against the government. The United Nations defines human rights as the "basic rights and freedoms

The United Nations Security Council Chamber, New York

to which all humans are entitled." This includes "civil and political rights, such as the right to life and liberty, freedom of expression and equality before the law and social, cultural and economic rights, including the right to participate in culture, the right to food, the right to work, and the right to education". Several conventions or codes of practice have been drawn up to safeguard human rights. The Geneva Conventions came into being between 1864 and 1949 to safeguard the human rights of individuals involved in armed conflict. The International Committee of the Red Cross is the controlling body of the Geneva conventions. On occasions Human rights abuses actually means death. There have been occasions where a government has attempted to kill an entire ethnic group. This is known as genocide. In Rwanda (1994) the majority Hutu population killed over 1 million of the minority Tutsi population in a three week period. Another example is the targeting of the civilian population of black Africans in the Darfur region of Sudan, contemporary at the time of writing. Over 200,000 civilians have been driven from their villages and many have fled to the relative safety of the refugee camps. Many of the female refugees have been subjected to gang rape by the Arab militias. The government of Sudan have been accused of serious human rights violations and genocide in Darfur. The United Nations Human Rights Council has a mandate to investigate violations of human rights. The Security Council hears reports from all organs of the United Nations, and can take action over any issue which it feels threatens peace and security, including human rights issues. However, it has at times been criticised for failing to take action to prevent human rights abuses, including the Darfur crisis, the Srebrenica massacre (in Bosnia 1995) and the genocide in Rwanda.

In some ethnically diverse situations, the allocation of resources seems to favour the ruling group. In South Africa the apartheid system was a deliberate attempt to keep the black South Africans an underclass and maximise the wealth and resources of the country for the white population. South Africa was ostracised by most western nations and by most of Africa during the apartheid era. In Zimbabwe many white farmers have had their land expropriated by the government and given to supporters of President Mugabe. Denying one section of the population fair access to resources or unfair political practices leads to dissatisfaction and often breeds conflict. When Northern Ireland was first set up, local government districts were created in such a way so as to maximise the unionist representation on the local councils. As the councils controlled the budget for housing and other services this was seen as an attempt by the unionist government to discriminate against the minority nationalist population. Business people were entitled to vote in council elections in their home address as well as at their business address. This meant business people could vote in more than one council area. As most business people were from the Unionist population this was also regarded as an unfair practice. The Civil Rights movement in the late 1960s was formed to protest against these injustices. Local government reform has removed both of these practices.

Resource 65 *Major ethnic groups in Sri Lanka*

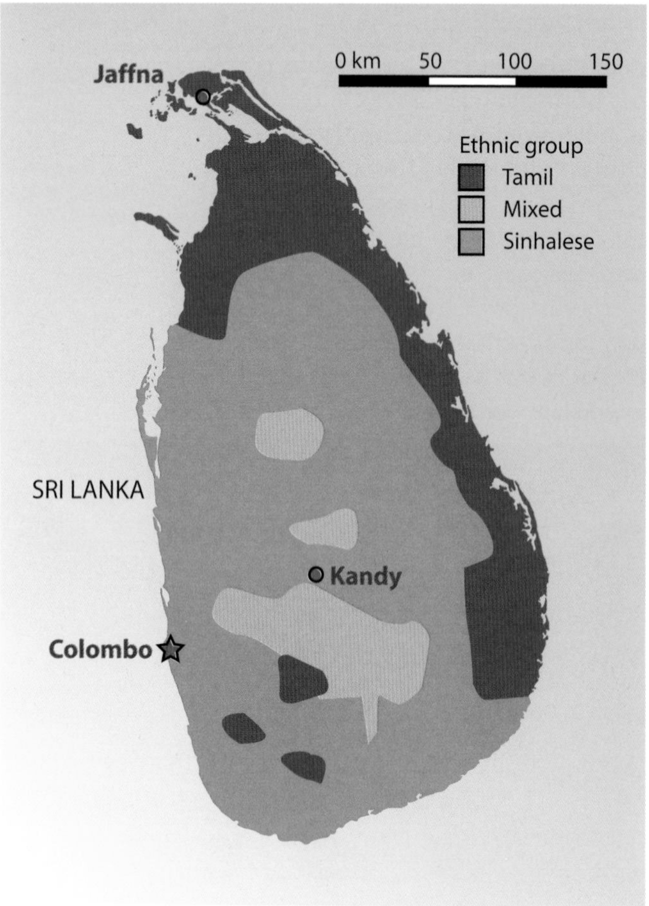

Jaffna
0 km 50 100 150
Ethnic group
Tamil
Mixed
Sinhalese
SRI LANKA
Kandy
Colombo

As stated earlier, ethnic conflict is usually the result of the interaction of a number of factors. The example of the conflict in Sri Lanka demonstrates this. Sri Lanka is a small island in the Indian Ocean (**Resource 65**). It has two main ethnic groups – the majority Sinhalese who speak Sinhala and are Buddhists; and the minority

Tamils who speak Tamil and are Hindu. Under British colonial rule the Tamils became the more prosperous group. When Sri Lanka became independent the Sinhalese formed the government. Historical animosities towards Britain were now directed at the Tamil population and the government embarked on a policy of discrimination against the Tamils. Tamils required higher grades to enter university than Sinhalese; Sinhala was made the official state language and all government documentation was only available in Sinhala and land close to sacred sites of the Hindu Tamils was taken over by the Sinhalese. A bitter ethnic conflict has taken place in Sri Lanka claiming the lives of over 60,000 people.

Exercise

Figure 1

Thailand's restive south

Members of Thailand's minority Muslim community – based almost exclusively in the country's southern provinces – have been at loggerheads with Bangkok for decades. Thailand's Muslims often complain of discrimination and a lack of opportunities, a resentment which occasionally leads to clashes with the authorities...

Thailand's Muslims are largely concentrated in the four southern provinces of Narathiwat, Pattani, Songhkla and Yala. The area is less prosperous than central Thailand, and many of the region's inhabitants complain they are at a disadvantage compared to the country's Buddhist majority...

The southern provinces were originally part of the ancient Kingdom of Pattani, a semi-autonomous Malay region which adopted Islam in the mid-thirteenth century. Thailand annexed the region in 1902, but the people living there had – and still do have – far more in common with their neighbours in Malaysia. They speak Yawi, a Malay dialect, and most importantly they are Muslims, abiding by Islamic rules and restrictions. Increasingly estranged from the Bangkok government, Muslim separatists began an insurgency in the 1970s. The violence eventually died down in the 1990s – but only after the government promised to channel more funds into the region and ensure the Muslim community an adequate political representation.

A raid on an army depot in January 2004 signalled a return to the violence. Four soldiers were killed and 400 guns, most of them M-16 rifles, were stolen from a store in Narathiwat province. Since then there have been frequent incidents in which symbols of authority – including police officers, teachers and Buddhist monks – have been targeted by Muslim gunmen.

The deadliest incident happened on 28 April [2005], when hundreds of suspected Islamic militants launched a series of raids on security posts in the region. The day ended in the massacre of more than 100 of the poorly-armed militants, and there was international concern over the degree of force used by security personnel.

The Thai government continues to insist that most of the attacks in the south can be attributed to local criminals. But it seems evident that organised Islamic separatist groups are playing at least a part in the violence. [In September 2006 a peacful coup in Thailand suggested that a new regime may be more successful in dealing with ethnic conflict in the future.]

Source: BBC News, 15 July 2005, http://tinyurl.com/thaires, accessed 21 August 2009

Figure 1 adapted from resource for CCEA January 2008

Exercise continued

Figure 2

Thailand's Muslim Divide

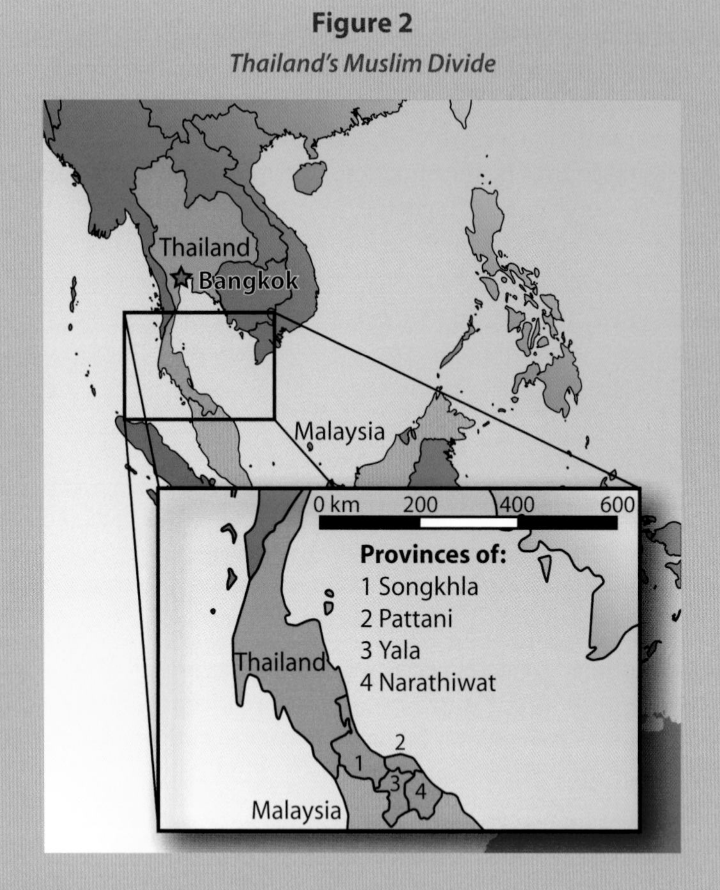

1 *Question from CCEA January 2008*

(a) Study **Figures 1** and **2** relating to recent ethnic tensions in Thailand.

(i) Identify and briefly discuss **one** primary and **one** secondary factor that identifies the ethnic population of southern Thailand. (6)

(ii) Use the resources **to help you** discuss the importance of discrimination and territorial disputes as causes of ethnic conflict. (8)

The nature of ethnic conflict

Ethnic conflict has to involve some confrontation between the rival sides in the dispute. In today's world of satellite media and twenty-four hour news bulletins it is possible to follow events as they unfold. Those involved in any conflict situation will strive to get their viewpoint broadcast sympathetically by reporting journalists. The form of ethnic conflict varies greatly from protest marches to full scale war.

Civil disobedience is the active refusal to obey certain laws or commands of a government. It is a non-violent protest where the protesting group withdraws its participation in the working of the country. It includes non-payment of rates, taxes, boycotting services or shops owned by the opposition, and mass strikes. To be effective civil disobedience needs the support of large numbers from the protesting group. If the protesting group are the dominant workforce in one sector of industry a strike can have a dramatic impact on the country as a whole. The civil rights movement in the USA under Martin Luther King and some of the protests in India against British control in India, organised by Mahatma Gandhi, constituted civil disobedience. At the other end of the scale there is civil war. This describes a situation where there are clearly identified armed forces within the country actively engaged in armed conflict with each other.

Civil wars develop for many reasons including ethnic conflict. In Europe the civil wars that occurred in the Balkans in the late 1990s, leading to the break up of the former Yugoslavia, were ethnically based. Africa has many examples of civil wars. At the time of writing the Democratic Republic of Congo is involved in a civil war between the government forces and the minority Tutsi population. The Democratic Republic of Congo is itself the product of another civil war in neighbouring Rwanda in the 1990s.

Many ethnic conflicts do not reach full scale civil war but take the form of a terrorist campaign. Terrorism involves armed conflict but the terrorist is a member of an illegal guerrilla organisation which operates within the community. Terrorism operates in pursuit of some ideological goal, such as a united Ireland for the IRA or a Tamil homeland for the Tamil Tigers in Sri Lanka. Terrorist groups do not openly display the trappings of a regular army, instead they operate secretively within their community. This form of conflict poses particular problems for the security forces because terrorists can blend unnoticed into the community. The tactics employed by terrorist groups include car bombs and attacks directed at the rival group, destruction of state property and killing members of the opposition. In Northern Ireland the IRA carried out terrorist attacks against the Unionist and British Army for over twenty-five years. Terrorism from one side often results in a terrorist response from the opposition and in Northern Ireland the UVF carried out terrorist attacks on the nationalist population. Terrorism reached a new dimension with the Al Qaeda attacks on New York on 11 September 2001. The term global terrorism is used to describe the world wide threat to western countries by Islamic extremists. Apart from the USA, other countries targeted as part of global terrorism include: the UK (London 2005) Spain (Madrid 2004) and Mumbai (November 2008). Western communities were also targeted in tourist resorts in Turkey, Morocco, Egypt and Bali.

Outcomes and response to ethnic conflict

Ethnic conflict has far reaching impacts wherever it occurs. The economy of a region experiencing ethnic conflict can be affected in several ways. There will inevitably be a direct loss of property and businesses through bombings but in addition conflict areas present a very negative image to outside investors. Since the end of 'The Troubles' Northern Ireland and Belfast in particular has received much investment which would not have occurred if there was still civil unrest. In Turkey the tourist trade has been negatively affected by the threat of terrorist attacks.

Society is also negatively affected by conflict. At the lowest level of impact communities become more segregated and polarised. Throughout the Northern Ireland conflict residential segregation ratcheted up either because people were forced out of mixed housing areas or people simply decided to move to be with their co-religionists. This type of segregation was always more pronounced in the inner city areas. The most extreme form of segregation is ethnic cleansing. This is the whole scale removal of an ethnic group from an area. Ethnic Cleansing created more than two million refugees and displaced persons in former Yugoslavia (**Resource 68**) during the war in Bosnia (**Resource 67**). Although Serbs were by far the most successful 'cleansers', all sides adopted this method in the course of war. One of the worst atrocities in modern times occurred at Srebrenica when over 7,000 men were murdered by the Serbian Army as part of ethnic cleansing in 1995. Conflicts of any kind can force people to flee from their homes in search of safety. Refugees are a particularly vulnerable sector of society. They are mostly women and children who have no possessions,

Resource 66 ***The ethnic cleansing plan in Bosnia***

1. **Concentration**. Surround the area to be cleansed and after warning the resident Serbs – often they are urged to leave or are at least told to mark their houses with white flags – intimidate the target.
2. **Decapitation**. Execute political leaders and those capable of taking their places: lawyers, judges, public officials, writers, professors.
3. **Separation**. Divide women, children, and old men from men of "fighting age" – sixteen years to sixty years old.
4. **Evacuation**. Transport women, children, and old men to the border, expelling them into a neighbouring territory or country.
5. **Execute** "fighting age" men, dispose of bodies.

Source: Balkans anti-war and human rights resources, http://balkansnet.org/

Resource 67 *Maps of Bosnia before and after ethnic cleansing*

Resource 68 *Map of the Balkans*

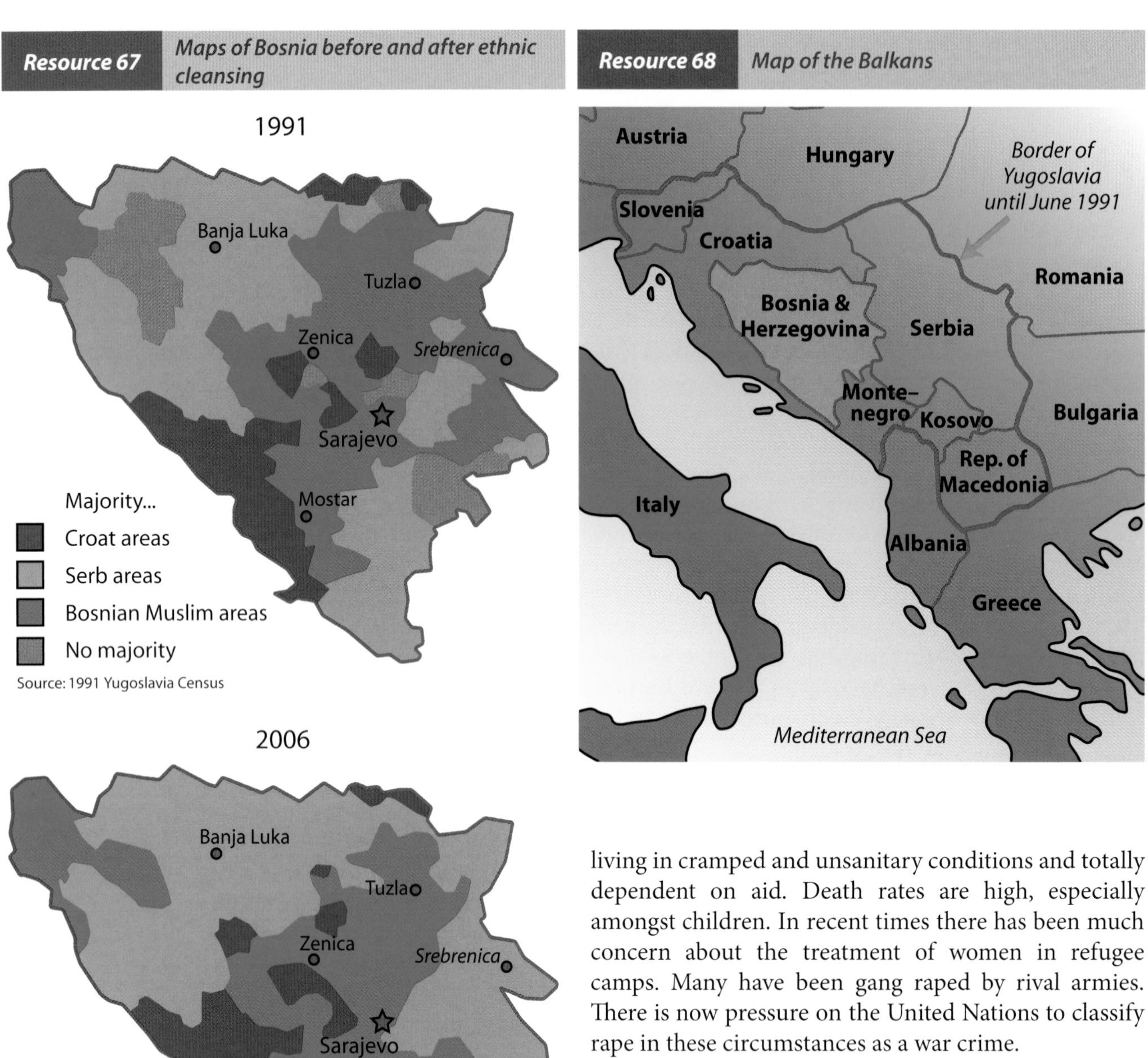

living in cramped and unsanitary conditions and totally dependent on aid. Death rates are high, especially amongst children. In recent times there has been much concern about the treatment of women in refugee camps. Many have been gang raped by rival armies. There is now pressure on the United Nations to classify rape in these circumstances as a war crime.

At some stage the opposing sides in any ethnic conflict will have to attempt a solution. The form that this will take depends on many factors, including the geographical distribution of the various groups involved. If the protesting groups have clearly defined territorial boundaries it may be that territorial division is considered. An example is the sub-division of British India into Hindu India and a Muslim West Pakistan (now Pakistan) and East Pakistan (now Bangladesh). Ireland was divided into a twenty-six county Republic of Ireland while the remaining six counties became part of the United Kingdom. A number of former Soviet republics, including Ukraine and Georgia, have broken away from Russia since the demise of communism. Ethnic identity played a major part in their quest for territorial separation from Russia. Territorial division can sometimes result in a region gaining some degree of political control while still remaining an integral part of the ruling country. This is known as autonomy. In Sri Lanka, the Tamils were granted autonomy in the Jaffna peninsula but they are still part of Sri Lanka. In May 2009 the Sri Lankan army defeated the Tamil Tigers and regained full control of Sri Lanka.

Exercise

Figure 1

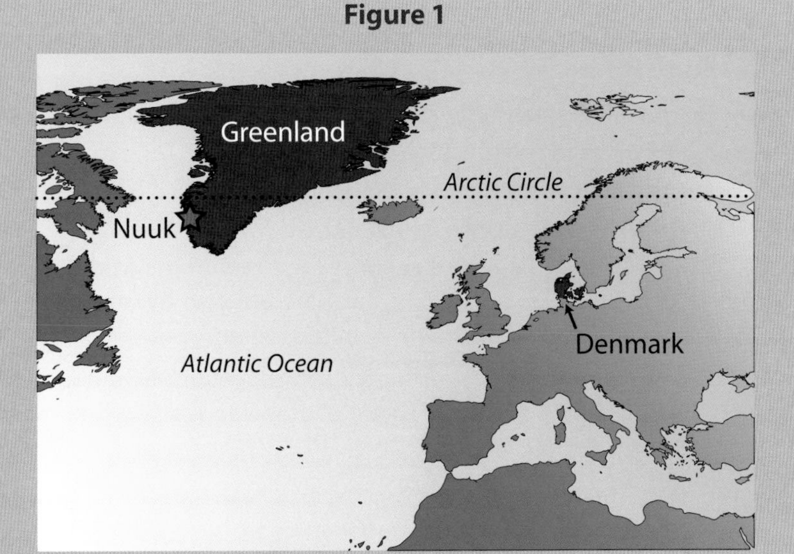

Figure 2

Greenland votes for more autonomy

The people of Greenland have voted decisively in favour of a plan to give it greater autonomy from Denmark. Officials said just over 75% of voters had supported the plan, which would see Greenland take a greater share of its annual oil revenues. It will also take control of police, courts and coast guard, and have some say in foreign policy. Correspondents say the vote could be a major step towards independence for the Arctic island of 57,000 people. Hans Enoksen, the head of the local government in the Danish self-governing territory, thanked Greenlanders for "this overwhelming result"...Final results showed that 75.54% voted in favour, while 23.57% said no – in line with predictions before the vote. Turnout was 71.96%.

Regaining rights

About 50,000 of the population are native Inuit. Greenland gained self-rule in 1979, after previously being a colony and then a province of Denmark. "It was time for us to regain our rights and freedoms that were stolen from our ancestors," David Brandt, a former fisherman, told the AFP news agency. Under the new arrangement, due to take effect in June next year, the island will take a greater share of its annual oil revenue, and Greenlanders will be treated as a separate people under international law. If the proposals are enacted, Kalaallisut would become the official language, instead of Danish. The plan would also see Greenland becoming less reliant on subsidies from Copenhagen. Currently these provide 30% of its GDP. In 1985, the island left the European Union to avoid subjecting its fishing grounds to EU rules.

Source: BBC News, 26 November 2008, http://tinyurl.com/grvote, accesssed 19 August 2009

1. Study **Figure 1** and **2** above relating to Greenland.
   (a) Identify the primary factors that make the Greenlanders an ethnic minority in Denmark.
   (b) Discuss possible reasons that might have prompted the Greenlanders to seek autonomy from Denmark.

Sometimes the international community, apart from the United Nations, becomes involved in foreign conflict situations. There are many reasons for this international intervention including:

- Moral concern for the human suffering that ethnic conflict brings, such as the support for the Muslim population of Kosovo by NATO in 1999.
- Political or historical links with one of the groups concerned, such as the French interest in its former colony of Chad.
- Strategic reasons, such as American support for Israel in the Middle East. This is partly because there is a Jewish population in the USA but also because during the Cold War Russia backed some of the Arab countries in the region.
- Security reasons, for example, the American involvement in Iraq and Afghanistan was justified on the basis of the perceived threat of global terrorism from these countries.

The effectiveness of international intervention has been mixed. In Northern Ireland the intervention of the USA made a positive contribution to the resolution of conflict. In other parts of the world international intervention has been more confrontational.

International intervention in ethnic conflict usually involves an attempt at conflict resolution and the formulation of a peace process. There have been some successful peace processes, notably The Dayton Agreement, which brought an end to the conflict between Bosnia and Serbia in 1995. Not all Peace Processes lead to an immediate and permanent cessation of hostilities as the Northern Ireland example illustrates. The Peace Process in the Middle East has been ongoing since the creation of Israel in 1948 and currently it is overseen by an international quartet of countries or regions – the European Union, USA, Russia and the United Nations. Former British Prime Minister, Tony Blair is the official international peace envoy to the region.

Exercise

Figure 1

Location of Darfur

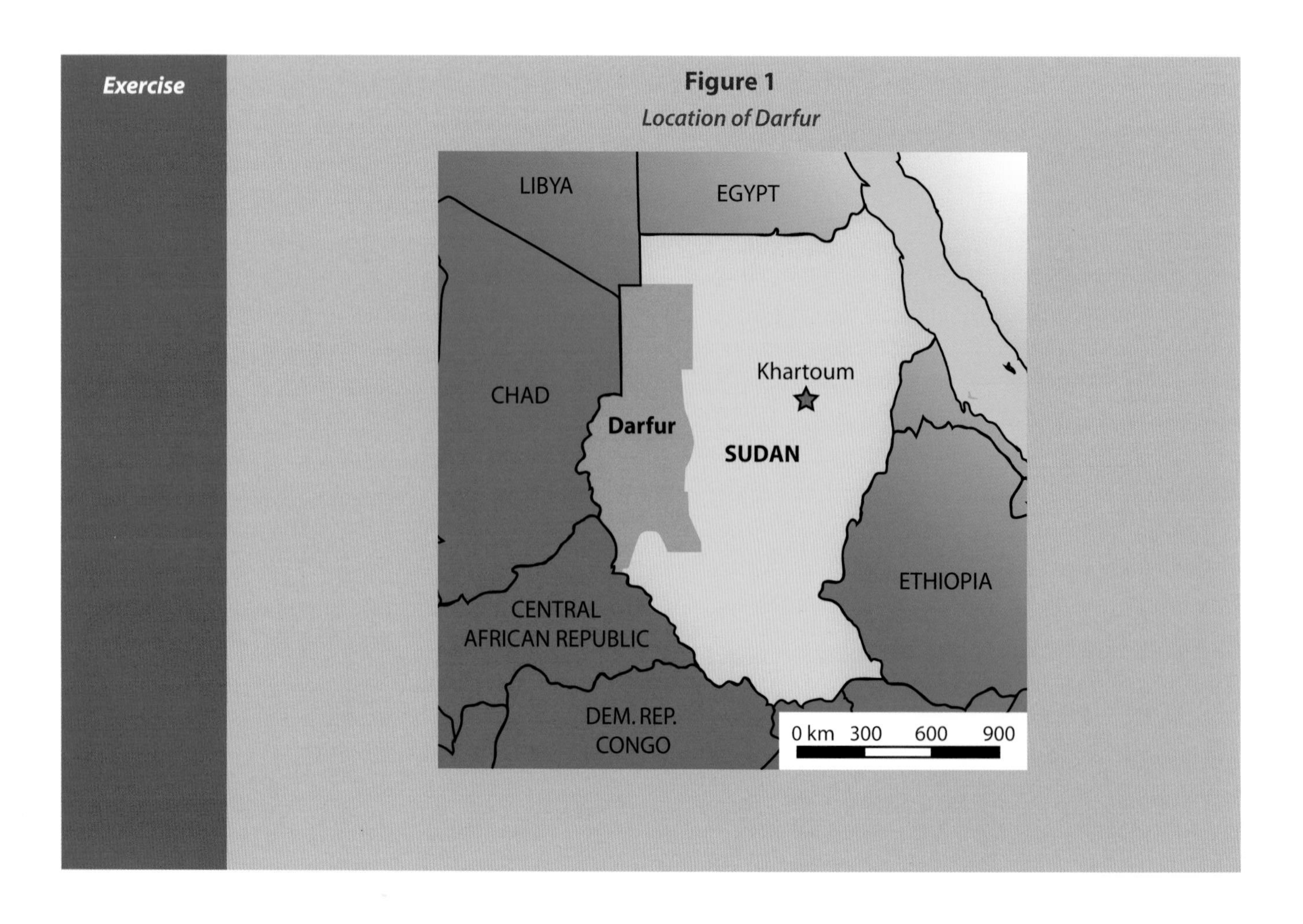

Exercise continued

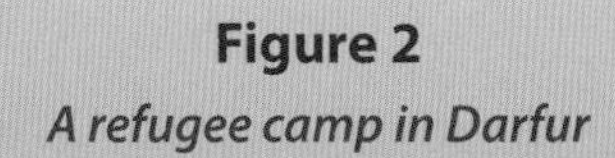

Figure 2

A refugee camp in Darfur

Figure 3

Ethnic conflict in Darfur

Darfur is a semi-arid western province of Sudan - Africa's largest country. Darfur alone is the size of France. In an Arab-dominated country, Darfur's population is mostly black African.

For years, there have been tensions between the mostly African farmers and the mostly Arab herders, who have competed for land.Opposition groups in Darfur say the government neglects their province, and discriminates against black Africans.

The conflict began in 2003, when rebel groups began attacking government targets. In retaliation, the government launched a military and police campaign in Darfur. More than 2milllion people fled their homes. Many spoke of government aircraft bombing villages, after which the Arab Janjaweed militia would ride in on camels and horses to slaughter, rape and steal. The refugees and some western observers said there was a deliberate attempt to drive black Africans out of Darfur. The government admits mobilising "self-defence militias", but denies links to the Janjaweed and says the problems have been exaggerated.

Those who fled the violence are now living in camps across Darfur. About 200,000 refugees have crossed the border into Chad. Those living in camps now depend on food aid from international donors. Aid agencies have repeatedly warned that continuing violence is making it difficult, or impossible, for them to provide the displaced people with the help they need.

Attempts by the African Union (AU) – a grouping of African states – to end the conflict resulted in a peace deal being signed in 2006. The Sudanese government backed the deal, but only one rebel faction – Minni Minawi's faction [a rebel faction] of the Sudan Liberation Army – signed up. As part of the deal, the government agreed to disarm the Janjaweed, but there is little to suggest that this has happened...

The AU has sent 7,000 soldiers to try to monitor a ceasefire. The Sudanese government agreed to allow this force to operate. But this relatively small force has not managed to end the violence.

Britain and the US have been pushing for the United Nations to take over the peacekeeping mission and the AU is happy to stand aside. Sudan, however, says it will not allow a UN force on its territory.

Source: BBC News, 6 September 2006, http://tinyurl.com/qgdarfur, accessed 29 August 2009

Exercise continued

Figure 4

Sudan 'kills hundreds in Darfur'

Hundreds of Sudanese have been killed in attacks in Darfur, with the apparent knowledge and support of the government, a UN report says...The report says that no evidence was found of any rebel activity in the area. Instead, the report says, the violence appears to have been a coordinated campaign to drive out black Africans before the arrival of UN peacekeepers...The area is now reported to be deserted, as most of the 10,000 inhabitants have fled.

The US says a genocide is being carried out in Darfur but Sudan says the scale of the problems is being exaggerated for political reasons.

Source: BBC News, 9 October 206, http://tinyurl.com/sk100s, accessed 26 August 2009

Figures 3 and 4 adapted from CCEA May 2008

1. *Question adapted from CCEA May 2008*
   Study **Figures 1–4** (pages 122–4) relating to ethnic conflict in Darfur (Sudan).

   (i) Identify and discuss **two** outcomes of ethnic conflict in Darfur. (8)

   (ii) Outside intervention has often been ineffective in stopping ethnic conflicts in Darfur and elsewhere. Use the Resources **to help you** discus why this is often the case. (4)

2. *Question from CCEA January 2006*
   Discuss any two of the following outcomes of ethnic conflict:

   - Refugee movement
   - Ethnic cleansing
   - Destruction of economic and social infrastructure. (10)

CASE STUDY: Ethnic conflict in Israel

The state of Israel was created as an outcome of ethnic conflict over sixty years ago and has remained at the centre of ethnic conflict in the Middle East ever since. The conflict in Israel is inextricably linked with major world events taking place in the surrounding countries of the Middle East and in Europe. In essence this conflict concerns territorial disputes, historical animosities, sectarianism, human rights abuses, discrimination including unequal distribution of resources and political power. The conflict has resulted in civil disobedience, civil war, terrorism, and international wars. There has been considerable international attention to events in the region, at one time becoming a potential threat of conflict between USA and the Soviet Union during the Cold War. There have been many Peace Deals brokered by international organisations but to date no deal has succeeded in achieving a permanent cessation of hostilities.

Background

The state of Israel was created in 1947 as a homeland for Jewish people from all over the world but especially from Europe. Israel is surrounded by the Arab Islamic counties of Jordan, Lebanon, Syria and Egypt and in the wider Middle East by Saudi Arabia, Iraq and Iran. Sectarianism in the form of anti-Semitism in the nineteenth and early twentieth centuries resulted in widespread discrimination against Jews in Europe and this had galvanised the Jewish people into a unified group. Large numbers had migrated in successive streams from Europe to what many considered to be their ancestral home in the Middle East – Palestine. These migration streams, referred to as Aliyah, were supported by the growth of Zionism or Jewish Nationalism in Europe during the nineteenth century. The Zionist movement formed institutions such as the Jewish Agency to facilitate Jewish migration to Palestine. The Jewish Agency promoted the Hebrew language and culture, established a Hebrew University in Jerusalem and purchased land in Palestine for future Jewish settlement. They also formed political parties and a Jewish defence organisation. In essence the Jewish Agency was moulding a unified Jewish nation from people who had lived in many different countries and spoke different languages. All of these institutions laid the foundations for the management of a state, which Jews believed, was their entitlement. Anti-Semitism in Europe intensified in the years leading up to World War II, culminating in the mass murder of six million Jews in the Nazi concentration camps during the Holocaust. In the immediate aftermath of World War II those Jews that had survived the Holocaust made even more strenuous demands for a Jewish Homeland in Palestine.

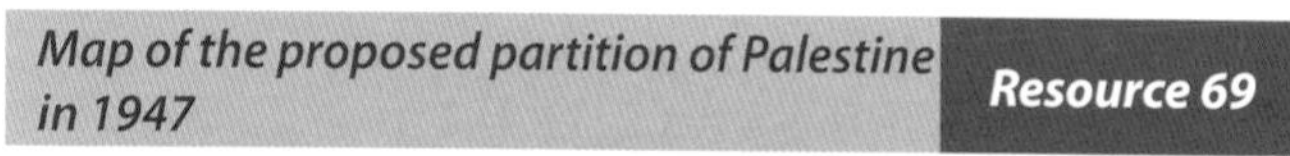
Map of the proposed partition of Palestine in 1947 **Resource 69**

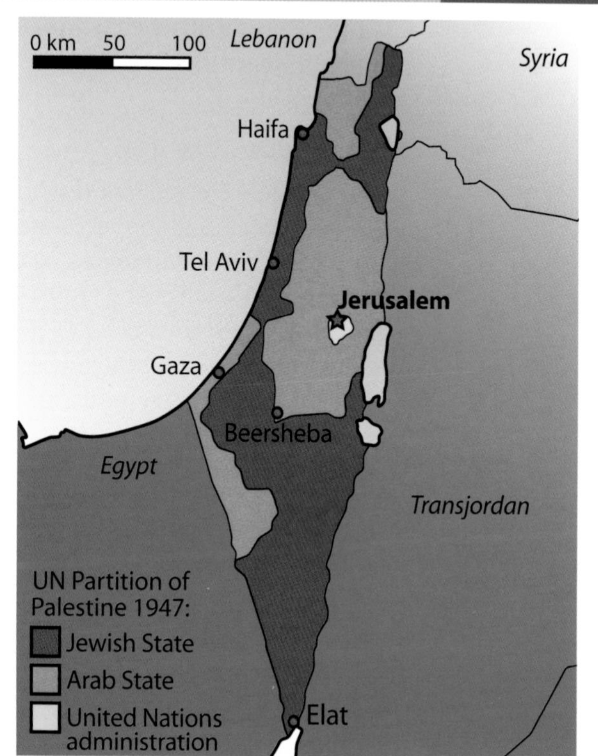

The partition of Palestine and ethnic conflict

Meanwhile a complex redistribution of land between the major world powers saw Britain in control of Palestine from 1917. Anxious to gain Jewish support against Germany, Britain announced its support for a Jewish Homeland in Palestine, in the 1917 Balfour Declaration. However, the intention was that this Jewish Homeland would live peacefully within an independent Palestine. In fact, Britain supported the idea of Arab nationalism in Palestine and favoured a reduction in the numbers of Jewish migrants to the region. Jewish migration gathered momentum from 1945 onwards and there were bitter clashes between Jews and Palestinians. Britain planned to withdraw from Palestine in 1947, leaving a United Nations Commission to decide the future of Palestine. The Commission decided that Palestine should be partitioned into a western Jewish homeland and an eastern Palestinian section of Transjordan, later known as Jordan. The city of Jerusalem was to remain under UN control. The western section was particularly fragmented as **Resource 69** shows, but the Jewish population reluctantly accepted it. The Palestinians rejected the partition completely because they resented the loss of territory to the Jews and there were a sizeable number of Palestinians trapped in the Jewish state. This territorial division marked the beginning of the first major incident of ethnic conflict in this region. In essence, this ethnic conflict had two main causes, which are still as pertinent today as they were in 1948:

- The territorial dispute between Israel and the Palestinians and the surrounding Arab countries
- Historical animosities between Jews and Muslims

The Palestinians first form of protest against the proposed partition was a general strike in December 1947, which led to inter-communal rioting and eventually a civil war. The civil war lasted for six months and the Jewish Agency declared the territory allocated to the Jews as the new state of Israel on 14 May 1948. The following day Egyptian, Lebanese, Jordanian, Syrian and Iraqi troops attacked Israel in what is known as the First Arab-Israeli war.

Map of Palestine in 1949 **Resource 70**

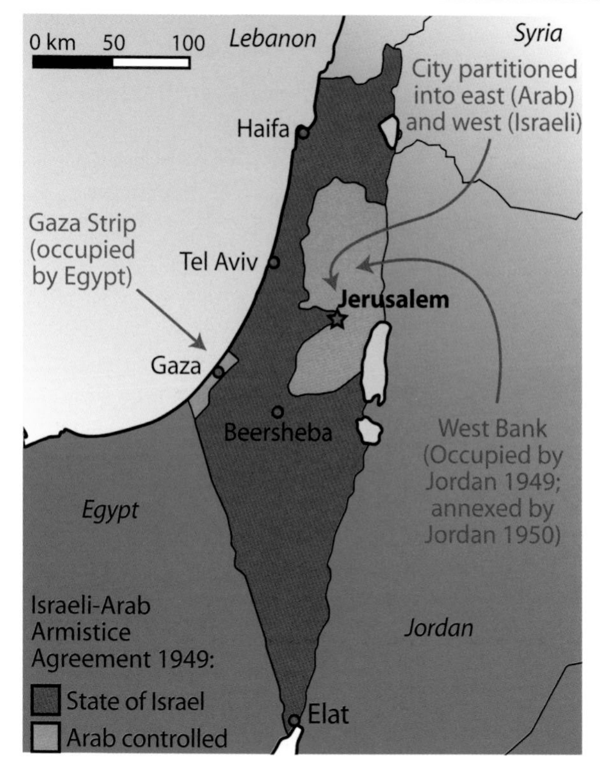

Israeli forces defeated the Arab armies and in 1949 a new territorial division of Palestine was agreed and Israel was formally recognised by the United Nations. Israel had increased its territory by about 21% (**Resource 70**). The Arab nations also took land from Palestine. Apart from the territorial issues, the Palestinians were now divided across several countries. Many Palestinians had fled from Israel during the fighting and became refugees in the hope of returning when peace was restored. Exact numbers are difficult to verify but it is reckoned that this war created somewhere between 750,000 and 900,000 Palestinian refugees. Immediately after the war, Israel encouraged further immigration of Jews to their newly enlarged state. Few of the Palestinians were allowed to return and most set up refugee camps close to the Israeli border, where they attempted to unite as a group and called for an independent Palestine.

The Six Day War 1967

The refugees created as a result of the first Arab-Israeli war exacerbated the territorial dispute between Israel and the surrounding Arab nations. In the refugee camps the Palestinians began to organise terrorist attacks against Israel. The Israeli security forces reacted to these attacks by bombing suspected terrorist enclaves, resulting in the deaths of many civilians. A war with Egypt in 1956 threatened to involve both the USA and Soviet Union. The USA had always supported Israel and the Soviet Union supported Egypt in this conflict. The United Nations secured a temporary peace in the region. The growing numbers of immigrants into Israel created increased demands for water. Israel set about laying an extensive irrigation network which relied on water from the River Jordan. This river has its headwaters in the Golan Heights (Syria) and flows for a short distance through Israel but most of the river flows through Jordan. Both Jordan and Syria accused Israel of overusing scarce water resources. Relations between Israel and her Arab neighbours were already unstable but this dispute over water added another dimension. In addition, Jews were unable to visit their sacred shrines in East Jerusalem and some of these sacred sites were vandalised by Muslims. Israel fearful of an Arab attack launched a pre-emptive strike against Egypt, Syria and Jordan in 1967. This war, known as the Six Day War, had far reaching consequences for Israel and the Palestinians. Israel defeated the Arab armies and annexed land from each of defeated countries. The main gains to Israel were:

- The Gaza Strip and the Sinai Peninsula from Egypt;
- The Golan Heights from Syria; and
- East Jerusalem and the West Bank (of the River Jordan) from Jordan.

Resource 71 *Map of Israel in 1967*

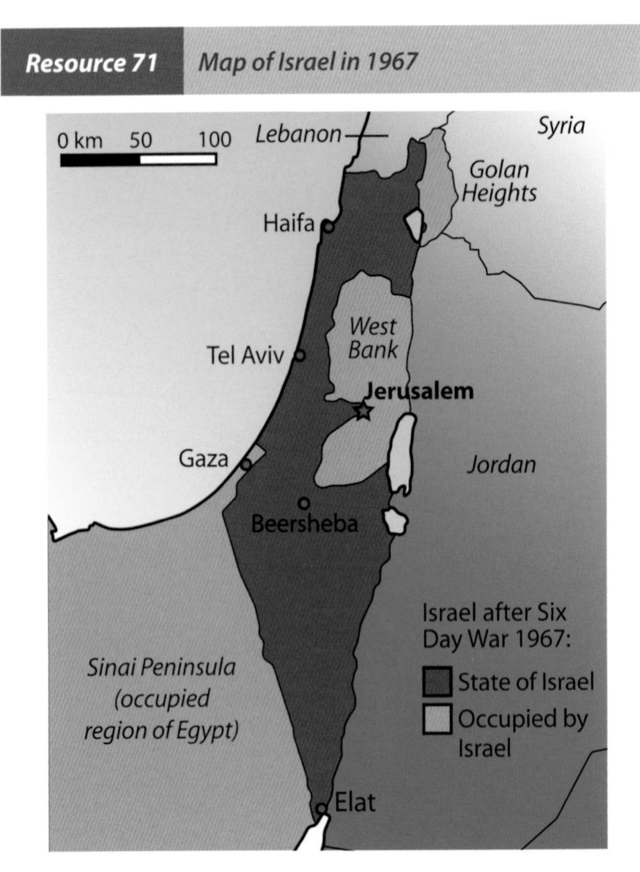

As a result of these annexations, Israel had brought about a three-fold increase in the land area of the country and secured control over the River Jordan. Although there has been no international recognition of Israel's claim to these Occupied Territories, Israel still claims ownership of East Jerusalem, the West Bank and the Gaza Strip. These territorial disputes exacerbated the existing territorial conflict in the region.

Growth of terrorism and the Palestinian Liberation Organisation (PLO)

A significant outcome of the Six Day War for the Palestinians was the realisation that their Arab neighbours were not going to achieve the liberation of Palestine. The Arab countries had been heavily defeated by Israel with over 15,000 deaths and many more injured while Israel recorded 350 deaths. Israel had gained control of a further 400,000 refugees as well as an additional 600,000 Palestinian residents. The United Nations Security Council passed a resolution calling for a 'land for peace' solution to the conflict. Basically, the UN was attempting to secure a cessation of attacks on Israel in return for an Israeli withdrawal from the Occupied Territories. Increasing frustration about lack of progress saw many Palestinians resort to terrorist attacks on Israel at home and abroad. They formed a number of paramilitary and political organisations under the umbrella name of the Palestine Liberation Organisation (PLO), led by Yasser Arafat. Initially the PLO operated within Israel but was forced from Israel first to Jordan and later to southern Lebanon. Their tactics included hi-jacking of aircraft and cruise liners as well as bombing perceived Israeli targets at home and abroad.

The Yom Kippur War and the search for conflict resolution

Israel maintained an uneasy peace with her Arab neighbours until 1973 when Egypt and Syria attacked Israel in what became known as the Yom Kippur War. This war had a very high human cost and the Arab nations were better organised than in previous wars. Over 3,000 Israelis and 8,500 Egyptian and Syrians were killed in this war. The Arab countries also banded together to form OPEC (Oil Producing and Exporting Countries) and restricted the supply of oil to those countries that had overtly supported Israel. All of these reasons increased the drive for a long lasting solution to the Middle East crisis.

There are four main areas of contention in this conflict:

- Israel's right to peaceful co-existence with her Arab neighbours.
- Palestinian demands for autonomy and statehood.
- The plight of the Palestinians within Israel and in the refugee camps.
- The Occupied Territories and the status of Jerusalem.

There have been many attempts by the international community to find an accommodation for some of these areas of contention since the end of the Yom Kippur War. The USA negotiated a cease-fire to the Yom Kippur War in 1974 and brokered a Peace Deal between Israel and Egypt, whereby Israel agreed to return the Sinai Peninsula to Egypt and to explore the possibility of granting autonomy to the West Bank and Gaza. In return, Egypt formally recognised the state of Israel in 1977 and a Peace Deal between Egypt and Israel was eventually signed at Camp David in 1979. However, it soon became clear that Israel was not going to allow full autonomy and set about a policy of increasing Jewish settlements in these Occupied Territories. The number of Jewish settlements in the Occupied Territories had increased from 5,000 in 1977 to 60,000 in 1987 which many Palestinians regarded as creeping annexation.

Israel had established peace with Egypt but there were still tensions with Syria. Throughout the remainder of the 1970s and early 80s Israel was attacked from southern Lebanon by the PLO with support from Syria. The PLO had effectively taken control of southern Lebanon and in 1982 Israel invaded southern Lebanon. The PLO was forced to leave Lebanon and Israel maintained a military occupation of southern Lebanon until 2000. The PLO no longer had a base close to the Israeli border but they continued their attacks on Israeli targets throughout the world.

The First Intifada and the formation of Hamas

Growing frustration by the Palestinians over lack of progress towards autonomy and increasing Jewish settlement in the Occupied Territories sparked an uprising of Palestinian youths known as the Intifada in 1987, which lasted until 1993. The Intifada started as civil obedience, including a Palestinian boycott of Israeli shops, a general strike and public demonstrations against Israel. However, the Intifada soon became a violent uprising. An Islamic resistance movement known as Hamas formed in the Gaza Strip, with the objective of establishing an Islamic state in the region, marking a new dimension to this conflict. Hamas was essentially a terrorist organisation but their ideology revolved around Sharia Law, which has a close connection between state law and religious beliefs. Their objective of the creation of an Islamic state increased the potential for a major cultural conflict to this region. Hamas waged a Holy war against Israel, including suicide bomb attacks targeting the Jewish civilian population. Throughout the uprising a number of committees were formed to lay the foundation for an independent state in much the same way as the Jewish population had done forty years earlier. The Intifada met with stiff Israeli retaliation and Israel was accused of human rights violations by some international pressure groups, including Amnesty International. There were mass arrests of Palestinians and claims of torture. Palestinians were subjected to curfews during periods of sustained unrest. Schools and universities in affected areas were closed. Arabic newspapers were censored and Charities supporting the Palestinians were forced to close. Suspected key figures in the uprising were targeted and assassinated. Over 1,100 Palestinians and 160 Israelis were killed during the Intifada.

The Oslo Accords

A second major international attempt to secure a permanent solution to the Arab Israeli conflict came after the First Gulf War in 1991. The USA helped secure the signing of A Declaration of Principles (the Oslo Accords) between Israel and the PLO in 1993. This set out a framework to grant autonomy to the Palestinians in the West Bank and Gaza. The proposals included elections in the West Bank to establish a Palestinian council. This was followed by the Cairo Agreement in 1994, which began the actual transfer of authority to the Palestinians and a phased withdrawal of the Israeli army. A peace treaty was also negotiated between Israel and Jordan. A number of amendments and redrafts of the peace deals took place but eventually in 1995 the Israeli-Palestinian Interim Agreement was signed. It extended the powers of the Palestinian council to include the Gaza Strip and parts of the West Bank and made some progress on the release of Palestinian prisoners held in Israeli jails. Elections were held in the Occupied Territories to elect a Palestinian Authority in 1996, with Yasser Arafat as the Prime Minister. This progress towards a lasting peace in the region had been supported by the USA, the EU, Russia and Egypt. In return, the Palestinians recognised Israel and agreed to give up terrorism. The agreement was opposed by Hamas, which increased their suicide bomb attacks on Israel. Some right wing Israelis also opposed the deal and the Israeli Prime Minister was assassinated two months after the deal was signed.

The Second Intifada 2000–2005

The right wing Likud party won the election following the assassination of the Israeli Prime Minister. The Peace Process slowed down and there were renewed violent attacks on Israel from Hamas. In addition, the Palestinians interpreted a visit to the Al Aqsa mosque by the Israeli government minister, Ariel Sharon, as proof that Israel was faltering on their agreement to withdraw from the Occupied Territories. Widespread rioting followed marking the beginning of the Al–Aqsa Intifada or Second Intifada, which resulted in the deaths of over 5,000 Palestinians and 1,000 Israelis. In response to a number of suicide attacks, Ariel Sharon, by this stage Prime Minister of Israel, ordered the construction of a barrier around the Jewish settlements in the West Bank. This barrier is over 670 kms long and varies in height from 5 to 8 metres. It has rolls of razor wire and is fitted with electronic sensors to detect attempts to breach the barrier. Israel claims this is necessary to protect Jewish settlements from suicide and sniper attacks. To the Palestinians this seemed to be further evidence that Israel intended to maintain control over much of the territory occupied by Jewish settlements in the West Bank. Barriers have also been built around the Gaza Strip. Several attempts have been made by the USA and others to work towards a two state solution to the conflict since 2000, including a Saudi Peace Plan in 2002 and a Roadmap for Peace 2003 proposed by the USA, EU, UN and Russia. Former UK Prime Minister Tony Blair was appointed Peace Envoy to the region in 2006.

War with Lebanon 2006

One of the many stumbling blocks to peace in the region involves the Israeli settlements in the Occupied Territories. While there appears little willingness to remove them in the West Bank, Israel has withdrawn 8,000 settlers from the Gaza Strip despite strong opposition in 2005. In a further development, Israel became the target of attack from another terrorist organisation based in Lebanon and supported by Syria-Hezbullah. Persistent attacks from Hezbullah led Israel to attack Lebanon beginning the Second Lebanon War in 2006. The war ended two months later with no conclusive victory for either side but civilian casualties were particularly high including 11,000 Lebanese and 150 Israelis. In the Gaza Strip the militant Hamas group won the 2006 election and Israel has refused to negotiate with Hamas because of the terrorist activities associated with that group. In response to an increase in violent attacks from Gaza, Israel has effectively blockaded Gaza, restricting all movement of people, fuel and food. A Peace Conference was held in Anapolis (USA), in 2007 and was attended by some of Israel's Arab neighbours and the newly elected President Obama has pledged to continue to work towards a two state solution and accommodation over Jerusalem when he assumed office in January 2009 but there is little optimism that a permanent solution will be found any time soon. An unstable truce between Israel and Hamas in the Gaza Strip ended on 19 December 2008. In response to daily rocket attacks from Gaza following the end of the truce Israel invaded Gaza on 27 December. For the next three weeks the citizens of Gaza suffered aerial bombardment and ground attacks by the Israeli army. Over 2,000 Gazans were killed before a ceasefire was agreed.

The sixty years of conflict have cost many lives but in addition the economy has also been negatively affected. Israel and Jerusalem hold much potential for tourism, which is as yet not fully developed because of the on-going conflict. While all sections of the community are affected it is the plight of the refugees that causes most concern. Since the creation of Israel and the annexation of the West bank and Gaza, more than half the Arabs of pre-Palestine are thought to have been displaced. Some observers have accused Israel of ethnic cleansing in the 1948 war but Israel disputes these claims. Some four million Palestinian refugees trace their origins to the pre-partition Palestine and 750,000 people belong to families displaced in the Six Day War, many of these for the second time. According to international human rights law civilian refugees should be allowed to return to their former homes once the conflict has ended. They should also be paid compensation for the loss of property and personal possessions. Many Palestinians fled to neighbouring Arab countries during the Six Day War but Israel has refused to allow them back into Israel or to pay them any compensation. In the last decade alone, the Palestinian people have lost almost 5,000 lives, close to $40 billion in income and 20 million square meters of agricultural land. Almost 1.7 million of the four million residents of Gaza and West Bank are refugees.

The Palestinians in Israel remain a seriously deprived group of people as **Resource 72** shows.

Statistical comparision between Palestinians and Israel — ***Resource 72***

Country/ Region	Population (millions)	GDP per capita US$	Infant Mortality Per 1000 live births	Total Fertility	Palestinian refugees
Israel	7.28	28,800	7.03	2.84	276,000
West Bank	2.80	1,100	19.62	4.90	665,000
Gaza Strip	1.38	1,000	22.93	6.42	923,000

The issue of the allocation of water resources has already been mentioned with regard to the Six Day War but the situation in the West Bank is particularly serious. According to the World Bank, 90% of the West Bank's water is used by Israelis, despite them making up only a fraction of the total population. Palestinians also claim that their water supplies are frequently rationed, threatening not just their agriculture but health and sanitation. Currently, less than one million Palestinians in the West Bank are connected to a running water supply.

Palestinians have been negatively affected by the building of the West Bank Barrier,

The West Bank Barrier as it appears at Abu Dis, in east Jerusalem.

which separates Jewish and Palestinian settlements in the West Bank. Parts of the Barrier are built on land confiscated from Palestinians. In the first two years of its construction Palestinians lost over 100,000 olive and citrus trees, 75 hectares of green houses and 37 kms of irrigation pipes. Many shops and houses were also demolished to allow for its construction. Because there are limited crossing points along the barrier, it is now more difficult for Palestinians to access medical care in Israel. Some estimates claim that almost one third of West Bank villages will have no access to healthcare in Israel. In towns near Jerusalem the average time for an ambulance to travel to the nearest hospital has increased from ten minutes to 110 minutes. Within Gaza, the recent blockade following the election victory by Hamas has caused serious humanitarian issues of food and water supply. In response to international criticism of these practices, Israel cites the potential threat to their security posed by suicide bombings and shelling from the Occupied Territories. Since the construction of the barrier and the blockade of Gaza there have been fewer suicide attacks but shelling from Gaza has continued. As noted above, some 2,000 Gazans died during the Israeli invasion of Gaza in December 2008.

Additional References

Gazans despair over blockade – news.bbc.co.uk/1/hi/world/middle_east/7739063.stm

Inside Gaza: Malnutrition and shortages – news.bbc.co.uk/1/hi/world/middle_east/7766509.stm

Israel delays detainee releases – news.bbc.co.uk/1/hi/world/middle_east/7771427.stm

Olmert condemns settler 'pogrom' – news.bbc.co.uk/1/hi/world/middle_east/7770384.stm

Anger as UN debates Gaza blockade – news.bbc.co.uk/1/hi/world/middle_east/7203863.stm

Profile: Gaza Strip – news.bbc.co.uk/1/hi/world/middle_east/5122404.stm

What is the West Bank barrier? – news.bbc.co.uk/1/hi/world/middle_east/3111159.stm

Palestinians' high-risk human shield tactic – news.bbc.co.uk/1/hi/world/middle_east/6166362.stm

Annapolis Peace Conference – www.voanews.com/english/archive/2007-11/2007-11-28-voa52.cfm

History of failed peace talks – news.bbc.co.uk/1/hi/world/middle_east/6666393.stm

Arab Israeli conflict-a brief outline with maps – www.guardian.co.uk/flash/0,,720353,00.html

Israeli leaders 'to topple Hamas' – news.bbc.co.uk/1/hi/world/middle_east/7794577.stm

Exercise

1. ***Question from CCEA May 2007***
   With reference to a case study of ethnic conflict: (15)

   (i) explain the underlying reasons for the conflict;

   (ii) discuss the outcomes of, and responses to, the conflict.

2. ***Question from CCEA January 2006***
   Explain how each of the following can be a cause of ethnic conflict in plural societies: (9)

   - Unequal distribution of resources and political power
   - Human rights abuses
   - Territorial disputes

A2 2 PHYSICAL GEOGRAPHY

A1 HUMAN DEMANDS ON FLUVIAL AND COASTAL ENVIRONMENTS

Increasing demands on rivers and coasts

The use and abuse of natural resources is a dominant theme of the twenty-first century. Building on the threat of mass overpopulation, the world now fears the ecological and economic fallout of climate change. At the same time, population growth and technological advance have combined to place increasing pressure on specific resources, including our fluvial and coastal environments. The majority of the world's inhabitants, now approaching seven billion, live in river valleys, estuaries or at coasts. The attractions of these zones are largely self-evident – water supply, transport routes, fertile soil and land suitable for building and agriculture. The addition of 75 million people each year to the world's population is enough to ensure growing stress on these resource areas. Add to this the demand for ever more material wealth, along with easy access to cheap energy, and such pressure may become unsustainable.

Rivers and valley zones

Rivers have been at the heart of human development. Along the desert rivers of the Indus, Nile, Tigris and Euphrates grew the earliest civilisations, prompting the development of writing, mathematics and science. The need to obtain, move and use water stimulated technology from the bucket, through the water wheel, to the hydro-electric dam and turbine. Resource demand on fluvial environments concerns the water, the flow of the river and the landscape created by the river system itself.

Domestic/residential use

Land adjacent to rivers provides many essential needs for settlement and consequently few significant urban centres across the world do not involve at least one river. Despite the risk of flooding, the ready supply of water for daily domestic needs, such as washing, drinking, cooking and cleaning, means proximity to rivers is a major location factor. Today, it is estimated that while rural inhabitants consume between 100 and 200 litres of water daily, the equivalent figure for urban dwellers lies between 400 and 600 litres. As a result of rapid urbanisation, especially within LEDCs in the last 50 years, the majority of people today are classed as urban and this proportion is increasing. While the population of the Earth tripled in the last one hundred years, the demand for water has increased six-fold. Today across Europe individuals on average use ten times more water in the home as 150 years ago. The widespread and increasing use of domestic equipment, such as automatic washing machines and dish washers, helps explain why growing demand outstrips the population growth rate. Delhi in India has a population of over 15 million and the city derives 86% of its huge water demand from the Yamuna River that flows through the urban area. In London too, most domestic water is supplied from local rivers – the Lee and the Thames.

Schemes for the movement and supply of water represent the single largest component of world engineering and construction. River flow is an all too convenient means of waste disposal, and the dumping of domestic waste and sewage into rivers has a long history. While most governments have policies on these aspects of river use, their effect is frequently limited and river pollution is common. Even where sewage is properly processed, rivers are still routinely the destination of the output from sewage works. The construction of housing, schools, hospitals, offices, shops and factories, all with drainage systems across floodplains, dramatically impacts basin hydrology. Such urbanisation increases surface flows and reduces the time water takes to reach river channels – flooding inevitably follows. Outside urban centres river valleys can be home to high concentrations of people. The floodplains and deltas of the Ganges, Indus, Nile and Brahmaputra rivers have population densities exceeding 150 per square kilometre.

Global freshwater use — ***Resource 1***

Use	Amount used in 1900 (cubic km)	Amount used today (cubic km)	Percentage of water used today
Agriculture	500	2,900	65
Industry	40	800	23
Domestic	20	380	12

Agricultural

Farming uses more fresh water than all other human activities put together. It also covers more river valley land than alternative uses. Some 30% of all the farmland in the world requires irrigation – the artificial addition of water. Much of this is lifted and pumped directly from river sources. The valleys of the Nile, Colorado and Ganges are prime examples of the close relationship between agriculturally productive zones and their proximity to rivers. Any atlas or GIS view of these drainage basins shows food production's affinity to river channels and their floodplains. The land adjacent to most rivers is subject to periodic flooding. Depending on the local climate, this may be a seasonal or occasional event, for example, the intense rains of the summer monsoon across South East Asia. This flooding, while a hazard in itself, provides alluvial sediment, rich in nutrients, to enhance the quality of soil on the floodplain. This explains why, despite the risks, farmers across the world utilise these flat fertile plains. The region is home to one in three of the planet's population and most of these two billion people are rural village inhabitants who depend on agriculture. The demands of agriculture and settlement are often in competition in river valleys, including the current controversy over proposals to build thousands of new houses in southern England, in areas at risk from flooding.

Industrial

Industrial processes, including washing and cooling, account for 20% of the global extraction of river water and the total increases rapidly year on year. Heavy manufacture makes high water demands. For example, an iron and steel mill uses 4,500 litres of water in the production of each tonne of steel, while an average-size car will require 30,000 litres of water for its production. In terms of industrial transport, rivers and linked canal systems form a vital route for the movement of raw materials and industrial products. The total freight moved by barge on the Mississippi River, USA, during 2004, was the equivalent of more than 40 million lorry loads. Waterway transportation of freight is eight times more efficient than road transportation. In a broader sense, river valleys act as corridors of access, and it is normal for major road and rail links to parallel the course of rivers, concentrating human activity in their valleys.

Energy production

Thermal power stations, whether fueled by oil, gas, coal, peat or nuclear, require large quantities of fresh water. While most of this water will be returned to the rivers, often at a higher temperature, the demand can amount to 500 million litres each day. Estimates suggest that across the USA the power industry daily extracts around 650 billion litres of water, mostly from rivers. Individual rivers may have a series of power stations along their course, such as the River Trent in the English Midlands. A river bank location has several advantages for power stations: proximity to the water supply required, available flatland suitable for construction and in some cases fuel can be transported along the river itself. Alternatively, river flow is harnessed using

Resource 2 *Examples of agricultural, recreational and transport use of rivers*

The fertile floodplain of Dordogne, France.

Leisure craft on Lower Lough Erne

Living and shopping on the river, Thailand

River bus, Bangkok

Hydro-Electric Power (HEP) systems. HEP stations, using dams and reservoirs constructed in the narrow confines of mountain valleys, provide a cheap and renewable source of electricity. In turn, this may attract power-oriented industry, such as smelting plants to the river valley region. The attraction of HEP as a renewable and green energy source has resulted in large areas of river valleys being permanently flooded. The Three Gorges dam project in China, completed in 2009, involved constructing a dam over two kilometres wide, across the Yangtze River. The reservoir created flooded 1,200 towns and villages, displaced over one million people and covers an area of 632 km^2; twice the size of Lough Neagh.

Leisure activities

A wide variety of recreational activities are associated with river and valley systems; from angling to white water rafting, and hiking to power boat racing. Rivers, lakes and reservoirs are a common destination for urban populations seeking relaxation in scenic environments at week-ends and holidays. Lake Mead, the huge reservoir behind the Hoover Dam on the Colorado River in the USA, is used by over eight million visitors each year.

Coasts

Around the world the significance of coastal zones is increasingly being recognised by governments as they develop new approaches to planning for these areas. Locally, the Department of the Environment (DOE) produced a report titled, 'An Integrated Coastal Zone Management Strategy for Northern Ireland 2006–2026'. The stated objective of this Integrated

Coastal Zone Management (ICZM) was, "...to establish sustainable levels of economic and social activity in our coastal areas while protecting the coastal environment." In its discussion of the report, the DOE reflected on the broad range and complex demands made on the coast:

> "This dynamic fringe supports tourism, agriculture, aquaculture, inshore fisheries, industry, military and civil firing ranges, commercial harbours and quays as well as being used for waste disposal, aggregate mining and power generation. All these activities and more, occur in a zone well known for its natural propensity to change".

Most of the world's population live within an hour's overland journey from the coast. Of the planet's 33 megacities (populations over 7.5 million), 21 are in coastal areas. These include cities in MEDCs, such as London, Tokyo and New York, as well as in LEDCs, such as Mumbai, Lagos and Shanghai. The coast, and particularly deltas and estuaries, have always been a focus region for settlement, communication and trade. More recently they are also seen as recreational resources. The coast is the interface between the land and the sea, and its definition is difficult as it includes both terrestrial and marine environments. As growing human pressures open up new areas of coast, so too redevelopment of existing sites is common. In Belfast, the Laganside Project, completed by 2008, has been followed by the Titanic Quarter, a fifteen year long project

An illustrated map of coastal demands around Belfast Lough **Resource 3**

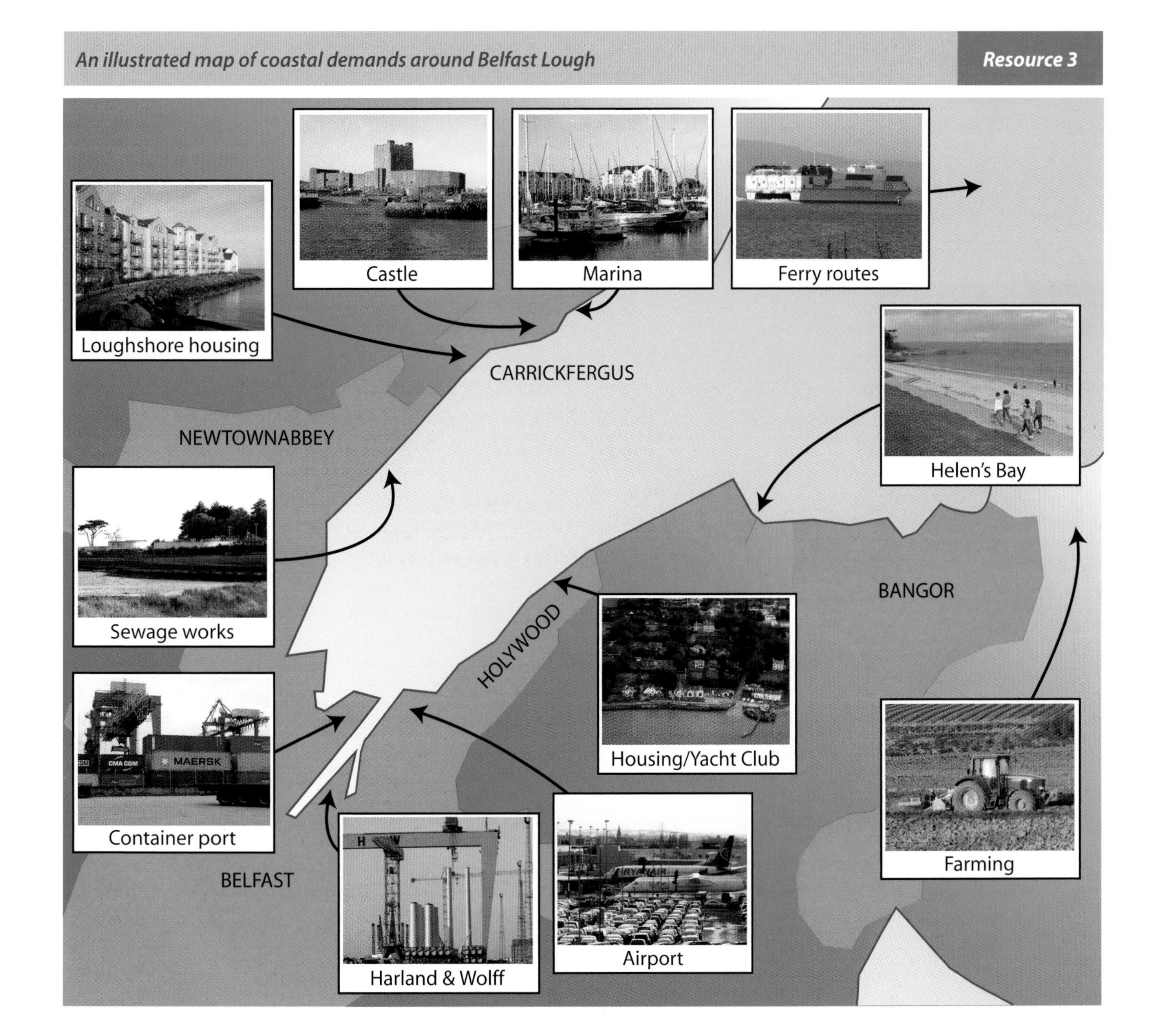

to renovate and develop the former docks and shipbuilding area on the southern shore of Belfast Lough.

Domestic/residential use

Location by the sea has numerous advantages for people, including proximity to work at ports and docks, and access to the shore and sea for recreation. The growth of world trade over the last few centuries means that in both MEDCs and LEDCs port facilities have grown rapidly, leading to expanding populations in many formerly minor colonial trading ports such as Sydney, Cape Town, Mumbai and Manila. In tropical regions coastal zones may be perceived as hazardous because of storm surges or even tsunamis. Malaria and other diseases are associated with stagnant coastal swamps and consequently, before drainage and reclamation these areas were avoided. Settlements on coasts often spread laterally along the shore to produce a linear or ribbon development as this provides views and access to the shoreline for fishing communities or leisure. The release of sewage into the sea is a major issue for coastal settlements. In 2008, under European Union regulations, the sewerage system in North Down was at its maximum capacity and until this was expanded no new house building would be permitted in the area. Coasts are commonly seen as desirable locations for both holiday and retirement homes. Since the 1950s, the flow of grey migrants from Greater London to the south coast of England amounts to several million and in towns from Eastbourne (East Sussex) to Torquay (Devon) the population structure is old and ageing as a result.

Agricultural

Coastal areas, in particular low-lying coasts adjacent to river estuaries, often provide an ideal environment for agriculture. Even in regions of poor soil, beaches can supply sand for improved drainage and seaweed for increased fertility. In many places the technical ability to control drainage and water flow has released large regions from the risk of floods. In Western Europe, the Dutch led the way from the fourteenth century in the reclamation of coastal wetlands from the sea in the Rhine Delta. Eventually the Netherlands was expanded out into the North Sea as dykes cut-off the Zuider Zee and drainage created the Polders, protected fields lying below sea-level. Aquaculture is the farming of both fresh and salt water organisms. While this has a long history in places like China, most aquatic species have only been domesticated within the last few decades. As stocks of wild fish and shellfish have suffered from overexploitation, aquaculture is growing by around 6% each year to meet the demand for these products. Salmon farms, in which fish are kept in large nets and cages in sea inlets, have become a common sight in Western Scotland and Ireland, including Lough Swilly, County Donegal.

Resource 4a *Greenhouse agriclulture on the coastal plain of south Turkey*

Industrial

Ports are good examples of break of bulk points – locations where goods have to be moved from one form of transport to another. This means a port site can be an advantageous location for an industry to process raw materials or to assemble products. A prime example concerns the world's most important traded material – oil. When crude oil is brought by ocean going tanker or by pipe from an off-shore field, it needs to be refined by a series of complex cracking and distillation processes into its many products. The coast is therefore a logical location for such oil refining. Consequently, numerous related industries, both manufacturing and service, will also locate nearby. The reclamation of land on both the north and south foreshore of Belfast Lough has been primarily to allow expansion of industrial premises in these areas, although commercial retail and recreational uses are now promoted. The development of containerisation has reduced the impact of break of bulk for many goods, but ports continue to attract investment from related industries. Extractive industries are also common in coast locations. The last commercial collieries in north-east England where at the coast, exploiting deposits up to five miles offshore beneath the sea bed. Dredging of sea bed aggregates and quarrying sand from shoreline deposits are other examples of primary extractive industries.

Farmland, settlement and port facilities near Whitehead, Co Antrim **Resource 4b**

Energy production

Many older power stations have coastal locations, either to facilitate easy port access to supplies of their fossil fuels (coal, oil or gas) or for remoteness in the case of nuclear plants such as Dounreay, Scotland, and Sellafield, Cumbria. In the search for alternative and renewable energy sources, the coast has become a key battleground between environmentalists and developers. The power of the sea in both its wave and tide energy is one source of this friction, added to which are the strong and persistent winds common to the region. Energy schemes using wave and tidal power have been in development for decades. In France, a large scale barrage across the Rance Estuary in Brittany has been producing electricity for over 40 years. A similar but much larger scheme has been proposed for the Severn Estuary (Bristol Channel) between England and Wales. In January 2009, electricity from a unique twin turbine, tidal stream turbine in Strangford Lough, County Down, was fed into the National Grid. The powerful tidal race at the mouth of the sea lough between the towns of Portaferry and Strangford is used to power the 16 m long turbine blades anchored to the seabed. Offshore windfarms have been developed at several sites around Great Britain and Ireland, including seven turbines on the Arklow Bank, 10 km off the coast to the south of Dublin. The new Robin Rigg wind farm, standing in the shallow waters of the Solway Firth, south Scotland, is designed to generate 180 MW of electricity, enough to supply 120,000 homes. This wind farm, due to operate from 2010, consists of a total of 60 wind turbines that were assembled by Harland and Wolff in Belfast.

Leisure activities

It was the advent of the railway and cheap excursion fares that lead to the mass tourism of the Victorian era and the concept of the seaside holiday. Coastal resorts – including Blackpool, Bournemouth, Scarborough, Llandudno, Oban, Bray and Portrush – received huge numbers of day trippers from their respective nearby urban centres. These resorts grew rapidly between 1850 and 1900 as job opportunities, though often seasonal, expanded with the demand. One outcome of this 'invasion' of the coast was that engineers designed piers and promenades along the coast to facilitate people 'taking the air' and bathing. These engineering structures and others designed to prevent beach erosion such as sea-walls and groyne fields, were the start of deliberate management of the coastline beyond the earlier development of ports and harbours. In the 1960s, another transport innovation, cheap air fares, helped create another wave of coastal development, this time in the poorer nations of southern Europe. Many of the towns

Resource 5a *Development in Koh Tao, Thailand*

Resource 5b *Second homes near Dunfanaghy, County Donegal*

along the Costas of east and southern Spain were mere fishing villages, that within a decade transformed into large towns, dependent on the annual summer influx of north European holiday makers. Active coastal recreation activities that are increasingly popular include wind surfing, parascending, scuba diving, yachting (land and sea), water-skiing, beach volleyball and snorkeling. However, walking is still the most common activity undertaken along the shore.

The trend in the growth of global tourism continues to impact on coastal settlements and environments worldwide. Exotic tropical locations such as Bali in Indonesia or the islands in the Gulf of Thailand have likewise been transformed from remote undeveloped backwaters to honey-pots of mass tourist development and building. The extension of what is termed the 'pleasure-periphery', through increased affluence in MEDCs and cheap travel, has had very direct impacts on attractive coastal scenery, especially in tropical and sub-tropical locations. At a more local scale, while holidays to traditional seaside resorts have declined, the aspiration of many to own their own holiday or second homes has increased. Such ownership is usually confined to quiet, rural regions or the coast. Around Dunfanaghy, County Donegal, the growth of the housing density, particularly from the construction of bungalows, has created friction between locals and weekenders, many of whom come from the North.

A2 RIVER AND BASIN MANAGEMENT STRATEGIES

There is a long history of human management of river channels, or would 'interference' be a more appropriate word? Only within the last one hundred years or so has this management started to approach rivers from the broader perspective of the drainage basin. This more holistic view has emerged as awareness has grown of the interdependence of river channels and their flow characteristics within their catchment area. In short, river channels are just one element in a complex, interacting basin system that involves climate, soil, geology, topography, vegetation and human activity.

The need for channelisation

Channelisation is a term that describes the deliberate modification of natural river channels. These involve changes to the width, depth or the plan form (vertical view) of the channel and also diversions of channels and the construction of embankments or artificial levées.

The most common reasons for the channelisation of rivers are to improve:

- Flood control
- Land drainage
- Navigation
- Erosion problems

Some methods used in channelisation schemes **Resource 6**

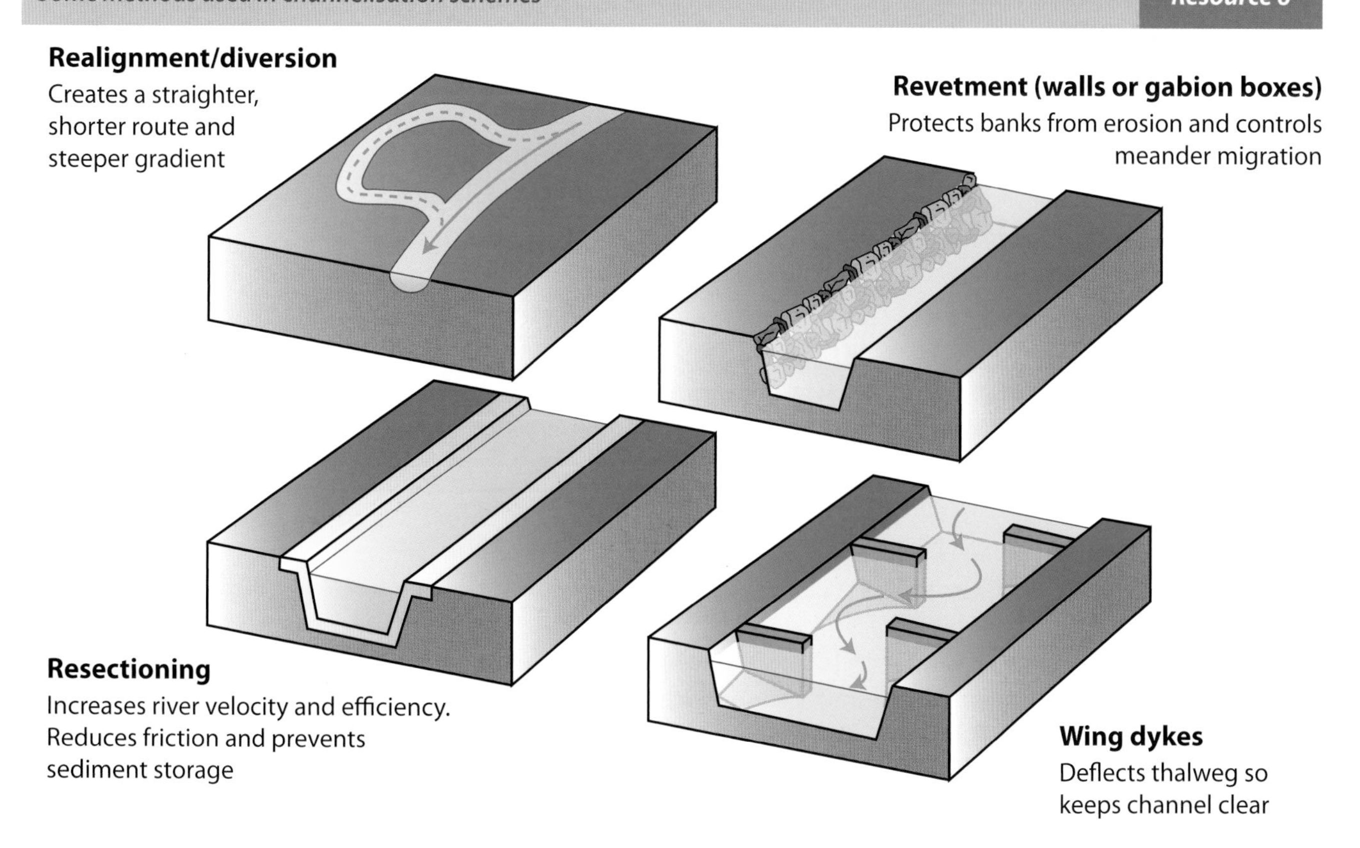

The shape of a natural river is controlled by the pattern of variation in its discharge and sediment load. The width, depth and path of a river channel continuously adjust as these factors change over time. This is called a **dynamic equilibrium**, where a change in any one variable causes change elsewhere in the river channel system. The essential aim of any channelisation scheme is to increase the efficiency of the river channel to move water and sediment downstream. Rivers are of vital importance to people but at the same time potentially dangerous. The tendency of rivers to flood, in some cases annually and regularly, in others much less predictably, has encouraged people to protect their homes and resources by modifying the offending channel. River floodplains have many attractive characteristics for people, including the availability of flat land, fertile soils and fresh water. To increase the prosperity of agriculture, the land quality can be improved by developing more efficient drainage of water from fields into the nearby channel. Using simple drainage ditches or more elaborate underground field drains and plastic piping, the outcome is that the river needs to carry the additional water away more effectively (**Resource 7**).

Resource 7 *Field drain at a river bank*

The prevention of flooding and the improvement of local field drainage are the two main aims of most channelisation projects undertaken in Northern Ireland, including the example of the River Blackwater during the 1980s, outlined in **Resource 8** below.

Resource 8 *The Upper Blackwater Land Drainage Scheme 1984–91*

Aims:

To improve drainage of farmland and to reduce damage and isolation caused by flooding.

Background:

Repeated flooding in the marshy valley of the Upper Blackwater, on both sides of the Irish border, limited the use of over 7,300 hectares of potentially productive farmland.

Methods:

- Dredging of the river bed to increase its flood capacity and reduce the water table in the adjacent floodplain. Most dredging was done by drag-line cranes operating from one bank of the river.
- The river course was shortened and straightened by the removal of 13 meanders, increasing the gradient of the channel bed to increase stream velocity.
- Protection measures were undertaken of river banks and existing bridges to ensure the lower riverbed and higher flows would not undermine these causing erosion.

Outcomes:

- Farmers reported that vegetables and cereal crops can be grown on fields that were previously flooded.
- In places anglers have reported that increased erosion has caused high sediment levels threatening fish stocks.
- The RSPB has expressed concern that the loss of habitat on the banks cleared for dredging and along the river bed itself has impacted on bird nesting sites and their food sources.
- Due to adjustments in the hydrology it is believed that engineering will have to be repeated if the improved channel capacity and river flow are to be maintained.

Other common reasons for changing channel profiles include:

- navigation – the use of rivers to transport people and goods.
- erosion problems – the concern that rivers are wearing away their banks in a way that threatens land or property.

Using rivers for transport has been an important activity around the world, especially where it allowed access to remote or isolated regions. Today river transport remains vitally important but the variation in river depth and in stream velocity poses serious hazards to shipping. A large-scale and on-going example of channelisation for this purpose concerns the Mississippi River in the USA (**Resource 9**).

The erosion of land adjacent to river channels is more than an inconvenience. For farmers migrating meanders can mean the loss of valuable farmland, while in urban environments buildings, transport routes and other structures in the built environment may be destroyed. This helps explain why rivers running through cities are normally strictly confined to reinforced or artificial channels (**Resources 10** and **15**).

The Lower Mississippi Navigation Scheme ***Resource 9***

Aims:

To maintain a deep navigation channel and shorten the journey distance along the river.

Background:

The shifting nature of the Mississippi's channel and sandbanks across its wide river bed meant that paddle steamers had an average working life of only three years before they were ran aground or sank. To allow the river to cope with the increasing demand for transport along its course, a reliable 2.75 m deep water channel was required. In 2001, 500 million tonnes of freight, worth $6 billion, was transported along the Lower Mississippi.

* (Navigation is only one aspect of engineering on the Mississippi River: other aims are flood prevention, water storage and hydro-electric power generation).

Methods:

- Wing dykes – hundreds of stone barriers were placed at regular intervals on the river bed from one bank of the river up to one third of the way across the channel. These were designed to block river flow and trap sediment. The aim is that the river uses its additional energy to cut a deeper channel in the remaining narrower channel (**Resource 6**).
- Meander cut-offs – dozens of large bends in the river channel were by-passed using explosives and dredgers to cut new channel across the necks of the meanders. The river was shortened by over 200 km. The aim was to increase the gradient of the river, and so speed up water flow to maintain a deep and shorter channel.
- Channel dredging.
- Revetments to protect river banks from erosion by currents deflected across the river by the wing dykes.

Outcomes:

- The river has developed and maintained a suitable deep water channel but large sand banks on the river bed shift and reform so they need to be constantly monitored.
- Erosion of the river bank opposite to where wing dykes were installed meant that additional dykes were needed from the second bank or additional bank protection was needed.
- Along some stretches of the channel the bank and bed have been entirely lined with concrete mattresses to keep the river in one place.
- The river has started to regain its former length by initiating new bends and meanders, increasing its sinuous plan.
- The on-going maintenance of the Mississippi hard engineering scheme, which includes flood prevention measures, costs over $300 million annually.

The methods of river channelisation

Channelisation may be applied to a stretch or **reach** of a river channel, or along the whole length of the stream. In Northern Ireland most channelisation schemes have involved all or most of a river's route, for example, the Upper Blackwater (**Resource 8**) and the River Main (**Resource 14**) schemes. In England it has been more common to use channelisation along short river sections.

At either scale the aim of most channelisation schemes is to increase:

1) the flow velocity of the channel

2) the carrying capacity of the channel

Discharge of a river measures the rate at which water passes a given point and is commonly stated in cumecs – cubic metres per second (m^3/sec). This is a function of the river's cross-section and its speed – its width and depth multiplied by its average velocity. Increasing any one of these three variables will increase the rate at which the channel can move water.

The most common approach to channelisation is **resectioning**, where the channel cross-section is enlarged, either widened by excavating the banks or deepened by dredging the river bed. The objective is to create a more energy-efficient, trapezoid shaped cross-section, with a broad bed and steep banks. Often associated with these modifications is the straightening of a channel's course or **realignment**. Meanders in the channel are cut through and filled-in to produce a straighter channel with a steeper downstream profile. This speeds up the water flow in a river that may appear more like a canal than a natural channel. Another approach is to increase a channel's cross-section by raising its banks by **levée** construction. A further refinement in channel modification is to reduce friction by **clearing** and **snagging** – removing obstructions from the bed such as boulders, sand banks or weed beds. One outcome of increasing a river's velocity is its increased ability to erode its bed and banks. This means that both up and downstream of channelised river sections banks may become unstable and thus require **bank protection**. This can be done using **revetments**, which may consist of concrete walls, sheet piling, rip-rap (loose boulders) or gabions (large wire cages filled with small rocks) (**Resources 6 and 10**).

In urban areas the need for river control and stability has led to whole channels being lined with concrete and ultimately directing rivers into underground tunnels or pipes, known as culverts. **River training** is a form of channelisation that can be used to improve navigation or to develop and maintain a new channel form. In some places, especially when periodic flooding is the issue, a second overflow channel is constructed to take the additional floodwater. These **diversion channels** or **spillways** run parallel to the existing river, re-joining it downstream of the section being protected.

Resource 10 *Photographs illustrating revetments and gabions*

Revetment bank on the River Ure

Gabions on a river bank

In practice, channelisation schemes usually involve more than one form of modification and the real outcome of these is not easily predicted. For example, if a river channel is widened this will tend to reduce its mean velocity but if at the same time the river channel is shortened by removing meanders, the steeper profile will tend to speed up river flow. In Northern Ireland, flooding and land drainage schemes are the most common reason for channelisation projects and almost all lowland river systems across the province have had some degree of channelisation in the last 60 years. In the USA, between 1930 and 1980, over 26,000 km of river channels were subject to major channelisation work.

The impact of channelisation

In recent decades, the concept and many of the methods of channelisation have become deeply unpopular largely due to the unforeseen negative consequences of the management. However, it should be stated that in many places channelisation has prevented flooding, improved land quality and allowed safe navigation on rivers. The issues with channelisation are various, ranging from concerns over the visual appearance of schemes, through problems of habitat destruction, to examples where the engineering has failed, making flooding worse. Frequently, channelisation is applied to one stretch of a river channel where a problem has been identified. Often while the modification of the channel has alleviated the issue locally, the net impact is to create another problem further downstream (**Resource 11**). A second common failing of these engineering management projects is that the required monitoring of their impact and on-going maintenance of the structures designed does not happen. In short, management ends when the builders move on. In the case of a flood reduction scheme along the River Thame in Oxfordshire, the enlarged channel was not maintained by regular dredging and within 30 years the river had reverted to its original water carrying capacity.

An analogy – river discharge and road traffic

The problems with river channelisation can be similar to issues facing planners attempting to improve traffic flow along roads. Imagine a commuter's drive to work. Along the journey there are four major junctions. At each of these junctions traffic builds up during the rush-hour. Planners then place a roundabout at the first junction and traffic flows more freely. Unfortunately this simply speeds more traffic to the second junction, where even longer tailbacks develop. Planners act again, placing a phased set of traffic lights at the second junction. This only results in sending even more traffic, more quickly, to the third junction causing longer queues and increased congestion.

Instability

Natural river channels are constantly adjusting their shape and form through processes of erosion and sediment deposition. Engineering schemes can immediately and radically change the channel characteristics. The response to this rapid and unnatural change often leads to instability. Change in the channel shape along one reach of a river not only alters its flow characteristics, it also creates a new regime further downstream beyond the section altered. If river velocity has been increased then downstream erosion may be enhanced. In a study of small but high energy streams in England, the channels of many were widened as an outcome of resectioning of the river upstream. Banks were worn back as higher levels and faster flows of water increased the river's erosion capacity. In several of these cases the work was designed to improve land drainage and alleviate the flood risk to agricultural land. However, the net impact downstream has been to erode river banks threatening land and property. The Mississippi navigation schemes (**Resource 9**) illustrates an example of instability following channelisation.

One of the oldest forms of channelisation involves the raising or creation of levées. Natural levées form when rivers flood and deposit coarse load immediately on their banks. These can be enhanced locally to improve the channel cross-section and thereby reduce the flood risk. However, levées alter how rivers move their sediment load. Firstly, reduced flooding means less alluvium is spread across the floodplain. Secondly, the load starts to be deposited on the river bed itself, raising the river channel above the floodplain level. This can not only make it difficult for water on the floodplain to drain into the river but should floods occur, their impact can be more severe. Embankments along the River Ganges, as it flows through the Bangladesh capital Dhaka, were designed to reduce the seasonal monsoon floods. In reality, the normal four to six weeks flooding of low-lying areas of the city was extended to four months. This was because monsoon rainfall that would previously have drained into the river was ponded back by the new embankments and could only drain away when river levels fell.

Increased flood hazard

Moving a greater volume of water more quickly to an unchanged section of river channel is inevitably going to increase the risk of that river exceeding its bankfull discharge and inundating its floodplain. Some observers suggest that the disastrous Mississippi flood of 1993 did not happen in spite of 100 years of management but rather because of it. **Resource 11** describes an example of how a scheme that aimed to reduce local flooding has increased the risk of such flooding happening downstream of the engineered river reach. In many countries attempts to reduce flooding of urban areas through resectioning, realignment and containing rivers ultimately creates a flood hazard downstream where the engineering of the channel ends. This is because the nature of surfaces and drainage systems in urban areas shed water rapidly and the newly modified channels accelerate discharge out of town on into the unaltered river channel with its lower carrying capacity.

Aesthetic consideration

As noted earlier, river courses are often highly valued as an amenity by the local community. This ranges from those who use the river for sport such as angling or canoeing, to those who walk along the banks, or others who view the river as an element of the scenic environment.

Resource 11 *The Raba River Resectioning Scheme , southern Poland*

Aims:

To reduce the risk of flooding of valuable farmland

Background:

In the 1960s and 70s repeated channelisation schemes were completed along sections of the Raba, a mountain tributary of the Wisla River, 20 km south of Krakow.

Methods:

- Sections of the river were straightened by cutting off meanders so that the total channel length was 7% shorter.
- Unusually, the river channel was made narrower by up to 60% in places. The aim was to create a more efficient channel shape and increase river velocity during high flow periods.

Outcomes:

- Up to three metres of bed degradation (erosion) has occurred along an eight kilometre stretch of the river.
- The river has a more flashy response to rainfall with shorter lag times, steeper rising and recession limbs and higher peak discharges.
- Bankfull discharge flows occur more than twice as often as before the resectioning scheme.

A later scheme, the construction of the Dobczyce dam in 1988, has only accelerated the erosion rate of the Raba's riverbed.

The most common response to channelisation is an objection to the canal-like appearance and the intrusive hard engineering structure built. In the words of David Shaw, an angler on the River Main before but not after its channelisation, "I have no interest in sitting for an evening's fishing at a glorified drainage ditch that was once a beautiful stretch of winding river" (**Resource 12**). Channelisation often results in the loss of the stream's riffles and pools and also produces a wider variation in discharge with low flow levels which expose the bed becoming more common.

Map and photographs of the River Main scheme ***Resource 12***

Modern sluice gates

View north from bridge

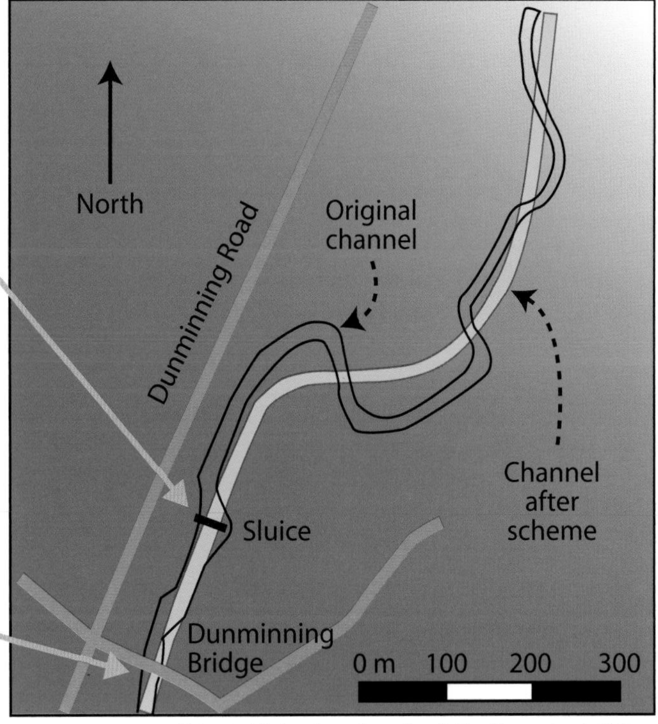

This material is based upon Crown Copyright and is reproduced with the permission of Land & Property Services under Delegated Authority from the Controller of Her Majesty's Stationery Office, © Crown Copyright and database rights. Permit number 90106.

Impacts to river ecology

Rivers provide a diversity of habitats and environments that interact with the biotic and abiotic elements of ecosystems in a complex way. Shallows or **riffles** and deeper sections called **pools** are natural elements of river meanders. These provide a range of habitats for both plant and animal life. Coarse gravel beds are used by fish laying their eggs, while pools provide shelter for resting fish, especially in times of low flow and where these are shaded by overhanging vegetation. **Resource 13** shows how channelisation can impact river bed and bank environments. Land alongside rivers is known as the riparian environment and this zone will be directly impacted under many engineering schemes. For instance, improved floodplain drainage will make them drier so the flora and fauna of marshes and wetland will suffer. Channelisation usually modifies river banks either through the clearance of their vegetation or the regrading of their shape. This may involve strengthening by the construction of revetments. Bank vegetation provides food and shelter for insects, mammals and birds that make use of the river. Plant cover on river banks reduces erosion, as roots bind the soil particles and plants shade the river, helping to moderate changes in stream temperature. This latter point is critical to many plants and animals that are sensitive to wide fluctuation in light and temperature conditions. Increasing concern for the ecological impacts of channelisation, as well as fears over their long-term effectiveness, led to a rethink in channel management. In Northern Ireland, both the Upper Blackwater and River Main drainage schemes used detailed public enquiries and environmental assessments as, gradually, a new school of thought emerged. This modern approach focuses on the creation of environmentally sensitive solutions, incorporating hard and soft engineering and river restoration.

Resource 13 *The impact of channelisation on river bed and bank environments*

Natural channel

Suitable water temperatures; shading; good cover for fish life; abundant leaf input.

After channelisation

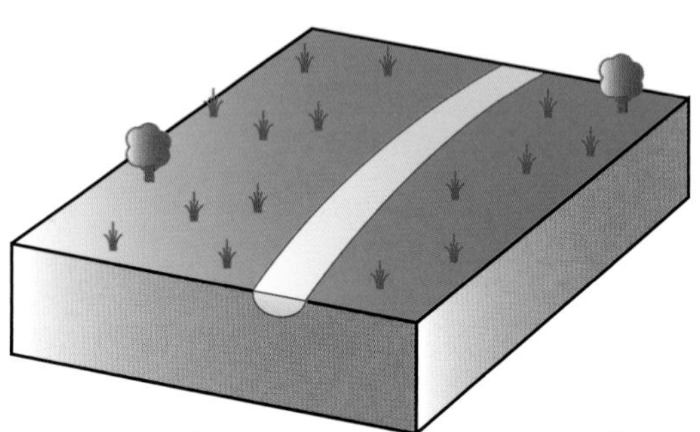

Increased water temperatures; no shading; no cover for fish life; rapid fluctuations in temperatures; reduced leaf input.

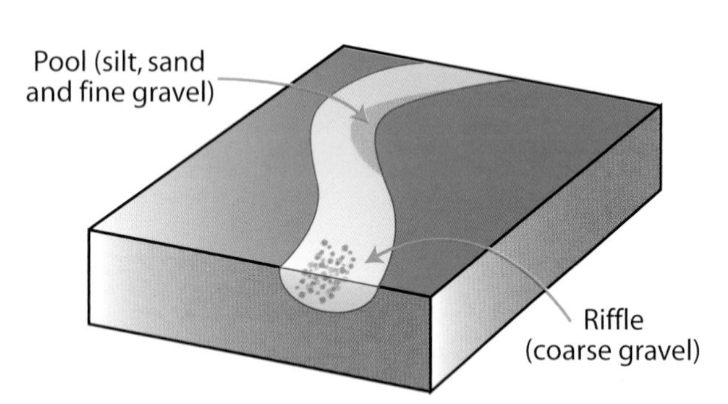

Pool-riffle sequence; sorted gravels provide diversified habitats for many stream organisms.

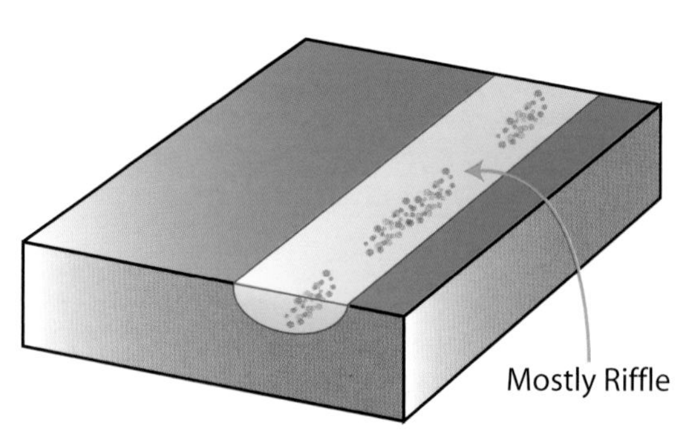

Unsorted gravels; reduction in habitat variation.

The pool environment

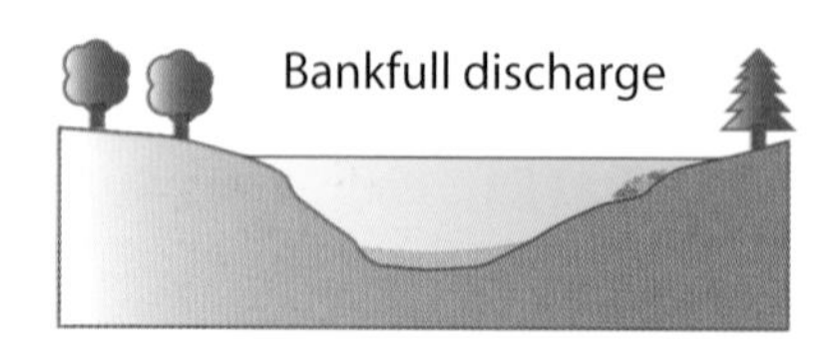

Disperse water velocities; high in pools, lower on riffles.

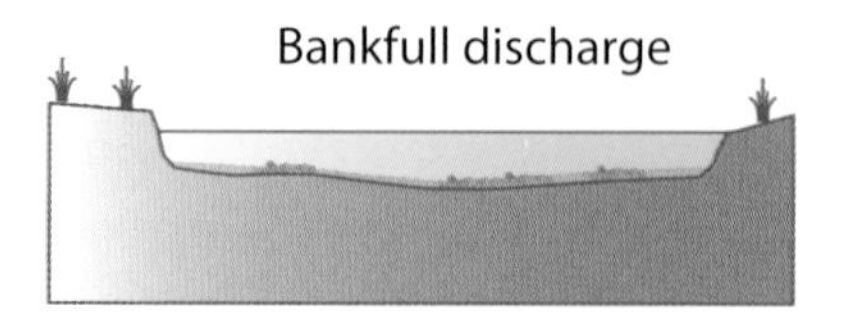

Increased stream velocities.

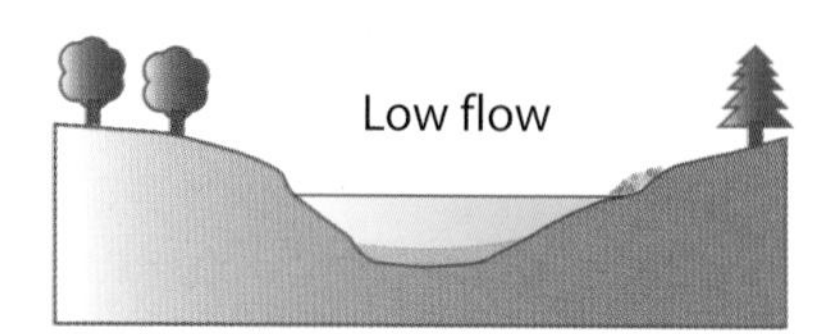

Moderate depth in dry seasons.

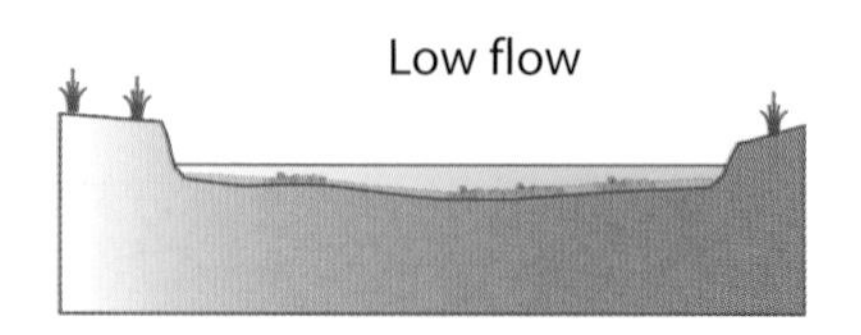

Much reduced depth of flow in dry seasons.

The River Main Drainage Scheme Public Enquiry ***Resource 14***

This engineering scheme was designed to improve the land drainage for 4,000 hectares along a 20 km section of the River Main in County Antrim. The river rises near Ballymoney and flows south past Ballymena into Lough Neagh. The proposal involved the enlargement, regrading and realignment of the river channel, and the replacement of an existing weir with sluice gates (**Resource 12**). The enquiry considered the views of all interest groups including:

- several local and national representatives of angling clubs.
- many local farmers and representatives of farming organisations.
- owners of industrial premises that used water from the Main for industrial processes.
- numerous conservation and heritage groups and experts.

A large part of the report and its conclusions dealt with the need to modify plans in the light of their potential ecological impact, especially of fisheries, riparian ecosystems and scenic amenity. Changes included:

- restoring pools and replacing boulders to maintain fish shelter.
- working from alternative banks to leave vegetation untouched.
- retaining some river bends for habitat variety.
- considering the construction of a fish pass at the sluice gates.
- increasing the number and scale of replacement trees on the banks.
- the relocation of the channel to avoid a particularly scenic landscape at Gracehill.

Creating environmentally sensitive engineering solutions

In reassessing the engineering and management of rivers it has been suggested that planners need to move away from the view of 'rivers as hazards and wealth' to 'rivers as resource'. Uses other than extraction and navigation need to be equally valued, such as recreation, conservation, aesthetics and ecology. The damaging impacts and expense of some channelisation projects encouraged the development of soft engineering methods to replace or mitigate hard engineered schemes. Hard engineering refers to the structural approach to issues. In the case of rivers these include dams, revetments, land drainage systems, culverts, sluice gates and artificial levées. Soft engineering is usually defined as solutions that work with nature rather than against it. In reality many projects incorporate elements of both hard and soft engineering. Modern planning for rivers has been influenced by local and global events and policies. In 1988, new legislation in the Town and Country Planning Regulations required that all planning not only required a Cost-Benefit Analysis but also an Environmental Impact Assessment (EIA). A United Nations Conference on Environment and Development in 1992 resulted in Agenda 21 (see page 64) and a call for sustainable development. By 1998, the supervision of rivers in the UK was delivered through Catchment Management Plans (CMP). These involve the integrated planning, management and development of water environments. One aim is the identification of conflicts between flood defence schemes and conservation of river ecosystems. Balancing the demands of the various groups interested in rivers and basins, while planning for the future, is a difficult task. Soft engineering techniques and 'softer' structural approaches can help achieve the goal of environmentally sensitive solutions.

Soft engineering techniques

Two examples of these techniques used in cases where river flooding is a hazard, are **afforestation** and **land zoning**. Planting trees or other vegetation across catchment areas has the dual effect of firstly, reducing the amount of rainfall that leaves the basin by river channels and secondly, slowing down the transfer of water through the basin into the river. Land zoning involves the management of the land use towards flood reduction. In places wetlands may be retained as water storage areas or low lying land that has not been developed may be set aside

Resource 15 *Photographs of flood defences on River Tay in Dundee*

Parkland adjacent to the River Tay

to temporarily store floodwater as required. In Dundee, on the banks of the River Tay, sports fields and public parks line the river bank both up and downstream of the city centre. During high water these can be flooded without causing great expense or long-term damage. In the town centre a more structural flood defence system is employed (**Resource 15**).

Softer channel engineering techniques

One approach is to modify the traditional resection approach by using partial channel dredging. Natural banks are retained while part of the bed is lowered to increase the channel capacity. This allows most of the ecological habitats to remain intact though it is not clear if it does help reduce flooding effectively. Another method has been to pull back from the channel itself to leave a river corridor along which the river is free to flow and even modify its own path and channel. Defences are then placed some distance from the edge of the river channel. Embankments along the floodplain rather than on the river banks mean that flooding can occur but only to a fixed point. This additional storage land may then protect land further downstream from inundation. Clearly such a scheme means some land cannot be developed along the river but the lower and more distance defences retain the natural and aesthetic value of the river amenity (**Resource 22**).

The provision of an additional channel running parallel to the existing river but only used during high, overbank flows, is an example of a hard engineering structure used in a soft way. The river is left untouched with all its diversity of ecological habitats intact. Biological engineering is a term sometimes applied to the use of specific types of planting. Green stakes of willow can be used to line river banks as a living revetment or woven willow cages used as gabions to stabilise banks at bends or bridges. These features encourage the trapping of sediment, allowing river plants to establish and flourish in and near the water's edge.

River restoration is the application of more environmentally sensitive methods to rivers that have previously undergone hard engineering channelisation. Over the last twenty years across the UK and Ireland many attempts have been made to recreate the more natural appearance of modified rivers in both urban and rural settings. 90% of British lowland rivers have undergone some degree of channelisation in the past so there are many places where restoration can be applied. Complete restoration to the original state is rare and often not possible, but some rehabilitation can be undertaken. Common changes are the reinstatement of bends and meanders, the restoration of pools and riffles on the bed, and varying the cross-section channel shape from the efficient but monotonous trapezoid plan. River banks can be vegetated and regraded to improve access for anglers, walkers and other recreational users. River restoration is usually applied to short sections of rivers – **Resource 16** describes some examples of these techniques.

Some examples of river restoration schemes **Resource 16**

Scheme	Result of earlier channelisation	Restoration scheme
River Skerne, Darlington	• small river straightened and deepened to reduce flooding • power lines, gas and sewerage pipes run alongside the river • habitat and biodiversity severely degraded	• along a 2 km stretch former meanders were restored, the stream bed was reshaped and backwaters developed • trees, shrubs and bulbs were planted • footpaths open the valley to the local community • the natural appearance is improving with pools and riffles restored • the plant diversity has increased
The Ballysally Blagh, Coleraine	• a straight, trench-like channel was created • wildlife numbers fell and biodiversity decreased	• flow deflectors used to recreate sinuous course • willow gabions used to protect banks • meanders and an island created • appearance more natural and vegetation cover increased
River Kissimmee, Florida USA	• channelised in 1940s to aid navigation and reduce flood risk • drained wetlands lost bird habitats • water flow reduced and supplies salinised (salt)	• 11,000 hectares of wetland restored • levées removed, meanders restored and canals filled in • due for completion 2012 • progress slower than planned

Additional References

Many examples of river restoration techniques and projects, including the River Skerne, can be viewed in the River Restoration Centre website:
www.therrc.co.uk

Basin management

River basin management operates at a scale beyond the modification of sections of a river's channel. It involves the control of water movement across and through a river network's catchment area. The most common method of basin management is the construction of dams and reservoirs that allow control over a river's discharge and storage of water. The need for river basin management is to match the variation in river flow to the demands made by people within and beyond the basin. The many aims of basin management are outlined below, but in modern management systems it is common for schemes to be multi-purpose in design. China's huge Three Gorges Project became operational in 2009. It is primarily designed to control flooding and generate electricity but it will also improve river transport on the Yangtze and is expected to generate an income from tourism.

Aims of basin management

1. Flood control

Annual and periodic variation in river discharge is a common problem for management and the need to avoid devastating floods is of paramount importance. Most schemes aim at flood control, recognising that total flood prevention may be too expensive to justify. The Aswan Dam in Egypt, completed in the 1970s, finally gave the nation control over the River Nile's discharge after thousands of years of living with annual summer flooding.

2. Water supply

Water for domestic, industrial and agricultural uses is a common aim of management. Growing populations and industrial development in river valleys increase demand for a water supply that must be reliable if development is to continue. India, with its population of over one billion people, is a leading builder of dams. In semi-arid regions the unreliability of rain-fed farming can be supplemented by irrigation water. In the Sudan, the Sennar Dam on the Blue Nile supplies water for the country's largest area of irrigated farmland, the Gezira, which consists of over one million hectares of productive arable land. Meeting water demands involves not only quantity but also the control of water quality.

Resource 17 *Diagram of aims and issues in basin management schemes*

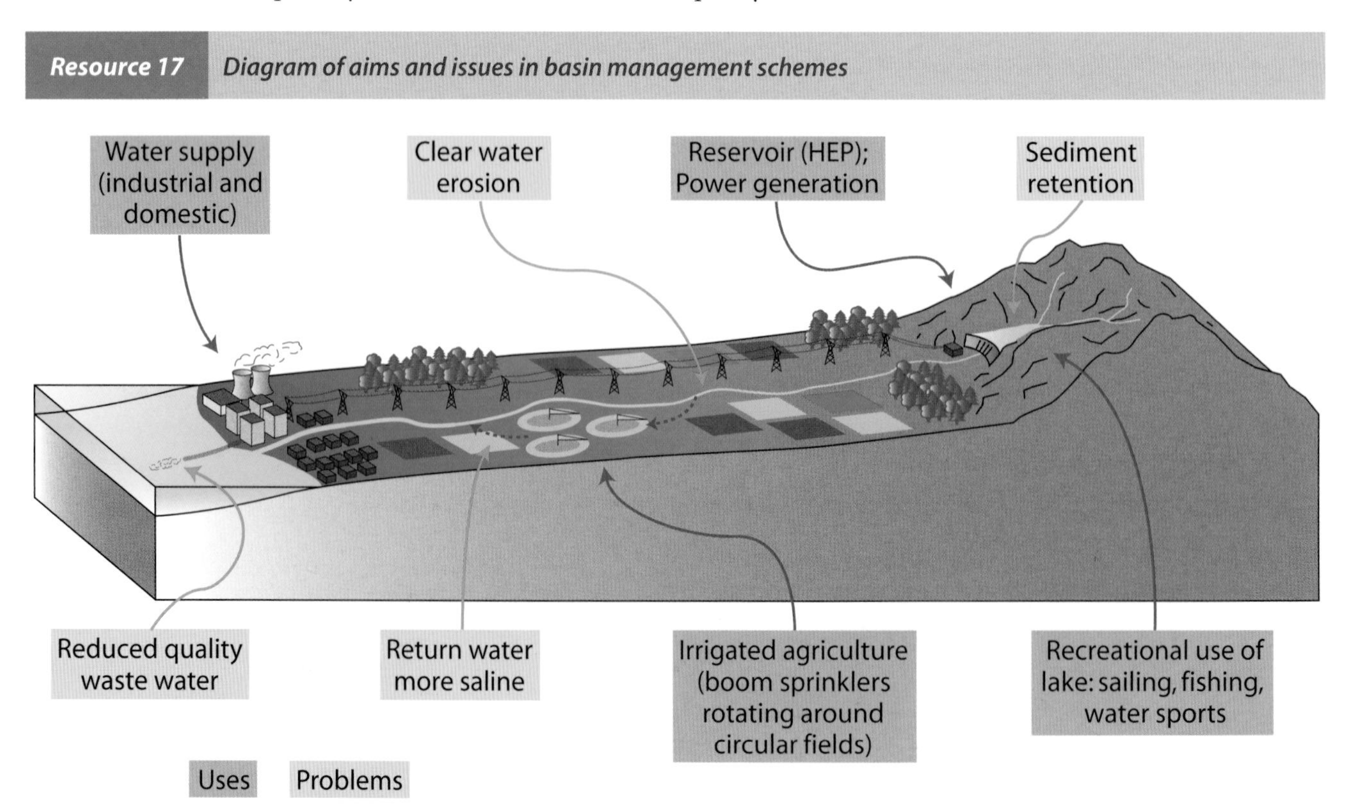

3. Power generation

As an environmentally friendly source of electricity, using well proven technology, Hydro-Electric Power (HEP) is both valuable and can offset the huge capital costs of dam building. The High Aswan Dam, primarily designed for flood control, also supplies almost 50% of Egypt's electricity needs.

4. Navigation and transport

Dams themselves may act as barriers to navigation but downstream they can reduce discharge variation to allow reliable transport to take place. Numerous dams on tributaries of the Mississippi allow the main river to be the single most important freight transport route in the USA.

At times these aims may not be compatible. For example, HEP requires reservoirs to be maintained at high (bankfull) levels, which allows little or no additional storage capacity during flood episodes.

Strategies of basin management

As noted, the construction of dams and the consequent creation of storage reservoirs is the most common strategy in basin management schemes. In some cases a single large dam and reservoir are employed, such as the Akosombo HEP Dam on the River Volta in Ghana. Elsewhere a series of smaller dams is preferred, including the Mississippi-Missouri basin in the USA. Many secondary management strategies may be employed. Canals and pumping stations carry water from reservoirs and river channels to urban and farming areas in remote parts of the basin or even into other river catchments (inter-basin transfer). All of the channelisation methods described earlier can be employed to modify flows and deal with discharge variation in river basin schemes.

Modern river basin management dates from the early decades of the twentieth century. The USA in the developed world, and India in the developing world pioneered the management of large-scale river basin projects such as the Tennessee Valley Authority (TVA) in 1934 and Damodar Valley Corporation (DVC) in 1948.

River basin management

Beneficial outcomes, conflicts of interest and interdependence between places

River basin management is demanding in financial and resource terms, therefore the outcomes need to be positive and significant in nature. Wealth generation and resource development are the benefits of such management schemes, with industries using the ready supply of cheap energy and the agriculture output increasing from land unusable without irrigation water. Interest groups will inevitably clash over their demands. Domestic, industrial and agricultural users are likely to argue over water costs and the quality of the supply. Increasingly, ecologists and environmentalists have taken issue with engineers and bureaucrats over the methods employed in water control and distribution. River systems link areas within their basins and consequently modification of any one variable has significant impacts both physically and politically elsewhere. Often basins cross internal and international borders, in which jurisdiction varies and relationships may be strained. The headwaters of the River Indus, that supply water to Pakistan's irrigation dependent farmland, lie in India. The two nations have a history of conflict from their creation over 60 years ago. Rivers themselves are complex, interacting systems of water and sediment flows. They use their energy to erode, transport and deposit alluvial material, creating and modifying an array of physical features and ecological environments. Any engineering strategy designed to modify flows must inevitably cascade impacts down and throughout the system.

A REGIONAL SCALE CASE STUDY: the Colorado River basin

Rising in the snow covered peaks of the Rockies and reaching the sea in the Sea of Cortez (Gulf of California), Mexico, after passing through the arid desert of Arizona, the Colorado River flows over 2,300 km, draining seven states of the South-West USA.

Resource 18 *Colorado Fact Box*

Area of Drainage basin – 632,000 km^2 (Double the land area of Ireland and the UK together)

Length of main channel – 2,304 km (Almost twice as long as the River Rhine in Europe)

Highest point – 4,200 m (Three times the height of Ben Nevis, the highest point in the British Isles)

Mean annual discharge – between 13.5 and 18.5 km^3 (Varying from 4.9 km^3 (1917) to 21.4 km^3 (1977))

Channel network – A total of 35 permanent river channels and numerous ephemeral streams.

States drained – USA (Upper basin) – Wyoming, Colorado and Utah
USA (Lower basin) – Nevada, Arizona, New Mexico and California
Mexico – Sonora and Baja California

Main tributaries – (Upper basin) Green, Gunnison, Yampa and San Juan River
(Lower basin) Little Colorado, Salt and Gila Rivers

In its natural state the Colorado was a wild and unpredictable system with over 70% of its flow confined to three months each year (May–July), resulting from the spring snow-melt released from the mountains at its source. Much of the basin is arid, receiving less than 25 mm of rainfall annually, due to the extreme rain shadow effect of the mountains of the Sierra Nevada. The southern part of the basin is hot, with daytime temperatures over 40°C, which can cause evaporation of 95% of rainfall. Apart from the seasonal spring floods, violent summer thunderstorms cause flash floods along sections of the river (**Resource 19**). Along 1,600 km of its course in the Upper Colorado Basin, the river passes through a series of deep canyons and gorges, including the most famous of all, the Grand Canyon. In the Lower basin, the Colorado winds across the desert state of Arizona, forming its border with Nevada and then California, before crossing the Mexico–USA border at Yuma. The river completes its journey a further 145 km south, in the Gulf of California, an inlet of the Pacific Ocean. The Colorado, from the Spanish word meaning 'ruddy', was named after its distinctive colouring caused by the high sediment load. Much of the sediment was deposited, creating rich alluvial land near the Mexican border and a broad delta at its mouth.

The Grand Canyon

Despite this harsh environment and the unpredictability of the river, archaeological evidence shows that Native Americans, including the Hohokam, had used the river to irrigate farmland for over one thousand years between 300BC and AD1130, when a prolonged drought appears to have ended their traditional economy.

Modern attempts to use the river date back a century or so, but these early efforts proved disastrous. In 1901 the state of California began extracting water by canal from the Colorado to irrigate farmland in Imperial Valley. In flood, four years later, the Colorado broke through the poorly constructed irrigation system and over the next two years flooded into a desert depression, creating a lake 64 km long by 20 km wide, called the Salton Sea. By 1909 over $500,000

Map of Colorado River Basin **Resource 19**

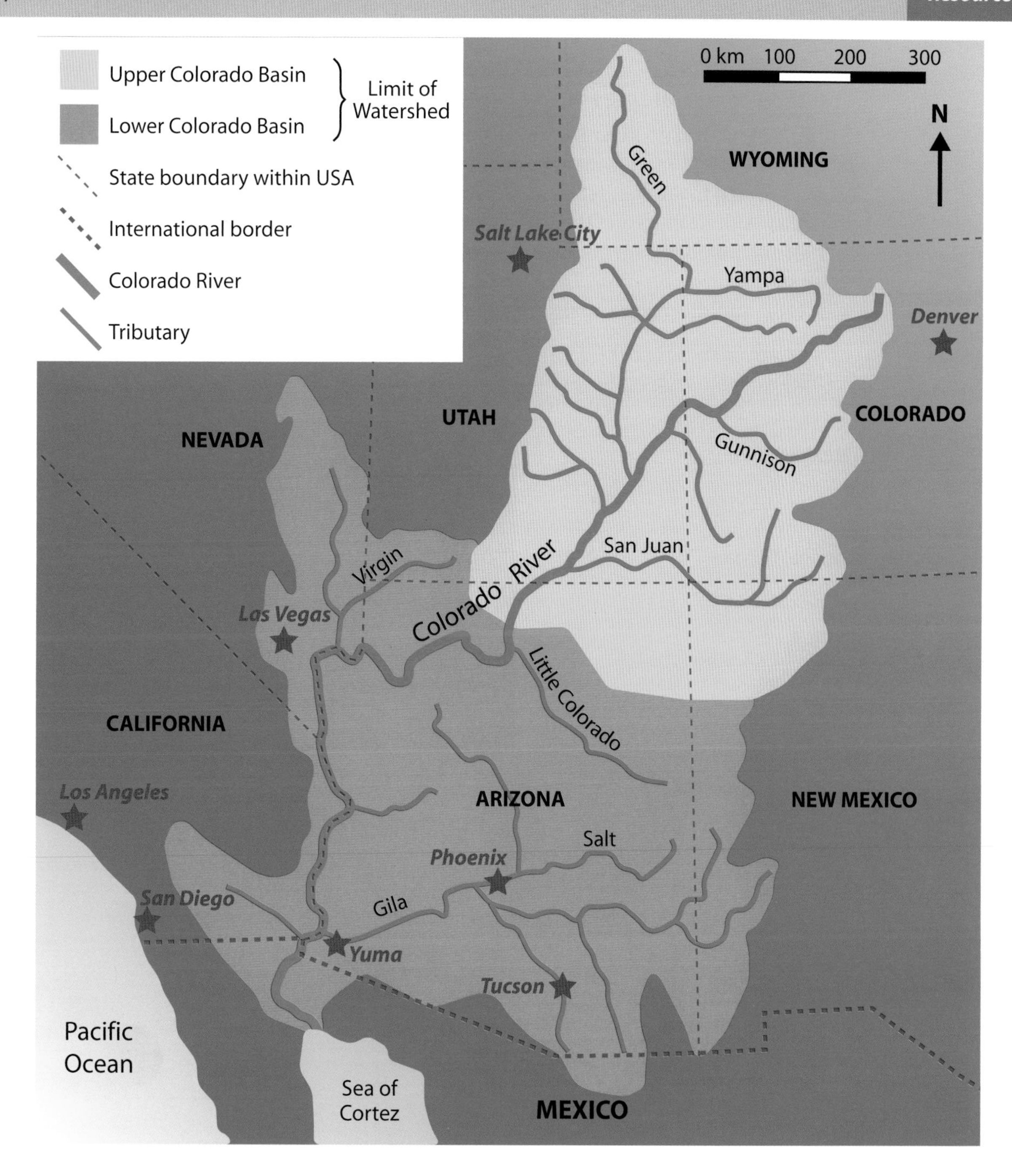

were being spent on levée construction just to prevent local flooding.

As the region's population grew, especially in California, the demand for water became increasingly important. In 1922 the first piece of legislation concerning water rights and allocation was drawn up – the Colorado River Compact. Its terms concerned the division of the river's water between the states of the Upper Basin (Wyoming, Utah and Colorado) and those of the Lower Basin (Nevada, California, Arizona and New Mexico). The final allocations involved legislation in 1948 for the Upper Basin states and as late as 1963 for the Lower Basin states. Initially, no official water allowance was made for Mexico but this was later ratified by agreement. A major problem with water allocation is that the figures used for the river's normal flow, 18.5 km^3, are certainly higher than the long-term average in the last 80 years, which is closer to 13.5 km^3. California's larger population has given it more political power over other states despite the fact that most of the river's water (83%) is gathered from the Upper

Basin states. This has led to friction over water rights and as demand issues continue to grow, especially following the drought years of 1999–2005, the potential for future inter-state conflict is clear.

The aims and strategies of the Colorado Basin Management system

The modern Colorado River is variously described as "an American Nile", "the most legislated… in the entire world" and "a giant plumbing system". Today it is the most managed system in the world. Located in a water deficient region of the USA, it supplies and exports more water than any other American basin. The first step was approved by the federal government in 1928 and by 1935 the Boulder Canyon was blocked by the Hoover Dam, designed to prevent flooding by water storage in its reservoir Lake Mead. The project rapidly became a multi-purpose scheme, with HEP and diversion canals employed for distribution of water for urban, industrial and

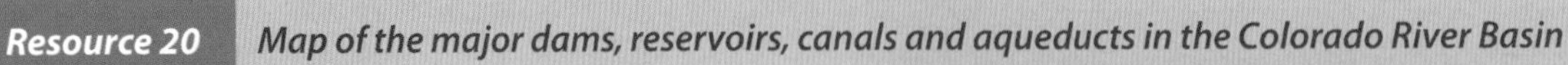
Resource 20 *Map of the major dams, reservoirs, canals and aqueducts in the Colorado River Basin*

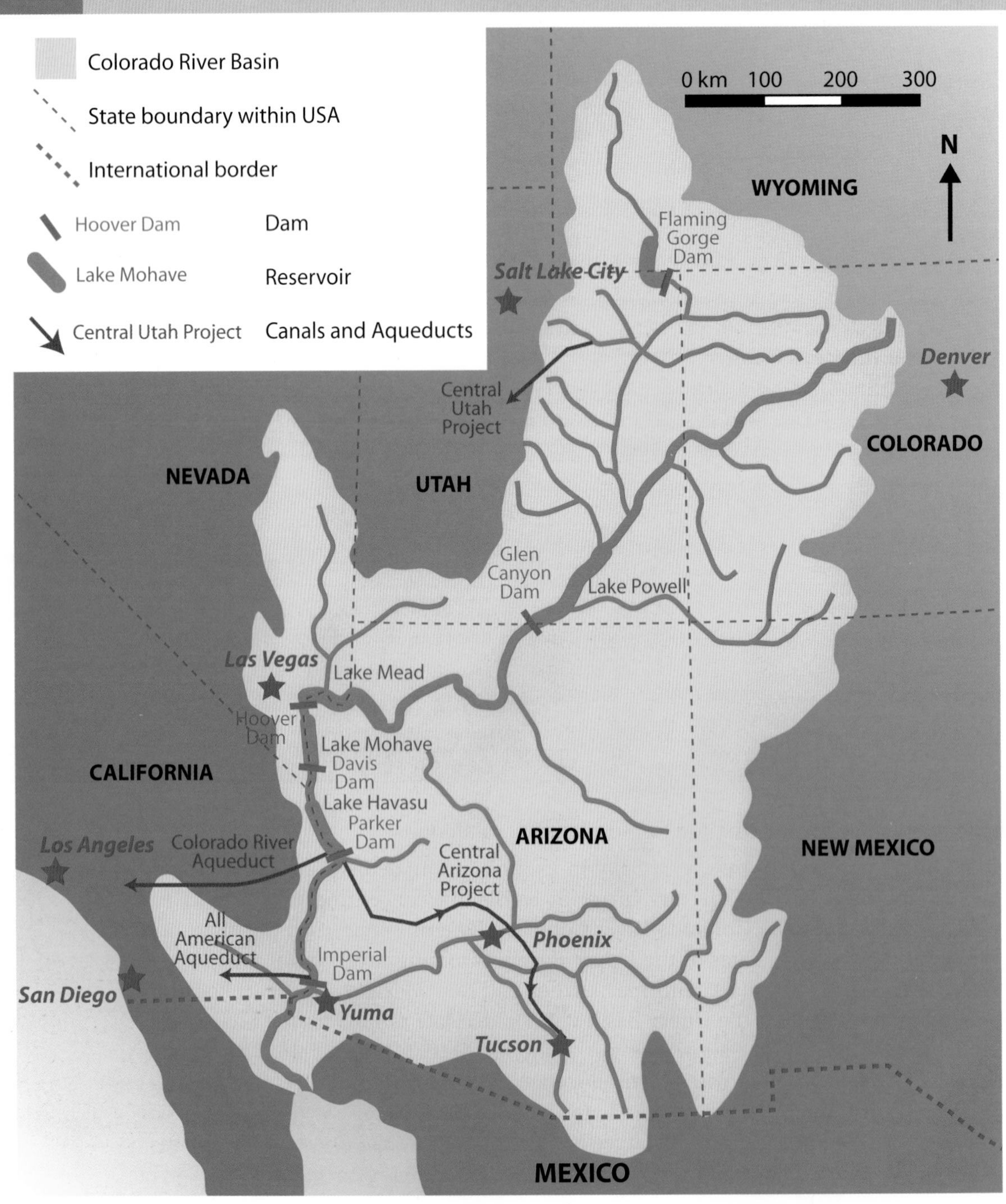

agricultural use. Other dams followed along the Colorado and its tributaries, totaling over twenty that significantly impact the river's flow. Eleven large dams are illustrated in **Resources 20** and **21**.

Dams and reservoirs are primarily concerned with the storage and control of water flow. River levels can be maintained below the dam and excess water stored during flood episodes to be later released safely downstream. The net effect of the Hoover Dam and later the Parker and Glen Canyon dams was to reduce variation of the Colorado's discharge further downstream. Other engineering elements of the system include the hydro electric power (HEP) turbines in many of the dams to provide 'green' electricity for domestic and industrial use. Seven of the dams, including those named earlier, incorporate HEP production. Reservoirs provide water for a range of uses. Water from Lake Mead is pumped west to support Las Vegas, a desert city that owes its existence to the liberal gambling laws of the state of Nevada. Lake Havasu, formed by the Parker dam, is the source of water for two major projects. The first is the Colorado River Aqueduct that takes water west over the Colorado's watershed into southern California. This, and three canals from other reservoirs – the All American, Coachella and Imperial Valley Canals – irrigate 364,000 hectares of farmland in California. This artificial addition of water to regions that have warm climates and fertile soils allows the production of valuable crops including oranges, dates, grapes, lettuce, tomatoes, alfalfa, avocados and wheat. The second scheme of water extraction from Lake Havasu is the Central Arizona project (CAP). This was a $3.6 billion plan to transport water 500 km across the Arizona desert, raising it 325 m in the process, to the cities of Phoenix and Tucson. These rapidly expanding urban centres had been using depleting groundwater sources and consequently water costs were soaring. In 1980 the two cities had a combined population of 1.1 million inhabitants, today it is 2.1 million and it is projected that they will reach 4 million by 2040.

Several other Colorado reservoirs are the source of water for long distance transfers. In the Upper basin water from the headwaters of the Colorado are diverted across the Continental Divide into the Big Thompson River by way of a 22 km long tunnel through the mountains. This water helps supply water for municipal and agricultural use as well as HEP from the rural and urban areas around the city of Denver. The Continental Divide is the name given to the principal hydrological watershed of North America that separates the river basins that drain into the Pacific Ocean (west) from those which drain into the Atlantic Ocean, including the Gulf of Mexico (east).

The Colorado system as a flow diagram **Resource 21**

Flaming Gorge
Colorado River
Fontenelle
Green River
Yampa River
Gunnison River
San Juan River
Central Utah Project
Lake Powell
Glen Canyon
Lake Mead
Nevada (Las Vegas)
Hoover
Lake Mohave
Davis
Colorado River Aqueduct (to southern California)
Lake Havasu
Central Arizona Project
Parker
Parker Valley
Headgate Rock
Palo Verde
Palo Verde Valley
Imperial
Gilla Valley
All American Canal
Coachella Canal
Morelos
Alamo Canal (Mexicall Valley)
Yuma
Imperial Valley
To Mexico and the sea

Purposes of Dam:
HEP plant
Flood control
Diversion channel
Desalination plant

Based on Doherty

Hoover Dam
Source: US Department of the Interior, Bureau of Reclamation

Resource 22 *Plan views of the Parker Valley 1968 and 1983*

1968

Part of floodplain is planned for emergency floodwater storage.

Levée built

River Colorado

Levée built

California

Arizona

Floodplain (up to 20 km wide)

1983

Areas of irrigated agriculture.

Resorts, jetties and homes built in a long strip near the river are inundated during the 1983 flood.

California

Arizona

California Orchard on irrigated land

Additional engineering schemes along the Colorado include flood protection measures. One of the principal organisations involved in the river's management is the Bureau of Reclamation. In their literature it is stated that "flood control does not mean flood prevention" but rather that downstream areas "are less likely to be flooded". An example of this can be seen in the Parker Valley south of the Parker Dam. The valley was designed to be used for irrigated agriculture but part of the floodplain was left for the storage of emergency floodwater. To facilitate this levées had been built at a distance from the river channel (**Resource 22**). The lack of flooding in the area for several decades after the dam's construction encouraged local county planners to allow the development of homes, recreational resorts and jetties along the river and on its floodplain. In 1983, during exceptional rainfall and rapid snowmelt, the storage reservoirs upstream were filled to capacity and higher than normal flows had to be released at Parker Dam. The temporary floodplain storage was then inundated and businesses lost millions of dollars in damage and lost revenue. Enquiries after the event suggested that engineers managing the network had retained high water levels in reservoirs upstream to maintain HEP production and supplies for the Central Arizona Project, underestimating the storage needs to cope with the flood surge.

Exercise

From the material provided:

1. Identify examples of the following engineering schemes on the Colorado:

   Dam and reservoir *Canal or aqueduct* *Floodplain levées*

2. Identify and outline with examples four aims of the Colorado management system.

The Colorado River: the impacts of basin management processes

Benefits

The obvious benefits are those that match the aims of the strategies employed, namely, flood control, hydro-electricity production, irrigation, domestic and industrial water supply. Other benefits have been identified during the expansion of the scheme and the growth of population in the region, such as recreation and tourism.

Flood control

It was estimated that in any one year, damage costs of up to $85 million are avoided by flood prevention. River discharge levels at the location of the Hoover Dam totaled 17–20km^3 annually before the dam but are now around 10–12 km^3. With careful management, including draining down of reservoirs before spring snow-melt, there is no reason why even the small flood event in 1983 cannot be prevented.

Hydro-electric power generation

Over 50 power plants now exist along the river, many associated with the largest dams. They generate over 4,000 megawatts of electricity, valued at around $21 million a year. The 17 HEP turbines at Hoover Dam alone could supply the electrical needs for a city of 750,000 people, roughly equivalent to the Belfast Urban Area. In energy terms this effectively saves the use of six million barrels of oil each year. HEP was initially seen as a secondary benefit, helping to offset the capital and running costs of the dams but it is now regarded as a central purpose. At several dams much of the power is used to lift water along aqueducts to supply regions outside the basin. At Parker Dam water is lifted over 1,000 m to supply municipal needs to the coastal Californian city of San Diego, via the Colorado Aqueduct.

Irrigation

Around 1.5 million hectares of land are supplied with irrigation water from the Colorado. This is by far the largest use of the river's water (**Resource 23**). Farmers have benefited most from the billions of dollars invested since the 1920s in Colorado River projects. Estimates put the annual value of agribusiness at $5 billion. It is also claimed that the water supplied is heavily subsidised by tax payers across the nation and that much of the agricultural production is either unnecessary or costs more than it earns. The most common product is alfalfa, a fodder crop used for cattle. However, nearly half the crops produced are already overproduced in other, non-irrigated regions of the USA. In short, irrigation water may benefit the region's farmers but not the nation as a whole.

State water use from the Colorado **Resource 23**

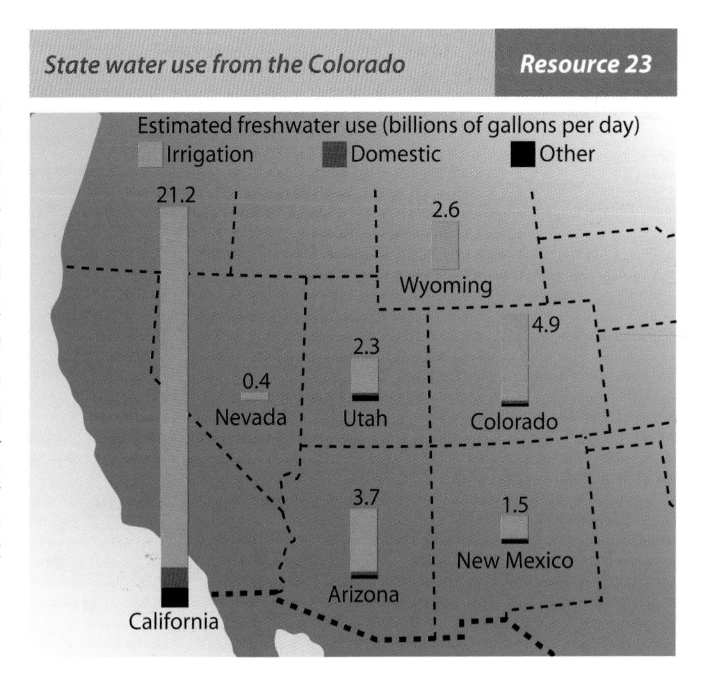

Urban/domestic water supplies

There is little doubt that the availability of water from the Colorado has facilitated the enormous growth of cities in the sout-west USA. Most of this growth is by migration to the sun-belt states of Nevada, Arizona and New Mexico from the traditional north-east cities, including Detroit and Chicago. Indeed, one popular bumper sticker in Chicago during the 1990s read, "Last one to leave Michigan switch off the light". From San Diego to Denver and from Salt Lake City to Tucson dozens of towns and cities have expanded rapidly in the last 60 years. Today water from the Colorado supplies the homes of over 24 million people. Even in the hottest desert cities water is now available for maintaining lawns, outdoor swimming pools and evaporative home cooling systems.

Industrial water supply

Water and electricity supplies have encouraged mining and heavy industry in the region, including Arizona's copper industry and the aluminium, borax and tungsten industries of California.

Sediment control

The high sediment carried by Colorado water had made it unsuitable for domestic use in the past. Dams help trap sediment, reducing the river's load and allowing clean water to be easily extracted.

Recreation and tourism

Lakes Powell, Mead and Havasu provide recreational opportunities for millions of tourists each year. Water based activities, such as boating and water skiing, as well as the dams themselves, attract tourist dollars. Each year 700,000 visitors are recorded at the Hoover Dam centre, with eight million using the six marinas around Lake Mead. The relocation of London Bridge to Lake Havasu in 1971 helped make it a popular attraction. Rafting and boating along the Colorado is now a more accessible, reliable and safer activity as water level is closely monitored. It is estimated that the tourism income is now ten times greater than the value of HEP.

Wildlife

The huge reservoirs have become both a home to resident birds, and a resting place for migrating species. Snow goose, blue heron and pintails are among 250 bird species recorded at the Lake Mead National Recreation Area.

Conflicts

It is of no surprise that, given the scale and range of the Colorado scheme, conflicts of interest have emerged. Some involve the demands of different groups for the water itself; others concern the impacts of the scheme on water quality, river processes, the natural landscape and the ecology of the basin.

Water politics: Inter-state, international and ethnic

In regions of water shortage, the rights and allocation of water frequently cause conflict, in the worse scenarios wars may ensue. In the case of the Colorado, friction has existed between the Upper and Lower basin states. Due to an overestimate of the river's discharge and California's large allocation under the initial Colorado Compact Agreement (1922), numerous legal battles have been fought. Perhaps more significant is the potential conflict between the USA and its southern neighbour Mexico. By 1992 the Lower basin states were using their full water allocation but the quality of water crossing the Mexican border made it unsuitable for use as irrigation water in the farmland area of the Mexicali valley. This was the result of salinisation. Water with a natural salt content of perhaps 200 parts per million presents no problem for plant growth. However, high rates of evaporation in desert regions causes water to increase its salt content, often to a level that is toxic to plant growth. The use and re-use of Colorado water for irrigation along the river increases its salinity. Between 1900 and 1990 the water crossing into Mexico went from a salt content of 400 to over 800 parts per million, a level at which crop yields can be impacted. While the USA was honouring an agreement in terms of the water quantity (1.85 billion m^3) that should cross the border, the water quality became an issue. In some years the salinity has reached 3,000 parts per million, a level likely to render soil unusable in the long-term. Around 20% of the land in the Mexicali Valley had to be abandoned. The US government agreed to build and run a desalinisation plant at Yuma, near the border, to improve the water quality. The plant completed in 1992 cost $280 million in capital costs and $20 million a year to run. Unfortunately, it worked for only nine months and did not work again until 2007, when the long drought forced the US government to make it operational. It is not currently in use. Salinisation is an increasing problem across the whole region, and plans to reline canals to prevent water seepage and to increase the use of drip and sprinkler systems of irrigation, which are less likely to cause salinisation, have been introduced in southern California. Mexican farmers fear that lining the All American Canal will prevent water seepage, which helps to recharge their groundwater supply used in local irrigation. To add insult to injury, the 1983 US management failure that flooded the Parker Valley also forced Mexican farmers off their land by destroying 25,000 hectares of farmland in the process.

Native American tribes claim rights to Colorado water based on their prior use. This was not recognised by the 1992 Colorado Compact and tribes such as the Chemuevi were forced to relocate when the Parker Dam flooded their tribal lands. The federal government now acts on the Native Americans behalf to protect their rights.

Conservationists and Ecologists

Many environmental groups find themselves in conflict both with the planners and users of the Colorado scheme. On the physical level the conversion of the river from a wild natural element to a regulated and administered regime has caused many changes in the processes and landforms of the basin.

Conservationists argue that the equilibrium of the river has been undermined. One issue concerns the movement of sediment. The deeply dissected canyons of the Upper Basin, such as Bryce, Zion and Grand Canyons, which are up to 4,000 m deep, were formed by the erosion and removal of the bedrock as alluvial sediment. The large dams along the river trap this sediment, which threatens their effectiveness as the reservoirs silt up, reducing their storage capacity and necessitating expensive dredging and dumping. More significantly for environmentalists, the water released from reservoirs through dams no longer carries sediment and is therefore able to use its energy to erode and transport the bed and banks of the channel downstream. This is termed 'clearwater erosion' and has led to the destruction of natural sand bars and beaches along the river. Alternatively, river discharge below dams is often lower than the natural pattern and under these conditions it is deposition of silt that can alter downstream habitats. These riparian environments had provided niches for vegetation and aquatic life that can no longer be supported. Native fish species, including the humpback chub, have been driven out of the river while other non-native species, such as the rainbow and brown trout, thrive. In recent years engineers have experimented with varying the discharge from dams to help recreate a more natural downstream environment (**Resource 24**).

Controlled flooding at Glen Canyon dam — ***Resource 24***

For one spring week in 1996, engineers released the maximum possible discharge from the Glen Canyon dam. While this represented only half the potential natural flood it was much higher than the normal flow rate. The seven day flood swept away areas of unwanted vegetation, created 55 new beaches and extended others over a 100 km stretch downstream. Marshes and backwaters were rejuvenated, which helped endangered native fish species but the hope than alien species, such as carp and striped bass, might be removed was not realised. The success of the scheme was limited as many of the new beaches were eroded by subsequent snowmelt flows.

A second major issue for conservationists concerns the Colorado Delta in Mexico. For most of the last 50 years, little or no water has actually reached the sea at the Gulf of California. The use and reuse of water along the river has ended, in all but years of high flood, the flow of sediment and water to the delta. Physically the delta area is being eroded by the sea and its soils are increasingly saline. The Colorado Delta had been described as one of the most diverse and abundant environments on the continent. Egrets, jaguars, beavers, deer and marine species including porpoises were native to the region. By the end of the twentieth century only 5% of the original delta wetlands remained and non-native vegetation had replaced the original species over most of the region. Many species of bird, land and marine animals were locally extinct or added to the endangered lists. Ironically, it was the failure of the Yuma desalinisation plant that helped one region of the delta to be restored. Water that the plant was designed to treat was temporarily allowed to flow across the US/Mexico border onto what had been part of the delta region. Vegetation responded and wildlife began to be re-established. The fear is that when the desalinisation plant is recommissioned, the wetland delta will again lose its vital water supply.

The flooding of large tracts of the Colorado's valley under the numerous reservoirs not only forced tribal groups to relocate and destroyed riparian ecosystems. It also drowned many natural features, some of which were sacred to Native American groups. Lake Powell, behind Glen Canyon Dam, covered the Cathedral of the Desert and threatens natural bridges including Rainbow Arch, a site associated with the Navajo Indians. The 'High Sierra Club' is a group of environmentalists who hope to maintain the wilderness status of regions such as the Colorado Basin. They have successfully blocked some Colorado water developments using court battles and referendums.

Economists and Farmers

As **Resource 23** suggests, agriculture is the principal benefactor of the Colorado system, but economists suggest that Cost-Benefit Analysis shows that the scheme is unsustainable. State and federal subsidies amount to over 80% of the costs of water projects, totaling around $1 billion annually. In some irrigation areas farmers were paying $3 to $4 for each acre foot of water* which actually cost $300 to supply.

*An acre foot is the equivalent to an acre of land covered one foot deep in water or 1,230 m³. One acre foot of water would supply the needs of an average urban family in the USA for one year.

In one scheme, where over $100 million was invested, it was shown that fewer than 100 farmers directly benefited from the project. It is also true that many of the crops grown are wasteful of water and most are actually overproduced elsewhere in the USA. In 1987 new legislation demanded that in any further schemes farmers must pay for the water and the relevant state cover half the cost of the project. Drought periods and reduced allocations in California have encouraged the use of more efficient water practice and conservation. Improved technology in irrigation can help avoid environmental issues such as salinisation and through tax incentives it is possible that a more sustainable pattern of use can be made of the Colorado's precious water resource.

Interdependence between places

River basins by their very nature link places. In the case of the Colorado, it links the wet but cold regions of the high Rockies of Colorado and Wyoming with the arid hot deserts of Arizona and New Mexico, and the mountain ecosystems of the Grand Canyon with the wetlands of the Colorado Delta. By controlling the river's discharge from source to mouth throughout the year, its natural rhythm and processes have been replaced by artificial flows and storage. Huge amounts of water are lost through seepage below reservoirs and canals as well as by evaporation. As noted, sediment stores and flows are changed with impacts on river processes and land features. The Colorado scheme has pushed interdependence beyond its own natural boundary – the watershed. Many of the diversion schemes carry water on inter-basin transfers into California, Utah, Colorado and even beyond the Great Divide. This means that these areas become dependent on artificial supplies of water, which in drought years the Colorado may be unable to supply. One answer to this issue has come from the water engineers themselves. They suggest an even larger scale of transfer from basins in Canada and Alaska, a scheme known as the North American Water and Power Alliance (NAWAPA). Currently unlikely to be developed, such a scheme would take interdependency to another level in the west of North America.

One example of an inter-basin transfer from the Colorado is the Central Utah Project (CUP). Started in 1967 and only recently completed, this scheme involves constructing ten new reservoirs and over 300 km of aqueducts and tunnels to transfer water from the Colorado's headwater streams to irrigate over 80,000 hectares of new farmland around Lake Utah, south of Salt Lake City. The land will grow fodder crops for cattle ranching.

The interdependent nature of the Colorado is not reflected in its management. Despite the demands for an integrated approach, a holistic planning and engineering system has not been developed. This is partly because seven states and two nations make various demands of the river and within the USA the central federal government attempts to balance impacts. The Bureau of Reclamation is not the only organisation involved in water management of the region. The US Army Corp of Engineers and the National Water Commission are also active. The latter was created in 1968, in an attempt to coordinate the use of the Colorado and reconcile its exploitation with conservation.

Exercise

From the material on the Colorado management system, identify examples of interdependence between:

- The southwest USA and the northeast USA.
- Dam construction and urban growth in Arizona.
- Sedimentation in dams and wildlife in the Colorado Delta.

Exercise

1. ***Question from CCEA May 2009***
   With reference to places for illustration, describe the ways in which river and valley zones are subject to a range of demands. (8)

2. (i) Explain how channelisation of a river may cause increased:
   - stream velocity;
   - channel gradient;
   - channel capacity. (6)

   (ii) Explain why these impacts are useful in reducing flood risk. (4)

   (iii) Study the photograph below which shows a channelised stretch of the Connswater River, East Belfast. Suggest how channelisation may have disrupted habitats within the river channel. (4)

3. With reference to a regional scale case study of a river basin system:

   (i) describe the management strategies used; and (5)

   (ii) discuss and evaluate the following statement in relation to your case study:
   "The beneficial outcomes of the scheme outweigh the conflicts of interest that it created." (10)

4. With reference to a regional scale case study of river basin management:

   (i) describe the reasons why river management was required; (5)

   (ii) discuss the physical and human impacts of the scheme. (12)

A3 COASTAL PROCESSES, FEATURES AND MANAGEMENT

While the term 'coastal zone' is generally understood it is hard to define. It is where the land meets the sea but, despite decades of debate, its offshore and landward boundaries are difficult to determine. What is agreed is that the coast represents a dynamic, ever changing environment, in which the features and processes of the land meet the vibrant fluid dynamics of the sea. At any one point in time the landforms created along this distinctive boundary represent a dynamic equilibrium between the nature of the land, the forces of the sea and human activity. At a simple level it can be said that the land provides the material for coasts; rock and sediment, while the sea provides the energy to form and shape these materials. The coast then is composed of features of erosion, such as cliffs, and/or features of deposition, such as beaches and dunes.

The energy from the sea

Waves, tides, currents and changing sea-level provide the flows and forces to modify and alter the shore. Coastal environments vary greatly over time and space. Twice daily tides, generated by the gravitation of the moon and sun, sweep across the coastal zone, constantly altering the point at which waves arrive. The coast of Western Europe has some of the highest tidal ranges in the world, meaning that, at low tide, huge stretches of land may be exposed, only to be covered again in a few hours. Waves are created by wind blowing over water and they transfer energy across the oceans until they reach land. Waves vary in their nature and impact. Steep, plunging waves may cause severe erosion of the coastline, while shallower but powerful surging waves may carry sediment onshore.

The nature of waves

Sea waves are generated by the friction of winds blowing over the open sea. The power of a wave reflects the speed of the wind and the time and distance (**fetch**) over which it blows. This is why waves on the west coast of Ireland tend to be powerful, as they can be generated across the width of the Atlantic Ocean. Waves in deep water merely transfer energy; think of sending a wave shape along a piece of rope you are holding. When waves enter shallower water near the coast an important change takes place. Friction with the seabed slows the base of the wave until it breaks, throwing water forward onto the shore – the **swash**. The same water then runs back down the shore – the **backwash**. The relative power of the swash and backwash will determine if each wave deposits or erodes material from the shore. The precise nature of a wave or wave train (as a group is called), varies according to variables of the wind and shoreline. In European winters storms often form high energy plunging waves, termed **destructive waves**, which commonly remove material from the shore making beaches steeper. In summer gentler winds create low energy waves that push material onshore adding to beaches. These are termed **constructive waves**.

An important relationship with coastlines is the direction from which waves approach. At first it would appear that this will be determined by wind direction. For example, to the west of Ireland the most persistent winds are from the south west so waves will commonly come from this direction. However, as waves approach the land and shallower water, the shape of the seabed will alter their form and, as they slow down, they often become increasingly parallel to the shape of the coastline. This is known as wave refraction (**Resources 25** and **26**).

Wave refraction concentrating energy onto headlands **Resource 25**

A wave front turning to parallel the shore **Resource 26**

Long Shore Drift **Resource 27**

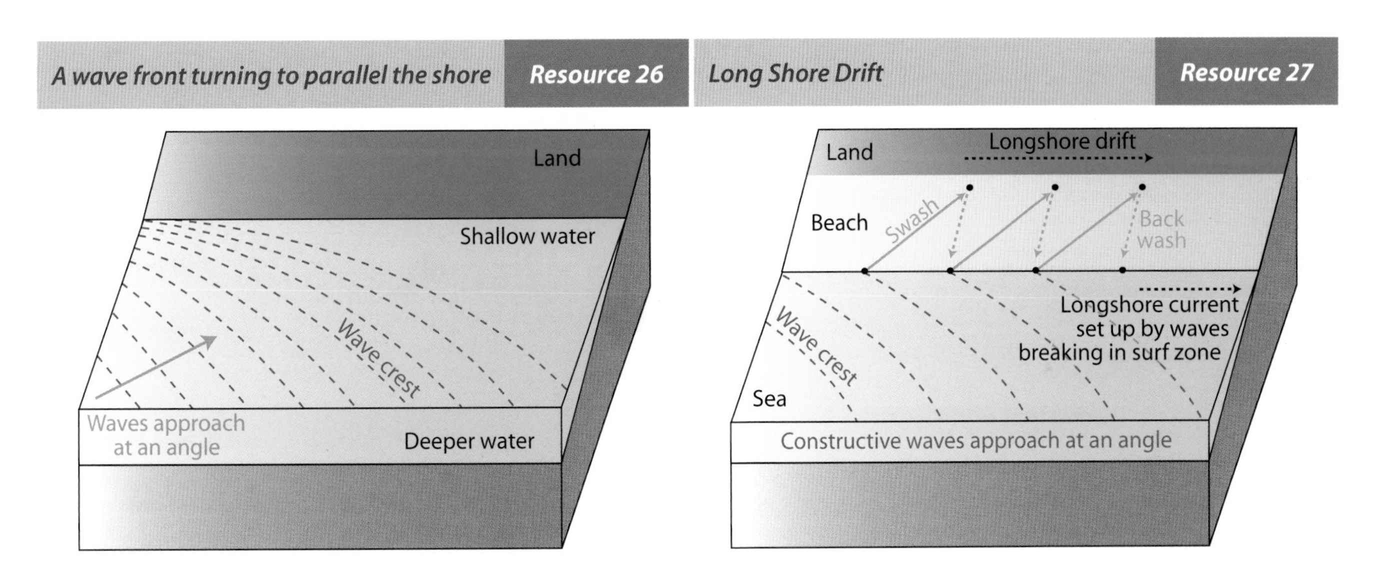

Despite refraction, waves often reach the coast at an angle to the shore. In these cases the swash will break at an angle, and on a beach they will carry water and sediment up the beach at the same angle. The backwash, under gravity, will run directly down the beach to the sea. This sets in place a process known as **long shore drift** (LSD), by which material, such as sand, is moved along the coastline in a zigzag or saw tooth manner (**Resource 27).**

Sea-level changes

Another complication to the story of coasts is the reality that the level of the sea in relation to the land is not a constant. On a global scale, world sea level is rising as a consequence of a warming climate but in the past a series of ice ages has meant ocean levels have changed repeatedly. Such worldwide sea level adjustments are termed **eustatic** change. However, not all sea level change is worldwide. On a local scale, vertical change in land height does occur. One example is **isostatic change**. Land under deep ice, such as Greenland today, or Northern Europe at the height of the last ice age, will be depressed down under the sheer weight of the ice pack. When this burden is removed, the ice melts and the land will slowly rise upwards. The north coast of Northern Ireland is still slowly recovering and as a result former beaches, cliff lines, caves and other coastal features can now be seen high and dry above modern sea levels around the Antrim coast (**Resource 28**).

Resource 28 *Former cliffs, raised beaches and arches in Northern Ireland*

Red Arch, a natural raised sea arch. Red Bay, County Antrim.

Raised beach, fossil cliff and caves, Ballintoy Harbour, County Antrim.

Raised beach and cliff line between White Park Bay and Ballintoy Harbour, County Antrim.

Fossil stack near Ballintoy, County Antrim.

Elsewhere in Northern Ireland the consequence of rising sea levels in the past can still be observed. In the shallow sea inlet of Strangford Lough the numerous islands and pladdies (shallows exposed at low tide) are the result of the sea drowning the rolling drumlin hills of that part of County Down (**Resource 29**).

Resource 29 *Islands and pladdies along the western shore of Strangford Lough, County Down.*

The nature of the land

The geology of the coastline is a key factor in determining the outcome of the interaction between land and sea. At its simplest, rocks may be classified as those that are easily eroded and those that resist erosion. Often it is the arrangements of the rocks that guides the coastline that is formed. Alternating bands of hard and softer rock running at right angles to the shore can form a headlands and bay topography over time.

Differential erosion rates will also be associated with existing weaknesses in geology, such as fault lines or the existence of river or glacier valleys. The distinctive indented coastline of southwest Ireland, Western Scotland and Western Norway are all the consequence of the sea invading and eroding valleys that were created by glaciers (**Resource 31**).

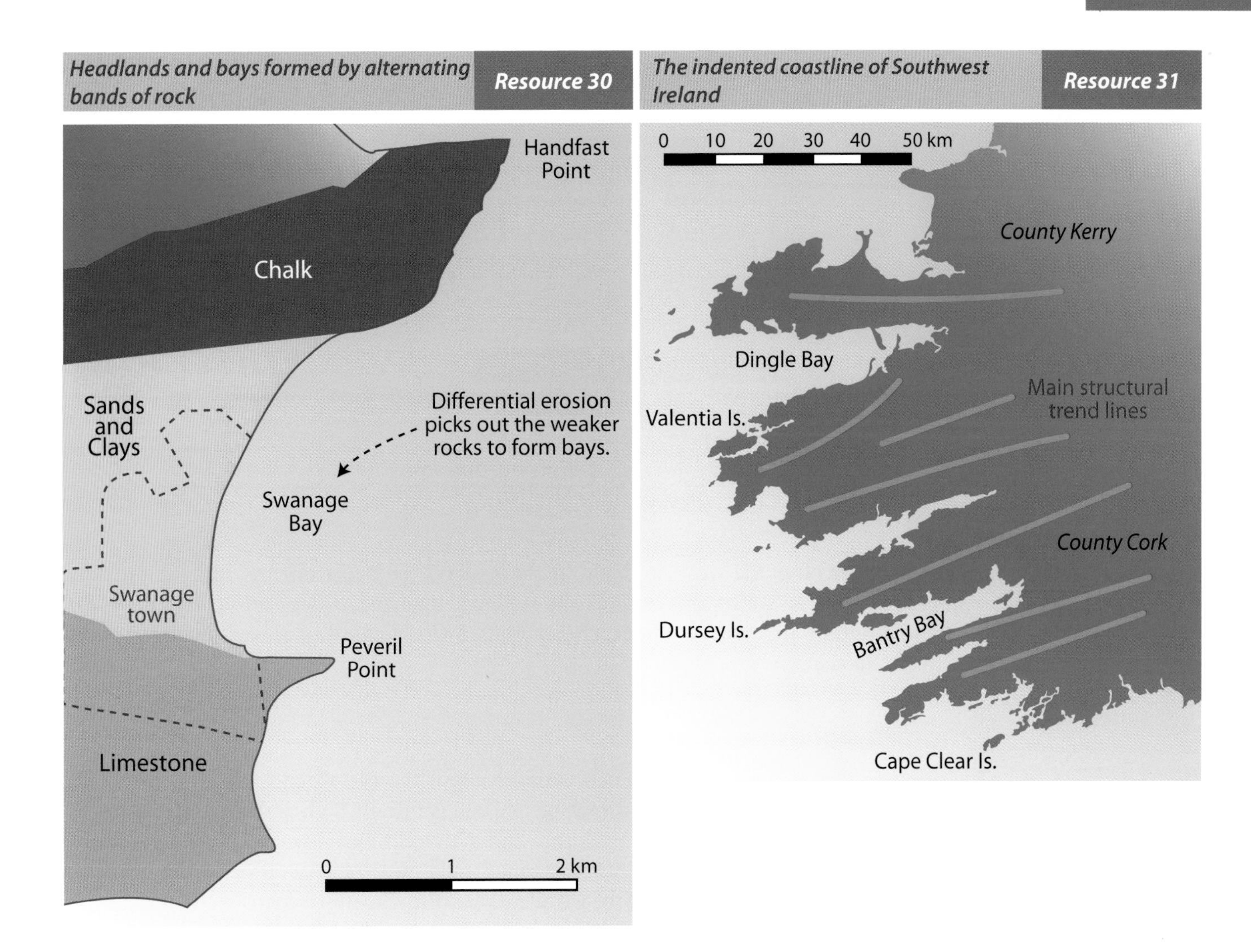

The processes of erosion

Both the sea and the atmosphere are at work on the coast to breakdown the rocks that form the shore. The sub-aerial processes of weathering – mechanical, biological and chemical – will all operate here. On rock faces freeze-thaw weathering will cause rocks to fall to the foot of cliffs; plant roots and wildlife can widen cracks and weaknesses in rocks; and the dissolving of calcium carbonate by rainfall will continue in limestone deposits. The coast has some special forms of mechanical and biological weathering processes. The abundance of sodium and magnesium compounds at the coasts produces salt weathering. As these compounds crystallize out and expand in the cracks and joints of the rocks they widen these lines of weakness. The repeated wetting and drying of rocks by the advance and retreat of tides produces water-layer weathering. Marine organisms such as mollusks, sea urchins, sponges and boring worms biologically attack rock surfaces along the shore. Waves use their chemistry and energy to erode coastlines in four specific processes: hydraulic action, abrasion, solution and attrition.

- **Hydraulic action** occurs when the air in cracks in the rocks is compressed by the force of breaking waves. As the wave subsides this air expands again and these pressure changes can open the joints and weaken the rock. The sheer weight of waves hitting rocks can send shock waves of 30 tonnes per m^3 through the cliff. This is known as **wave pounding**.
- **Abrasion** is a highly effective form of erosion along exposed coastlines. Waves throw sediment, including sand, gravel and boulders, against the base of cliffs, wearing them back. Abrasion and Hydraulic action are both concentrated between the high and low tide marks.
- **Solution** results from salts and acids in the seawater attacking the chemistry of rocks. It is particularly effective on lime-rich strata.

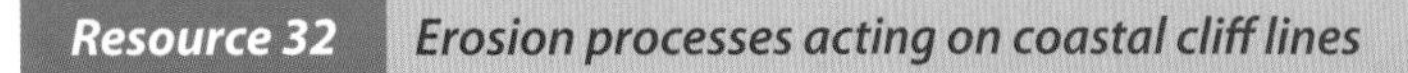

Resource 32 *Erosion processes acting on coastal cliff lines*

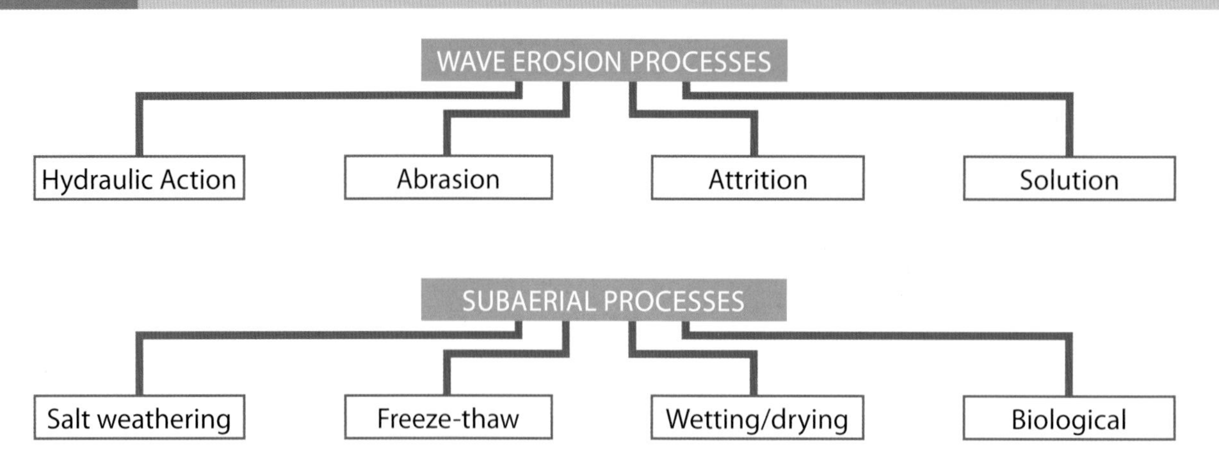

- **Attrition** involves the wearing down of the material eroded from the cliffs. It provides the tools used in abrasion as well as the sediment that forms depositional features. The rapid rounding and polishing of beach materials, including broken glass, is evidence of the effectiveness of this process.

Landforms of erosion

The primary coastal landform associated with erosion is the cliff or cliff line. This is a break in slope between the land and sea that may be low and gentle, or high and steep. Cliffs are the outcome of sustained erosion along the shore and active cliffs are associated with retreating coasts. **Resource 33** illustrates how cliffs are formed and how they grow in size as the coastline retreats, creating the related feature of the wave-cut platform. Erosion is focused in the relatively narrow zone between high and low tide. At this point a small notch will form as material is weakened and removed. Over time this wave-cut notch will undermine the rock above and collapse will occur. The fallen material can prevent further erosion for a time along the cliff base but eventually attrition and other marine erosion processes will remove this material and erosion of the cliff base will be renewed. Gradually the cliff face retreats and the residual wave-cut platform, often covered by sediment, is widened. The rate of cliff retreat, assuming the wave energy conditions are unchanged, will slow over time as waves will have further to travel across the wave-cut platform before reaching the cliff base. Finally, sea erosion of the cliff base may

Resource 33 *Diagram and photograph of cliff and wave-cut platform formation*

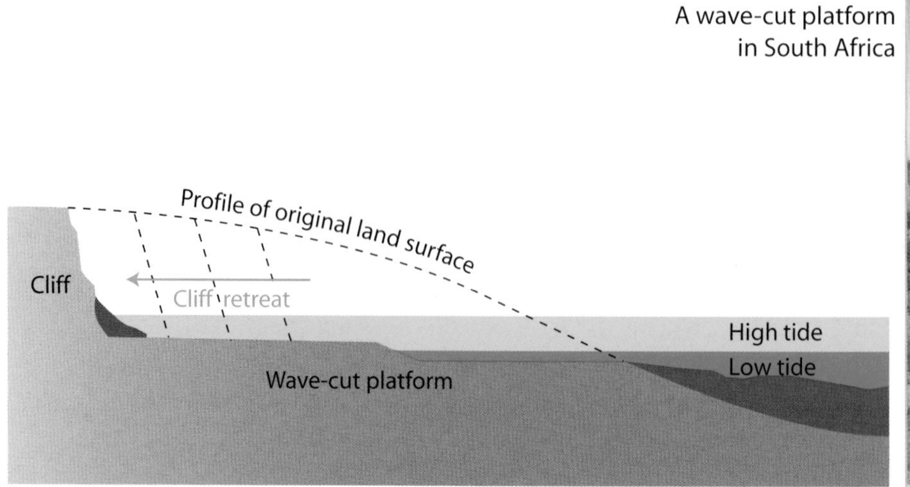

A wave-cut platform in South Africa

virtually cease and cliffs become degraded by sub-aerial processes. In the UK, cliff retreat rates of 50 cm per year are not uncommon, while the government regards rates of 100 cm or more per year as a cause for concern.

The precise cross-section shape and plan form of a cliff depends on wave energy and the nature and structure of its geology. Hard rocks that are horizontally bedded can form vertical cliffs, such as the 210 m high shale and sandstone Cliffs of Moher in western County Clare. Softer geology or rocks that dip towards the sea create more gentle profiles. The cliffs along the coast of Holderness in Eastern England are formed in unconsolidated (loose) glacial mud and are among the most rapidly retreating in the world.

Earlier in the discussion of wave refraction (**Resource 25**) it was demonstrated that wave energy can become focused onto headlands and in such settings a series of distinctive erosion landforms is often found.

Headlands, arches and stacks

The coastline of Ulster has many dramatic erosion landscapes. At Fair Head (Benmore), County Antrim, a band of hard volcanic rock known as a sill juts dramatically out into the North Channel. To the south, along the County Antrim coast, each of its famous Glens is separated by headlands and promontories, between which lie long curving bays and beaches. Many headlands show the impact of concentrated wave erosion at their base, where a wave-cut notch is evident, especially at low tide. Where there are weaknesses in the geology, faults, jointing or weaker strata, the sea will widen and open **caves**. Caves in a headland can be worn backwards, perhaps to meet a similar feature on the opposite side. Where this happens a hole through the headland leaves the upper rock spanning an **arch**. Ongoing erosion, both by waves and sub-aerial processes, will widen the arch, undermining the spanning rock until it collapses to the sea below. The remaining part of the headland is now separate from the land and often surrounded by the sea as a **stack**. Even stacks in their turn will be eroded and reduced to **stumps** of rock that only appear at low tide. **Resources 34** and **35** describe and illustrate examples of these features of coastal erosion.

Illustration of headlands, arches and stacks ***Resource 34***

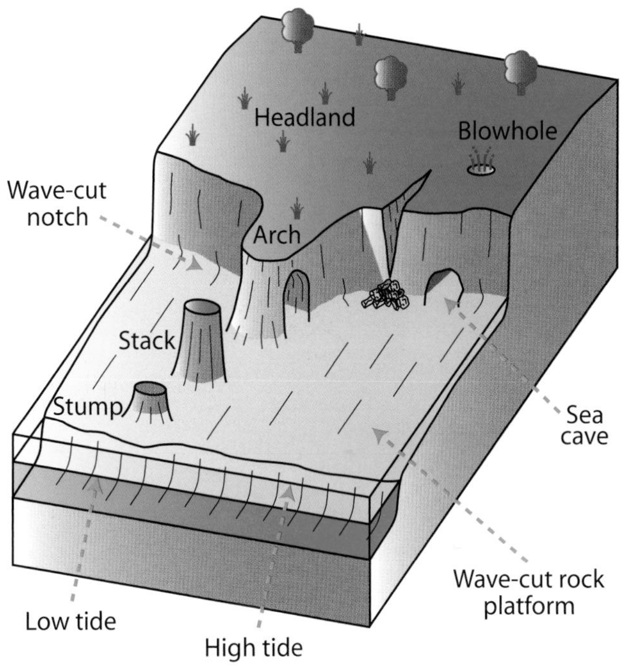

The collapse of an arch is a dramatic event and several have happened in recent decades, including the collapse of one of a double arch known as the London Bridge, in a headland in south-east Australia. Well known stacks include the Old Man of Hoy, in the Orkneys and a series of stacks off the coast of the Isle of Wight called the Needles. At White Rocks in County Antrim there are a number of caves, arches and stumps, including the Wishing Arch (**Resource 35**).

Other landforms of erosion that can be seen at coastlines include **blowholes** and **geos**. These may form in headlands or along cliffs. A blowhole, as the name might suggest, involves the blowing out of water at the top of a cliff. This is the result of the sea eroding a hole in the roof of a cave. At high tide waves sweep into the cave and force air and water out through this hole. These dramatic features can be short lived as erosion continues. A geo is a narrow, steep sided inlet that may have been a constricted cave in which the roof has collapsed.

In order to satisfy the laws of physics, it is not possible to have processes of erosion without the production of sediment. This sediment will have to be transported and deposited somewhere. While some of it is carried offshore into deeper water, much is moved along the shoreline to lower energy environments, where it is deposited forming other distinctive coastal landforms.

Resource 35 *Coastal erosion features at White Rocks and Magheracross, County Antrim.*

(Note that due to isostatic uplift in this region, some stacks, arches and stumps are raised out of the sea except at high tide.)

Landforms of deposition

Just as the features of coastal erosion are associated with areas of high energy, including wide tidal variation and powerful storm waves, so the landforms of deposition are closely associated with low energy coastal zones. Low and high energy zones are frequently close together. An offshore island can shelter a section of otherwise storm torn coast or the change in orientation along a shore, from say north to north-west, may expose the coast to the full force of an ocean wide fetch, creating surfing breakers. The earthquake induced tsunami wave of Boxing Day 2004 devastated many coastlines. However, in places shores only a few metres from destruction were virtually untouched as the shape of the land and sea bed sheltered them from the enormous waves. In short, it is possible to find erosion and deposition landforms adjacent to each other. Between most headlands bays are found, which are dominated by the most common of all deposited landforms – the bay-head beach. Clay and silt sized particles are often too light to remain on beaches so the coarser sand particles are left. Beaches can be made of a wide variety of materials, including sand, pebbles and cobbles. These particles in turn are often sorted into size either up and down the beach or along the shore (**Resource 36**).

Two forms of beach/deposition coastlines can be distinguished: the swash-aligned and the drift-aligned shore. In swash-aligned environments the prevailing wind, and thus wave

The variation of materials on the beach near Newcastle, County Down **Resource 36**

direction, acts at right angles to the shore, whereas in drift angled environments the wind and wave fronts arrive at an angle to the shore, driving water and sediment along the beach (**Resource 37**).

Swash-aligned environments

In swash-aligned environments the swash and backwash of waves move material up and down the beach, sorting it into different grades or sizes of materials and forming long ridges or berms across the beach. In some cases, ridges of coarser pebbles are deposited near the high tide mark, often with a cusp or saw-tooth shape along their edge. At low tide ripple marks stretch across the sandy beach and shallow ponds or runnels lie parallel to the coast. Where tidal ranges are high and the waves are pre-dominantly constructive in nature, wide and shallow sand beaches may form. These in turn can form the source area for wind blown sand to form sand dunes above the high tide mark of the beach.

Dunes

Strong onshore winds blowing across a wide stretch of beach can lift and transport fine sands onshore in a bouncing motion termed 'saltation'. Above the strand line high water mark, organic material and/or litter obstacles can trap this sand forming small foredunes. Specialist plants that are adapted to this salty, windy and arid environment thrive in this shifting sand, including seacouch and marram grasses. The complex root network of the vegetation binds these embryo dunes, allowing them to grow in height and breadth. A cover of marram creates a 'dead-zone', some 10 cm

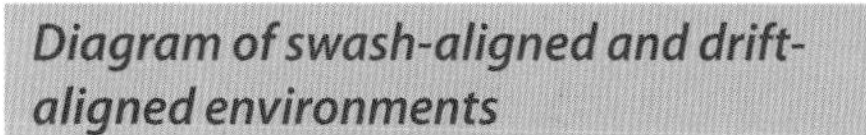
Diagram of swash-aligned and drift-aligned environments **Resource 37**

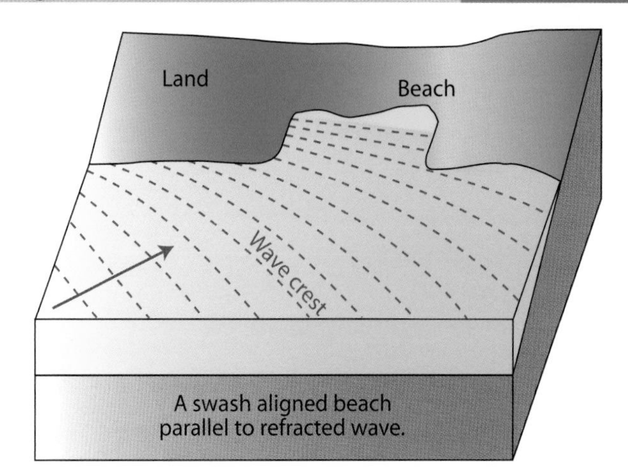

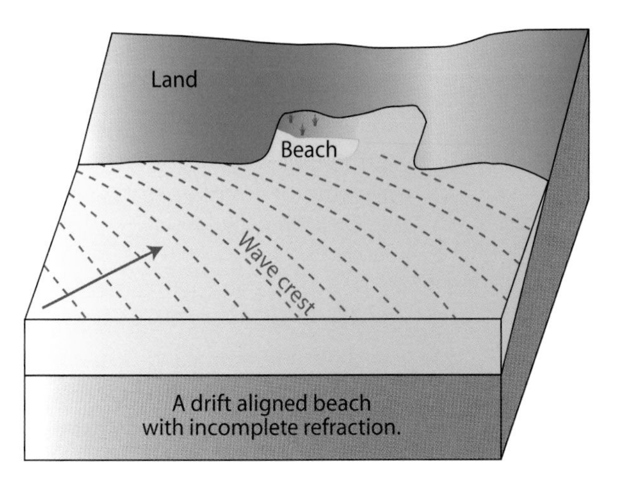

Resource 38 *Photographs of dune formation, structure and erosion at Murlough Nature Reserve, Dundrum Bay, Newcastle, County Down.*

above the dune surface, where wind falls to almost nothing and windborne sand is trapped. Over time, assuming a continuous supply of fresh sand, a successive line of dunes can develop with linear low-lying dune slacks running between them. Near the beach dunes are almost pure sand and are described as mobile yellow dunes. Inland, older fixed dunes have a wider range of vegetation and plant species, and the soil is less alkaline and arid. These are termed the grey dunes. Dunes may be 15 or even 20 m high but are very fragile features. Damage to the vegetation cover or storm waves at high tides can cause them to erode rapidly. Blow-outs are large hollows where exposed loose sand has been swept away by storm winds.

Drift-aligned environments

A drift-aligned beach is one where the prevailing onshore wind generates waves that arrive at an oblique angle and therefore carry sediment along the shore in the zigzag process mentioned earlier – longshore drift (**Resource 27**). The beach will continue to exist if there is a continuous supply of sand available, for example from an eroding cliff line or from sediment brought down to the coast by a river. If no such supply exists, the beach will gradually be depleted of sand at one end, possibly leaving only coarser pebbles or cobbles which the waves cannot remove. In this case, people often attempt to keep the sand beach in place by building barriers across the beach to trap the drifting sediment. These are called groynes and normally many are constructed, creating groyne fields.

In either case, the longshore drift of sand down the coast will only continue until the shape of the coast changes. If the shore turns to face the direction of the drift then deposition will occur and a wide swash aligned beach can form (**Resource 39**).

Alternatively, if the coastline turns away from the direction of drift by 30° or more, such as at an estuary or river mouth, then one of the coast's most distinctive landforms may develop – a spit. Essentially, a spit is simply a beach that continues to extend out into the sea (**Resource 40**).

Longshore drift and a swash aligned beach **Resource 39**

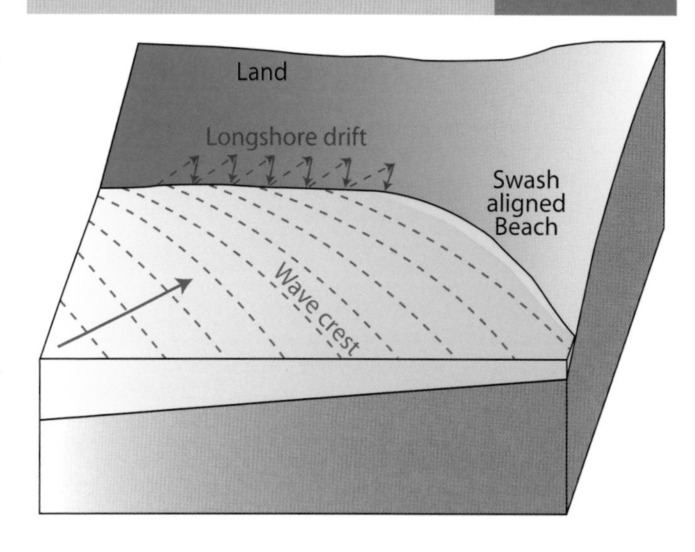

Longshore drift and the initiation of a spit **Resource 40**

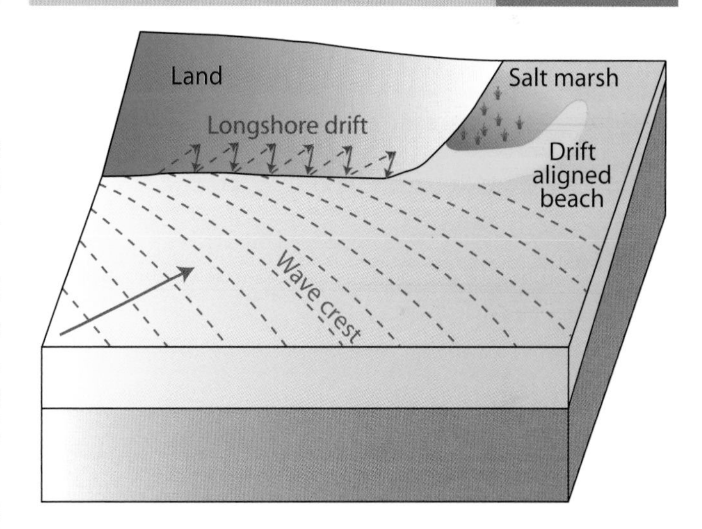

Spits

These are stores of sediment that form as drift processes continue at the change of trend of the shoreline and where the tidal range is not too extreme. **Resource 41** shows the formation sequence of a spit.

- The dashed line shows the position of the original coastline. In this region the prevailing winds and the direction of maximum fetch are from the southwest. As a result the strongest and most common waves come from this direction, transporting material eastwards by long shore drift along the beach at A.
- Where the trend of the coastline changed direction dramatically, at the headland, the drift of material continued out into the river estuary, and pebbles and cobbles were deposited on the bed at B.
- Deposited materials extend the beach to C, and storm waves and wind add sand to the upper beach.
- The beach continues to grow across the estuary to points D and E. At this end of the spit, the distal end, occasional storm winds or a second common wave direction can curve the end into a hook.
- Onshore winds carry sand landward, forming sand dunes above the high tide mark. Behind the spit the sheltered area of the estuary allows fine silts and mud to form a flat, wet saltmarsh (G).
- The spit reaches point F but deeper water and the scouring of the river flowing into the sea prevents further growth and expansion.
- Spits may be breached by winter storms and their position and size can be altered, slowly or dramatically.

The formation of a spit **Resource 41**

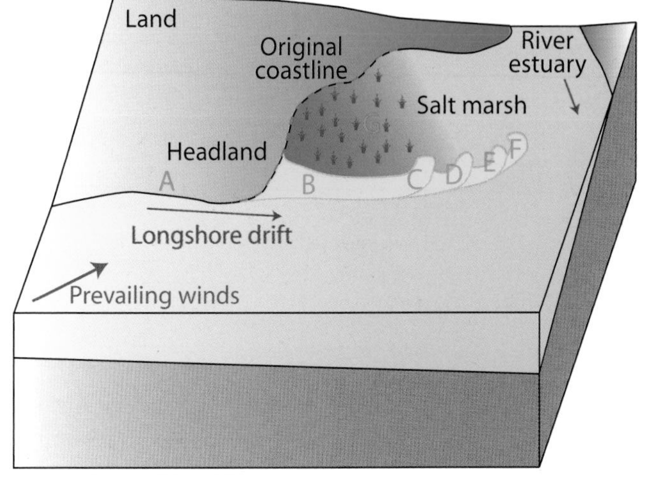

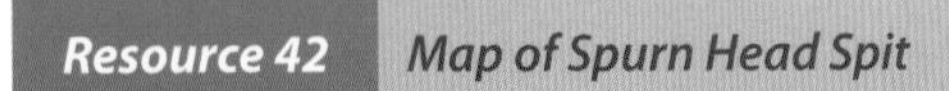

Resource 42 *Map of Spurn Head Spit*

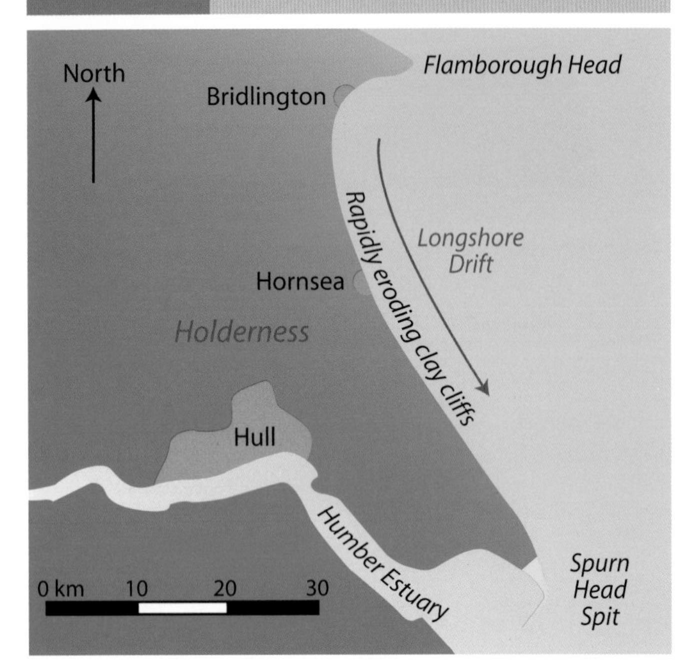

Resource 43 *Map of Murlough and Dundrum*

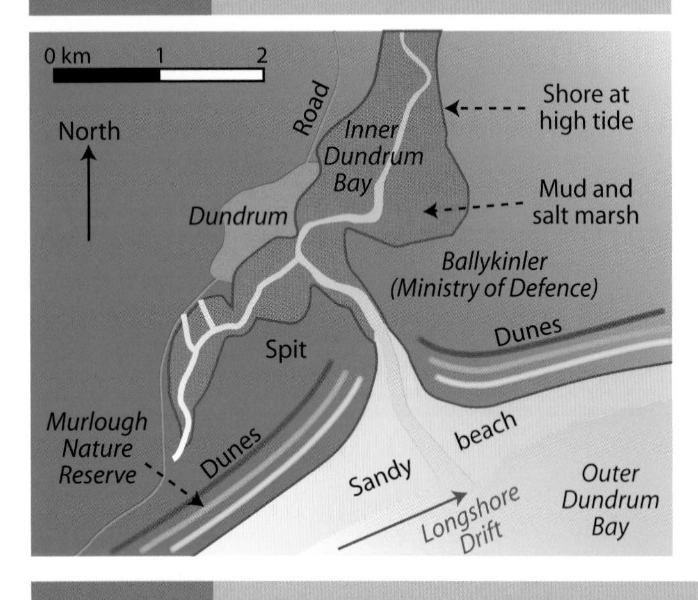

Spits are fed by active erosion further back, 'upstream', along the coast. A classic example of such a situation is the Spurn Head Spit, Yorkshire, where erosion from the cliffs along Holderness feed its growth (**Resource 42**).

Another example is the spit that is home to Murlough Nature Reserve, County Down and helps form Inner Dundrum Bay (**Resource 43**). The source of this sediment lies offshore and was deposited during the last Ice Age. It appears that, in recent decades, this source is declining as the beach is reducing in width and scale, providing less natural protection from storm winds. Remedial action has been taken to protect the foredunes from erosion by waves, especially where Royal County Down Golf Links is threatened (**Resource 44**).

Spits come in many forms, such as double spits across both sides of a bay or estuary and bars where a spit extends right across a bay. Where a spit extends from the mainland and links a former island to the shore it is referred to as a 'tombolo'. The most famous UK example is at Chesil Beach. Where a shingle spit over 10 km long connects Dorset to the Isle of Portland (**Resource 45, 52** and **60**).

Tombolos are often much smaller features, where an island causes wave refraction to build a spit (causeway) from the land to the island itself. Some are only evident at low tide (**Resource 46**).

Resource 44 *Groynes and other defences to protect the foredunes from erosion*

Map of Chesil Beach (also see Resource 60) **Resource 45**

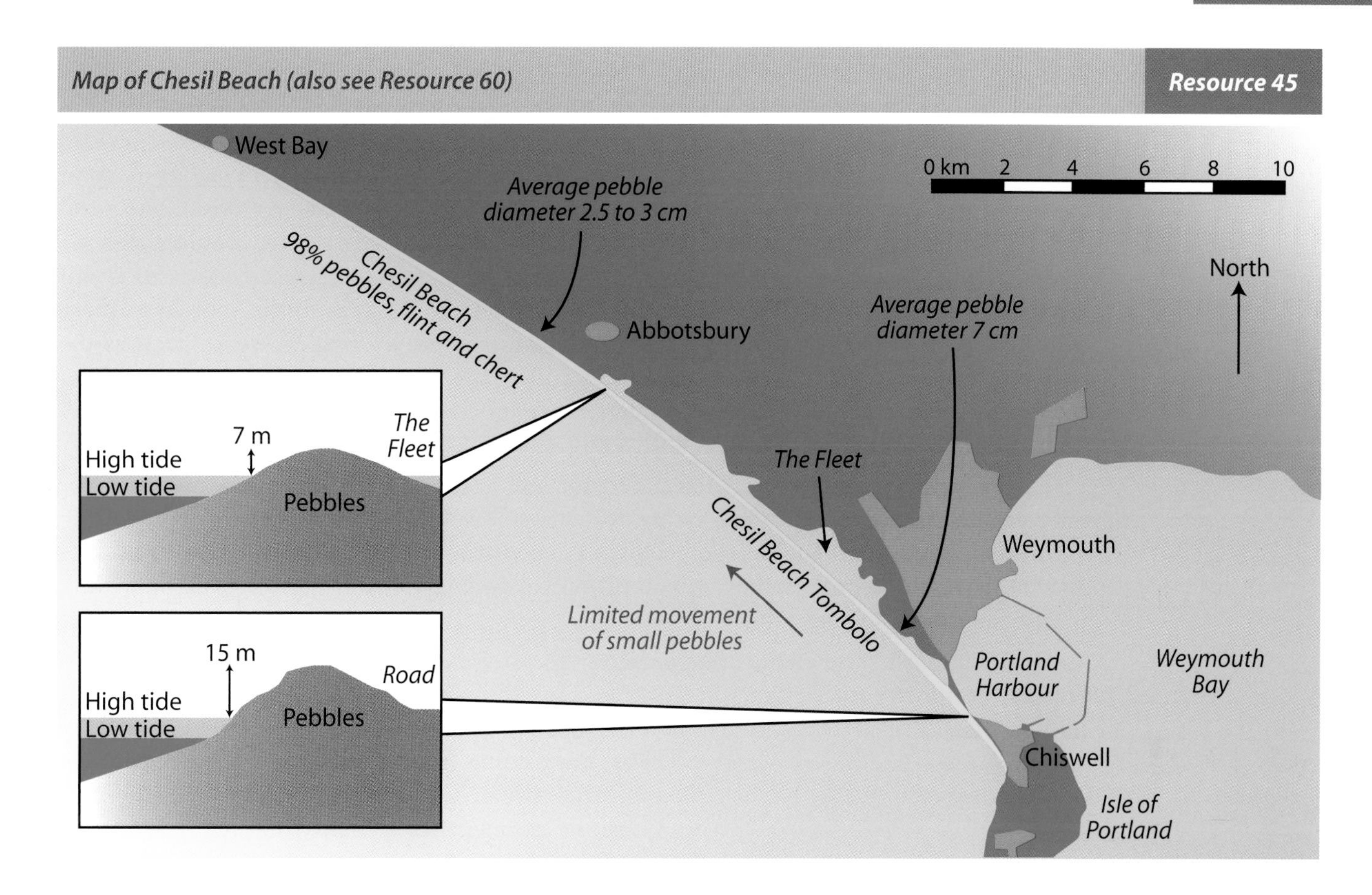

Wave refraction around islands **Resource 46**

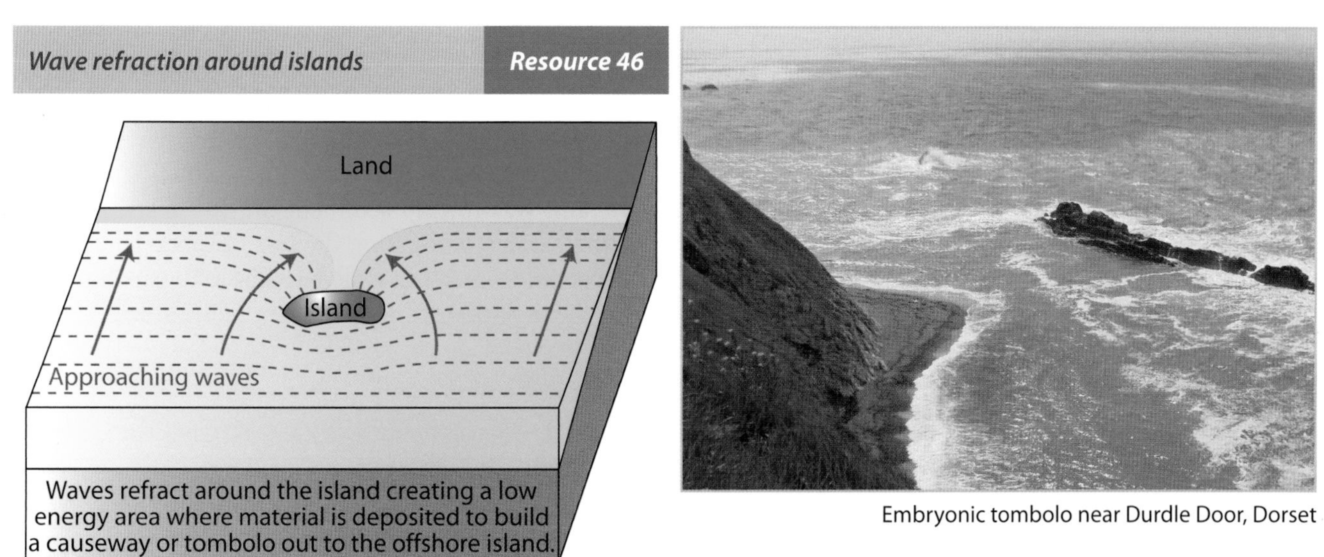

Embryonic tombolo near Durdle Door, Dorset

Exercise

1. ***Question from CCEA May 2005***
   Why might a coastal zone be of economic value? (6)

2. ***Question from CCEA January 2007***
   With the use of a diagram or diagrams and with reference to an example, explain how physical processes operate to create any one coastal landform. (9)

The need for coastal protection?

In the UK one in three people live within the coastal zone. Around the coast dramatic erosion events, such as hotels collapsing onto beaches and lighthouses having to be jacked-up and moved inland, suggest coastal processes cannot be ignored. The earliest direct management of coastlines probably involved the improvement of natural harbours for trading, fishing and naval craft. The primary purpose of such work was to allow boats to safely dock, avoiding damage caused by wind and wave. As technology improved and ambition increased, dock creation and extension added piers, breakwaters, harbour walls and promenades to the shoreline. These engineering projects had secondary, often unforeseen impacts along the coast, such as the build-up of sediment alongside the structures and/or the depletion of beaches further along the coast. Another aspect of historical interference on coastlines was the reclaiming of land, such as salt marshes, from the sea.

As the variety and scale of demand made on coastlines has grown so the need for management has increased. Initially, this management was done, almost exclusively, by using hard engineering. Hard engineering involves the construction of structures, often large-scale and intrusive, to control or prevent natural processes that threaten property, harbours and tourist amenities (**Resource 48**).

One example of hard engineering involves the rise of seaside tourism in Victorian Britain. During the nineteenth century the coast became the preferred destination for the earliest mass tourism. The advent of the railways had opened up the possibility of families holidaying away from home. Within reach of all the expanding industrial urban centres seaside resorts developed. Coastline promenades stretched for miles along the shore and piers ran out to sea. Where beaches were not wide enough or where erosion moved the precious sand away from the tourist areas, the most common hard engineering solution was the groyne. These were wooden walls constructed across the beach at right angles to the shore. Built at regular intervals, some groyne fields had dozens of individual barriers. The aim was to trap sediment on the 'upstream' side of the barrier, preventing the loss of sand. These were successful in creating wide beaches for recreation and also helped protect promenades from storm waves.

Degraded groyne field at Newcastle, County Down

Resource 47 *Diagram of groyne management*

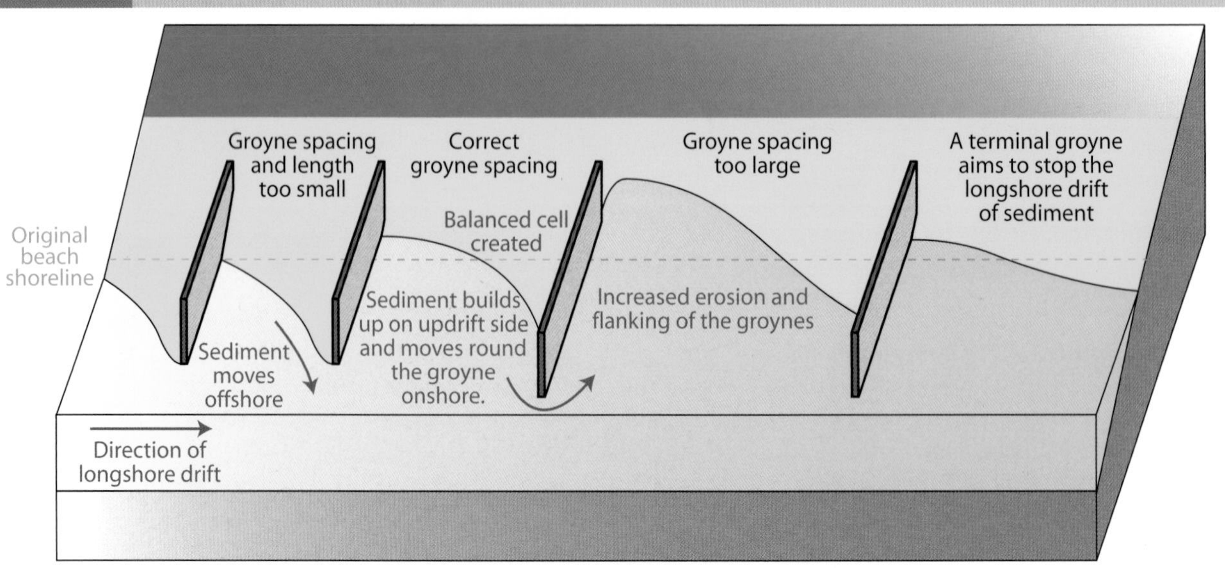

Table of hard engineering methods used in coastal defence **Resource 48**

Hard engineering strategy	Outline drawing	Nature and operation	Limitations and common issues
Sea walls	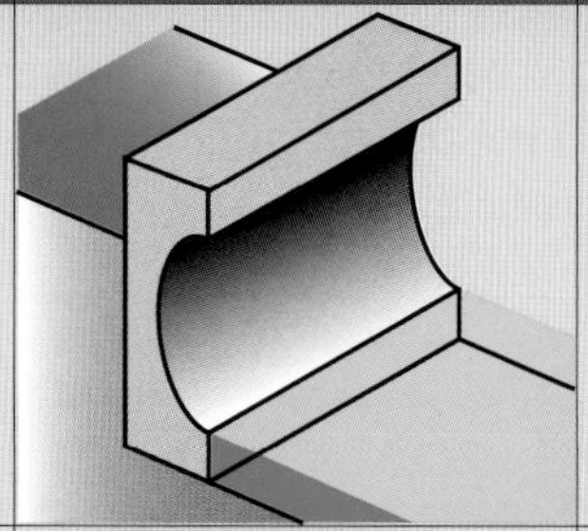	Solid walls separating land and sea. They support the land while holding back the sea. They can be designed to absorb and deflect wave energy. Common along promenades and at harbours (also see **Resource 61**).	These can often be the most expensive structures and need deep foundations. Poorly designed sea walls can deflect wave energy downwards and undermine the wall itself.
Rock Armouring or Rip-rap	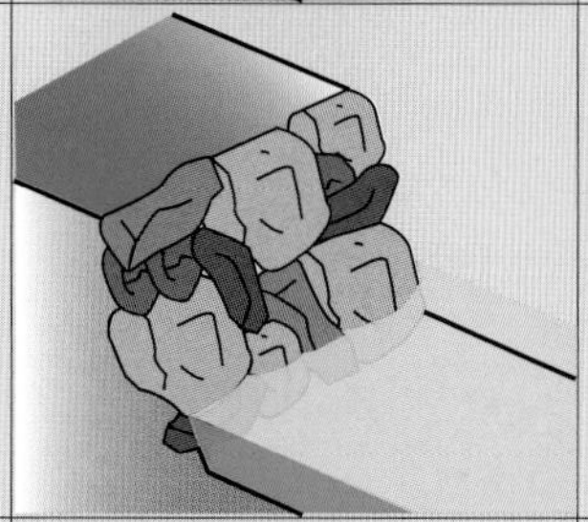	Large boulders used as an alternative to a sea wall. Being permeable they can absorb wave energy and have a more natural appearance (also see **Resource 67**).	Boulders may move or be undermined if placed on sand. Can be unattractive and relatively expensive.
Gabions	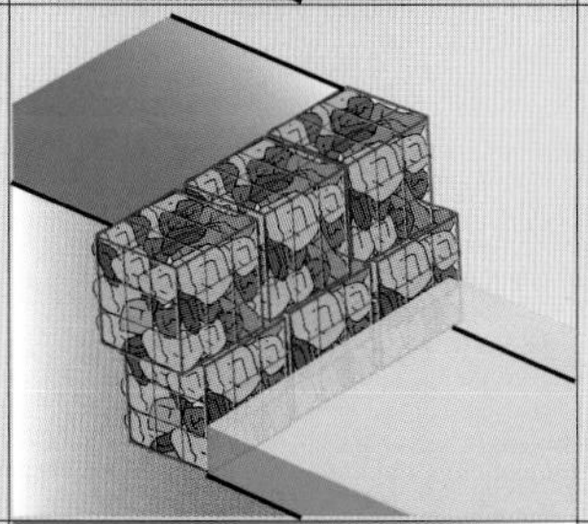	Metal cages filled with rocks often used to build walls. Wave energy is absorbed as water percolates and moves rocks around within cages (also see **Resource 61**).	If cages split over time rocks can be used to erode shore. Storms can knock down gabions piled up as walls.
Groynes	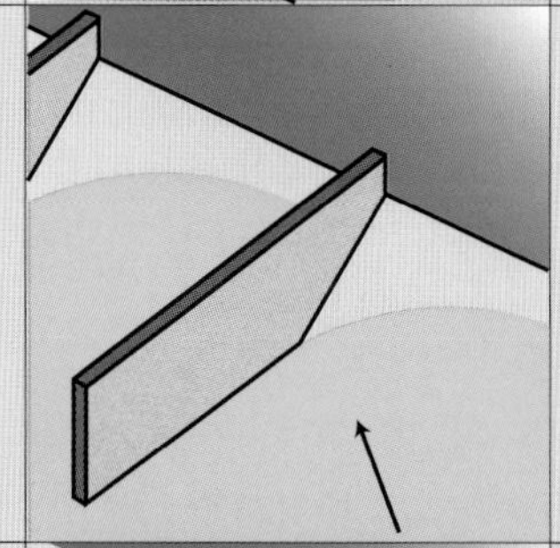	Wooden, concrete or rock barriers built out perpendicular to the shore to trap sediment carried by longshore drift. They are usually build in sets called groyne fields (also see **Resource 70**).	If too efficient they trap sediment, starving places further down the beach. Groynes need maintenance and replacement. They are visually obtrusive.
Revetments	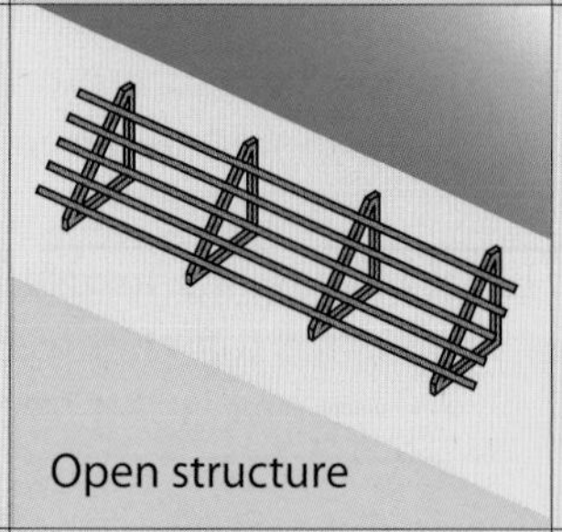 Open structure	These are sloping ramps build with open baffles of concrete, wood or rocks. They are designed to absorb wave energy.	Visually intrusive they can be undermined and can damage beach and shore ecosystems.
Breakwaters	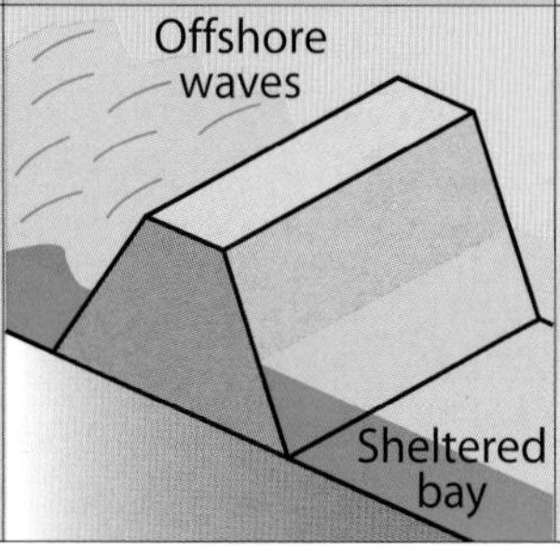 Offshore waves Sheltered bay	Offshore structures of concrete or boulders, they deflect or absorb wave energy before it reaches shore.	If poorly aligned they can deflect waves to erode at other points on the shore.

Groynes needed to be maintained and eventually replaced so, while effective, groyne based beach management was not cheap.

Groyne management not only illustrates the potential effectiveness of hard engineering in protecting the coast but also its potential for destruction. As the concept of coastal sediment cells suggests, the stores and flows of sediment along coasts are in a state of dynamic equilibrium. Any interference is likely to have consequences and beach groynes proved this. In many places the groyne fields that held and expanded the pleasure beaches of Victorian seaside resorts also caused rapid beach and shoreline erosion further along the coast. Long shore drift continued to remove sediment from beaches beyond the groyne field but their supply of sand and pebbles had been reduced, and the beaches narrowed to the point that storm waves eroded the shore.

Coastal sediment (littoral) cells

In nature sediment is transported within sediment cells involving large sections of the coast. In these cells sand and shingle movements are largely self-contained. Cells are normally separated by major headlands or dramatic changes to the coastline trend. Within each large sediment cell, sand and shingle can move more freely between smaller sub-cells. These facts should sound a warning that too much human interference along any one coastal section might permanently upset the balance within that sediment cell (**Resource 50**).

An alternative approach?

The expense and failure of many hard engineering strategies around the coast encouraged discussion of alternative approaches, in particular soft engineering. Soft engineering is described as schemes that make use of natural processes and work with them to achieve the desired end. Environmentalists have encouraged planners to develop such solutions, if not to replace, then at least to reduce the impact of hard solutions. Two examples of soft engineering at coasts are: beach nourishment (replenishment) and dune or cliff stabilisation.

1. The concept of **beach nourishment** is that material can be added to beaches to enhance their natural ability to protect the shore from erosion. It is commonly believed that a broad expanse of beach sand is the best protection for a shore, as waves are dissipated by friction, with their energy used up in shifting sediment on the beach itself. Beach nourishment may be as simple as lorry loads of sand being deposited at one end of a beach to then be redeposited by the natural long shore drift down the beach. Effective beach nourishment needs to use sediment size that matches the natural material and it must be sourced from a location, most likely inland, where it does not create environmental issues.
2. **Dune and cliff stabilisation** usually involves planting vegetation or covering damaged areas with matting that protects the area and encourages the trapping of sediment. In the case of sand dunes the aim is to prevent the loss of wind blown sand so that it remains available to replenish, by natural processes, the beach itself. In the case of eroding cliffs, trapping sediment at their base reduces the power of incoming waves and therefore slows down the rate of erosion.

For a time the debate over the management of Britain's coastline focused on whether the traditional hard engineering solutions should be replaced with a soft engineering approach.

The debate over coastal protection

Two factors are responsible for the current debate over how coasts should be managed.

1. The enormous costs of using engineering schemes for protection. Some countries, including Belgium and Japan, now protect most of their shorelines with hard engineering structures. Annually in England and Wales alone over £300 million is spent just to maintain a total of over 1,200 km of coastal defensive structures that already exist.
2. The environmental impact of many schemes is now regarded as unacceptable and unsustainable.

Three techniques are commonly employed when considering any coastal management scheme: Technical Viability, Cost-Benefit Analysis (CBA) and the Environmental Impact Assessment (EIA).

Technical viability examines whether or not the proposed scheme will actually accomplish the task that is required. CBA seeks to find the net balance between the financial outlay required in the construction and maintenance of a proposed coastal defence scheme and the value and income from the property and land that is being protected. The EIA evaluates the scale and nature of a proposed scheme's impact; including effects on the area's ecology and its visual result. A negative outcome for any of these studies is likely to result in the scheme being rejected unless it can be modified.

Another factor in the debate over coastal management policy concerns the complexity over who is responsible for making decisions. In the past this often meant planning was mired in confusion. All levels of local government had some responsibility and frequently plans were drawn up piece-meal so that a local council might protect their shoreline despite the damage it might cause to the coast nearby (**Resource 49**).

Hallsands, Start Bay, South Devon: an example of disastrous interference in a sediment cell **Resource 49**

Over ninety years ago the small fishing village of Hallsands in southern England was destroyed by a storm after sediment stores from offshore had been removed for the construction of large naval docks in nearby Devonport. The engineers had not realised that these offshore shingle banks provided the material that protected the coastline of Start Bay and the village of Hallsands from storms.

After the dredging began in 1897, the shingle beach that fronted the village and on which the fishermen of the village kept their boats became lower and narrower, as the natural supply of beach material from offshore declined. Despite facing east, the more sheltered direction in South Devon, the coast of Start Bay does suffer from some occasional severe, easterly storms in winter.

In January 1917 such a storm swept in and without its beach the village had no protection. Most of the buildings were swept away and 100 hundred people that miraculously survived the night lost their homes and livelihoods.

In 1993 one government agency, MAFF (Ministry of Agriculture, Fisheries and Food), recognised the need for an integrated approach to coastal protection based on the natural sediment cells that exist along the coast. From this they developed the concept of a **Shoreline Management Plan (SMP)**, which MAFF defined as:

> "a document which sets out a strategy for coastal defence for a specified length of coast taking account of natural processes and human and other environmental… needs."

SMPs are created by voluntary groups of local authorities and others and, although they are not statutory, their purpose is to provide an overview for a region within which local authorities can undertake schemes that fit in with the aims of the strategic plan (**Resource 50**).

Currently, in the UK, DEFRA (the Department for Environment, Food and Rural Affairs), a Government department, sets all coastal defence policies. These policies are then implemented by other agencies known as 'operating authorities', including the Environment Agency, local county councils and drainage boards. There is now a clearer definition of who is responsible for what along the coast but the debate has also shifted from "whether to use hard or and soft engineering" to a more fundamental question, "should we protect the coast at all?"

Until recently it has been assumed by most people that using any means to prevent coastal erosion was, by definition, the right thing to do. Indeed the loss of land and property by coastal erosion was essentially a bad thing. Now, partly from the use of Cost-Benefit Analysis and environmental impact studies but also as a result of concern over global warming and rising sea levels, a new concept has emerged, " do nothing". In other words, let nature take its course and through natural processes the coast will find a new equilibrium and balance. A slight modification to this view is termed **managed retreat**. Under this approach any existing coastal defences would be gradually removed and the sea allowed to alter the morphology of the shore.

Resource 50 *The development and nature of Shoreline Management Plans (SMP)*

Shoreline Managemet Plans

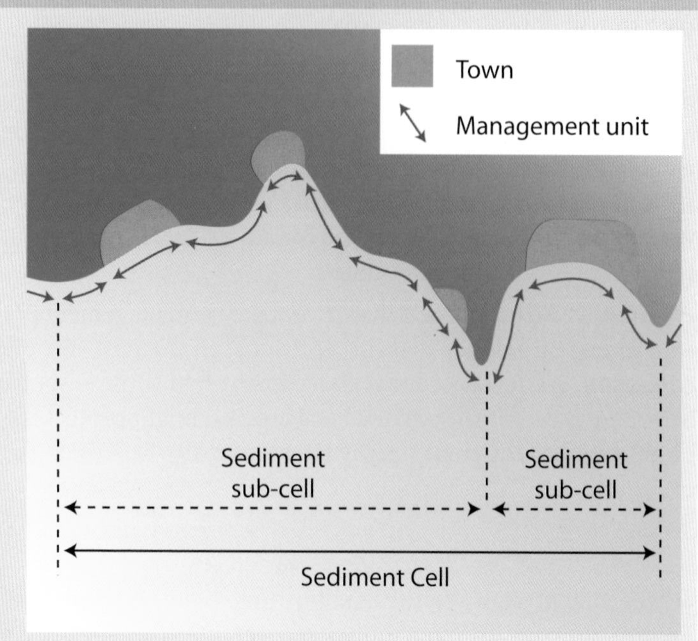

Between 1995 and 2000 the first Shoreline Management Plans were drawn up for each of the 11 different sediment cells that form the coastline of England and Wales. Within each of these major sections of coastline sub-cells had to be identified and within these sub-cells coastline segments known as management units were marked.

For each management unit of a cell the following four options were proposed:

- Do nothing
- Hold the Line
- Advance the Line (a rare choice)
- Retreat the existing defence line

Each management unit choice must be considered in relation to the neighbouring management units and the sediment cell as a whole. The choice also needs to link to the objectives for the plan area and be evaluated on economic (CBA), engineering (Technical Viability) and environmental (EIA) terms.

In 2006 DEFRA (formerly MAFF) launched the second generation of Shoreline Management Plans, known as SMP2. The guiding principle for these SMP2s is that they should seek to promote 'sustainable shoreline management policies' for a coastline into the twenty-second century.

The recommended SMP2 policies to achieve management objectives are:

- Hold the existing defence line (formerly Hold the Line)
- Advance the existing defence line (formerly Advance the Line)
- Managed realignment (formerly Managed Retreat)
- No active intervention (formerly Do Nothing)

Resource 51 *An example of managed retreat in East Anglia*

UK's largest man-made wetland created in Essex, July 2006

The sea wall at Wallasea Island in Essex was breached today, creating the UK's largest man-made marine wetland. DEFRA's Wallasea Wetlands Creation Project is creating a 115 hectare wetland to replace similar bird habitats lost to development during the 1990s. The wetlands will improve fish nurseries, and create opportunities for recreation. Wetlands will also provide additional flood and storm protection. Damaging storm waves lose their energy as they pass over the area, and the new sea defences will provide better protection than the old ones, which were in very poor condition. A total of 330 m of existing sea wall were breached today in an operation involving around 25 large hydraulic excavators, bulldozers and dump trucks.

The project has created 115 hectares of wetland, including seven artificial islands, saline lagoons, mudflats, new public footpaths, and 4 km of sea wall. It will be used by birds including Brent Geese, Oystercatchers, Grey Plovers, Dunlins, Shelducks, Curlews, Avocets and Little Terns. It will also provide a nursery habitat for fish such as bass, herring and mullet. The project has been delivered to time and cost £7.5 million.

DEFRA worked closely with the Environment Agency, RSPB, English Nature, Harwich Haven Authority and landowners Wallasea Farms Ltd, who had serious concerns about the stability of their existing flood defences. The project started in 2004 and completed by August 2006. It will be subject to intensive independent monitoring until 2011.

Source: adapted from 'UK's largest man-made wetland created in Essex', Government News Network, www.gnn.gov.uk, accessed 21 November 2008 [website no longer functions]

Some soft engineering strategies might be used to slow down the rate of change. In parts of rural Essex and Suffolk the sea has been allowed to breach defences and flood farmland in a plan to re-create a saltwater wetland habitat (**Resource 51**).

Another example of the new thinking is illustrated by Norfolk County council, who were the first in the UK to ban the locating of new developments on the coast. In the light of Norfolk's rapidly eroding coastline, the council proposes to establish at setback line at 75 m from the present shore. This means no new buildings, roads or other developments can be placed within that distance of the present shoreline.

At the national level, the UK government, faced with an estimated bill of over £5 billion to stop coastal erosion by future rising sea levels, has adopted a plan to stop maintaining coastal defences, except where flooding threatens settlements.

A REGIONAL CASE STUDY – South Devon and Dorset

The geographical setting

The complex geology and the variable orientation of the shore along the south coast of England creates a wide diversity of environments, habitats and landforms. Part of this coast is the newly designated SMP2 cell of South Devon and Dorset, stretching from Durlston Head in the east to Rame Head in the west, a distance of over 300 kms. The coastal environments in this region include sea cliffs and slopes; estuaries; sand dune systems; spits; and both fresh and salt water lagoons. Much of this coastline is highly valued for its distinctive rocks, including rich fossil deposits, and its historic role in the development of the science of geology. A large section of the shore is now protected as England's only natural UNESCO World Heritage Site – Jurassic Coast.

While landforms formed by both erosion and deposition are found in this region, the long-term pattern of change is slow coastal retreat, called transgression. One suggested rate over the last 2,000 years, is an average of 1 mm annually. Climate change, producing more severe storms and rising global sea level, is set to continue and accelerate this process of erosion with serious consequences for the future. In many coastline cells sediment is produced, moved and deposited by natural processes. In Devon and Dorset many of the deposition features, including the shingle beaches and bars, are now understood to be relict features. This means that they were formed from material left, possibly at the end of the last Ice Age, but are no longer being actively formed. This long-term sequence of change can be disrupted by short-term

Map of the South Devon and Dorset Shoreline Management Plan region **Resource 52**

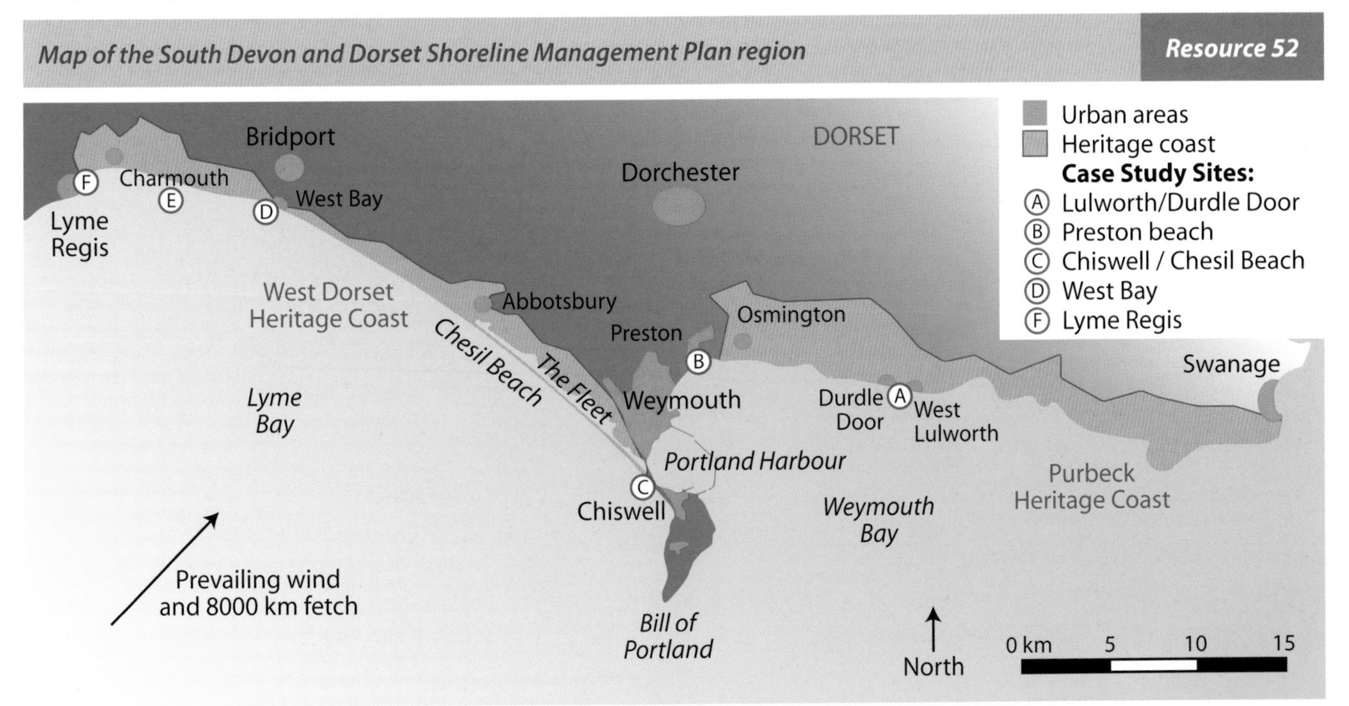

Resource 53 *Some of the management groups involved in the region*

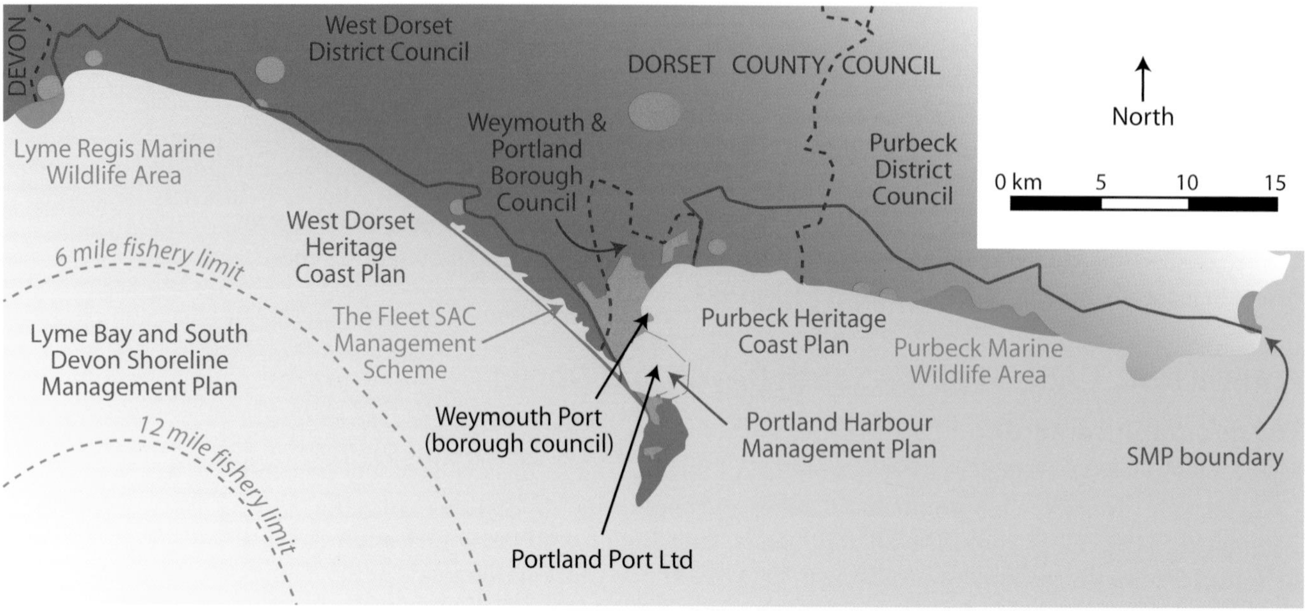

Resource 54 *The main recreational pressures on the South Dorset coast*

Activity	Locations	Level	Importance	Impacts
Walking	SW coast path	Very popular. Over 1 million each year	National and international	Erosion to paths on beach and cliff lines
Beach bathing	34 beaches	Very popular	Regional and national	Congestion and noise
Climbing	Limestone cliffs at Portland and Purbeck	Fast growing	Regional and national	Disturbance and vegetation damage
Cycling including off-road	Purbeck cycle path and rural routes	Growing demand	Regional	Nuisance and damage to coastal paths
Jet skiing	Weymouth and Poole harbours	Growing	Local and regional	Controversial activity safety concerns. Incompatible with other uses
Power boating	Races at Weymouth and Poole	Popular events	Regional and national	Noise and safety issues
Sailing and marinas	Poole and Portland Harbours, as well as West Bay, Lyme Regis, etc	Growing – Portland to host 2012 Olympic sailing events	Regional, national and international	Limited moorage availability and pollution/sewage issue
Sub-aqua diving	Popular wrecks in Lyme Bay, Portland Harbour and Purbeck	Growing popularity	Regional and national	Wildlife and marine archaeology impacts
Water skiing	Lyme Regis, Weymouth and Poole clubs	Steady demand	Regional	Noise, safety and incompatibility issues
Wind surfing	Poole, Portland Harbour and Ferrybridge	Expanding	Regional – international in Portland Harbour	Litter, car parking and shingle vegetation erosion issues

events. In recent decades storm events have not only damaged the local communities but in places caused the equivalent of a century's worth of erosion in one night. Add to this scenario the impact of people, both in their attempts to defend the coast and their other activities, and a complex picture emerges. At best, human action may slow down the erosion and retreat of the shore; at worst, such as in Hallsands (**Resource 49**), it may accelerate the natural change. People make high demands on the coast both from the land-based and sea resources **(Resource 54).**

One consequence of the many demands made on this coastline is that, along some sections, it is heavily defended. In low-lying areas the defence is to prevent flooding, whereas along cliffs it is designed to reduce or prevent erosion. The most common defence structures are linear seawalls and groynes. In the long-term, if the seawalls were retained, as the unprotected areas eroded landward, then these seawalls would form promontories along the areas of coast highly exposed to waves in deep water. In short, given a future of eroding shorelines, managed retreat in all but a few key locations is the only sustainable option. The story goes that almost one thousand years ago, Canute, king of England, commanded the tide to stop in order to demonstrate to his subjects that he was not all powerful. Perhaps the long-term and sustainable future of our coastline requires the modern day decision makers, the engineers and planners to take a similarly radical position.

The planning framework and the proposed Shoreline Management Plan

The concept of the Shoreline Management Plan is described in **Resource 50** and in this case two cells identified in the first SMP (1998) have been amalgamated. The SMP2s in England and Wales stress the need for long-term sustainability and the emphasis is less on maintaining the existing coastline and more on managing the seemingly inevitable process of retreat. The four options for planners at this stage are:

- Hold the existing defence line
- Advance the existing defence line
- Managed realignment
- No active intervention

The procedure also requires that the plan addresses the future at three timescales: short-term (next 20 years), medium-term (20–50 years) and long-term (50–100 years). The South Devon and Dorset SMP2 initially divides the coast into 17 sub cells, these are further divided so that proposals are stated for 190 sections of coast (management units). For each of these, the preferred policy for each time scale is stated. The consultation document for the plan was made public in April 2009 and the final plan implemented from 2010. Finally, it should be remembered that SMPs are drawn up as guidelines for the regions and that numerous groups are involved in the decision making process for any one scheme or management unit.

Examples of management and impacts from along the Dorset and East Devon coast (located on Resource 52)

A) The hard rock geomorphology at Lulworth

Beloved by geomorphologists, the Lulworth section of the Dorset coast appears in more textbooks on coastal erosion landforms than any other place on these islands. A dramatic and unique sequence of landforms is the product of bands of rock of varying resistance to erosion running east and west parallel to the shoreline (**Resource 55**).

Along this coast the land is almost entirely agricultural or is under the control of the Ministry of Defence (MOD). In the past there has been no major attempt to defend the coastline, except for some small site construction to maintain public access to the beach and shore. The SMP for management units along this section of coast in the short, medium and long time scales is to minimise any intervention as erosion rates are low due to the resistant nature of the hard rock geology. The only possible exceptions concern retaining the short sea wall defences that protect car parks and access points (managed realignment).

Resource 55 *The landforms of the Lulworth Cove region*

Durdle Door – a sea arch

Lulworth Cove

Cliffs

Erosion at Stair Hole

Resource 56 *Map of the coast along Weymouth Bay*

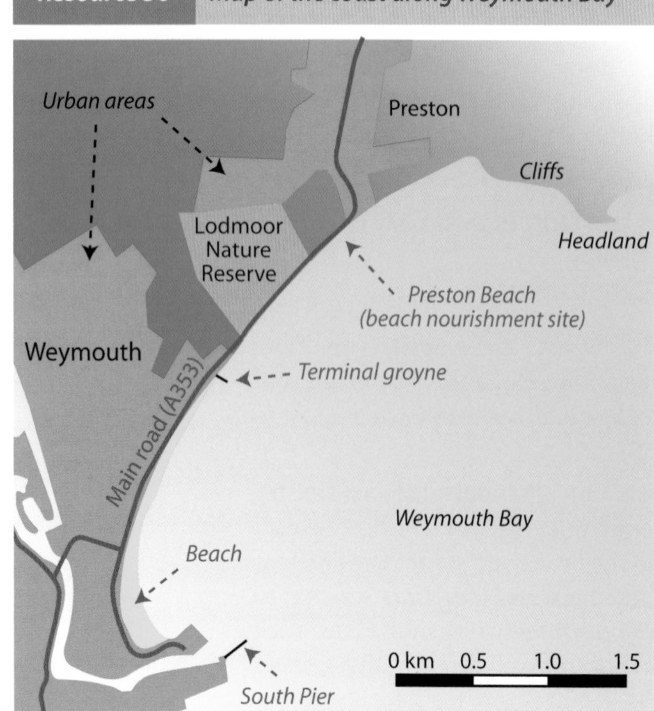

B) Weymouth Bay and Portland highly developed resorts and ports

Further west from Lulworth, in the more sheltered environment of Weymouth Bay lies one of the regions largest port towns, Weymouth. This section contains a great deal more development as well as numerous coastal defence structures. The Isle of Portland is connected to the coast by a narrow strip of land that is part of the Chesil Beach shingle bar. Behind this natural shelter from the severe south west winds and waves, Portland Harbour, over 10 km^2 in area, has been constructed surrounded by extensive breakwaters. This was formerly a naval base, and while it remains a commercial port it is increasingly important as an amenity for leisure and tourism (**Resource 57**).

The National Sailing Academy was developed here and opened in 2005. It will be the venue for the sailing events in the 2012 Olympic Games. Within Weymouth Bay sand and shingle beaches have formed and, unusually for the south coast, longshore drift moves material from east to west (**Resource 56**).

Photomontage of Portland harbour including the National Sailing Academy and recreation activities **Resource 57**

Portland Harbour

Recreation

National Sailing Academy

Photomontage of the situation at Preston Beach and Lodmoor nature reserve **Resource 58**

Lodmoor Nature Reserve

Preston Beach nourishment scheme

A353: main road, below sea level

Behind the sea bank

While beaches adjacent to Weymouth harbour are wide, in the centre of the bay the main coast road is threatened by erosion. Between the sea and the Lodmoor Wetland RSPB Nature Reserve, a two kilometre long section of the Preston Beach Road (A353) lies just below the height of the shingle beach (**Resource 58**).

In the past during winter storms, waves swept over the old sea wall and the road was often cutoff by floods. On studying this problem a working group, including the local and county councils and the National Rivers Authority, decided that either wave energy reaching the coast must be reduced or a coastal barrier designed to absorb wave energy was needed. After considering the construction of sea walls, offshore breakwaters or a groyne system, a beach nourishment scheme was implemented in the 1990s. In this scheme, initially costing £6.5million, thousands of tonnes of shingle were added to the beach. The shingle was similar to that found naturally on the beach and was sourced from elsewhere on the south coast. Because this material will continue to be subject to longshore drift a sum of £250,000 is needed for annual maintenance of the beach. Under the proposed Coastal Management Plan for this management unit of the Dorset coast, the short and medium term policy is to hold the existing line. In the long-term, before the year 2105, it is suggested that a policy of managed realignment will be required. **Resource 59** is an extract from the South Devon and Dorset proposed preferred policy SMP2, 2009.

For the remainder of Weymouth Bay to the south west, including Weymouth town, harbour and Portland Harbour, the policy for the foreseeable future is to hold the existing shoreline. The harbour and town are regarded as too valuable to be lost.

C) Chesil Beach and the Fleet – habitat protection

Chesil Beach is a world famous shingle beach or bar that stretches 29 km from West Bay in the north-west to the Isle of Portland to the south-east. It varies in height from 5–15 m and in

Resource 59 *An extract from the South Devon and Dorset proposed preferred policy SMP2, 2009*

Section of Coast	Policy: Short-term (2025)	Policy: Medium-term (2055)	Policy: Long-term (2105)
Preston Beach Weymouth	Hold the Line	Hold the Line	Managed Realignment
* Coastal squeeze: This is the process that may occur when rising sea levels moves the high tide mark further inland reducing the area of a particular coastal habitat.	The Preston Beach sea defence consists of a sea wall and a recharged beach with a terminal rock groyne at the southern end. These defences would require maintenance during this period. Ongoing beach management activities along Preston Beach prevent breaching of the sea defences and so reduce flood risk to low-lying land behind. Due to longshore drift of sediment…it is likely that further beach recharge (nourishment) will be required at Preston Beach towards the end of this period, to maintain the standard of protection.	Maintenance of the defences along this section is likely to be required to retain the standard of protection at Preston Beach during this period in response to coastal squeeze caused by sea level rise. There is a possibility of cliff erosion to the north… leading to this area standing several metres seaward of the adjacent…cliff to the north… it may be that maintenance of defences becomes unsustainable during this period…it may be necessary to consider bringing forward the long-term policy of managed realignment.	At Preston Beach the provision of flood defence through beach management activities will become increasingly unsustainable as sea levels rise, therefore realignment of the defences (along all or part or of this section) through construction of new defences in a set back location is the preferred policy. This would require… the relocation of assets, including the main road that runs behind the current defences. (A353) under this policy the shoreline (will) roll back in response to sea level rise…into an embayment between Weymouth and Furzy Cliff.

width from 50–200 m. The sediment along the beach is graded in size from pea-sized gravel in the north to potato-sized in the south (**Resource 60**). There are many theories about its origin and the movement of sediment along the beach. It is widely agreed that Chesil is a relict landform feature, an offshore bar formed after the last Ice Age ended from material deposited on the sea-bed. As the ice melted, raising world sea-levels, this bar was driven onshore to form the tombolo we see today. As a relict feature, virtually no new sediment is being added to the beach. The importance of Chesil Beach as an effective natural line of defence should not be underestimated. The prevailing south-west winds have an enormous fetch of 8,000 km of open sea all the way from the Caribbean. Wave energy is absorbed by the continuous movement of the shingle up and down the beach, as each wave breaks and with construction and destruction of ridges along the beach. Water also percolates in and through the beach sediment. Chesil Beach protects a 13 km long tidal lagoon called the Fleet, a rare feature on Europe's coast and the largest in England. The Fleet has a national conservation designation as a Site of Special Scientific Interest (SSSI), European status as a Special Protection Area (SPA) and internationally it is recognised as a Ramsar site for its wetland bird habitat. If, as seems probable, Chesil Beach is forced east by rising sea-levels, the distinctive ecosystem of the Fleet will be threatened and potentially destroyed. As noted earlier, Chesil also helps provides shelter for the built environment and activities in Portland Harbour and Weymouth Bay.

Most of Chesil Beach, and all its length parallel to the Fleet, has no artificial defences and the short to long-term policy is to allow nature to take its course. This would mean a landward shifting of the crest of Chesil Beach of between 6 and 12 m in the next century if current rates are maintained. This will cause coastal squeeze of the special ecology of the Fleet lagoon as well as increasing the risk of storm flooding. At small settlements to the north and south beach

Graded sediment along Chesil Beach **Resource 60**

Resource 61 *Hard engineering strategies at Chiswell at the southern end of Chesil beach (Also see Resource 45)*

protection does exist and will be maintained at least for the next 50 years. At the southern end of Chesil lies the small fishing village of Chiswell. Here the threat of flooding has been met by a series of hard engineering structures (**Resource 61**). These include a 300 m sea wall constructed in 1959 and modified in the 1980s with steel toe piles to prevent undermining by storm waves. In 1981 a short section of steel gabions filled with pebbles was constructed to prevent flooding. This scheme met with opposition from environmentalists who were concerned with both its visual impact and interference with the natural processes of the beach.

Resource 62 *Map of West Bay*

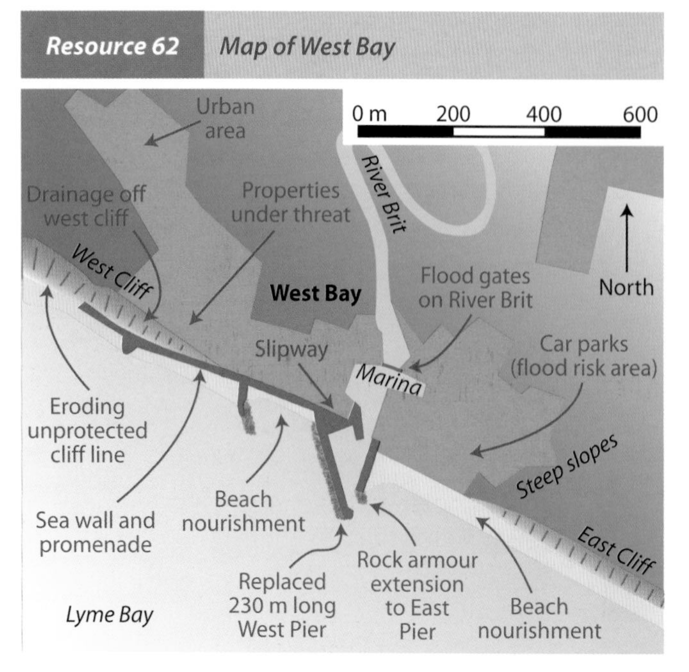

D) Settlement, harbour and tourist amenity protection at West Bay

The harbour at West Bay lies at the mouth of the River Brit and in the centre of the Jurassic heritage coast. To the south-east lies the start of Chesil Beach, dramatically backed by the East Cliff, a layered wall of vertical orange brown sandstone. To the north-west the geology of West Cliff is very different and the highly faulted and weak clay cliffs are in constant danger of collapse.

Photographs of West Bay (May 2009) **Resource 63**

Rock groyne beach protection

Beach nourishment ridge with sea beyond

Collapse of unprotected West Cliff

Overview of the harbour at West Bay

These photographs and text are an introduction to an on-line description of the coastal defence and flood management scheme of the Dorset town of West Bay available at:
www.dorsetforyou.com/index.jsp?articleid=1835 See also: www.dorsetforyou.com/index.jsp?articleid=1274

Management issues include the need to:

- prevent flooding of low land to the east of the harbour.
- deal with erosion rates averaging 0.5 m per year that threaten property on West Cliff.
- reconstruct a more sheltered harbour for fishing and pleasure craft.
- conserve protected environments and the aesthetic appearance of the coast.

Resource 63 illustrates some of the policies that have been implemented in recent years in West Bay.

E) Cliff erosion and landslides between West Bay and Lyme Regis

This section of the Dorset coast is famous for its geology and in particular its fossil wealth. For three hundred years it has been the centre of a fossil hunting industry and many of the founding fathers of British and world geology have spent time researching the region. It is not only an interesting coastline it is also extremely dangerous. Active landslips, slides and mudflows are common along its length, such as at Black Ven near Lyme Regis, which is described as the largest land slip in Europe.

It is hard to envisage how any engineering policy could protect this stretch of coastline from erosion in the future and indeed with the exception of a small section at the settlement of

Resource 64 *Map of coastline from West Bay to Lyme Regis*

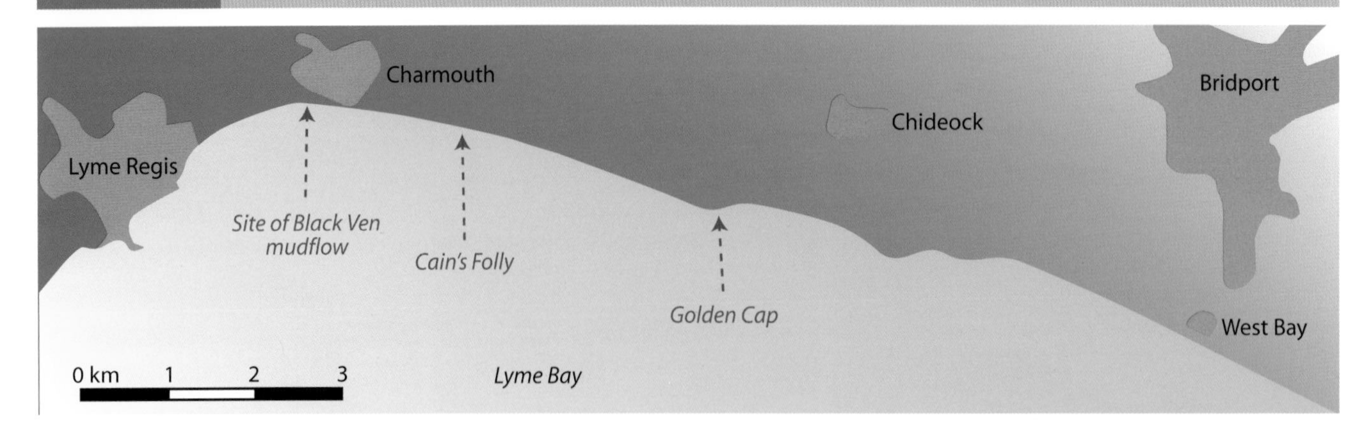

Charmouth (managed realignment), the long-term policy under the proposed SMP2 is one of "no active interference". It is envisaged that the cliff line may retreat by between 50 and 100 m in the next 100 years and that properties and amenities along the coast will inevitably be lost. This amount of erosion would suggest that a great deal of material would be added to the sediment cell operating along this coast and therefore local beaches could be widened and replenished. In reality, much of the eroded material is composed of fine clays and silts that would most likely be swept offshore into deeper water and little additional sand or shingle would be produced. It is true that landslides and slips can delay erosion of the coast as the material forms a barrier along the shore. However, rising sea-levels, storm waves and a lack of artificial protection means that these barriers would be short lived and rapidly removed. **Resource 65** shows recent

Resource 65 *Photographs of mass movements of the cliffs at Cain's Folly*

Map of Lyme Regis **Resource 66**

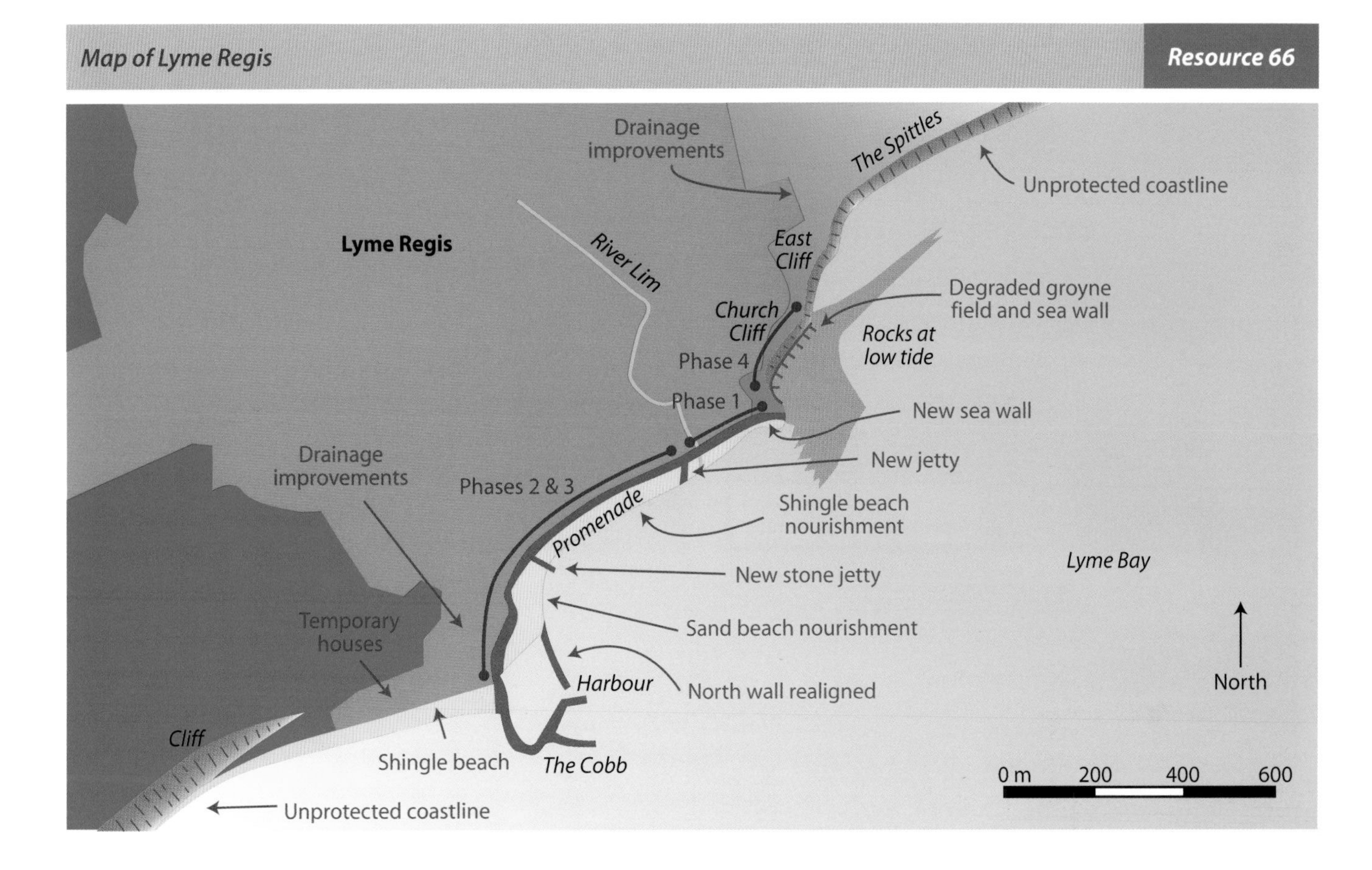

mudslides and flows along one short section of shore at Cain's Folly, east of Charmouth. Locally the rate of retreat will vary and existing headlands, such as Golden Cap, between West Bay and Charmouth, may become more prominent as the land to each side retreats more rapidly, forming deep embayments. As a consequence of this, sediment may be less able to move along the coast to replenish lost beach material.

F) Lyme Regis – Property protection

The beautiful resort town of Lyme Regis has the misfortune not only to be surrounded by retreating cliffs but also to have much of its settlement built on unstable geology. Porous sandstone lies on top of clay. This arrangement allows water to seep through the solid sandstone rock into the clay, which becomes plastic, causing the heavy rock layer above to slide downwards. Engineering projects in the area are therefore not solely concerned with coastal erosion but also with ground stability. The current plan to protect the town has five phases estimated to cost a total of £33 million. The first three phases have been completed and the remaining two are subject to planning and the availability of funding. The full plan is designed to protect 532 properties worth around £54 million, with a further £10 million worth of infrastructure and services conserved.

Phase 1: completed in 1995, consists of a new sea wall and promenade to the east of the mouth of the River Lim. The wall is protected by large quantities of boulders as rock armour (**Resource 67**).

Phases 2 and 3: were completed in 2007 and involve the section of shore between the Cobb, the large stone

Phase 1 of the Lyme Regis protection scheme **Resource 67**

Resource 68 *Photographs of the new structures associated with Phases 2 and 3, completed in 2007*

jetty that has sheltered the harbour for centuries, and the mouth of the river. On the shore this included the building of new stone jetties, between which extensive beach replenishment of sand and shingle took place, as well as a section of new sea wall. The Cobb was also protected and its sheltering impact enhanced by the use of rock armouring (**Resource 68**).

Phase 4: The BBC news item in **Resource 69** describes events in the spring of 2008 when Phase 4 of the plan for Lyme Regis was announced.

Resource 69

Preserving the coast

What was described as "the worst landslip to strike Lyme Regis for 100 years" occurred on a stretch of coast which was due for coastal protection work...In February 2008 the latest phase of the £21 m project to protect Lyme Regis from falling into the sea was unveiled. A new sea wall under the East Cliff is planned at a cost of £4 m. But on the evening of 6 May 2008 the East Cliff started rumbling and tonnes of debris slid onto the beach below. No homes were lost and no-one was injured but the landslip vividly illustrates how fragile this area of coast is. The proposed work would protect up to 170 homes, a football pitch, the historic St Michael's Church and Charmouth Road, the main route out of the town...The protection work will help to pin the cliffs to the harder rock below.

Source: J Sainsbury, BBC Dorset, 13 February 2008 http://tinyurl.com/ptcdor, accessed 18 August 2009

Church Cliff, East Cliff and the Spittles to the east of the town are highly unstable. The existing defences are inadequate, poorly maintained and failing (**Resource 70**). At the shore a new sea wall with associated walkway will be constructed, while inland the unstable surface rocks will be anchored by piles to the more solid layers beneath it and an improved drainage system will be installed to prevent clays becoming saturated.

Exercise

Research:

What is the current stage of development of Phases 4 and 5 of the Lyme Regis scheme?

For details of the Lyme Regis plan see:

www.dorsetforyou.com/index.jsp?articleid=1277

The failing seawall and groyne field defences at Church Cliff **Resource 70**

Exercise

1. ***Question from CCEA Summer 2005***
   Why might a coastal zone be of economic value? (6)
2. ***Question from CCEA Summer 2009***
   "As a response to coastal erosion, hard engineering strategies offer only a partial solution."
   Discuss this statement with reference to your regional scale case study of coastal protection. (15)
3. ***Question from CCEA Summer 2002***
   With reference to a regional coastal case study:
   (i) describe the nature of the hard and soft engineering strategies adopted; and (5)
   (ii) explain the impact these strategies have had on both the human and the physical environment. (10)

Selected textbooks and articles

Publications

V Bishop and R Prosser, *Landform Systems*, Collins Educational, 1997

D Brunsden, *The official guide to the Jurassic coast*, Coastal Publishing, 2003

A Doherty and M McDonald, *River Basin Management*, Hodder & Stoughton, 1992

M Hill, *Coasts and Coastal management*, Hodder & Stoughton, 2003

B Hordern (Ed S Warn), *Rivers and Coasts*, Philip Allen, 2006

D Knighton, *Fluvial Forms and Processes: A new perspective*, Arnold, 1998

G Nagle, *Rivers and Water Management*, Hodder & Stoughton, 2003

M Raw, *Rivers*, Philip Allen, 2004

***Geofile* articles**

388 'Coastal erosion: Back to nature Holderness, Yorkshire and Sidmouth, Devon'
460 'York: flood defence systems'
467 'Managing the River Wandle'
472 'Coastal management: a new perspective'
491 'Landforms of coastal erosion: examples from East Yorkshire'
501 'Large-scale River Management – The Colorado'
537 'North Norfolk Coast Shoreline Management Plan'
551 'Coastal Fieldwork: Case Study of a particular beach in the UK'
575 'Coastal systems: Waves, Tides, Sediment, Cells'
585 'Pressures on the Coastline'
594 'River flood management strategies (DME)'

Geoactive

364 'Coastal Management at Lyme Regis'
386 'Coastal processes and landforms in East Devon and West Dorset'

B1 LOCATION AND CLIMATIC CHARACTERISTICS OF MAJOR TROPICAL BIOMES

Living on the islands off the coast of continental Western Europe it is difficult to imagine any connection to the climatic extremes of the tropics but in reality geologically, geographically and ecologically speaking, the links are strong. The history of the rocks of these islands reveals that slowly shifting continents have drawn them on a 100 million year journey through the low latitudes around the Equator (**Resource129**). The jungle, grassland and desert climates of our past have left traces such as the desert sandstones beneath the summit of Scrabo, County Down and seams of coal, the fossilised remains of a wet equatorial forest, that later fueled our Industrial Revolution. Today the fear of global atmospheric change firmly links our futures to the regions where the high sun reigns supreme – the tropics.

The Tropics of Cancer and Capricorn are the lines of latitude that circle the world at 23.5° north and south of the Equator (0°). They mark the locations on the Earth's surface where the overhead sun reaches its most northerly and southerly position each year. The region of the Earth's surface between these lines is known as the **tropics** and within these low latitudes lie a variety of environments and ecosystems with distinctive communities of plant and animal life (flora and fauna).

These large-scale tropical ecosystems are examples of **biomes** and our aim is to examine their nature and the sustainability or otherwise of their management. **Resource 71** shows the global extent of three tropical zones – the **tropical forests**, **tropical desert** and **tropical grasslands.**

Distribution of tropical biomes

1. **Forest** covers about one quarter of the tropic's land area, representing 5% of the Earth's surface area. Tropical forest coverage is declining significantly in many regions. Most forest lies between 10° north and south of the Equator with three concentrations:

Resource 71 *The global distribution of the tropical biomes*

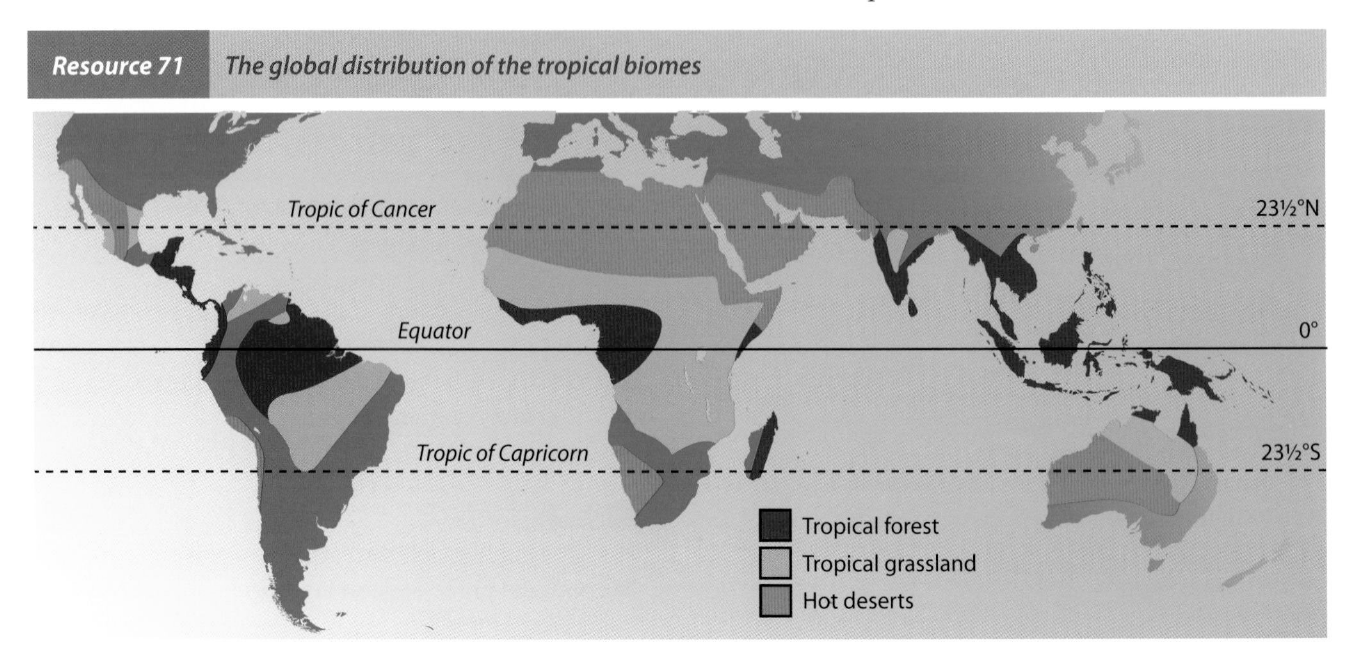

- **Latin America**, including the Amazon and Orinoco basins, 56% of the world total.
- Western Equatorial **Africa**, including the Congo basin, 18% of world total.
- South-East **Asia**, 25% of world total area.

2. **Hot desert** is also found across a range of continents, most lying between 15° and 30° north and south of the Equator, and commonly in the centre or towards western coasts. In the northern hemisphere lie the Sonora Desert of South-West USA (**North America**) and the largest of all deserts, the Sahara across North **Africa**. Further east the hot desert biome runs across Saudi Arabia, through Iran, to the Thar Desert of Pakistan in **Asia**. Their counterparts in the southern hemisphere are the Atacama Desert of **South America**, the Namib or Kalahari Desert of southern **Africa** and the Great **Australia** Desert.

3. **Tropical grassland or savanna** covers a wide zone within the tropics. This biome incorporates a range of vegetation communities, from open woodland with grass, through pure grasslands to scrub. Most are located between 5° and 20° north and south of the Equator. **Africa** dominates the distribution, with a belt stretching across the continent from West to East Africa and as far as Zambia in the south. In **South America** it comprises the Llanos of Venezuela and the Campos of the Brazilian Plateau. Finally, in North **Australia**, Queensland and the Northern Territory have tropical grasslands.

Within each tropical biome there may be great variation. In North Africa alone at least four types of tropical grassland are normally distinguished. For our purposes we will describe and study each of the three biomes by examining their common features.

Numerous physical factors influence ecosystems including geology, relief, time for development and most importantly of all **climate**.

Tropical circulation

The Hadley Cell

In the tropics, or low latitudes, one circulation feature dominates the pattern of annual climate – the Hadley Cell. First described in the eighteenth century by the then British Astronomer Royal, George Hadley, this model of circulation of both surface and upper atmosphere air is fundamental to the climatic controls on our three tropical biomes. The Hadley Cell is one element in the tri-cellular global circulation model of the dominant airflows around planet Earth. Although modern research has shown that the mid-latitude and polar cells of the model are oversimplifications of reality, the Hadley Cell still remains a useful starting point. As **Resource 72** shows, in each hemisphere the surface element of its Hadley Cell is a pattern of persistent winds, blowing from about 30°N or S, towards the Equator.

These are the north-east and south-east **trade winds**. These winds meet around the Equator at a zone dominated by surface low pressure and a related vertical uplift of air. This is the **ITCZ** (Inter Tropical Convergence Zone) and above this region, rising air (convection) commonly leads to the development of cloud filled skies and heavy convection rain, especially in the late afternoon. High in the atmosphere, near the tropopause (16 km), the rising air moves laterally away to the north and south to sink towards the surface around 30°. Here, this subsiding air creates the sub-tropical high pressure zones found on the surface at these latitudes. As the air descends towards the surface it is compressed and is warmed. This means that condensation is unlikely, so clouds and rain rarely

The Hadley Cell – the primary element in tropical circulation **Resource 72**

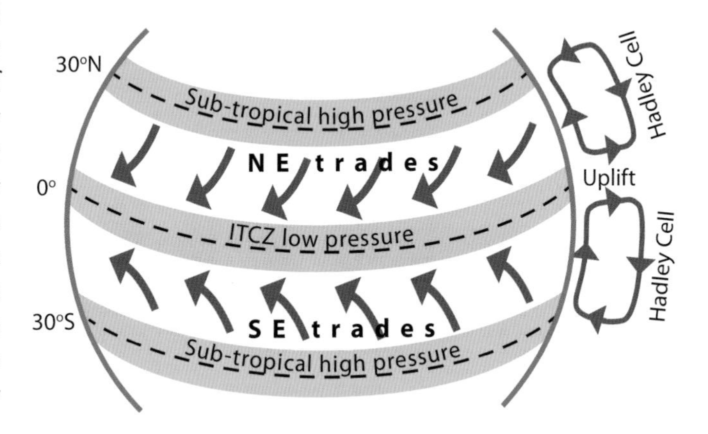

develop. Consequently, under the subsiding air of these sub-tropical high pressure zones lie the world's hot desert environments.

While it dominates the circulation of air and energy in the tropics, each Hadley Cell itself is not fixed in location. As **Resource 73** illustrates, its position follows the annual migration of the overhead sun so that in the northern hemisphere summer (June–August) it moves north, shifting the winds, pressure belts and the region of equatorial rainfall. Surface weather conditions near 30°N and S remain hot and arid all year. At the Equator the climate remains hot and wet all year round, but between these regions lie the tropical semi-arid grassland regions where rain falls for only part of the year and temperatures are high.

Resource 73 *The annual migration of the Intertropical Convergence Zone*

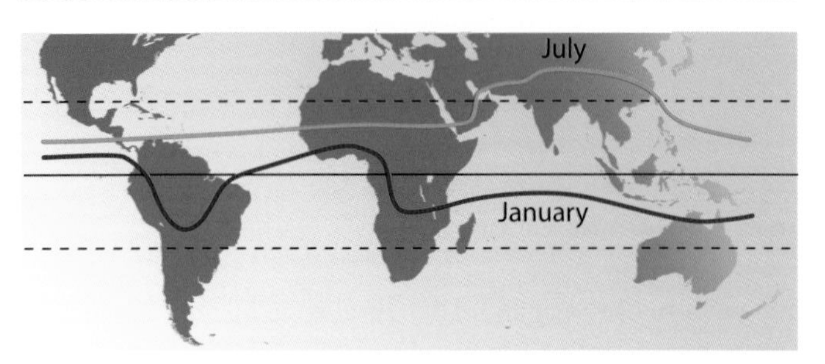

Tropical climates

The climate characteristics of tropical forests

The climate statistics for Uaupes in the Amazon basin (**Resource 74**) show this region has:

1. High temperatures, around 25°C throughout the year, with a low annual temperature range of 1–2°C. This is due to days that are consistently around 12 hours long, giving large quantities of solar insolation along with a high overhead sun angle.
2. High annual rainfall, a total of at least 1,800 mm a year but often up to 2,800 mm, this rain falls in thunderous downpours on most days of the year. The annual rainfall total varies by 15–20% from the long-term average (similar to UK variation).

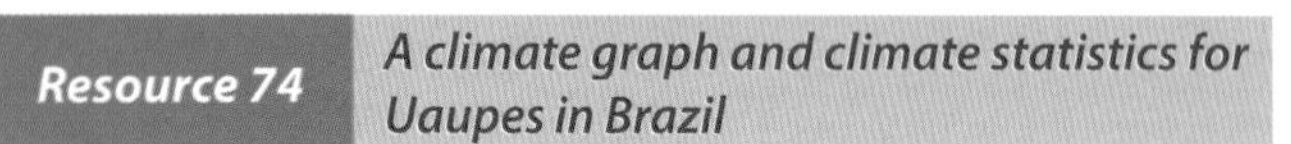
Resource 74 *A climate graph and climate statistics for Uaupes in Brazil*

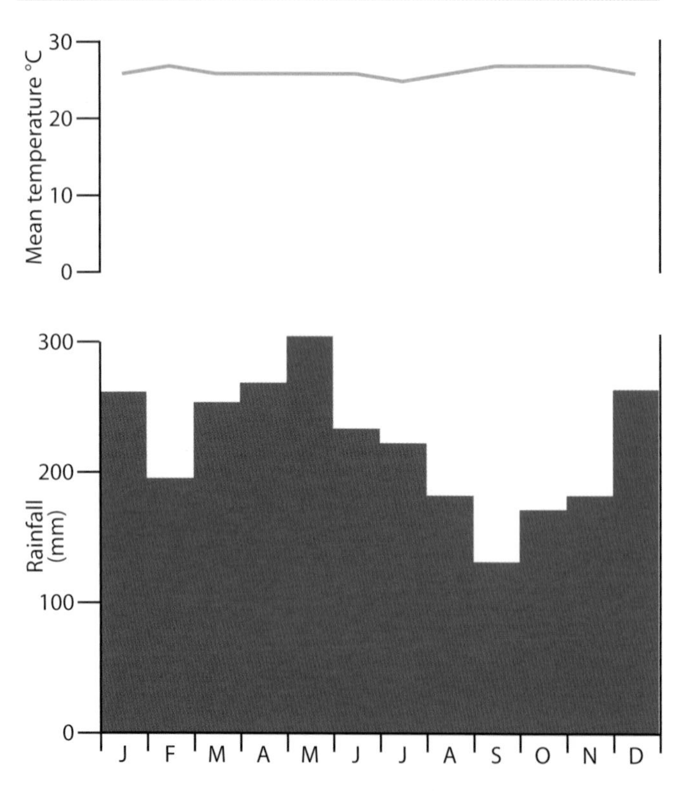

Explanation of the nature of the tropical forests climate

Despite the annual migration of the overhead sun between the Tropic of Cancer (23½°N) and the Tropic of Capricorn (23½°S) (**Resource 75**) it always remains high in the sky in the vicinity of the Equator where it shines for around 12 hours every day. This accounts for the consistent high monthly average temperatures in this region, which rarely vary by more than a few degrees. Rainfall is likewise persistent. The region is dominated by the meeting at the surface of the trade winds, the north-east trades from the northern hemisphere and the south-east trades from the south; the region known as the Inter Tropical Convergence Zone (ITCZ). Despite this year round convergence of winds the surface air pressure remains low. The only possible explanation is that the air rises upwards into the atmosphere as a series of convection currents. Indeed this is the main mechanism at the ITCZ, where

Uaupes (0°)	J	F	M	A	M	J	J	A	S	O	N	D
Temp (°C)	26	27	26	26	26	26	25	26	27	27	27	26
Rain (mm)	262	196	254	269	305	234	223	183	132	172	183	264

Uaupes, Amazon Basin, Brazil, latitude 0°
Annual temperature range is 2°C
Total rainfall = 2,677 mm

cells of rising air lift and expand up to the tropopause, on average some 16 km above the surface. As the warm, humid air rises it expands and cools reaching its dew point temperature. Condensation of water vapour commences and clouds form. The strong uplift continues, especially in the late afternoon when the ground is at its maximum heat, and towering vertical clouds develop. These are cumulonimbus clouds and are associated with thunderous bursts of intense rainfall. The equatorial forests have such late afternoon heavy rain for an hour or so most days of the year. In the city of Manaus (3°S) on the Amazon River in central Brazil rain falls on average 265 days a year.

Annual migration of the overhead sun **Resource 75**

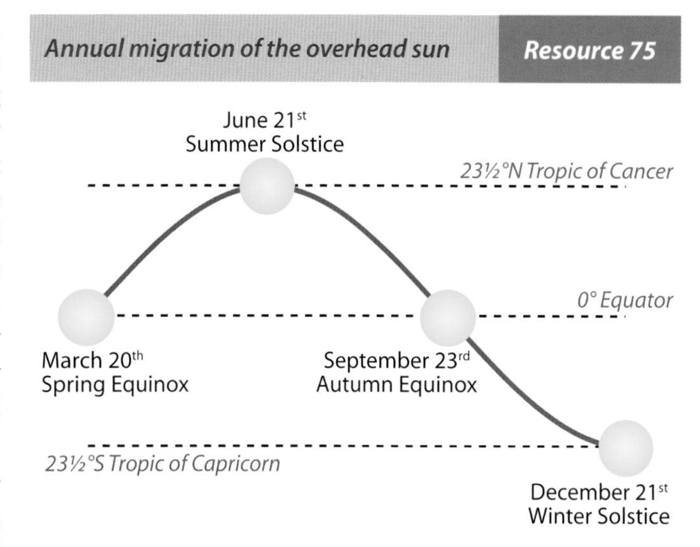

These conditions of abundant heat, light and water are an ideal growing environment helping to explain the abundance, productivity and biodiversity of tropical rainforests. It is worth noting that with increasing distance from the Equator a marked seasonal variation in rainfall emerges with a drier season during 'winter' months. This seasonality does not restrict the growth of forest until 10 to 15 degrees away from the Equator (**Resource 76**).

Resource 76 *A model transect of biome change from the Equator to the Tropics*

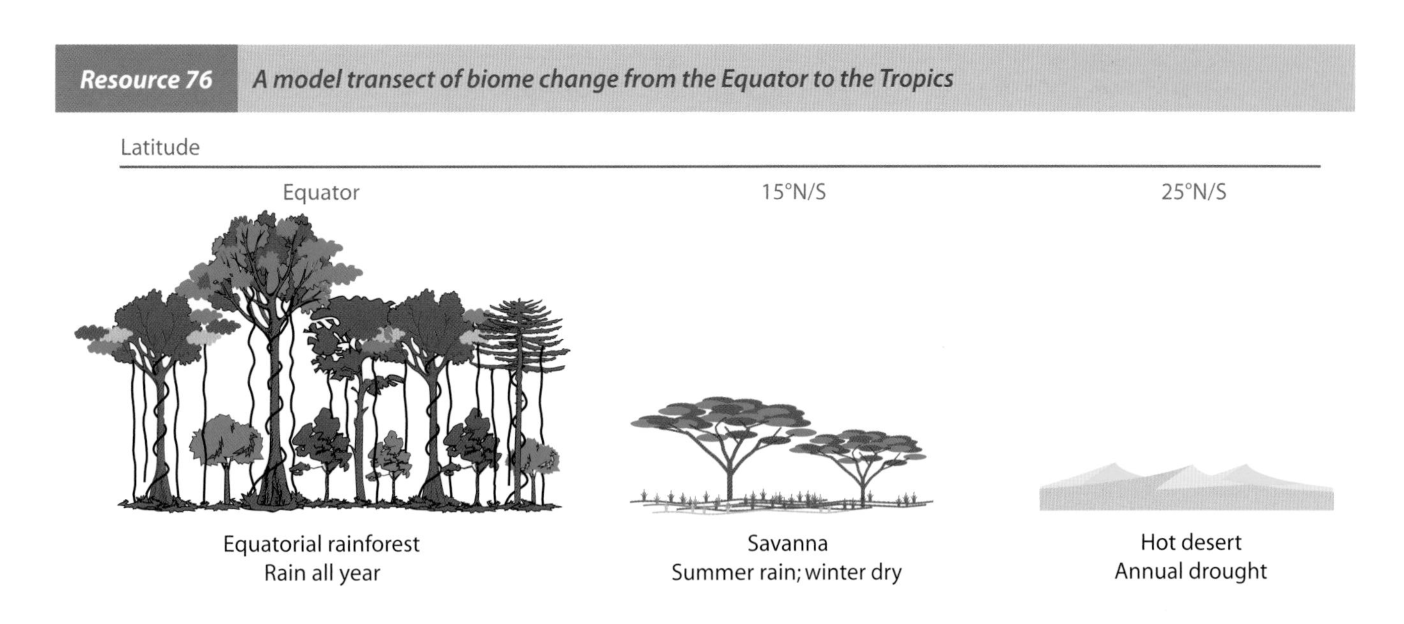

The climate characteristics of tropical (hot) deserts

1. Temperatures are high due to:
   - the clear skies that allow for high levels of daily and annual insolation
   - the long days and high angle of the sun during the summer
2. The seasonal difference in temperatures is between warm and very hot.
3. Rainfall totals are low; the technical desert limit is an annual total below 250 mm. Any rainfall is most likely in the summer months, and is often confined to a few scattered periods of rain.

Explanation of the nature of the hot tropical desert climate

The hot desert climate is primarily the product of the second limb of the Hadley Cell.

Resource 77 *Climate statistics for a tropical desert location*

Ain Salah (27°N)	J	F	M	A	M	J	J	A	S	O	N	D
Temp (°C)	12	14	19	25	28	33	36	33	28	23	18	14
Rain (mm)	4	3	0	1	0	2	3	7	2	3	12	3

Ain Salah, Algeria – latitude 27°N
Annual temperature range is 24°C
Total rainfall = 40 mm

Resource 78 *Detail of subsiding limb of the Hadley Cell*

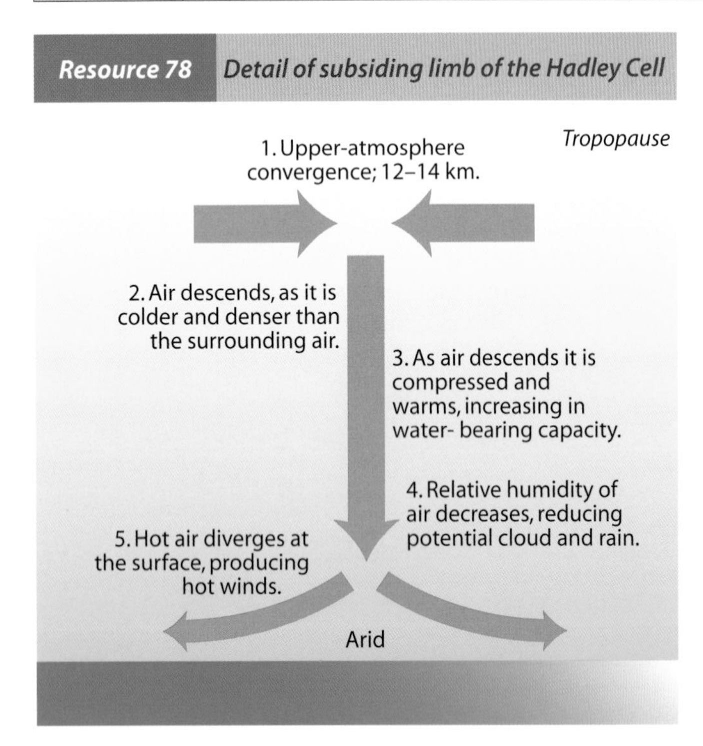

Around 20–30° north and south air descends from the tropopause towards the ground surface. This same air had risen above the equatorial region becoming dry as it lost its moisture as convectional cloud and rain. Having traveled away from the Equator in the upper tropopause the air now sinks to form high pressure conditions on the surface. The tropical high pressure region is the source of the surface trade winds (**Resource 72**). As the air descends it becomes compressed and warms, this ensures that condensation of water vapour is unlikely and so cloud and rain rarely form over these regions (**Resource 78**).

As skies are clear in these latitudes then daytime temperatures are likely to become hot (up to 45°C), especially in the summer when the sun is at its highest and the days may be up to 14 hours long. A feature of the tropical deserts is that the daily or diurnal temperature range is often very high, even 30°C or more. Surfaces heat up rapidly during long cloudless days but under the same clear skies they cool rapidly at night.

Other than the Sahara and Arabian Deserts, most tropical deserts are focused on the western sides of continents. This is due to the occurrence of offshore cold ocean currents that prevent moist air being carried onto the land bringing rain to these regions. The Atacama Desert of Peru is the world's driest, with some places having no recorded rain in over 60 years.

The climate characteristics of tropical grasslands

The climate statistics for Sokoto in Nigeria (**Resource 79**) show the seasonal contrasts of the tropical grassland region between a 'winter' drought and the 'summer' rain. The wet or rainy season lasts between five and nine months, with annual totals between 400 and 1,500 mm. The annual rainfall total often varies unpredictably by 50–70% from the long-term average. Temperatures vary little, remaining hot, normally over 22°C during the year. The expected summer maximum is reduced by the cloud cover associated with the seasonal rains. Annual solar energy inputs are high and desiccating (drying) winds are common, especially in the winter drought season.

Resource 79 *Climate statistics for a tropical grassland location*

Sokoto (13°N)	J	F	M	A	M	J	J	A	S	O	N	D
Temp (°C)	24	26	31	33	33	30	28	29	27	29	27	25
Rain (mm)	0	0	3	10	43	94	152	244	132	13	0	0

Sokoto, Nigeria, latitude 13°N
Annual temperature range is 9°C
Total rainfall = 691 mm

Explanation of the nature of the wet or dry tropical grassland climate

The tropical wet and dry climate is one of the most significant in the world. Around one third of the world's six billion plus population lives under it. The most extreme version is the monsoon climate of south-east Asia but it is common to all regions between the Equatorial hot, wet climate and the hot dry deserts. At its simplest these areas are the transition zone between the two systems, humid and desert, already described.

The low pressure and rains of the ITCZ follow the overhead sun as it migrates during the year, so regions further from the equator receive a period of rain during their summer months. Six months later, as the overhead sun moves away, the high pressure dry conditions of the higher tropics move in to give a dry winter season. It should be noted that while the position of the overhead sun travels between the Tropics of Capricorn (23.5°S) and Cancer (23.5°N), a total 47 degrees of latitude, the pressure and wind belts do not, normally shift so far.

Map of low latitude surface winds and pressure belts ***Resource 80***

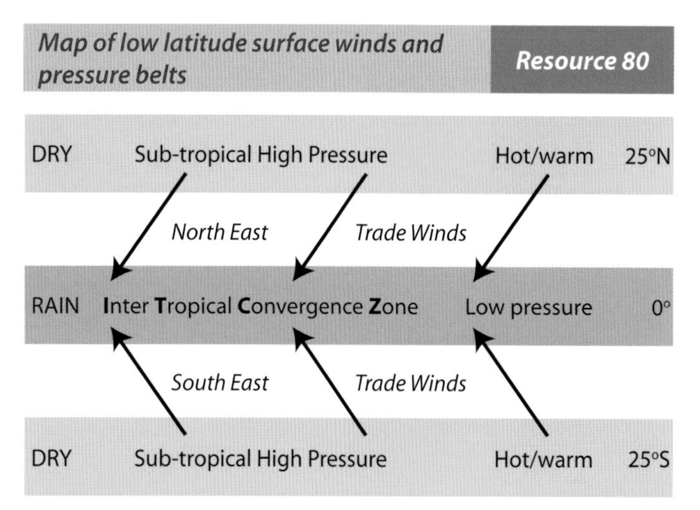

An illustrative exercise of wet and dry tropical climate

To illustrate the seasonal variation make a tracing overlay of the pressure belts and winds shown on **Resource 80**, then move them 10° north of the equator to represent their position in the northern hemisphere's summer and then move 10° south of the equator to represent its winter position, you can recreate the seasonal wet and dry seasons for regions around 6–15° in each hemisphere.

Exercise

Using the same scale as the climate graph for the tropical forest climate, Uaupes **Resource 74**:

1. Draw, on tracing paper the climate graph for Ain Salah, tropical desert location, using the figures in **Resource 77**.
2. Draw, on tracing paper the climate graph for, Sokoto, tropical grassland location, using the figures in **Resource 79**.
3. Describe and account for the impact of latitude on:
   a) the annual temperature range
   b) the total rainfall
   c) the seasonal variation in rainfall

Figures 1 and **2**, overleaf, for Australia and Papua New Guinea.

(i) Identify the tropical biomes that would be found at A, B and C. (3)

(ii) *Question from CCEA June 2006*
Account for the rainfall and temperature patterns at any two of the locations. (10)

Exercise continued

Figure 1

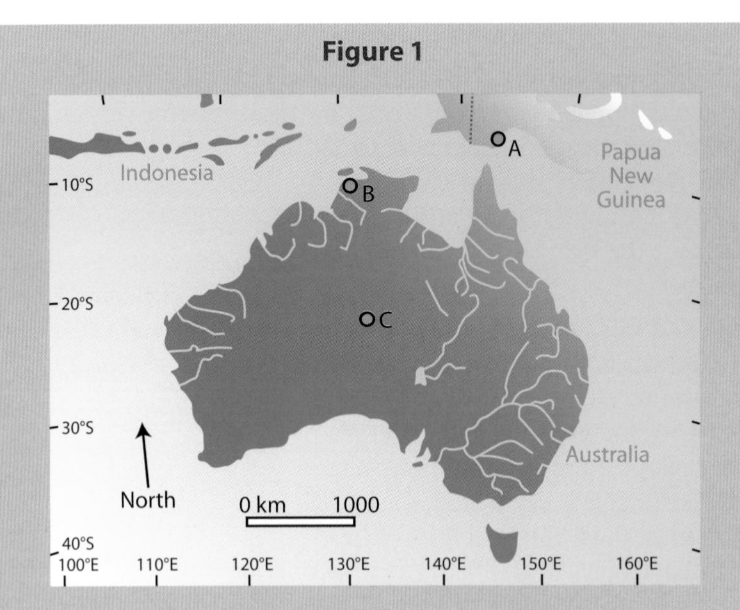

Figure 2

A – Daru, Papua New Guinea, Latitude 9°S	
Temperature (°C)	January – 28°C July – 26°C Annual range – 2°C
Rainfall (mm)	Total Annual – 2,500 mm Months with over 40 mm rain – 12

B – Darwin, Australia, Latitude 12°S	
Temperature (°C)	January – 29°C July – 24°C Annual range – 5°C
Rainfall (mm)	Total Annual – 1,630 mm Months with over 40 mm rain – 7

C – Alice Springs, Australia, Latitude 24°S	
Temperature (°C)	January – 29°C July – 12°C Annual range – 17°C
Rainfall (mm)	Total Annual – 256 mm Months with over 40 mm rain – 1

B2 ECOSYSTEM PROCESSES IN THE TROPICAL FOREST ENVIRONMENT

Biomass and productivity

These are terms that are used to measure and describe how effective an ecosystem is in converting solar energy (insolation) into plant energy. Photosynthesis takes place in plants when light energy from the sun allows carbon dioxide and water to be transformed into glucose and oxygen. The product of photosynthesis is chemical energy, the basis for the exchange of energy in the feeding (trophic) levels of the ecosystem.

The term **biomass** is used to describe the total amount of living organic matter in an area or biome. It comprises both plant and animal material and is usually measured by weight either as a total or an average per unit of area. In a particular woodland area the biomass could be stated as the total weight of all the trees, all other plants and animals living in or on the trees and in the soil. The table in **Resource 81** contains biomass figures, both total and average for several tropical biomes.

Biomass and productivity figures for three tropical biomes **Resource 81**

BIOME	Total Biomass (billion tonnes)	Average Biomass (kg/m^2)	Total NPP (billion tonnes/yr)	Average NPP ($g/m^2/yr$)
Grassland (Savanna)	60	4.0	13.5	900
Tropical Rainforest	765	4.5	37.4	3200
Tropical hot desert	13	0.7	1.6	90

Productivity

The rate at which an ecosystem is able to produce material is called its **productivity** and the first or **primary productivity** concerns the plants or producers that form the foundation of any ecosystem or biome. The **Primary Productivity Index (PPI)** is a measure of the rate at which sunlight energy is fixed by plants through photosynthesis in a given area. In simple terms, it is the amount of plant growth in a given area over a given period of time. Primary productivity is recorded by two indices:

1. **Gross Primary Productivity (GPP)** is the rate of energy fixed by green plants.
2. **Net Primary Productivity or (NPP)** is equal to the GPP less the energy used by plants for respiration and other life processes. Productivity in ecosystems is often measured in grams per square metre ($g/m^2/yr$) or as kilograms per hectare per year (kg/ha/yr).

Net primary productivity shows the amount of energy available from plants for the consumers at the next trophic level, namely the herbivores. Figures for net primary productivity in tropical ecosystems vary widely, with the highest values of around 3,200 $g/m^2/year$ found in tropical rainforest (**Resource 81**).

Trophic structure

All ecosystems are based on the 'capture' of solar energy (insolation) by the process of photosynthesis. This chemical energy (food) is then used, transferred or lost through a series of feeding steps or **trophic levels**. The diagram, **Resource 82**, shows a standard outline trophic structure which may be applied to both large and small-scale ecosystems, terrestrial (land-

Resource 82 *Trophic Pyramid*

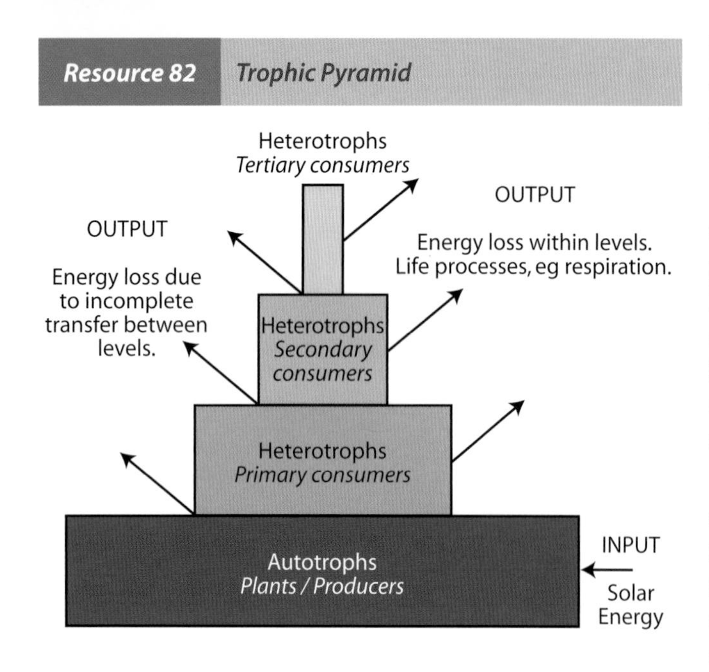

based) and aquatic or marine (water-based). The diagram is commonly known as a trophic pyramid as the energy and amount of living matter (biomass) declines from the base upwards.

Plants or **producers** are the organisms at the base of the food chain (**autotrophs**). Animals which eat the plants, **herbivores,** are the first or **primary consumers**. Herbivores are the energy source for secondary consumers, the **carnivores**. The fourth trophic level is occupied by the **top carnivores** or **omnivores**. All organisms that depend on other organisms for their energy and food are called **heterotrophs**.

The trophic pyramid is a representation of the exchange of energy through an ecosystem. At every trophic level organisms use energy in their life processes (termed **respiration**) and this energy is lost from the ecosystem into the environment, usually as heat. Also, at each transfer of energy, such as a caterpillar consuming a leaf or an anteater an ant, energy is lost from the system. This is why ecosystems rarely have more than three levels of consumers: herbivores → carnivores → top carnivores as so much energy is lost in life and at each transfer point. Remember energy can only enter the system at the producer level by photosynthesis and it cannot be recycled back into the process. In short, ecosystems always need an input of solar energy to keep going. That is why in temperate latitudes, including Ireland, plants have a season of inactivity during the short days of winter when the quality and quantity of sunlight is inadequate for active photosynthesis. There is no such problem in the tropics where the length of daylight and the high angle of the sun ensure abundant light is available throughout the year.

Nutrient cycling

Energy is transferred through ecosystems but not recycled, as it is lost through the life and transfer processes into the environment (**Resource 82**). On the other hand material, including essential plant nutrients, is recycled by decomposition and incorporation into the soil. This is **nutrient cycling** and it is vital in the efficient and long-term maintenance of any ecosystem. Plant foods or **nutrients** include a range of materials such as nitrogen, potassium, oxygen, sodium, calcium and phosphate. The key players in this recycling process are the **decomposers** (the fifth trophic level). These include bacteria and larger organisms, such as fungi, that breakdown the dead organic material (DOM) that falls to the ground as **litter**. Decomposers cause this material to decompose and to become incorporated back into the underlying soil. From here the nutrients are then available to be taken up in soil water by plant roots and re-enter the living part of the ecosystem. All these elements and processes are combined and illustrated in **Resource 83.**

The nutrient cycle model, first developed by Gersmehl (**Resource 84**), shows that any ecosystem, from a simple freshwater pond to the most complex global scale biome has three stores of nutrient material:

1. Soil – the physical medium in which plants grow
2. Biomass – the living material itself, plants and animals
3. Litter – dead organic material often on the soil surface

Nutrients move between these three stores in a unidirectional way: from soil to the biomass, then to litter, before returning to soil.

Resource 84 also shows the two inputs and two outputs of nutrients in an ecosystem.

Energy and material flows in an ecosystem **Resource 83**

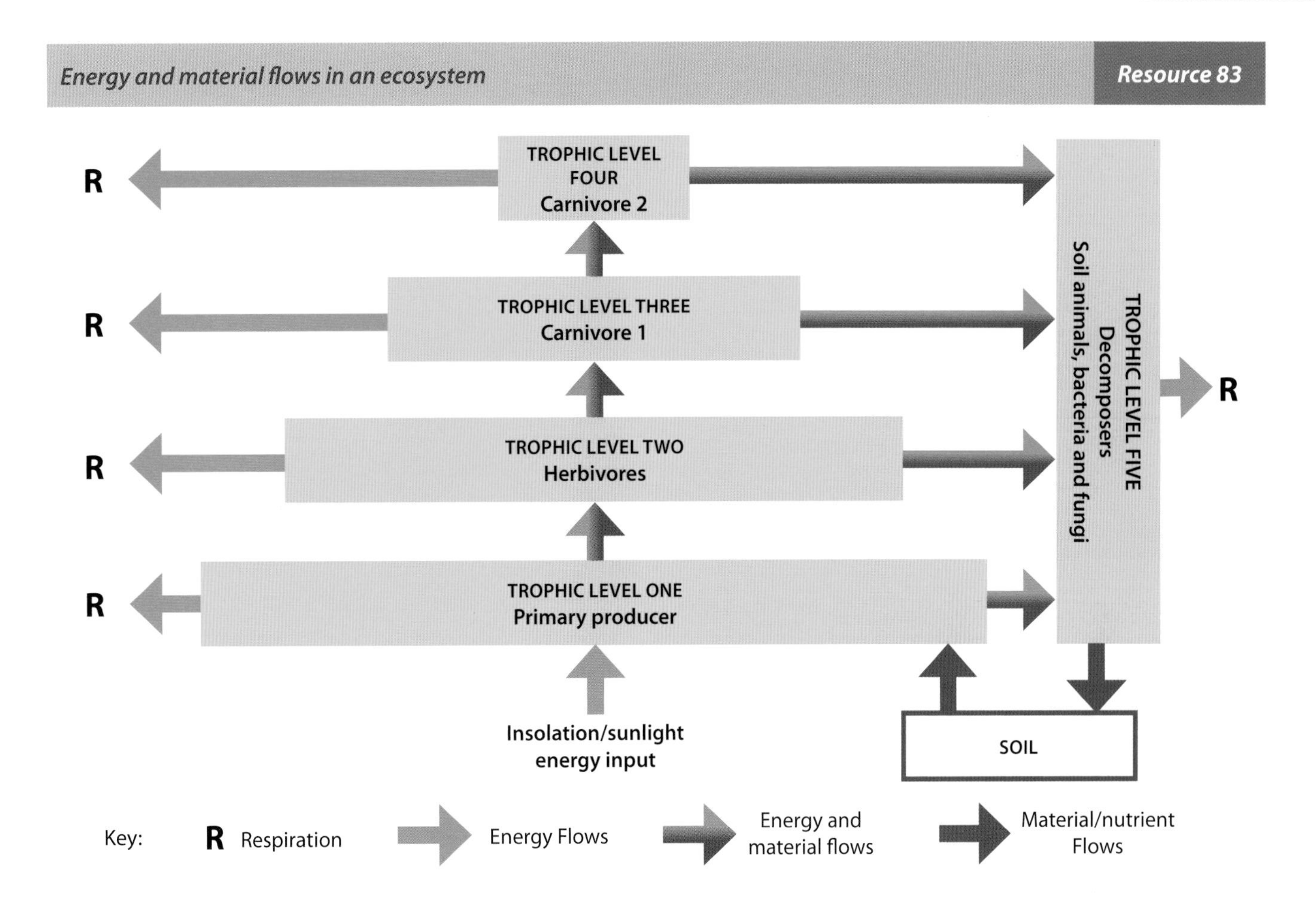

Rainfall and the rock beneath the soil are sources of nutrient material, while water in the form of surface runoff and leaching through soils cause nutrient loss. The most useful feature of the nutrient model is that when it is applied to a particular ecosystem, the width of the arrows and the size of the circles may be used to indicate the relative importance of the flows or stores in the ecosystem (as in **Resource 94**).

A model of nutrient cycling **Resource 84**

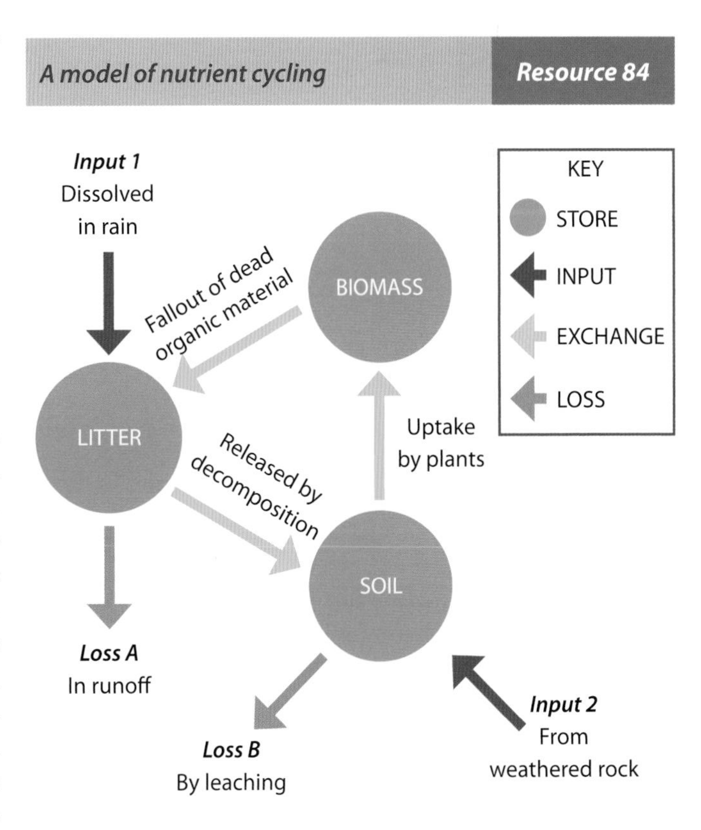

Zonal soils

Soils are defined as zonal when their nature is determined by and reflects the climatic nature of a world region. In reality soils vary over short distances, for example, at different points on a hillside or where the underlying rock type changes but zonal soils illustrate the dominant control of a region's climate. Soils are commonly represented by drawing a cross section showing their nature from the surface down to the underlying rock or **parent material.** Such a diagram with layers or **horizons** identified along with other characteristics is called a **soil profile**. All soils are said to have three horizons, each of which may be sub-divided to show distinctive characteristics. The layer or horizon near the surface is the **top soil** or **A-horizon**

Resource 85 *Outline soil profile model*

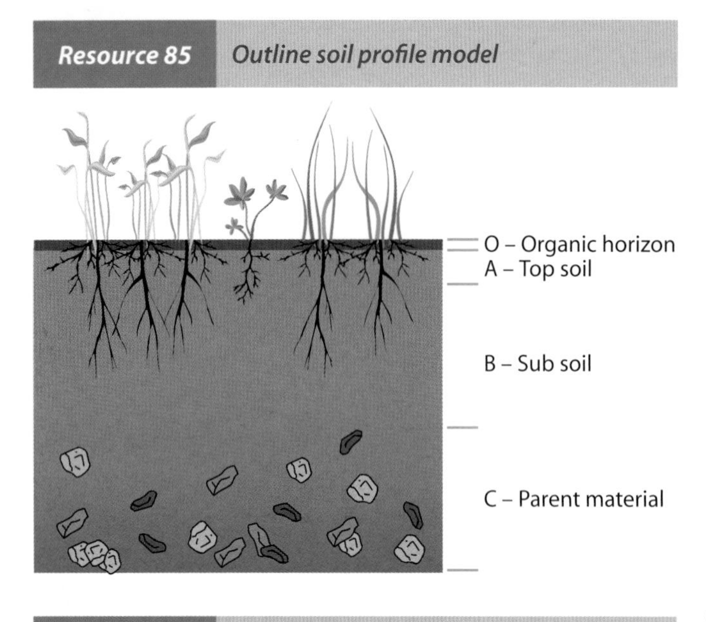

Resource 86 *Oxisol Profile*

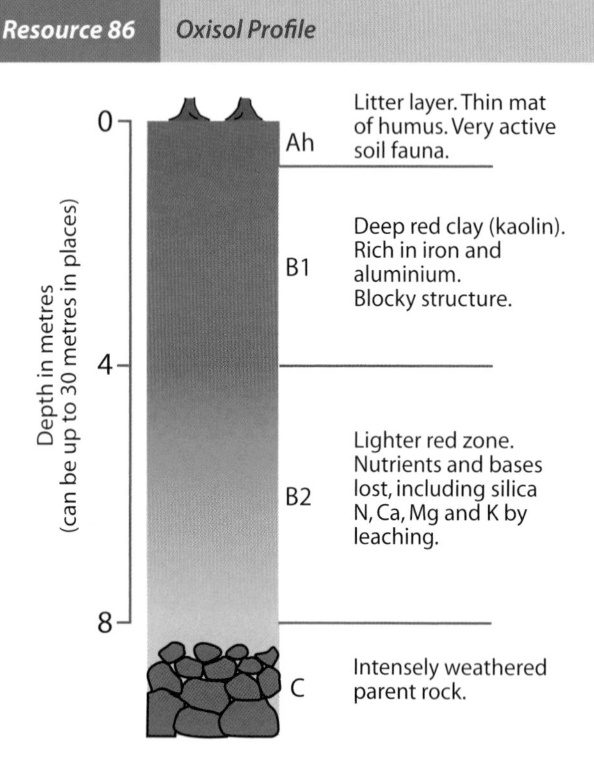

and often contains organic material from dead plants and animals. Beneath this is the **sub-soil** or **B-horizon**, which rests on the underlying geological rock which may be hard rock or soft deposited material such as sand or clay – the **C-horizon** (**Resource 85**).

Oxisol zonal soil – the zonal soil of the tropical forests

Soils beneath most tropical forests have severe limitations due to acidity, low nutrient status or poor drainage. The terms **oxisol**, **latosol** or **ferralitic soil** are all used to describe the zonal profile, though a great deal of local variation exists due to differences in geology, relief and drainage conditions. The use of the term ferralitic to describe tropical forest soils reflects the importance of iron compounds in their appearance and chemistry. The soil profile diagram (**Resource 86**) shows the most common features of these soils and the processes involved in their development.

The tropical forest ecosystem

Tropical rainforests cover 5% of the Earth's land surface. The forest varies in nature from swamp or wetland forest, montane forests in highland regions, to the classic closed forest of lowland equatorial regions known as **selvas**. Closed forest refers to biomes with a complete canopy cover high above the ground. Plant and animal species are numerous and the number of known species increases almost daily as remote forests in places such as the Congo Basin, Peruvian highlands and Borneo are explored (**Resource 87**).

Resource 87

New monkey species found in remote Amazon

A previously unknown species of uakari monkey was found during recent hunting trips in the Amazon... [Jean-Phillipe Boubli a New Zealand primatologist announced] he found the animal after following native Yanomamo Indians on their hunts along...a tributary of the Rio Negro [in the Amazon Basin] in Brazil. "They told us about this black uakari monkey, which was different to the one we knew..." Boubli said...Boubli named the new monkey Cacajao ayresii after a Brazilian biologist José Ayres...[Worryingly the newfound monkey] appears to live in a very small area outside any preserve [(protected zone)] and is hunted by locals. "We're going to have to create a park or reserve, because [its habitat is] not a protected area," he said. "The population is quite small, so they are quite vulnerable. I'm a bit concerned...Finding a relatively large monkey as a new species these days is pretty cool...It shows how little we really know about the biodiversity of the Amazon."

In 2003 Boubli described another new species from the region, the bearded saki. And he believes that new types of spider monkeys, squirrel monkeys, and capuchin monkeys await confirmation. "If we are still finding monkeys, imagine how many invertebrates and things like that are still out there. It's pretty amazing."

Source: D Hansford, National Geographic News, 4 February 2008, http://tinyurl.com/nwmnua, accessed 21 August 2009

Photograph montage of rainforest producers and consumers **Resource 88**

CASE STUDY: The Amazon Basin

Location and environment

Despite nearly 40 years of large-scale clearance and development, the tropical rainforest of the Amazon Basin in South America remains the largest single extent of this biome on Earth. The Amazon, now officially the world's longest river, has a total of 80,000 km of channel and drains 40% of South America (6.4 million km^2). While most of the basin consists of flat lowland below 200 m, in the west it rises on the high slopes of the Andes Mountains. The Amazon Basin extends beyond Brazil's borders into Ecuador, Bolivia, Colombia and Peru, but within Brazil itself lies over five million km^2. This river carries to the sea each day a discharge equal to the total annual flow of the River Thames! The Amazon Basin includes land adjacent to its river channels which is flooded annually. The river level at Manaus, 1,600 km from the mouth, varies annually by 12 m with the result that places up to 50 km from the river itself are flooded. These floodplains, called **varzeas**, cover about 2% of the basin; have more fertile soils; and a distinct and abundant ecosystem. The higher drier forests are referred to as **terra firme**. Here, despite infertile soils the diversity of plant and animal life is astounding, for example, one fifth of the entire planet's bird species live there.

Resource 89 *The varzea (flooded forest) near Manaus*

Source: H Adams and M Stanley

Resource 90 *Amazon Basin map*

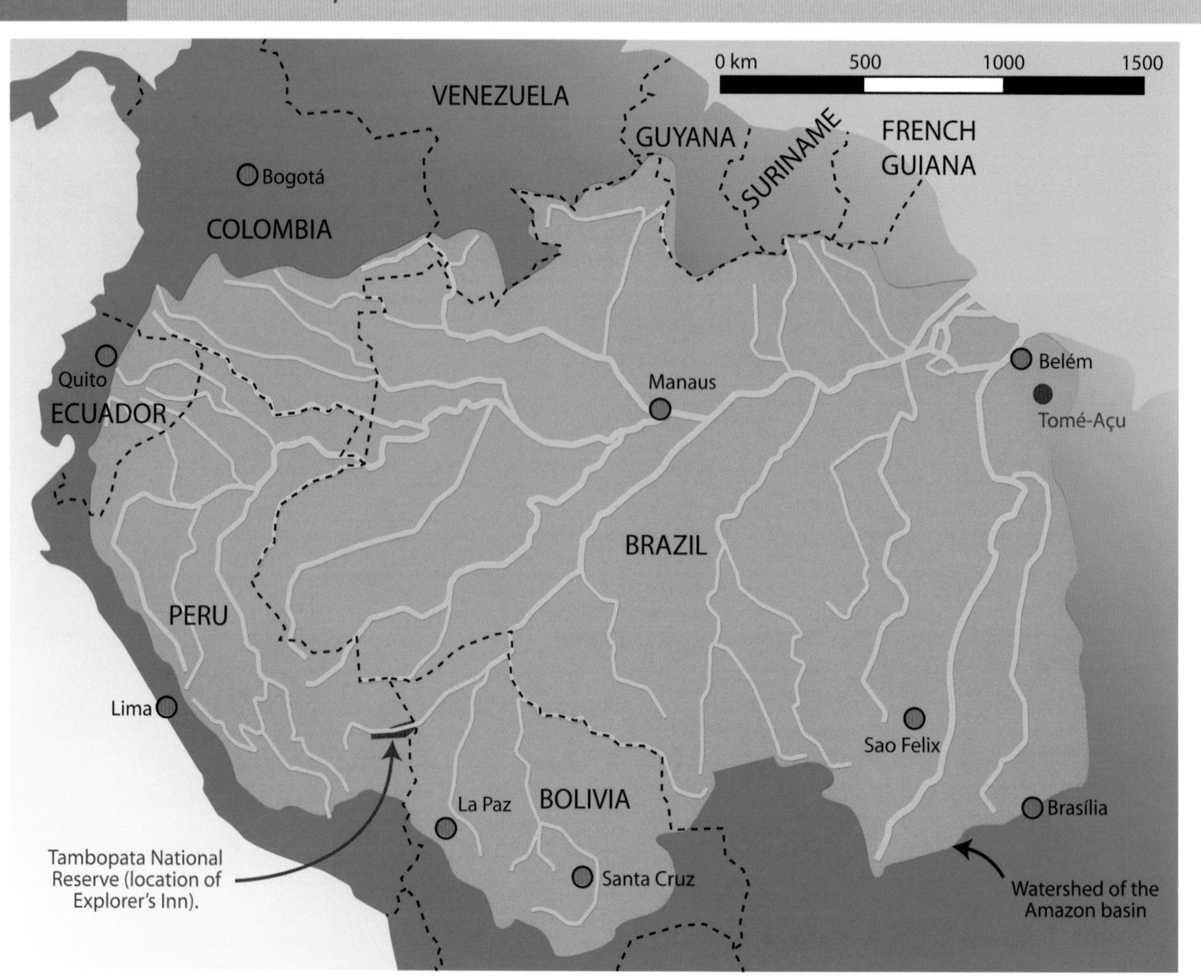

Biomass, productivity and trophic structure

Superlatives abound when describing the tropical forest. Statistically its enormous biomass and its incredible rates of productivity make it the world's leading land-based ecosystem. A typical **biomass** figure for the Amazon forest is **48 kg/m²** compared to 26 kg/m² in the temperate deciduous forests of Europe. In Brazil's forests **net primary productivity** (NPP) values of up to **3,200 g/m²/yr** are recorded. The ideal climatic growing conditions have ensured that a vast range of species thrive in the region. In Peru 43 species of ant have been recorded in a single tree. The 40,000 recorded plant species of the Amazon forests include some prized for hardwood timber: mahogany, ebony, rosewood and greenheart; others for food: brazil nuts, from the castanheiro tree, cocoa (chocolate) and sweet potato; and still others for industrial raw materials: the rubber tree (Hevea brasiliensis). **Resource 91** shows a cross-section view of the forest ecosystem with the key plant features identified. Trees are very tall, with the highest emergent species reaching 50 m, the height of an 18 storey building. The trees have long, smooth, relatively narrow trunks with few branches until the large crown near the top. This height, trunk form and heavy crown combined with shallow roots makes for an unstable tree but many have buttress or plank roots (**Resource 88**). These extend above ground reaching three or four metres above the soil surface to support these giant plants. The tree root networks are shallow as they extend to gather nutrients from the thin surface organic layer. Beneath

Tropical forest structure and plant adaptation **Resource 91**

Structure	Micro-habitat	Organisms
Emergent layer	Exposure to winds and full sunlight. Large daily temperature variation.	The tallest trees with broad crowns, slender trunks (boles) with few branches. Lianas and epiphytic flowers.
Canopy layer	Absorbs 70–80% of solar insolation.	Continuous layer of crowns of smaller or younger trees. Lianas and creepers. Main habitat for forest animals, including climbing mammals.
Shrub layer	Dark, drier with less temperature variation.	Young trees, often species that bear flowers and fruit on trunks and branches. Animals often move between trees and ground.
Ground layer	Sheltered, little daily temperature change. Little wind and slow growth due to heavy shading.	Tall ferns but little else, buttress roots of trees and some seedlings especially below any gaps in canopy. Termites, ants, bacteria and fungi are common.

the taller emergent trees is a continuous canopy of green, like a vast sea when viewed from above. In the gloom beneath this is an understorey of young tree saplings, the immature future canopy, along with smaller tree species. One common misconception of the Amazonian forests is that they are impenetrable at ground level. In reality it is only along river banks and in clearings that any ground flora is able to flourish. In the closed forest the canopy created by tree crowns blocks out almost all light, 90% in many cases, severely limiting the ground flora. Some ground species have seeds that will remain dormant for decades until light triggers their growth cycle. When a break appears in the canopy, perhaps due to a tree fall, a range of small species will germinate, grow and seed all within the short time it takes for the gap to be closed. Unable to survive beneath the canopy, numerous smaller plants actually live on the trees. These are epiphytes – ferns and flowers including orchids, which commonly seed themselves where a branch meets the main trunk. Here organic material gathers with moisture, enough to support these symbiotic plants in the sunshine of the canopy layer. The Amazon Basin alone supports over 500 species of orchid. Woody lianas hang down from the tree branches and take root in the ground while other plant species grow up the tree using it for support. Some plants live off the trees as parasites and these may eventually kill their hosts.

Micro-habitat

The fauna of the forest also has a layered element, often termed **stratum specificity**. Squirrel, howler monkey and bird species including macaws are found high in tree canopies with poison frogs, tapir, peccary and antelope species on the ground. The jaguar, a large cat, prowls both environments while insect species by the thousand inhabit every habitat. Within the streams that drain the Amazon Basin are 2,000 known species of fish, more than in the whole of the Atlantic Ocean itself. Some 600 bird species (20% of the Earth's total) are found in this one region and the total animal species present is several million, mostly insects. However, such abundance does not mean that the biome is a stable and resilient system. Despite the biodiversity of these forests, the number of any one species may be small as they inhabit one highly specific niche in the habitat. This in turn means that plants and animal species are vulnerable and that any interference, even over a small area, may cause extinction.

Resource 92 *A simplified Amazon rainforest food web (Brazil)*

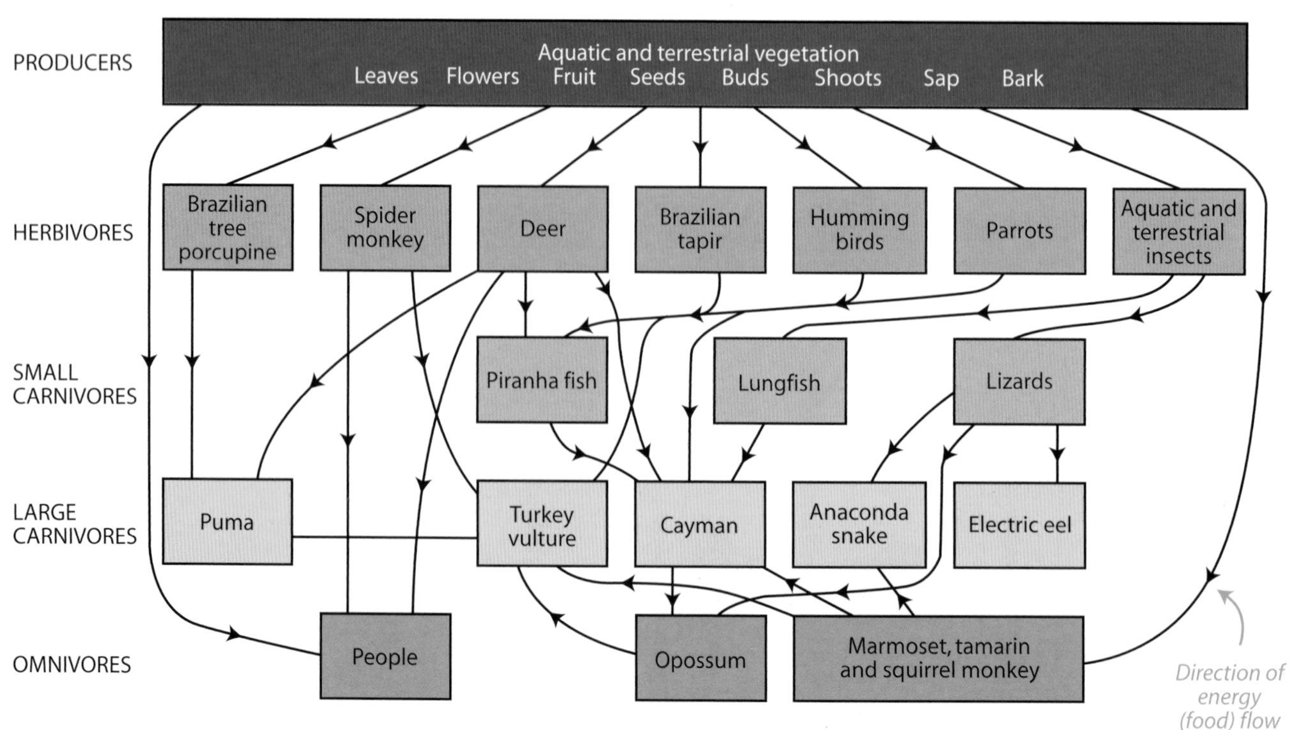

An outline trophic structure of the Amazon forest **Resource 93**

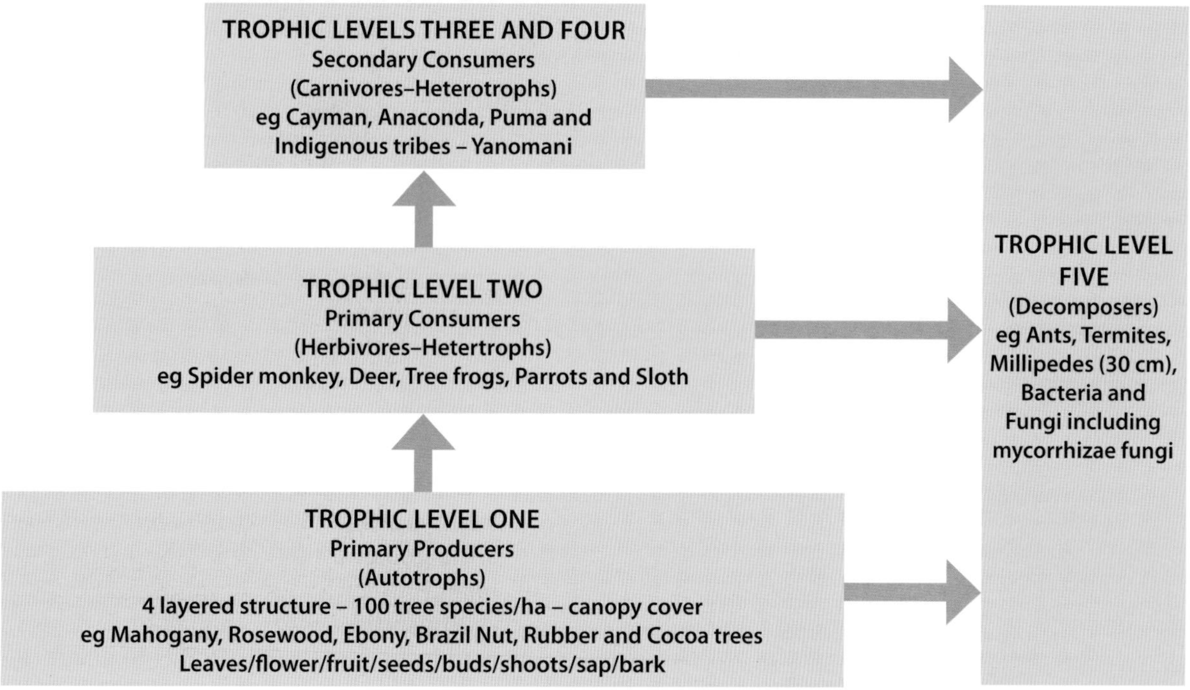

TROPHIC LEVELS THREE AND FOUR
Secondary Consumers
(Carnivores–Heterotrophs)
eg Cayman, Anaconda, Puma and
Indigenous tribes – Yanomani

TROPHIC LEVEL TWO
Primary Consumers
(Herbivores–Hetertrophs)
eg Spider monkey, Deer, Tree frogs, Parrots and Sloth

TROPHIC LEVEL ONE
Primary Producers
(Autotrophs)
4 layered structure – 100 tree species/ha – canopy cover
eg Mahogany, Rosewood, Ebony, Brazil Nut, Rubber and Cocoa trees
Leaves/flower/fruit/seeds/buds/shoots/sap/bark

TROPHIC LEVEL FIVE
(Decomposers)
eg Ants, Termites,
Millipedes (30 cm),
Bacteria and
Fungi including
mycorrhizae fungi

As in all ecosystems these fish, bird, mammal and insect species depend on the producers or plants and these are as diverse in nature and number as the fauna. The interrelationships within the ecosystem are incredibly complex and research has only begun to comprehend their nature. Many species depend utterly on another species for survival. For instance, some orchid species are pollinated by a single species of bee while some sloth species can consume the leaves of only one type of tree. In the Amazon River itself up to 200 of its fish species depend on a diet of tree seeds that fall from overhanging branches.

The vast productivity of the Amazonian forests, illustrated by its huge biomass and wide diversity of species, is a reflection of two key factors: climate and time.

1) Climate is fundamental to the richness of the Amazon's luxuriant flora and fauna. As far as vegetation is concerned the bright, hot and humid climate of this region represents the perfect environment for growth:
   - Long hours of uninterrupted photosynthesis throughout 12 months of the year.
   - No temperature limitation – frost is unknown.
   - A continuous and abundant water supply from rainfall.

2) The Amazon Basin forests are ancient. While successive glaciations have repeatedly rewritten the landscapes and climate of the higher latitudes, including the hot deserts, many equatorial regions have remained stable. While Europe's ecosystems are less than 20,000 years old, it is estimated that the Amazon forest is five hundred times older as it has existed for ten million years. This fact alone may explain its bio-diversity, as evolutionary processes have developed numerous responses to the various ecological niches available. Stability is a critical element in the development of an ecosystem.

One puzzle is that despite the luxuriant vegetation and diverse animal life, the underlying soils, known as Terra Rosa in the Amazon, are often nutrient poor. The abundance of these

Resource 94 *Nutrient cycling in tropical forest ecosystems*

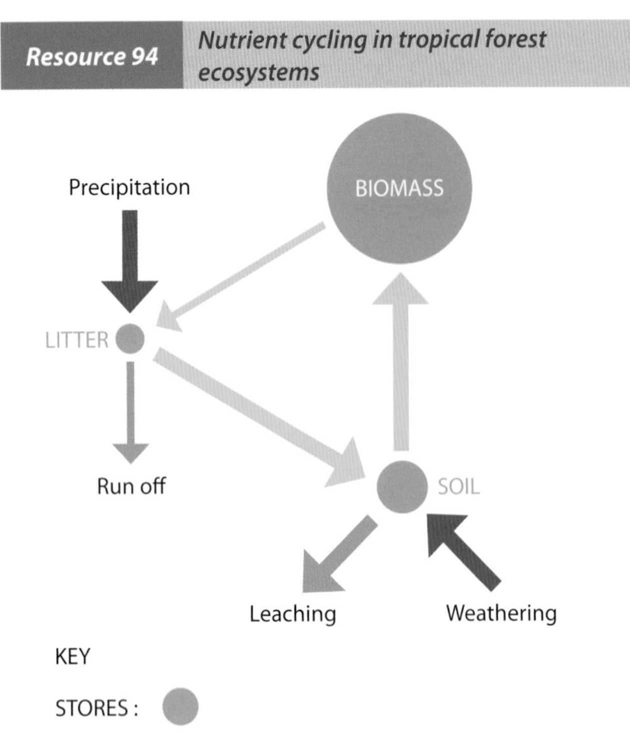

tropical forests does not depend on good soil nutrition but rather on the ability of these ecosystems to recycle dead organic material extremely rapidly.

Nutrient cycling

The nutrient cycle model for tropical forests (**Resource 94**) indicates that most nutrients, up to 90%, are locked into the living elements of the ecosystem (the biomass store). Litter is continuously falling to the ground where it rapidly decomposes in the presence of hot, wet conditions and abundant active decomposers – bacteria, fungi and insects. Experiments have shown that leaves can be broken down and recycled ten times faster under tropical forest than in European forests. The soils contain minimal quantities of nutrients as these are rapidly taken up by plant roots or risk being leached downwards beyond their reach. In tropical forests the soil is less a store, as it is in most other ecosystems, and more a routeway for nutrients. In the Amazon Basin, organisms including termites, leaf cutter ants, moulds and parasites ensure that all litter decomposes rapidly under the forest cover. In this highly developed ecosystem some nutrient transfer processes actually by-pass the soil altogether. Litter may fall onto plant roots above the ground and these are commonly covered by specialist fungi termed mycorrhizae. These break down the litter and can directly transfer the nutrients to plants through the finer roots themselves. Experimental work in the Amazon showed that recycling was highly efficient with up to 99% of nutrients such as calcium and phosphorus being taken up by vegetation, leaving only 1% in the soil water.

The characteristics of oxisols beneath the Amazonian forest

- Deep profiles due to long-term and intense chemical weathering of the parent material. Soils are commonly 10–20 m deep, resting on even more weathered rock or regolith beneath.
- Iron and aluminium compounds are left to dominate the top-soil as other minerals are leached downwards to the subsoil or out of the soil in solution. The high iron content of the heavily weathered and leached soils of the Amazon rainforest earned them the name Terra Rossa or red earths, though yellow-red soils are also common. In the 1970s the clearance of forest to make the Trans-Amazonian Highway left, on the unsurfaced road section, bright blood red scars where the soils were exposed to the sky.
- In fertility terms studies show that 90% of Amazonian soils lack the essential nutrients, nitrogen and phosphorus, while 80% are short of aluminium and potassium. Only on the varzea floodplains are fertile soils found. Here the regular inundation of the land provides new nutrients to replace those so efficiently leached beyond plant roots by the intense rainfall (**Resource 89**).
- The boundaries between the soil horizons are normally indistinct, due to mixing by soil organisms and the downward movement of soil water. Humus is limited in quantity and often confined to the surface 10 cm of the top soil.
- As precipitation exceeds even the high evapotranspiration rates of these climates, downward soil water movement dominates and thus strong leaching occurs.
- Intense leaching and rapid organic decay creates acid soils with low pH values. Water passing through the soil increases its acidity from the organic acids released by decomposition.

Hydrogen cations in the water replace soil nutrients carrying them down and out of the soil. Even the normally stable silica is leached and a concentration of iron and aluminium oxides (sesquioxides) is left in the soil. This may inhibit soil drainage but the greatest impact is seen after forest clearance. Soil erosion may expose this layer at the surface and under these circumstances it dries and hardens into a crust or **laterite** which will support little if any vegetation.

Exercise

1. Distinguish between biomass and productivity giving values for a tropical rainforest you have studied. (4)
2. ***Question from CCEA June 2004***
   Study the diagram showing nutrient cycling in tropical forests under: (A) Natural Conditions and (B) under Plantation Agriculture.

   Describe and explain the changes in the store and flows of nutrients caused by the introduction of the plantation system. (10)

(A) Natural Conditions

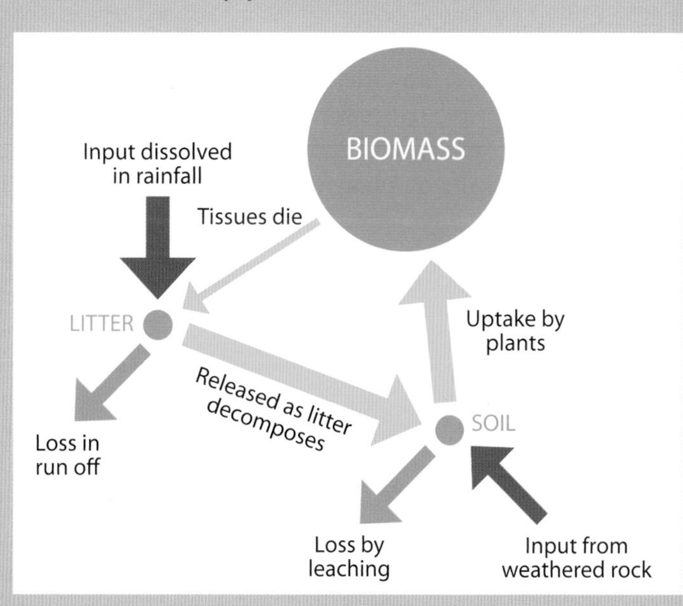

(B) Plantation Agriculture

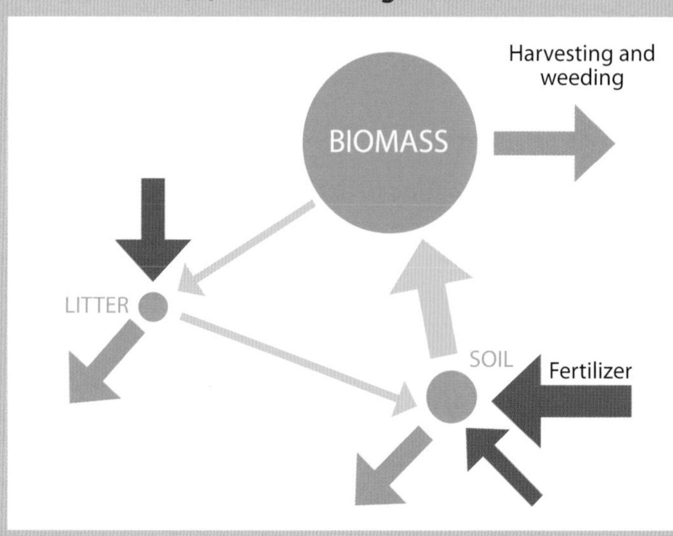

Note: **Plantation Agriculture** is a form of commercial farming in which large areas are planted with tree crops often as a monoculture. It is commonly used in tropical regions and examples include oil palm, rubber and banana plantations.

B3 MANAGEMENT AND SUSTAINABILITY WITHIN TROPICAL ECOSYSTEMS

Background

The tropics probably contain the origins of our own species, Homo sapiens sapiens. They certainly have helped to shape the development of human culture through the rise of some of the world's earliest civilization. In the arid and semi-arid tropics the need to increase food supply acted as a spur to develop effective agricultural systems linked to annual river flooding and irrigation. In the equatorial forests small groups of people have supplemented a hunting and gathering economy with small-scale agriculture for thousands of years. In most places trial and error led to systems that were in balance with their environment and therefore sustainable. The last 200 years have seen an unprecedented change in the tropics. World population growth and mass migration has put pressure on many of these tropical environments, forcing change and threatening destruction.

The rapid clearance of rainforests in the 1970s helped to stimulate the world to recognise the environmental threat and to develop the concept of sustainable development. Satellite images showed the Amazon Basin forests disappearing as roads opened the interior to thousands of migrants. Environmentalists quoted rates of expediential destruction that would leave the world without tropical forests within a lifetime. By the 1980s tropical environments were constantly in the news with headlines of drought, desertification and famine in the semi-arid regions and wanton clearance for short-term gain in the forests. The outcry reached a peak at the Earth Summit at Rio de Janeiro in 1992. This UN conference produced three essential documents:

- the Climate Change Convention, an international response to the threat of global warming;
- the Biodiversity Convention, concerning the protection of plant and animal species; and
- Agenda 21, a document proposing the adoption of policies to conserve and protect resources and the environment, ie Sustainable Development.

All three have important implications for development of tropical environments.

Sustainable development

Entire texts have been written attempting to define this term, but in essence it can be described as economic growth and social progress that does not damage the prospects of future generations. One approach to the issue is to identify distinct aspects of sustainability that need to be addressed in any integrated management scheme. In the context of a region where a subsistence primary economy exists then three forms of sustainability might be identified:

1. Environmental sustainability – can a management system be devised so that both local and global systems; soils, water and climate remain undamaged?
2. Agricultural sustainability – can the region produce a profitable output that can be maintained long-term?
3. Social sustainability – can the system maintain the existing social structure and not lead to exploitation, overpopulation or serious cultural change? Will all the social groups in the area benefit from the system?

Study 1: Management and sustainability in arid and semi-arid tropical environments

Water management in all its forms has numerous implications for any environment and most obviously in a semi-arid one. These implications are both positive and negative, in economic, social and environmental senses. Semi-arid environments are inherently fragile and reliance on their productivity is hazardous. Repeatedly the evidence indicates that people, both within and outside the region, must take a large proportion of the responsibility for the problems that have been created. Adding water to the land, or **irrigation**, has a long tradition in many regions, including the floodplains of rivers such as the Nile in Egypt, the Indus in Pakistan and the Colorado in the USA.

Irrigation is necessary if the limited and unreliable nature of rainfall in these regions is to be overcome. In arid or semi-arid tropical regions the length of the growing season is only limited by water supply: crops could be grown throughout the year if water was available. Indeed two or even three annual harvests may be possible. In some places irrigation has been used for thousands of years creating an effective and sustainable system. However, in many cases irrigation schemes have been plagued with problems and in particular salinisation of the soil.

What is irrigation and what forms does it take?

Irrigation is the artificial addition of water to the land. Some irrigation schemes entail simple redirecting of water, others are more radical in scale and transport.

Irrigation water in arid or semi-arid regions comes from one of the following sources:

- groundwater stores;
- perennial (permanent) rivers originating in wetter regions; or
- reservoirs filled during wet seasons.

Traditional irrigation schemes include **flood** or **basin irrigation** in which the water, usually diverted from a river in purpose-built canals, floods the fields and soaks downwards. Alternatively, water raised from rivers or wells flows along small channels or furrows onto the land. In either case water may be raised using a variety of people or animal powered devices. Modern systems can simply replace the lifting mechanisms with diesel-powered pumps or use more sophisticated and often more water efficient distribution, such as **drip** or **sprinkler irrigation**.

Irrigation and irrigated land Egypt and India **Resource 95**

Does irrigation work?

There are numerous large and small-scale irrigation schemes operating in the dry lands of Australia, Africa, the USA and the Indian sub-continent. Their aims are often similar and they also share common problems.

Resource 96 *Aims and problems of irrigation schemes*

Aims	Problems
• to extend the growing season • to overcome the unreliability of seasonal rain • to increase food production • to support a growing population • to grow cash crops to earn foreign income	• expense in set-up and running of scheme • overuse of the fragile soil • salinisation of soil due to evaporation • water logging as the water table rises • cash crops replace staple food crops • dependency on world cash crop prices

The problem of salinisation

Salinisation is a natural process. It is associated with environments in which evaporation rates are high and the water table is also high, ie near the soil surface. This second factor means that salinisation is less common in very arid regions but it is an issue in many semi-arid regions. Salinisation is a problem for, and often created by, irrigation schemes. The mechanisms that cause salinisation are illustrated in **Resource 97**. High temperatures rapidly dry out the top soil and a process of capillary action then draws moisture in the soil upwards towards the surface. Soil moisture contains soluble salts which, when the water evaporates into the air, are left at or near the soil surface. The most common deposited salts are various compounds of sodium, calcium, magnesium and potassium. The closer the underground water table is to the surface, the more chance there is that salinisation will occur – one common outcome of irrigation is the raising of water table levels.

While some plants, such as alfalfa, are tolerant of saline soil most do not thrive in these conditions. Salts necessary for plants may quickly become toxic to growth and development processes at higher concentrations. At between 0.5 and 1% concentration, salt will inhibit healthy plant development by preventing the uptake of water and essential nutrients. Consequently

Resource 97 *The salinisation process*

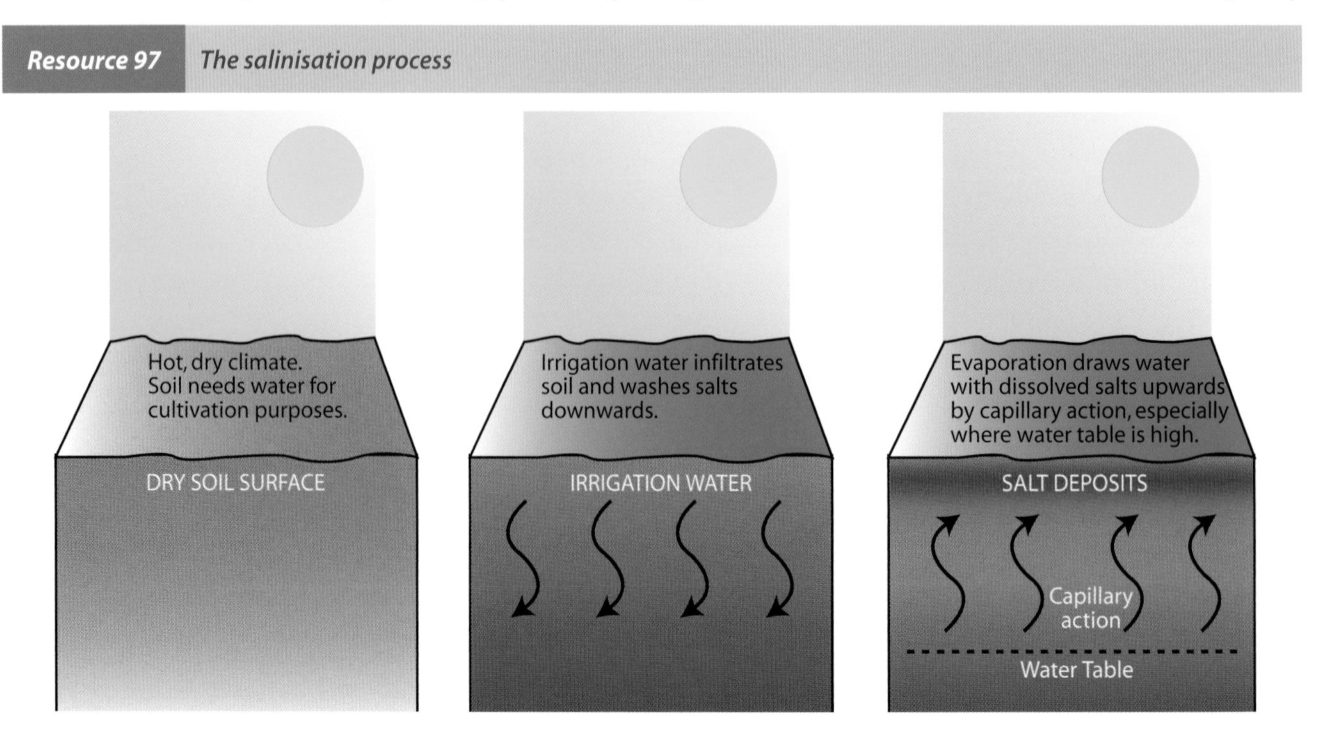

crop yields fall, reducing the economic viability of schemes and in extreme cases a salt crust forms on the soil surface and the land is abandoned entirely. The crux of the salinisation issue is excess water at or near the surface, if plants use up the available water or if the ground drainage system is effective then salinisation is unlikely to develop.

Several factors increase the risk of salinisation as the result of irrigation in tropical regions. Firstly, the sources of irrigation water are often saline in nature due to high evaporation rates associated with these climates. For example an exotic river, that is one that flows from a wet source environment into an arid region downstream, will quite naturally lose water by evaporation to the atmosphere. Even irrigation water of good quality, with a salt content of only 100 parts per million (ppm), may deposit 314 kg of salt on each hectare of irrigated land per year. If poor quality water is used, with a dissolved salt content of say 500 ppm, then evaporation could leave 5000 kg per hectare per year on or in the soil. Secondly, by definition semi-arid tropical areas have high rates of evaporation as a consequence of their hot and dry climate. Thirdly, the zonal soils of arid regions are termed aridisols and due to a lack of organic matter and chemical weathering they have low clay content so their sandy open texture may allow capillary action to occur. Further, while the aim of all irrigation is to add water for plant growth, too much can raise water table levels to within two or three metres of the surface. Ironically this may waterlog the sub-soil and the plant root zone, hindering growth while also encouraging capillary action and salt deposition. Finally, in low lying regions or where poor drainage exists, water can pond in the soil leading to evaporation and the risk of increasing salt concentrations in the upper soil.

Globally, it is estimated that 25% of all farmland is irrigated and over 40% of the world's food supply comes from irrigated land, but the Food and Agriculture Organisation (FAO) has calculated that for every new hectare of irrigated land, another hectare is being abandoned somewhere as a result of salinisation.

Solutions to salinisation

Preventing or reversing salinisation is dependant on the effective management of water flow. Although easily stated, this is often very difficult to achieve. For irrigation to be successful the supply of water must be enough to promote healthy plant growth but without causing water logging. At the same time there must be efficient drainage of surplus water. There are various options. Salts can be washed down and out of the soils by flushing them with water. This risks water logging the soil and making the issue worse unless adequate, usually expensive, drainage systems are provided. This may also increase the alkalinity of soil water to intolerable levels, pH8 or 9, as well as washing downwards important clay particles, so damaging the structure of the soil. Another possibility is to reduce the water input using drip or trickle irrigation systems. These involve underground or surface piping of water directly to plant roots and so virtually all water is used by the plants and returned by transpiration to the atmosphere without any infiltration or percolation to soil stores. An important drawback to such schemes is the high initial or capital expense which puts them beyond the reach of farmers in the marginal lands of semi-arid LEDCs.

CASE STUDY: The salinisation issues in Pakistan

Background and irrigation

Pakistan, a developing nation, struggles to meet the basic needs of its large and rapidly expanding population; currently 168 million and increasing by an average of three million per year. The region's ancient civilisation was based on the waters of the River Indus flowing through the Thar Desert. At their height the cities of Harappa and Mohenjo-daro rivaled any contemporary culture in Egypt or Mesopotamia. The climate of Southern Pakistan is that of a true hot desert, with less than 250 mm of annual rainfall, most of which falls during the brief summer wet monsoon in July and August. The high summer temperatures, often over 40°C, ensure a high rate of evaporation, leaving little effective rainfall for plant growth. The north of the country

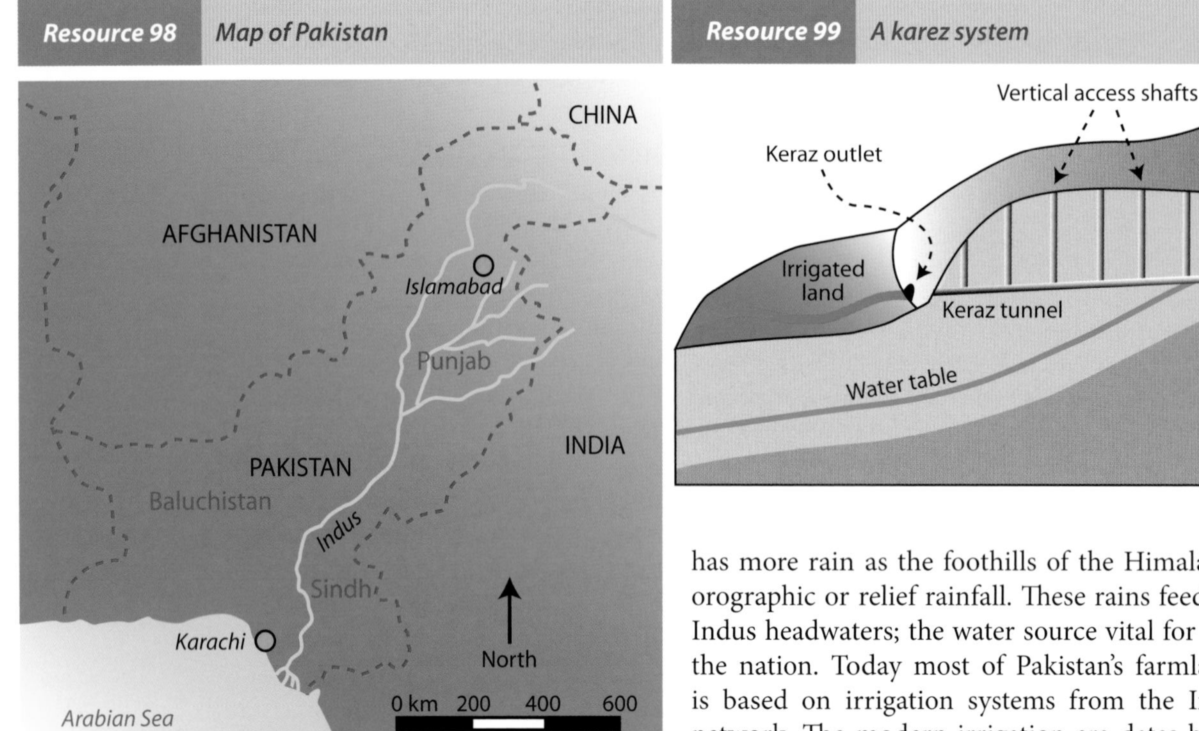

Resource 98 *Map of Pakistan*

Resource 99 *A karez system*

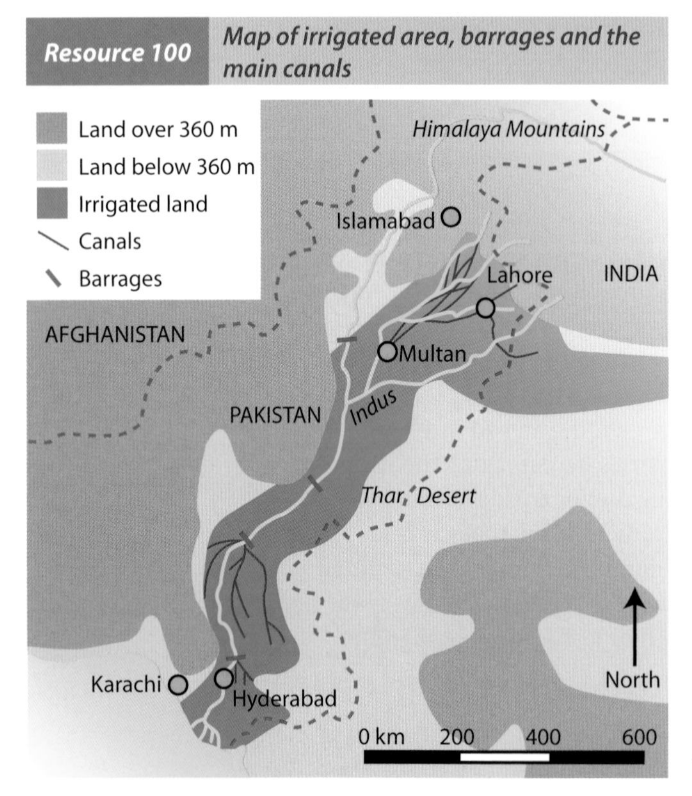

Resource 100 *Map of irrigated area, barrages and the main canals*

has more rain as the foothills of the Himalayas create orographic or relief rainfall. These rains feed the River Indus headwaters; the water source vital for the rest of the nation. Today most of Pakistan's farmland (80%) is based on irrigation systems from the Indus river network. The modern irrigation era dates back to the mid-nineteenth century when the region was under British colonial control (the Raj). The gently sloping canal systems, totaling 650,000 km today, carried water to the farmlands. An older traditional system, the **karez**, was developed to raise ground water using long, sloping tunnels and the lands natural gradient (**Resource 99**).

Pakistan's modern irrigation system is based on a series of barrage and canals system. Minor dams or barrages across the main river channel form small reservoirs of water from which canals distribute water across and down the wide floodplain. Some of the larger barrages and canal networks are shown in **Resource 100**. The system requires careful control of water flow including regular clearance of vegetation from the canals. In more recent decades, in common with most semi-arid regions, **tube wells** have been introduced in large numbers. These use both hand and electrically powered pumping systems. The vital importance of irrigation for Pakistan is reflected by the fact that irrigated land supplies 90% of the nation's agricultural output, accounts for 26% of its GDP and employs over 50% of its labour force. Today the very complex system is responsible for most of the country's food crops (wheat and rice) and industrial crops, such as cotton, sugar cane, tobacco and oil seed, that bring vital foreign revenue to the nation.

Causes of salinisation in Pakistan

Physical causes

In some respects nature has been unkind to Pakistan because several natural physical factors serve to make salinisation a real risk. Firstly, in the distant geological past the region was a shallow tropical sea bed. This has resulted in a large store of chemical salts in the rocks underlying the country. Secondly, the extreme aridity and heat of the region's climate produces high rates of evaporation. Thirdly, the fact that geomorphologically the Indus basin is low-lying, with gentle slopes that do little to promote good drainage, means that water logging is a constant risk. Finally, in parts of Pakistan the quality of groundwater available for irrigation is poor. The scene is set for problems once attempts are made at water management.

Human and management causes

The role of people in Pakistan's salinisation issue concerns the nature and management of the irrigation systems. As noted earlier, the modern era in Pakistan's irrigation history stretches back around 150 years. During the Raj the entire Indian sub-continent was administered by the British, and the barrages and canal distribution systems were introduced. For decades these successfully helped the region's people maintain agriculture production. However, from the outset there were built-in weaknesses that promoted a threat of soil salinity: the lack of lining in the canal systems and the very limited development of adequate drainage for surplus water. In 1947, independence from Britain involved the division of the Indus basin between a Hindu India and a Muslim Pakistan (West). Conflict between the states has been an ongoing problem and it often involves water supply issues. To some extent the management of the irrigation system was neglected and in places it fell into a state of disrepair. The total canal network used to carry irrigation water across Pakistan's agricultural land is over 650,000 km long. Unfortunately, the largely unlined canals network allows water to seep away into the soil. In places this raised the underlying water table from 25 m deep to only a few metres from the soil surface. At this level, water and salts can be drawn up into the plant root zone by capillary action initiating the process of salinisation. Annually some 120 million tonnes of salt are added to Pakistan's soils but only 20% of this is removed and carried to the sea.

Between 1965 and 1995 the Indus Basin irrigation network, begun one hundred years earlier, was largely completed becoming the world's largest single irrigation system. Not only was the country one of the world's top five in total irrigated land area but at over 80% it had the highest proportion of its cultivated land irrigated (**Resource 101**).

The top 10 countries in terms of area of irrigated land (2003) **Resource 101**

Nation	Irrigated area (million hectares)	% of cultivated land that is irrigated	% of irrigated land damaged by salinisation
India	55.81	33.4	27
China	54.59	35.3	15
USA	22.39	13.8	25–30
Pakistan	18.23	80.6	30
Iran	7.65	46.2	33
Mexico	6.32	23.1	20
Turkey	5.22	18.1	10
Thailand	4.92	27.5	7
Indonesia	4.81	14.3	10
Russia	4.61	3.20	18

Source: Figures taken from The World Factbook, https://www.cia.gov/library/publications/the-world-factbook/ and NationMaster, www.nationmaster.com

In Pakistan the government moved to make more use of groundwater resources through the sinking of tube wells. While their scheme largely failed many landowners followed their lead by sinking wells. Between 1964 and 1993 the number of such wells across Pakistan increased from 25,000 to 360,000. Ironically, the tube wells that were designed to lower the water table and reduce the salt issue encouraged the use of poorer quality saline water (over 500 ppm) for irrigation purposes. In some regions, including the Punjab, the clearance of vegetation from the land also increased the rate of evaporation, enhancing the salinisation of land still more. By 2003, the total area of irrigated land in Pakistan was 18.23 million hectares.

A key failure in the management of the Indus irrigation system is its high cropping intensity. It was designed to operate at 65% cropping intensity. This suggests that land that is irrigated should be left fallow, or unused, for a third of the time. However, the growing population demands have resulted in a current intensity of cultivation over 100% and up to 150% in places. Figures over 100% are due to land being used for more than one crop each year.

The impacts of salinisation in Pakistan

By 1960, salinisation levels across Pakistan had become a very real problem for the country and the first scientific investigations into the scale and cause of this were launched. Aerial photographs and field surveys showed that five million hectares were highly saline and a similar sized area suffered local salt problems. Several irrigation related issues impacted the country; in the western province of Baluchistan over pumping had reduced the water table to a level below the karez shafts and in the dry season many tube wells ran dry. Elsewhere, in the North West Frontier Province, the Sindh (south-east) and Punjab (north) the issue was **salinisation** associated with a rising water table. By 1992 98% of Sindh irrigation land was saline to some degree, with 50% heavily affected, and with the Punjab having equivalent figures of 25% and 6%. In the sub-soil the range of chemical salts has increased, reducing crop yields, especially of vital wheat production. Current estimates suggest that between 30% and 60% of Pakistan's irrigated farmland is affected, and in places a salt crust has formed on soil surfaces and cultivation is abandoned. Despite attempts to address the issue around 40,000 hectares of saline land is taken out of production annually in Pakistan. Some areas are so badly affected that surface salt deposits are blown over adjacent regions, spreading the problem. Tube wells that were introduced to tackle the problem by lowering the water table and slowing salinisation have succeeded in several regions, only to cause other issues concerning sustainability of water supply. Testing by the International Water Management Institute showed that even after 40 years of intervention, the salinity problem still persists in irrigated regions of the North West Frontier Province and the Punjab.

Losing irrigated land for cultivation in Pakistan is deeply troubling as the population grows by one million every three to four months. The falling yields from remaining areas, with salty soil and the need to switch to less productive or valuable crops in some regions, undermines the Pakistan economy. Food may need to be imported and there is a decline in export wealth from selling cash crops, such as cotton. The country's balance of trade is affected and capital investment in development projects of both an economic and a social nature falls. By 2005, the various attempts to control salinisation had cost the Pakistan government over £1.5 billion and at one stage the remedial work used up 43% of all its annual spending on the nation's water supply system.

Solutions to the salinisation issue

The response to these problems includes both individual and government action. Farmers have shifted from wheat to rice, which tolerates both more saline and waterlogged conditions; others leave their farmland fallow for a time to allow the rains to wash salts out of the surface soil. As mentioned earlier the Pakistan government initiated SCARP (the Salinity Control and Agricultural Reclamation Programme) and with the help of the World Bank sunk over 13,000 tube wells. These were to provide non-saline water for farmland and to lower the water table itself. The scheme was also designed to introduce improved drainage for the canal system but this was never developed and in fact the government abandoned the scheme when landowners took control and privately sank over 300,000 tube wells. Eventually in the lower Indus region groundwater levels have been lowered by seven metres and 45% of the area with saline soil has been reclaimed.

Commonly proposed engineering solutions include building surplus water drainage systems and lining the canals to prevent the seepage of water to the groundwater store. Given the scale of Pakistan's irrigation scheme the costs of this are prohibitive, though they might be possible at a local level. Several modern irrigation systems have been developed that could improve the situation, these include:

- the use of boom-arm sprinkler systems as seen in the mid-west of America; and
- a drip irrigation system, where valves in plastic hoses release water to the base of individual plants.

Both systems have the advantages of using less water, needing little drainage and fertilizer, and pesticides or herbicides can easily be added with the water. In Pakistan the capital expenditure required by such schemes means they remain desirable but unreachable aims. A move to small-scale schemes with more individual farmer responsibility for water management is seen as a key strategy in long-term control of this issue in Pakistan.

The focus of much recent research is to maximise the potential of land that is damaged by salinisation using what is known as **saline agriculture**. Studies have experimented with hundreds of halophytes (plants tolerant of saline soils) to identify those with commercial value. Some species have been shown to help reduce water tables, acting as 'biological pumps', helping to prevent salinisation. Genetic modification and conventional plant breeding have been used to develop strains of wheat, rice and other staple crops that have increased salt tolerance (**Resource 102**).

Research on Saline Agriculture in Pakistan **Resource 102**

After more than a decade of research and experimentation, Pakistan is now learning to live with salinity. Almost 11 million hectares of land in Pakistan has salt deposits, making the land unsuitable for normal agriculture. Scientists estimate that finding a way to cultivate on this land could contribute up to £2 billion to the economy annually. Several salt-tolerant grain, fruit and fodder species have been identified for practicing saline agriculture. This approach, if carefully adapted, can help to reduce the need to import agricultural goods.

Crops suitable for moderately saline soil

i) **cereals:** paddy rice, sugar cane, oat, sorghum
ii) **oilseed:** rape, canola, mustard
iii) **vegetables:** spinach, sugar beet, red beet, tomato
iv) **fodder and forage:** guar, lucerne
v) **fibre:** cotton, sunhemp, kenaf
vi) **fruits:** fig, grape, pomegranate

Crops suitable for highly saline soil

i) **fruits:** date palm, wild date palm and coconut
ii) **grass:** kallar grass, orchard grass, bermuda grass, para grass, sudan grass
iii) **woody species:** jojoba, guava, jujube, mesquite, mangroves, acacias, mustard tree
iv) **miscellaneous:** aloe, reed plant, bottle palm, cactus, drumstick tree, wild banana, senna

Source: Adapted from information from the Nuclear Institute of Agriculture and Biology, www.niab.org.pk/

Exercise

1. Identify five factors, physical and human, that helped to create Pakistan's salinisation problem. (5)
2. Describe the impacts that salinisation has had on the soil, agriculture and economy of Pakistan. (9)
3. Evaluate the attempts made to address the salinisation issue in Pakistan and outline any other possible solutions. (8)
4. *Questions from CCEA June 2006*
   Study **Figure 1**, which is an article on alternative cropping systems used in regions with a salinisation problem. Describe the three different methods by which cropping systems may be used to keep land productive. (9)

Figure 1

Alternative cropping systems in salinised regions

One option in regions where salinisation has started is to switch to more salt tolerant crops. The best choice for any particular farmer will depend on soil type, climate, the quality of both the incoming irrigation water and the drainage, and the farmer's management practices. Better matching of crops to soil and water salinity can be a key to keeping irrigated agriculture productive as salinity problems worsen. A salt-sensitive crop such as onions, for example, may experience an 80% drop in yield when grown in soils with salt levels that do not affect barley or cotton at all.

Farmers and scientists in Australia, California and elsewhere have also experimented with planting thirsty trees, such as eucalyptus, and deep-rooted crops, such as alfalfa and lupins, to lower the water table in regions threatened with salinisation. As with the engineering approaches, however, the long-term effectiveness of these biological options has yet to be proved. Studies on the west side of California's San Joaquin valley have shown that a plantation of eucalyptus trees was able to consume salty groundwater and thereby lower the water table from about half a metre below the soil surface down to 2.3 metres.

If irrigators cannot completely avoid the combined risk of waterlogging and salt buildup, can salinised land at least be reclaimed or used for some other productive purpose? Again, the answer seems to be a qualified yes. Salt-loving plants, called halophytes, can thrive in many salt environments that are completely unsuitable for even the most salt-tolerant of conventional crops. More than 20 years work in Western Australia has demonstrated that planting saltbush can convert salty wasteland into profitable grazing land, in some cases netting $100 per hectare. Many saltbushes are perennial shrubs that remain green all year round, and are good forage crops in dry regions. In Pakistan, a deep-rooted, highly salt-tolerant perennial called kallar grass shows promise. A nitrogen fixer, kallar grass grows well without fertiliser and is a useful forage crop, producing about 50 tons of biomass per hectare. In some areas its growth has restored soils to the point where a few varieties of barley and moderately salt-tolerant crops will grow again.

Source: S Postal, Worldwatch Institute, Pillar of Sand, www.worldwatch.org

Study 2: People and development in the tropical forests

Today more than ever before, the world's population depends on tropical ecosystems. An increasing proportion of humanity lives within the tropics and many of the rest of us find that our food supplies, our industrial resources, our medical needs, even the air we breathe are largely dependant on the fragile ecosystems of the tropics. In the last few centuries, development has changed many people's way of life from traditional to modern. Unfortunately traditional came to mean primitive, while modern meant progressive. More recently it has been realised that traditional activities, which had grown from years of trial and error into a balanced system, had lessons for current practice. Modern production methods, though very productive, can put too much strain on the environment. Today, as noted earlier, more thought is given to sustainability. In the case of the tropical forest ecosystem the question can be posed in the following way:

> "How can we use these resources to satisfy the legitimate needs of people, without allowing development to destroy the rainforest?"

The historical context

Until recent decades the tropical rainforests, protected by their remoteness and difficult climate, were largely ignored by outsiders. The people of the forests were studied by anthropologists, fascinated by their lifestyles and economies. The worldwide population explosion that occurred from 1950 forced governments of many LEDCs to re-examine their available natural resources in order to address the threat of overpopulation. Many tropical countries permitted or even encouraged the opening up of their forests for development by their own people or by foreign companies. The nature of this large-scale clearance of tropical forest and its impact locally and globally have been documented since the 1970s. Common reasons for the development and some of the negative impacts are illustrated by **Resource 103** and **104**.

The reasons for recent large-scale deforestation of tropical forests — **Resource 103**

The negative impacts of large-scale deforestation — **Resource 104**

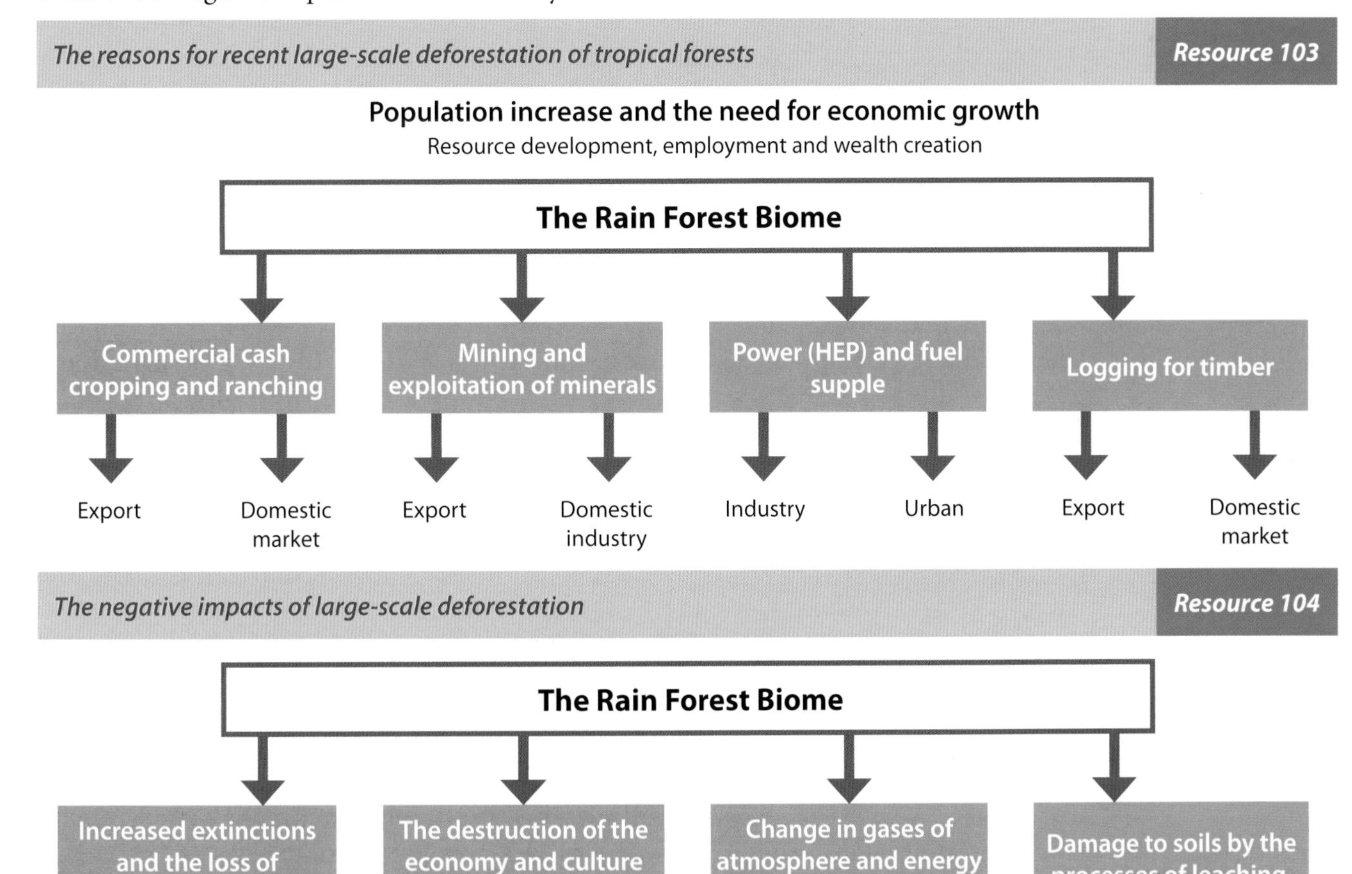

Today, the drive is to find ways to conserve the forests sustainably. To create approaches and technologies that use this vast resource to aid the development of nations without compromising the long-term health of these special biomes. Some have suggested a return to the traditional lifestyle of the hunter-gatherers or the shifting system of cultivation developed across these forests by the indigenous peoples. While their systems were models of sustainability (**Resource 105**) they can only support small numbers and often at a standard of living seen as unacceptable to most people today.

Resource 105 *Shifting cultivation the traditional sustainable economy of tropical forests*

Until recent years, across the world the use of tropical forests has had a common theme – **shifting cultivation** or slash and burn agriculture. From Papua New Guinea in South-East Asia, to Ghana in West Africa and the Amazon Basin of South America, tribes and indigenous groups have independently developed farming systems that are both effective and have a minimal long-term impact on the ecosystem. The clearance of small patches of forest, followed by a few years of suitable cultivation and a long period of abandonment is an attempt to maintain the cycling of nutrients within the local ecosystem. For many centuries, versions of this economic pattern have successfully allowed millions of indigenous natives, to live in harmony with their forest home. Shifting cultivation only becomes an unsustainable economy when either, the local population density rises above the capacity of the land or the amount of forested land available is reduced often as a result of competing land use from outsiders.

The various causes of large-scale rainforest clearance

The root of these is either population growth or the desire for economic gain.

1. Agricultural expansion for subsistence cultivation

Even traditional sustainable economies cannot cope with increased population densities caused by natural increase or by spontaneous and government sponsored migration.

2. Commercial agriculture

Often initiated by governments and through foreign-based businesses, territory in sparsely populated areas is opened up for cash cropping or cash grazing from livestock ranching.

3. Commercial logging (silviculture)

Many tropical species are prized for their timber. Unfortunately many others are not but will be cut down to enable the few desired trees to be reached and removed.

4. Mining and quarrying

New techniques and exploration have revealed the vast wealth contained in the rocks beneath these forests, including mineral deposits and metal ores.

5. HEP schemes

Population growth, industrial development and increased prosperity all make demands on energy supplies in wet regions. HEP may prove an easy source, which while non-polluting and renewable, creates reservoirs that flood huge forest regions with untold loss of habitat and life.

6. Transport

The principal security of the vulnerable tropical forests was their remoteness and general inaccessibility. Newly developed transport routes – road, rail, river and air – have undermined this natural sanctuary.

In certain regions some of these economic activities have been practiced for centuries. African forests were the first commercially exploited by Europeans in the seventeenth century and plantation farming in South-East Asia goes back over 200 years. Some regions are closely associated with one economic activity, for example in Sarawak, Malaysia, on the north coast of Borneo, commercial logging dominates forest development.

Management for sustainability

Tropical forests are diverse and fragile environments. In recent decades their development has accelerated at a phenomenal rate and today pressure groups, both local and international, are seeking to slow down and even arrest the process. Economic and environmental values have clashed and at times resulted in sporadic and sustained violence. In December 1988, the murder of Chico Mendes, a Brazilian leader of rubber tappers, by rival cattle ranchers was a pivotal moment in the global awareness of the conflict between sustainable and unsustainable exploitation of the forest. Since that event the world's media has highlighted the issue, if not consistently, at least more frequently. Somewhere between the reckless destruction for short-term economic gain and the traditional subsistence shifting cultivation system lies a compromise – a newly evolving attitude of responsible management.

Sustainable development, as noted earlier, involves the well-being of the local community, as well as environmental protection at both local and global scales. One lesson from the search for sustainable management systems is that no single approach will be applicable to all forest areas and that a wide variety of solutions will be needed. While successful examples of sustainable development are not abundant, their number and their impact is growing. The table below contains some of the common approaches to sustainable use of tropical forest resources.

Examples of proposed sustainable development projects in tropical forests **Resource 106**

System	Elaboration	Example
Agroforestry	An agricultural system that mimics the forest by having a canopy of productive trees with annual crops grown below.	The coconut farms of the islands of southern Thailand. The Tome Acu cooperative farms near Belem, Brazil (page 224).
Forest product resources	Extracting resources from standing forest, such as rubber tapping or Brazil nut gathering.	The state of Acre in the Amazon basin.
Ecotourism	Bringing in tourists to see and learn about the forest biome and its native people with minimal impact on the local environment.	The Explorer's Inn, Peruvian Safaris in the Amazon Basin, Peru (page 230).
Mining	Controlled exploitation of mineral reserves beneath the forest	The Grande Carajas project in Para state, Brazil.
Selective logging	Small-scale managed logging, including strip logging or 'highgrading' (the removal of only the most valuable trees).	The Amuesha Indians in the Yanesha Forestry Cooperative, Peru.
Nature reserves	Ranging from zero use, to areas for scientific research, including medical gene pools and tourism.	The Korup Nature conservation reserve, in SW Cameroon (page 227).

The success of these and other schemes in tropical forests depends on many factors. The local people and their governments along with NGOs (Non-Government Organisations) play important roles in this process but market forces are critical. Western economies control market demand and if suppliers adopt a policy to only handle goods from forests managed sustainably they may hold the key to success.

Three exemplar case studies of management for sustainability at a local or small scale

1. Agroforestry system

Agroforestry combines agricultural and forestry techniques to establish an integrated, diverse, productive and sustainable land use system. The concept is that by mixing tree crops and short-term or annual crops, the land can provide an income without having to expose the delicate soil to the heat of the sun or the torrential rainfall of convectional storms. The trees provide both a canopy layer that intercepts rain and a root network that binds the soil. As most

Resource 107 *An agroforestry scheme in Thailand.*

The coconut palms act as the tree cover vegetation with banana plants interplanted between them. Both provide a cash crop for the local tourist industry and the national market.

farmers cannot wait the ten or more years for trees to reach productivity, the interplanting of bush or ground crops produces a potential food or cash crop supply in the short-term.

Researchers into agroforestry schemes around the world have identified several necessary requirements to make these successful as sustainable enterprises:

- The locals or colonists must be aware of the limitations and problems of rainforest environments, including the nature of the soil.
- Schemes need to be well resourced and maintained so that any environmental issues can be addressed as soon as they appear – this requires appropriate technology and specialist labour.
- Both the profits made and any external subsidies must be controlled to prevent damaging, short-term strategies, where land is abandoned and new areas of forest cleared.
- Individuals and companies must be held responsible for any environmental consequences.

CASE STUDY: The CAMTA Cooperative, Tomé-Açu, Para, Brazil (Japanese community)

One of the few well documented and generally successful agroforestry schemes involves a small community of farmers in the Brazilian state of Para. Over the last 60 years they have developed farming from a poor subsistence economy to a cooperative-based commercial enterprise based on local plants. The history of the community is an unusual one but the lesson of their past is that with care and attention it is possible to develop an economy that is sustainable in social, environmental and economic terms.

A brief history

During the 1920s and 30s the government of Japan, fearing overpopulation, encouraged many of its citizens to emigrate to find new lives elsewhere. One group of around 40 families arrived in Brazil and settled at Tomé-Açu, around 130 km south of the Amazon port of Belem. More families arrived and over the next twenty years the immigrants cleared areas of secondary forest and subsisted on rice and vegetables, including varieties they had brought from Asia. After World War II the small community seized on a unique opportunity – the conflict had destroyed the black pepper plantations of South East Asia and consequently its market price soared. From a few seedlings that had been brought over in 1933, the Japanese farmers developed a highly profitable export economy based on a monoculture of black pepper. From 1947 until the mid-1980s production expanded and at one point the Tomé-Açu region supplied most of the world's black pepper. By 1985, the combination of a fungal disease, Fusarium, and foreign competition from new asian producers undermined this success. The community responded by developing a more broadly based agricultural system using small family farms. The community had learned the perils of over dependence on one crop and unpredictable world markets. They also learned from indigenous farmers that a system based on tree crops replicating the forest's natural nutrient stores, with most held in the biomass. One other advantage the community had was they had established a farmer's cooperative, **CAMTA** (Cooperative Agricola Mista de Tomé-Açu), which from 1931 had supplied seed, fertilizer and advice; while also helping the community socially by funding a hospital, schools and a supermarket. The cooperative promoted a more sustainable form of agriculture, when in 1987 it built a frozen fruit pulp processing plant as local farmers began to experiment with local fruit crops for the growing drinks market. The processing plant separates the pulp using both hand labour and machinery; it then freezes the pulp in plastic bags. CAMTA sends the fruit pulp to major urban markets, including Sao Paulo through the port at Belem, and abroad to US based companies, such as Sambazon.

A location map of Tomé-Açu region **Resource 108**

GUYANA
SURINAME
FRENCH GUIANA
Amazon River
Belém
Tomé-Açu
PARÁ
BRAZIL
0 km 250 500 750

The nature of the Tomé-Açu farms

Individual family farms are between 100 and 150 hectares in size, however, less than half of this may be in production at any one time. The cultivated plots are one to four hectares in size and normally have two, three or even four crops mixed and interplanted. For example, in one plot, under rubber trees, passion fruit may be grown, while on an adjacent plot cupuaçu and pineapple fruits may be found, beneath a canopy of coconut palm and citrus trees (**Resource 109**). Today, mostly native species are used, such as the shade tolerant cupuaçu and cacao. As many as 25 different species may be grown on one farm and a complex and sophisticated pattern of production emerges. This is a risk avoidance strategy, allowing flexibility if market conditions alter. In areas not cultivated, many farmers have planted valuable hardwood timber tree species, including mahogany, rosewood and jacaranda, as a future income for their children and future generations. Currently, less than one in five farmers grow staple food crops, such as rice, beans or corn, such is the confidence that the commercial success of this enterprise will continue.

A typical farm pattern in Tomé-Açu **Resource 109**

Scale: ☐ = 1 hectare (100 m × 100m)

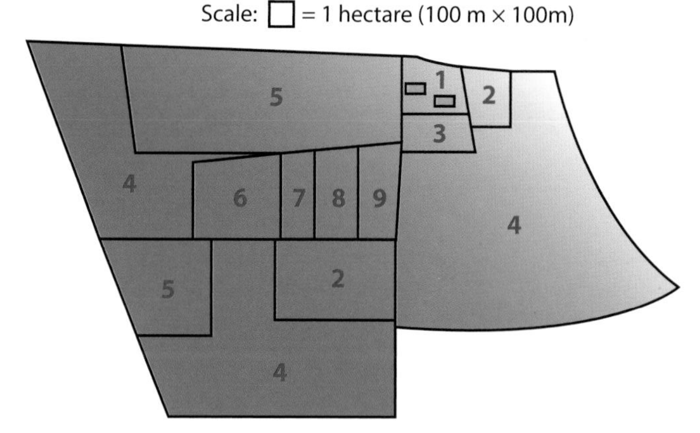

Land use:
1 Home and farm buildings
2 Brazil nut, cacao, pineapple
3 Mahogany, papaya, vanilla
4 Secondary forest regeneration
5 Coconut, citrus, cupuaçu
6 Rubber tree, passion fruit
7 Cacao, mangosteen, banana
8 Rubber tree, black pepper
9 Andiroba, cupuaçu

Economic sustainability

CAMTA trades over $6 million worth of fruit pulp to Brazil, Japan, USA and Europe annually, making it one of Brazil's most successful cooperatives. It has 124 member farms, about 70% of which are owned by descendents of Japanese migrants. The pulp comes from 13 different species and cacao and black pepper are also traded, though mainly for the domestic Brazil market. This broad based and growing market has helped to avoid the dependency of the past and the risk of a collapse due to world market prices or the blight of plant disease. One concern is that setting up new farms of this type is capital intensive. Income is low in the early years and costs are high. The cooperative, however, can provide access to credit and reduce costs by its bulk purchase of seeds, fertiliser and other inputs (**Resource 110**).

Social sustainability

At one time, concern was voiced that the complexity of these systems meant that only the specialist farmers from Japanese families could maintain these farms. Today, nearly a third of CAMTA members are Brazilian in origin and many are migrants from outside the Amazon

Resource 110 *CAMTA's operations in Tomé-Açu*

A - Logo of CAMTA the cooperative organisation in Tomé-Açu.

B - The range of fruit that are supplied as pulp from the CAMTA processing plant.

pineapple
açaí
acerola
cashew
star fruit
cupuaçu
guava
graviola
passion fruit
murici
taperebá

Source: Images from http://www.amazon.com.br/~camta/topE.htm

region. The farms themselves are labour intensive, with each small farm needing a skilled workforce of seven or eight people. This is an advantage in a region with high population growth and in-migration. One issue is that in recent years members of the younger generation, including the Japanese community, are leaving for the bright lights and opportunities in the cities of Brazil or beyond.

While it is true that the Tomé-Açu farms have not received help from outside foundations or NGOs (Non-Government Organisations – charities), it is not strictly true to say they are fully independent. Many families gain income from members working outside the area, including in Japan, for periods of time.

Environmental sustainability

The model mimicking the natural structure of a tropical forest for cultivation seems to work. Testing at Tomé-Açu shows that the creation of a tree canopy, with a second under-storey layer, is both productive and has maintained soil quality even after 20 years. This is superior to the two to three year output under traditional shifting cultivation systems or the eight to ten year use under cattle ranching. Some simpler agroforestry systems have been shown to be capable of maintaining a significant range of bird, small mammal, reptile and insect species. While more research needs to be completed on the impact of the Tomé-Açu system on natural biodiversity, it is worth noting that most of the farms were established in areas of damaged forest, including the pepper plantations and land previously clear felled by logging companies. Little virgin forest is now cleared and it is claimed that, even to the trained eye, a typical farm in normal production appears similar to the natural forest. To maintain soil fertility the black pepper plantations had relied on large inputs of inorganic chemical fertilizer brought into the area, but the new system focuses on the recycling of organic material. Cacao produces beans for chocolate but their hulls can be recycled, returning nutrients such as potassium to the soil. Weeds are routinely cut but left to decay and decompose as mulch for the soil.

Exercise

1. Re-read the four requirements for successful sustainable agroforestry schemes in the agroforestry introduction (page 224). Prepare notes for a discussion on the extent to which the modern farmers of Tomé-Açu have met these four requirements.
2. Evaluate the sustainability of the Tomé-Açu farming system with respect to Economic and Social issues.
3. Study the quotation in the box below.

   (a) To what extent is it accurate concerning the nature of nutrient cycling in rainforests? (3)

   (b) How does the farming system practiced at Tomé-Açu reflect these ideas? (10)

> "In agricultural school we were taught to pay attention to the soil. Prepare the soil and you will get a big harvest," he nodded. "Very modern. Very Wrong". In the Amazon, however, "the nutrients are above the ground. The soil is very poor. The fertility is in the vegetation."
>
> He continued, "It's in the trees. They control light, humidity, and protect the soil. In Amazonia you have to take care of the trees."
>
> **Noburo Sakaguchi, a Japanese resident and farming pioneer in Tomé-Açu for over 30 years**
>
> *Source: Mac Margolis, Japanese in the Amazon: The riddle of farming the tropics, http://tinyurl.com/nsakta, accessed 2 September 2009*

2. Nature or Biosphere Reserve

The designation of an area of land as a protected region of natural forest has developed over the last 150 years, originating with the National Parks of the USA. Research has shown that such areas need to be substantial in area to retain the full range of habitats and ecological niches that forests provide. In short, small areas of conservation may prove inadequate. Within nature reserves a range of conservation is possible, from complete exclusion zones, through areas solely reserved for scientific research, to zones open for ecotourism or resource extraction by locals on a sustainable scale.

CASE STUDY: The Korup National park in SW Cameroon

This forest area in the central African nation of Cameroon (**Resource 111**) contains the greatest diversity of plant species of any African rainforest, including 52 tree species. The Cameroon government are involved in protecting, managing and integrating the development of the Korup National Park.

Cameroon's first Tropical Rainforest National Park was designated in 1986. The Korup National Park is part of the government's plan to conserve 20% of its territory with National Park and Forest Reserves. In 1988 the government and a range of other agencies,

The Korup Project, South-West Cameroon Conservation area Forest — **Resource 111**

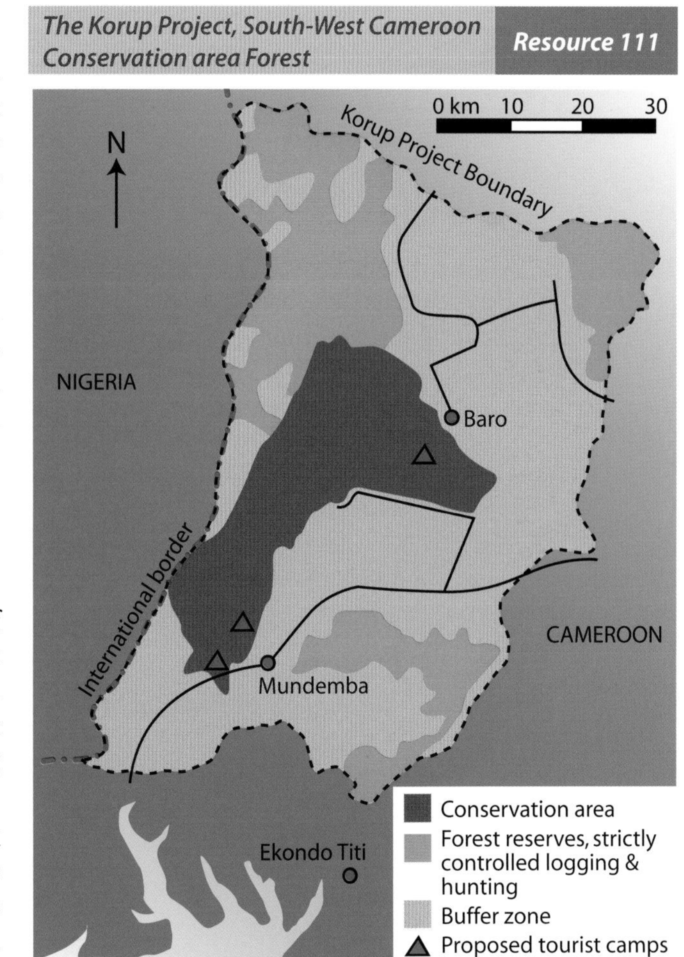

including the WWF (World Wide Fund for Nature) agreed on a master plan, known as the Korup Project, to run for 15 years until 2003. The management objective was not only to protect this pristine forest but also to benefit scientific research, education and tourism in a sustainable way.

The nature of the Korup National Park

Within the lowland forest the underlying geology influences the soil type and therefore the potential commercial use of the land. The western forest that borders Nigeria is remote and undeveloped. Here the soils are poor for agriculture, however, the forests contains a wide diversity of birds and mammal species, some unique to the region. The eastern forest has richer soils, mainly volcanic in origin, and these have been developed for agriculture, including commercial cocoa and coffee farming. In the south poor soils limit development, however, some cash cropping of oil palm has existed.

The Korup Project (1988–2003)

While people and development may be viewed as threats to the forest, the Project recognised the need to balance the needs of people with protection of the environment. The boundary of the Korup Project encompasses the National Park itself and a large buffer zone (**Resource 111**).

The aims of the Korup Project

1. Sustainable agriculture – developed on areas with better soils in the buffer zone.
2. Resettlement – of villages from the National park zone.
3. Hunting zones – outside the Forest Park and forest reserves.
4. Tourism – ecological tourism in the Forest Park itself.
5. Roads – improved access for agricultural and tourist development.
6. Services – enhanced education, health and water services for the local population.

1. The National Park

Within the 1,260 km^2 designated as the Korup National Park there were six small villages. While these had an economy partly based on subsistence and cash cropping, hunting was often their vital source of income. Most adult men had firearms for hunting and also used traps to snare game. This bush meat was then sold to villages that lay just outside the park itself. Cameroon law states that both settlement and hunting in National Parks is illegal. As a result, one important but controversial part of the Project was to move the people from the six Korup villages to resettle them at sites outside the forest. The National Park zone is inaccessible as it is bounded by fast flowing rivers with only two foot bridges, including the recently rebuilt 120 m span Mana suspension footbridge. The Project initially placed a fence around the Park and locals, often ex-poachers, were employed as guards to discourage poaching of its wildlife.

2. The Buffer Zone

In this large region outside the Forest Park new roads and bridges were constructed along with schools and health centres. An area with agricultural potential was set aside for the re-settlement of the forest villagers. Locals were taught new cultivation and livestock rearing techniques in order to reduce the need for hunting in the rural economy.

3. Tourism

The aim of developing tourism was to earn foreign income, provide jobs for local people and a market for local products. The ecotourism was to be strictly controlled, with access only by foot into the Forest Park and clearly marked trails and camps. While Korup has a diversity of bird and butterfly species it lacks distinctive large animals. Access for tourists is very limited and facilities are basic at best.

The outcome of the Project

By the end of the project in 2003 the six villages in the Forest Park had not been re-located and there is debate as to whether its National Park status can be retained if the residents remain. The tourism infrastructure in the Park consists of a well developed and maintained 115 km trail network, which visitors explore on foot. There are also three self-catering tourist camps in the Park. The camps all have fresh natural drinking water and bathing points, latrines or pit toilets, screened sleeping accommodations and kitchens. However, due to poor access, tourism involves only a few hundred adventurous individuals each year and the total income to the region is very modest. Unfortunately, the new farming skills promoted by the project have not been widely adopted and villagers outside the forest continue to attempt to poach bush meat and other forest products illegally from the National Park itself.

Research among the local population **Resource 112**

In 2005 a questionnaire study was carried out in the southern sector of the Korup region. A random sample of 78 respondents was selected from villages in and around the National Park. The results indicated:

(i) low levels of participation of the local communities in the biodiversity conservation and rural development aspects of the Korup Project;

(ii) that a difficult relationship existed between the international funders and the local communities;

(iii) biodiversity conservation was only temporarily successful; and

(iv) the attempts at rural development were a failure.

Research by scientists, including botanists from Kew Gardens in London, has identified many new plants, including one new genus and sixteen new species of fungi. Another discovery, unique to the region, Ancistrocladus korupensis, a canopy liana, may have a role in fighting the HIV virus. If so this may become a valuable source of local income as well as a breakthrough for world health.

At conservation conferences Korup National Park is often quoted for its high level of wildlife protection within the Forest Park. Even after the end of the Korup Project itself in 2003, the forest park has continued to attract funding from the World Bank as well as NGOs from Europe and the USA. Since 2007, with funding from a German bank, the 23 guards employed to protect the forest have used satellite linked GPS systems to monitor wildlife poaching and the extraction of non-timber forest products. The level of illegal activity is said to be under control and not a threat to the region's biodiversity status. In the past, funding for guard patrols has been insecure; in 2006 they went without any salary for eight months, while on a previous occasion only three poorly equipped guards were employed.

The elements of the Korup Project, 1988–2003 **Resource 113**

Four key elements of the Korup project were to:

- encourage environmental education of local people to reduce their impact on the rainforest;
- promote scientific research;
- develop ecotourism by providing tourist camps; and
- preserve the forest's diverse fauna and flora.

Exercise

For each of the four elements in **Resource 113:**

(i) describe how the project attempted to achieve this; and

(ii) evaluate the degree of success that has been attained.

3. Ecotourism

Tourism in tropical biomes has long been associated with the grassland biomes, where herds of migrating herbivores could be more readily seen along with the carnivores that prey on them. Safaris, initially as hunting expeditions have been popular, albeit with wealthier westerners, for a hundred years or more. Tropical forests until the last few decades have been regarded as the preserve of the adventurer. Mass tourism and improved access have allowed for the development of tourism and its supposedly sustainable cousin, ecotourism, bringing visitors and their valuable foreign currency into many LEDC nations.

Resource 114 *Photographs of rainforest tourism. Do they represent sustainable ecotourism?*

Mounted Red-bellied Piranha from Manaus, Brazil

Elephant trekking in Thailand

Orangutan feeding in Sarawak, Borneo

Source: O Glenn

CASE STUDY: Tambopata National Reserve, Peru – The Explorer's Inn (Peruvian Safaris)

Tambopata is a nature reserve on the Peru-Bolivian border within the Amazon Basin. Its establishment in 1990 is in part the result of a successful research centre opened in 1975/76, called Explorer's Inn, run by the Peruvian Safaris company in cooperation with the Peruvian government. By 2000, the Tambopata National Reserve (TNR) with 275,000 hectares was linked to the newly designated 1.1 million hectare, Bahuaja-Sonene National Park. Across these protected regions it is estimated that 20,000 tourists visit each year. Most stay at 13 purpose built lodges, generally outside the protected zone. Explorer's Inn and the nearby Posada Amazonas lodge, run by an indigenous community, lie within the TNR. The lodges vary in nature from basic to luxury, with most focusing on direct observation of wildlife. One claim for the area is that it has the world's highest species count for birds and butterflies at nearly 600 and 1,200 respectively.

The Explorer's Inn

Situated within the TNR, the lodge is located near the confluence of the Tambopata and La Torre rivers. Designed as a base for scientific research it has combined this role with educational ecotourism. Visitors stay at the complex in a small clearing a few hundred metres from the river bank (see Google earth exercise below). The Inn consists of seven separate bungalows with palm-thatched roofs, and a central hexagonal building that houses the dining area, lounge, research area, bar and a small library and museum (**Resource 116**). Local materials were used in the original construction of the Inn and today materials are supplied by local people from sustainable sources. The bedrooms are lit by candlelight with electricity only available in the public areas. The electricity is supplied by solar cells, which also power the radio link to headquarters in Puerto Maldonado. In the surrounding forest over 37 km of walking trails are regularly maintained. These lead to a variety of environments including the rivers, ox-bow lakes and pristine forest. Additional facilities include eleven viewing platforms, high in or above the canopy, from which wildlife can be observed by day and night. All visitors come in from Puerto Maldonado, some 60 km downstream, by motorised long boat. On-route they have to check into the biological reserve at a nearby riverbank control post, one of five in the reserve. Tourist stays vary from two to five nights, during which guided walks and open canoe trips are undertaken. Highlights of the 'Jungle Expedition' package include:

Map of the Tambopata National Reserve and location of Explorer's Inn **Resource 115**

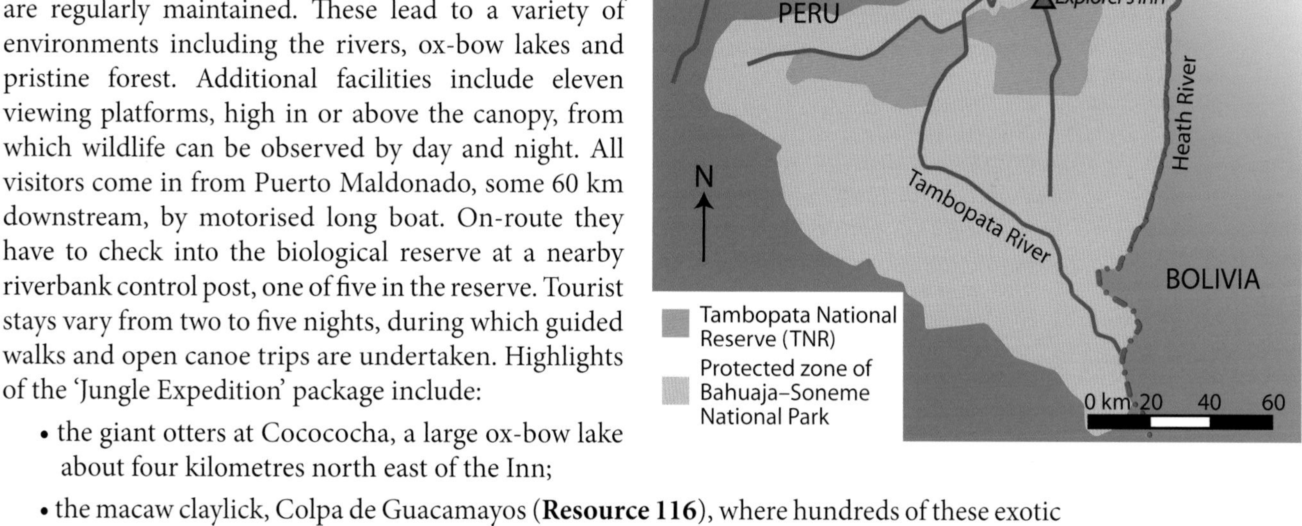

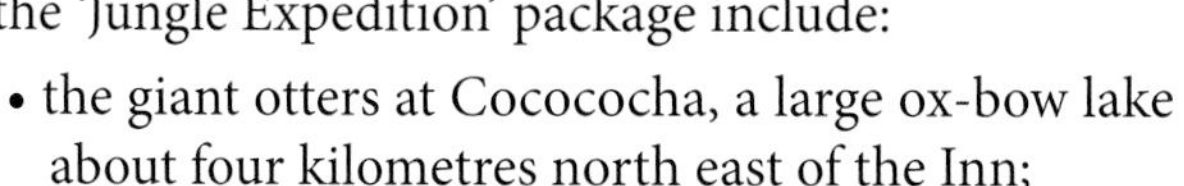

- the giant otters at Cocococha, a large ox-bow lake about four kilometres north east of the Inn;
- the macaw claylick, Colpa de Guacamayos (**Resource 116**), where hundreds of these exotic birds feed on a clay river bank; and
- night boat trips to spot cayman and turtles on the riverbanks.

Google Earth Exercise – Tambopata National Reserve ***Exercise***

Enter (or download) Google Earth.

Type in these latitude and longitude coordinates: 12 50' 12"S 69 17' 37"W

This location will take you to the clearing containing the Explorer's Inn, near the confluence of the Tambopata and La Torre rivers. Zoom in to study the buildings on the site itself. You can use the scale icon to measure the size of the clearing.

- Scroll 4 km to the north-east to the Cocococha ox bow lake where the hide for giant otters is found. Click on the blue squares that are normally photographs, showing the buildings, river or wildlife in the region.
- Scroll the map downstream (north and north-east) towards Puerto Maldonado. Notice how agricultural clearings, including cattle pastures, appear along the river and widen to dominate the area around the town. Note also the largely pristine forest of the TNR itself, especially away from the rivers.
- Other tourist lodges in the region can be seen, invariably near the river. These include Posado Amazonas, a native run lodge downstream and Libertador Tambopata, upstream of Explorer's Inn.

Sustainability at the Explorer's Inn

The express purpose of the Explorer's Inn is part of, "a unique experiment in cooperation where research, tourism and rainforest conservation are being combined to the mutual benefit of all involved and for tomorrow's generations". To this end, the Inn offers free accommodation and food for any researcher in return for their acting as guides to visitors. Numerous theses, published and unpublished, along with many well informed tourists have resulted from this creative symbiotic relationship. One study identified the risk of soil compaction along the walking trails. Consequently the centre built a raised walkway over paths in the lodge clearance and each year some trail routes are left unused to allow restoration. The same research suggested that trail clearance may allow more light to reach ground plants, positively promoting greater species diversity and helping insect life on the forest floor. The first clue to the number of species contained by rainforest canopies was from experiments carried out at Tambopata by Terry Erwin of the Smithsonian Institution. Biodegradable insecticides released into the canopy brought down a rain of thousands of unknown insect species. These findings indicate a possible 50 million insect species in the rain forest canopy – ten times more than the total number of life species previously imagined.

During the 1990s, tourist itineraries often included visits to nearby native communities where handicraft products could be purchased. These were discontinued at the request of community leaders but the centre continues to source as much of its food and other resources, such as canoes, locally. Native neighbours have priority in filling vacancies for permanent staff jobs at the Inn. Peruvian Safaris also supply books and materials for children at local schools. Recently the Inn has developed a link to a Medical University in Lima and consequently locals have access to regular medical checks at the Inn. The Inn also offers radio communication and transportation in case of emergency.

Waste disposal is an important issue in these vulnerable environments. At the Explorer's Inn any biodegradable waste is buried where it can decay safely and not attract unwanted visitors. Non-biodegradable waste is routinely removed downstream to local towns outside the TNR to be added to the urban waste system. Current threats to the environment include gold mining, illegal logging, hunting and expansion of farming along the rivers.

Resource 116 *Photographs of Explorer's Inn*

The Library

The macaw claylick

Accomodation

Source: O Glenn

Defined as "tourism which seeks out the attractions of natural elements in an area without undue stress imposed on them", ecotourism is one of the fastest growing sectors of the economy, attracting in excess of 20,000 visitors a year to the Bahuaja-Sonene National Park and the Tambopata National Reserve.

Exercise

1. With reference to detailed case study material answer the following questions.
   a) How has the development of the Tambopata National Reserve, and Explorer's Inn in particular attempted to address the environmental risks associated with tourism? (6)
   b) To what extent has the sustainable development succeeded in social terms. (4)

2. *Question from CCEA May 2008*
   Study **Figures 1–3** which illustrate agricultural land use in a tropical forest in Thailand.

   Describe and explain how this forested area is being managed for socio-economic and environmental sustainability. (10)

Figure 1

Palm plantations and secondary rainforest

Figure 2

Intercropping of coconut palms and banana plants

Source: CCEA, Principal Examiner, Geography

Exercise continued

Figure 3

Agroforestry – a sustainable approach to forest agriculture

In tropical forest ecosystems from Brazil to Congo, Sri Lanka to Papua, farmers, businesses and governments are seeking to use forest lands in ways that are both environmentally and socio-economically sustainable. One common solution is to use an agroforestry system:

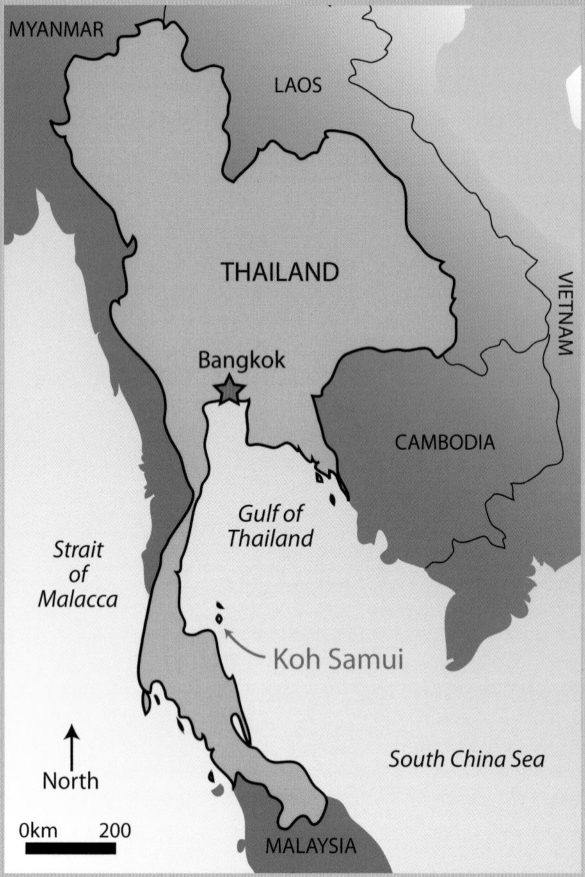

under such schemes tall tree-based products such as rubber or oil-palms are grown as long-term perennial (annually productive) crops. Beneath and between these trees other crops are grown. These may be smaller perennials such as cacao or coffee or even subsistence root crops such as yams or manioc. **Figure 1** shows a forested hillside on the island of Koh Samui in the Gulf of Thailand. In the past, the primary forest here was cleared and has been replaced, either by secondary forest re-growth or by planted coconut palm plantations. The palm trees mimic the natural forest structure by forming a canopy layer that provides shade and shelter for the vulnerable soil and vegetation beneath.

The combination of long-term cash crop production from the tree species and the other crops grown beneath the canopy, gives the farmers flexibility when it comes to market changes. As **Figure 2** shows, beneath the palm tree cover, a second cash crop has been grown, in this case bananas. These supply the local market for the Thai people and tourists alike. This agricultural system depends on careful management and abundant labour, one commodity readily available on the island. Koh Samui supplies over one million coconuts to the country's capital, Bangkok, every harvest season.

Selected textbooks and articles

Publications

K Atkinson, *Biogeography*, Philip Allen 2007

R Heelas, *Tropical Environments*, Nelson Thornes, 2001

M Hill, *Arid and Semi-arid Environments*, Hodder & Stoughton, 2002

A Kidd, *Managing Ecosystems*, Hodder & Stoughton, 1999

S Postel, *Pillar of Sand*, Wordwatch Institute, www.worldwatch.org

M Thom, *The Nature and Vulnerability of Tropical ecosystems*, Colourpoint, 2001

J Woodfield, *Ecosystems and Human Activity*, 2nd Ed, Collins Education, 2000

Geofile articles

495 'Tropical Rain Forests'

Geo Factsheet

201 'Sustainable Development – Case studies in Ecuador'

C1 PLATE TECTONICS AND RESULTING LANDFORMS

Introduction – The structure of the Earth

Modern research and current theory suggests that the Earth has layers. Despite the fact that the deepest hole drilled into the Earth so far is only 13 km, a mere scratch of 0.2% of the planet's radius, scientists have built a picture of the Earth's internal structure. In essence a basic three sphere model of the planet has emerged – central **core**, surrounded by a **mantle**, with a thin outer **crust** of continents and ocean floors.

The evidence for this structure comes mainly from the interpretation of how energy released by earthquakes and nuclear weapons testing travels through the planet. Such events emit several forms of energy wave that can help identify changes in the Earth's composition, deep beneath the surface. The speed at which compression waves (P waves) and shear waves (S waves) travel will vary with the density of material, and shear waves will not pass through liquids at all. As early as 1909, a Yugoslavian pioneer seismologist uncovered a line of change or discontinuity where the rocks of the crust meet those of the mantle. This line, named after its discoverer – the **Mohorovivic discontinuity** – is thankfully usually known as the **Moho**. Since then more discoveries and on-going refinements of the theory have produced a model of the Earth's internal structure (**Resource 117**).

Model of the Earths internal structure **Resource 117**

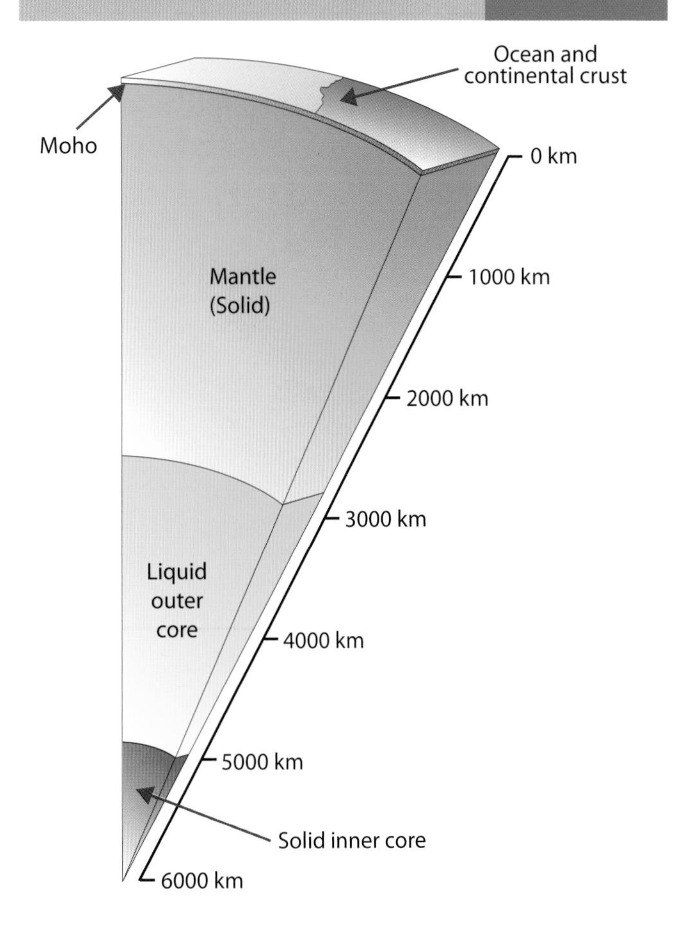

The Earth's **core** has a diameter of around 7,000 km, making it larger than the planet Mars. It has two distinct sections: an **inner solid core** surrounded by an **outer liquid core**. The inner solid core is largely made of iron and, along with the liquid core, they help create the planet's magnetic field. The composition of the core is known from calculation of densities, melting points and clues provided by meteorites that have fallen to Earth from space. At volcanoes molten rock or magma reaches the surface but as this originates no more than 1,000 km below the surface, it tells us more about the upper mantle than the core.

Enveloping the core is the **mantle**, a 2,900 km thick layer that contains 80% of the Earth's volume. The mantle is solid rock but near its outer edge, beneath the crust, it can behave like a liquid and flow or deform. This layer of the upper mantle is termed the **asthenosphere** and its existence is crucial to the current theory of **plate tectonics.** Above this layer the upper mantle and the crust form a final shell of solid rock termed the **lithosphere** (**Resource 118**).

The crust itself is the thinnest element of the model, averaging only 20 km in thickness, and ranging from 60 km in the continents to a mere 5 km beneath the

Resource 118 *Model of the first 100 km below the surface*

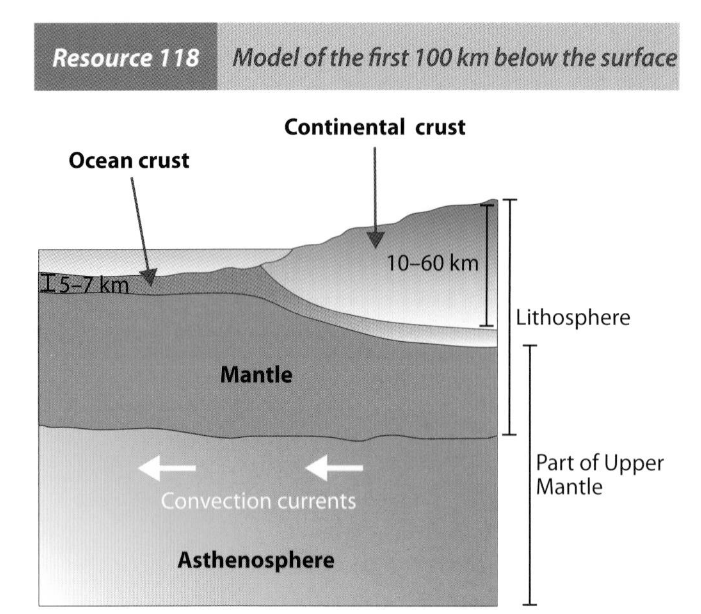

oceans. Other differences between continental and oceanic crust are their density and composition, with oceanic crust composed of denser basaltic rocks, while continental rocks are lighter and more granitic in nature. As we shall see, the modern concept of tectonics suggests that the lithosphere is not a single unit but rather it is composed of at least 13 huge and separate slabs or plates of continental and oceanic material. Together they form, like pieces of some enormous jigsaw puzzle, the Earth's outer layer on which all life exists. It is worth noting that if the Earth were scaled down to the size of an ordinary balloon, the relative thickness of the balloon's skin would over-represent that of the crust.

Resource 119 *The two contrasting types of crustal rocks*

	Oceanic Crust	Continental Crust
Thickness	Thin 5–7 km	Thick 10–60 km
Rock density	Denser 3–3.3 (gm/m³)	Less dense 2.7 (gm/m³)
Rock type	Basaltic SIMA (Silica and magnesium)	Granitic SIAL (Silica and alumina)
Rock age	Less than 250 million years	From 1,000 to 3,5000 million years

Resource 120 *Parallel coastlines*

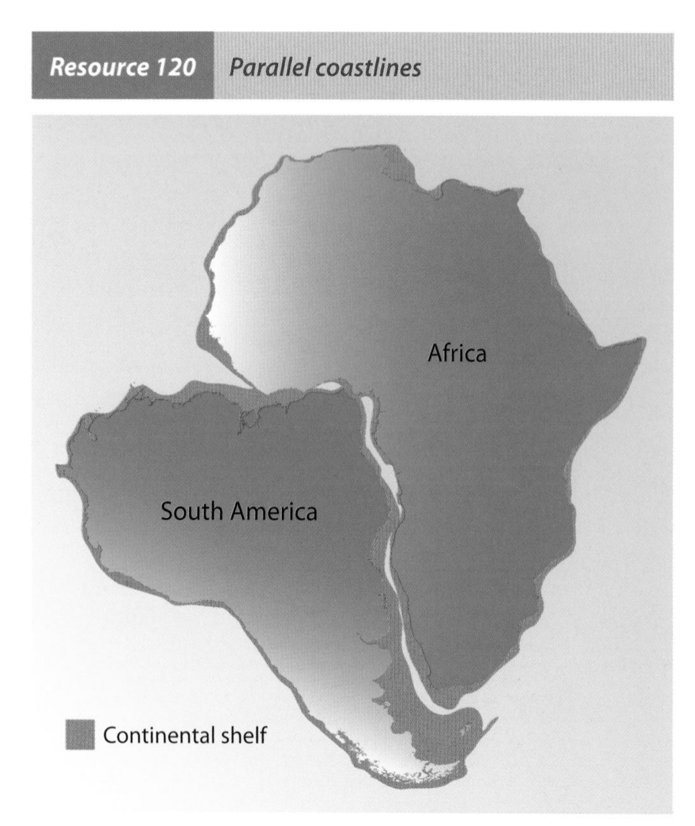

Plate tectonics and resulting landforms

Plate Tectonics

For centuries observers and scientists have been fascinated by the night sky. They often describe the beauty of 'the Great Dance' of the planets, stars and galaxies. The last one hundred years has revealed another Great Dance, much more earth bound, beneath our feet. The modern theory of plate tectonics suggests that our current world map is but a step in a continuum of change. It appears while the rocks of the continents are often ancient, even billions of years old, the ocean floors that form most of the Earth's outer skin are young. The huge jigsaw pieces that carry these oceans and continents jostle and move in three common patterns, in opposing directions: towards, away or past each other.

The idea of Continent Drift

It was during the great era of European discovery – when the Spanish, Portuguese, Dutch and British fleets ruled the waves – that the gaps in our knowledge of the world

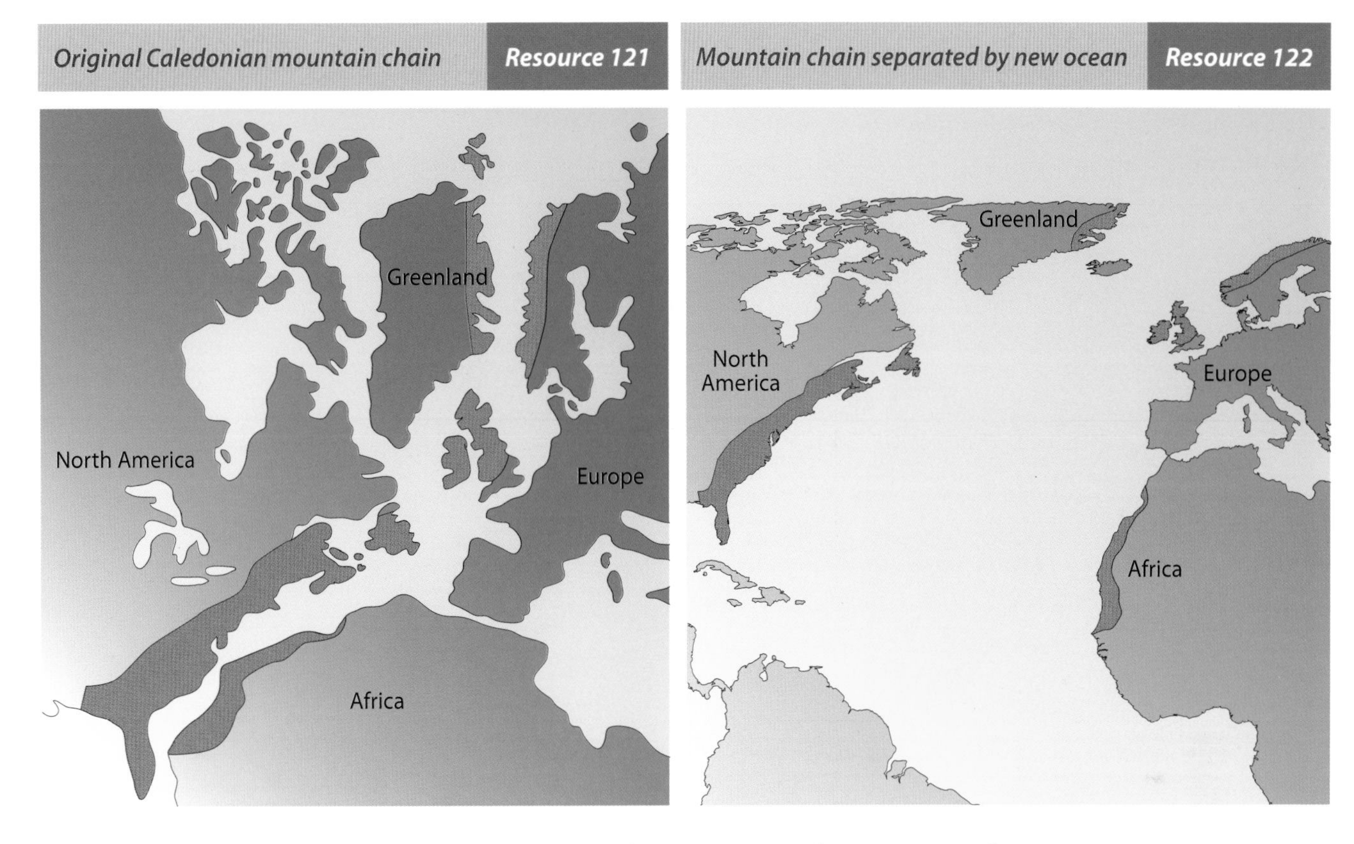

map were gradually filled in. In 1620, Francis Bacon, the eminent British scientist noted, as most schoolchildren have since, that the coastlines of western Africa and eastern South America run parallel to each other. Their coastlines, and more so the edge of their off-shore continental shelves, would form a neat junction if the South Atlantic did not exist (**Resource 120**).

Not until around 100 years ago did any scientist take such an idea much further. In 1915, Alfred Wegener proposed that the world's continents had formerly been a single land mass. He called this Pangaea ('all lands'), which over the past 200 million years had gradually broken up to form today's familiar outline. Wegener spent 25 years and all his energy in the search for evidence of continent drift and a process capable of explaining it. In the first part he succeeded but failed to convince the scientific world before his death, aged 50, on a research trip to Greenland in 1930.

The evidence he gathered included the parallel nature of some continental coastlines, along with other rock, fossil and past climate evidence.

- The distribution pattern of both rock types and the mountain chains they often form made more sense when the separate landmasses of contemporary continents were placed together. Past periods of mountain building, including the Caledonian and Hercynnian epochs, created long fold mountain chains across the world, many of which now exist as weathered fragments on the opposite shores of the world's ocean basins (**Resource 121** and **123**).
- Within these rocks, fossil evidence included the remains of ancient mesosaur reptiles and gigantic glossopteris ferns. These were found in similar aged rocks in South America, Africa, India and Antarctica, places now separated by thousands of miles of salt water in which these animals and plants could not survive (**Resource 123**).
- It was also clear from the landforms on their surface that these continents, including tropical hot desert regions, had in the distant past been covered and carved by huge ice sheets, similar to those found in Greenland today. Again, the location and direction of flow of such sheets seemed to make sense only when these continents were placed together, as a huge southern landmass Wegener named Gondwanaland (**Resource 124**).

Despite building this array of evidence, one British geologist, when talking of Wegener's

Resource 123 *Fossil evidence for contental drift*

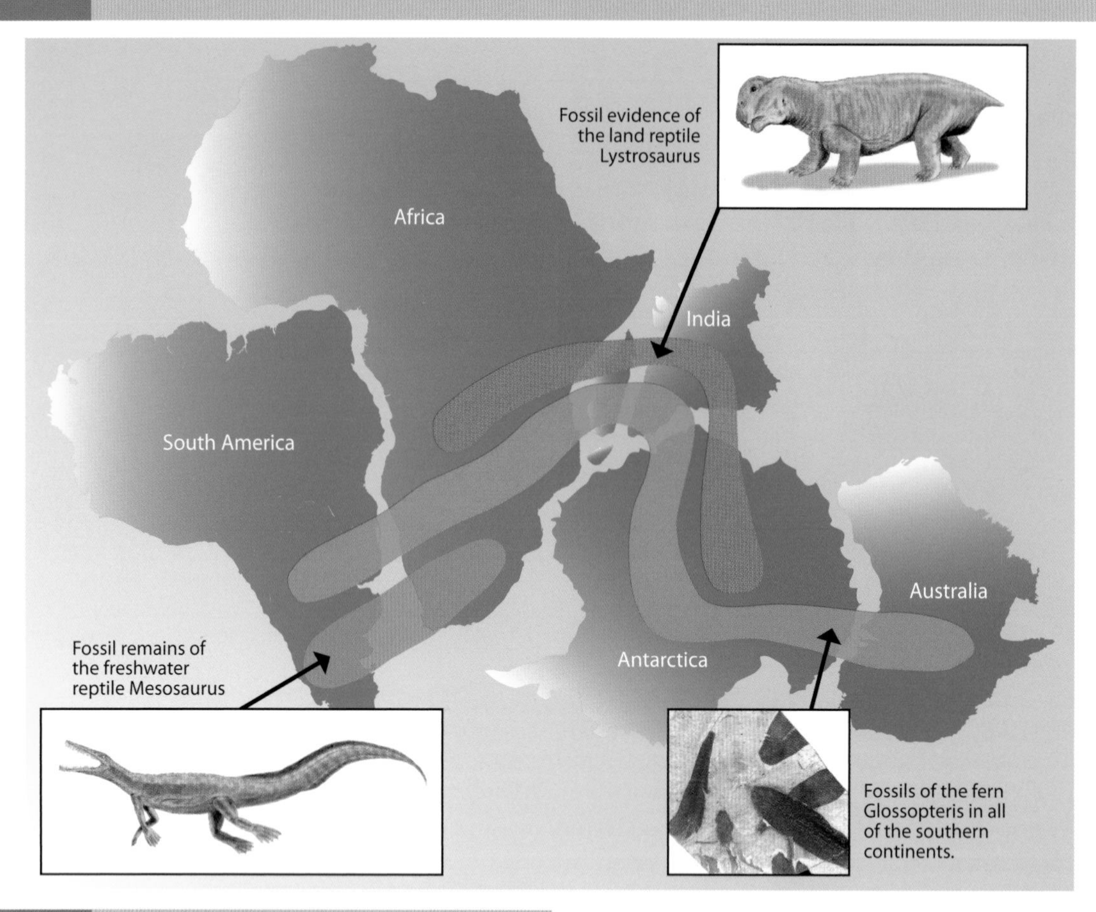

Resource 124 *Fossil glaciation and Gondwanaland*

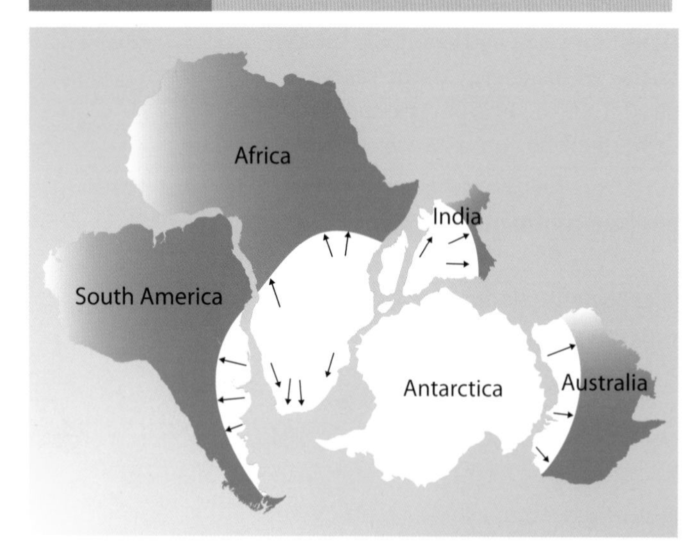

theory of continental drift, stated that anyone who, "valued his reputation for scientific sanity" would never dare support such a theory.

Alfred Wegener did not live to see the final proofs of his theory and the discovery of the possible mechanism for continent drift. These emerged after World War II ended in 1945 and continue to be refined today. This is the theory of Plate Tectonics.

Plate Tectonic Theory

This modern theory describes a mechanism that explains the moving continents. The evidence for it is almost entirely derived from study of the ocean floor that has only been technically possible for the last 60 years (**Resource 125**).

Resource 125 *The exploration of the Ocean floor*

The first piece of evidence that the rocks of the ocean floors differ from those of the continents was that waves from earthquakes moved more quickly through ocean floor material. Later the development of sonar, initially to detect enemy submarines in war, allowed the depth of the ocean to be plotted. In the 1950s, using magnetometers, ships crossed the oceans, uncovering patterns of change in the direction of magnetism from the rocks deep below. Finally, robotic and later manned submarines collected samples of ocean bed rock. All these sources of data meant a radical new comprehension of the ocean floor developed.

The evidence for the theory of Plate Tectonics

1. The topography of the oceans

The first accurate maps created by sonar, of the great ocean basins, showed that rather than being deepest near their centre, they had huge, linear, underwater mountain ranges, with deep central valleys. These submarine mountain chains ran in a continuous line for 50,000 km around the Earth, making them the largest single feature on its surface. These are referred to as the mid-ocean ridges and both the North and South Atlantic provide perfect examples (**Resource 126**).

The mid-Atlantic ridge **Resource 126**

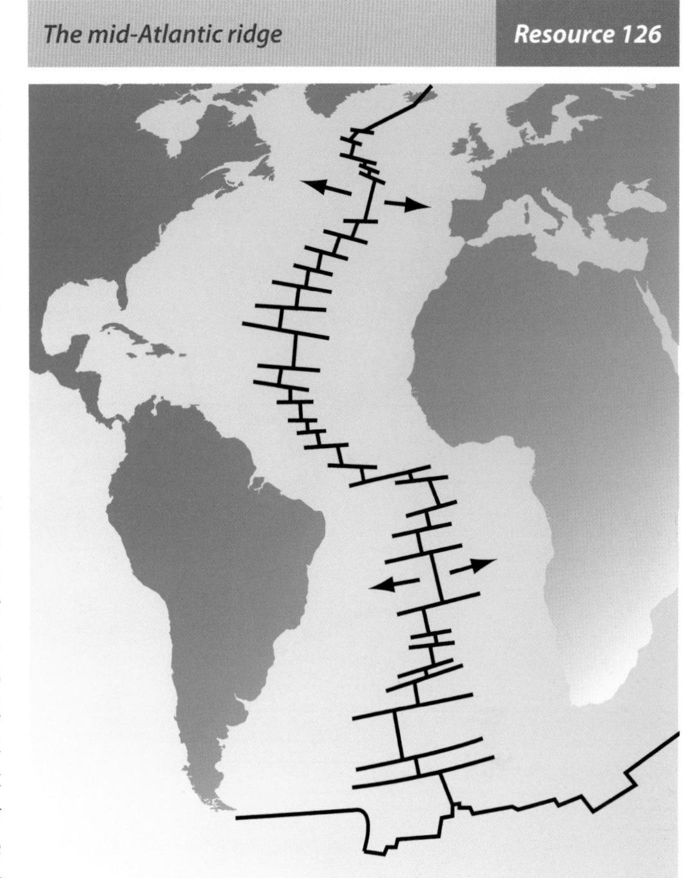

2. The age and pattern of ocean basin geology

One early and puzzling discovery was that the amount of sediment lying on the ocean floor was much less than expected. If the ocean floors were, like the continents, billions of years old, then they should be buried under thick layers of sediment. But the sediment was thin. When ocean rocks were finally dated, their age was numbered in millions or tens of millions of years and not billions. In fact the world's ocean floors, that form 70% of the surface, are young, recently formed. This fact alone sent shockwaves through the scientific community but a related finding was even more astonishing. The mountains of the mid-ocean ridges were made of very young rocks and the age of rocks increased away from them in a mirror pattern (**Resource 127**).

The mid-Atlantic ridge and rock age **Resource 127**

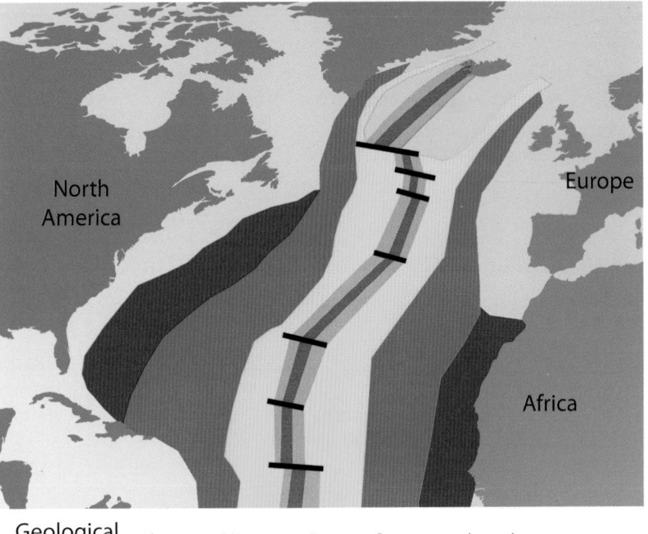

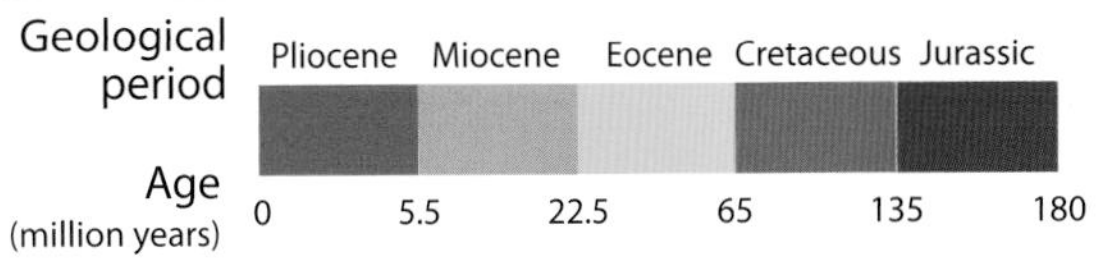

— Transverse faults

3. Paleomagnetism and magnetic striping

At the same time the ocean floors were being mapped, scientists studying ancient or palaeomagnetism (**Resource 130**) had identified a strange pattern in the ocean off the coast of the USA. The pattern of magnetic striping in rocks only made sense when Harry Hess, a scientist, wrote a paper describing a process, later known as sea-floor spreading.

4. The distribution of earthquakes and volcanoes

Mapping of the global distribution of active volcanoes and earthquake activity was continuously improved, and distinctive and repeated patterns emerged. Both volcanic and seismic activity tended to occur in long, narrow, linear bands, sometimes along coastlines or through oceans. Perhaps the most noted was the so called 'ring of fire', a line of volcanoes that marked the circumference of the Pacific basin, including the volcanoes of Washington State, USA and the island volcanoes of Japan and New Zealand. Identifying these active zones also highlights huge regions of the surface that have little or no such activity today (**Resource 128**).

Resource 128 *World earthquake distribution*

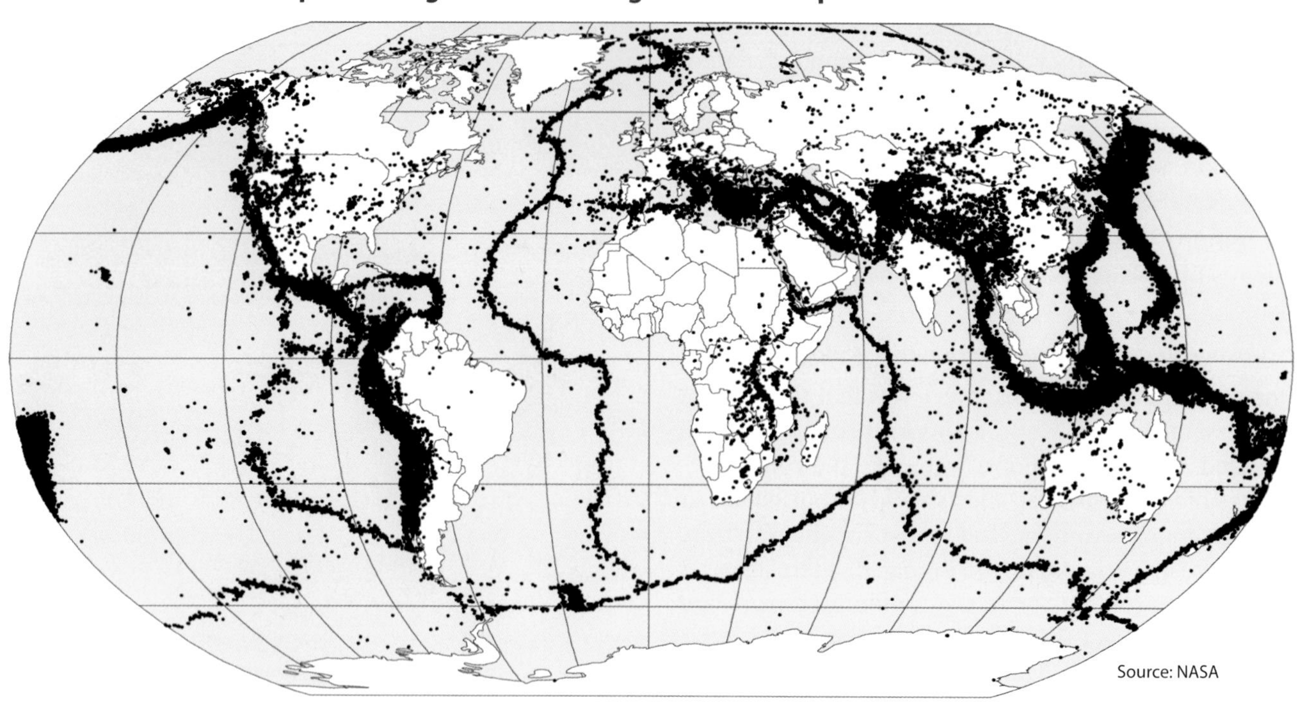

Resource 129 *The changing location of the British Isles*

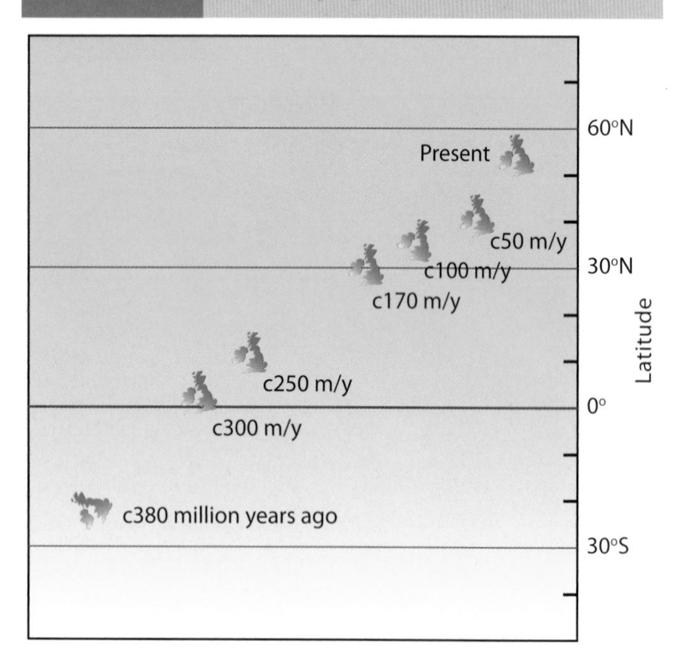

Resource 130 *The science of palaeomagnetism*

Scientists working on the nature of the Earth's magnetic field noted that metal particles in molten volcanic rock become magnetized as the rock cools and solidifies. Just as a compass needle points to the magnetic north pole, so these particles then retain the direction of the field. The rock permanently records this direction and angle of dip, therefore the location of the rock when it was formed can be calculated. Using this method it was shown that many rocks in the British Isles were formed near the Equator. This, along with the vast coalfields of Great Britain, formed by fossilised tropical swamp material, suggested that northward continental drift had occurred (**Resource 129**).

Even more dramatically, it has been shown that, for some reason not yet fully known, the Earth's magnetism reverses direction. In other words, all compasses would swing to point south and not north. This reversal from the present 'normal' pattern is also recorded in volcanic rocks. Across mid-ocean ridges, patterns of normal and reversed polarity have been recoded and linked to the age of the rocks. This magnetic striping provides further evidence, almost a recording, of the process of sea-floor spreading.

Plate Tectonic Theory – Harry Hess, seafloor spreading and subduction

In the 1960s, Harry Hess and others suggested that mid-ocean ridges are weak zones in the crust where the ocean floor is being pulled apart along the ridge crest. New magma from deep in the mantle rises easily through these weaker zones and eventually erupts along the crest of the ridges, creating new oceanic crust. This process, later named seafloor spreading, has operated over many millions of years forming the ocean basins. The hypothesis made good sense of the new evidence:

- The existence of the great submarine mountain chains and rift valleys at the ocean centres.
- Along the mid-ocean ridges the rocks are very young and become progressively older away from the ridge.
- Bands of rock parallel to the ridge have alternating magnetic polarity, reflecting the repeated reversal of the Earth's magnetic field.
- The patterns of submarine volcanoes along the ridges revealed active processes at work. In 1963 one rose above the surface of the Atlantic near Iceland to form the new island of Surtsey.

Harry Hess reasoned that if the Earth's crust was expanding along the oceanic ridges and the Earth was not expanding, then somewhere the crust must be shrinking. As new ocean crust forms and spreads away from mid-ocean ridges like a conveyor belt, millions of years later it is destroyed at deep ocean trenches. These features were another finding of sea-floor mapping along the edge of the Pacific – long narrow deep trenches on the sea floor with associated volcano and earthquake activity (**Resource 131**). In effect, the rocks of the ocean floors are continuously recycled, with new lithosphere plate material created at ridges and old oceanic plate melted and destroyed at destructive boundaries. The theory then neatly explains:

1. why the earth does not get bigger despite sea floor spreading;
2. why there is so little sediment accumulation on the ocean floor; and
3. why the rocks forming ocean basins are much younger than continental rocks.

Pacific ocean trenches **Resource 131**

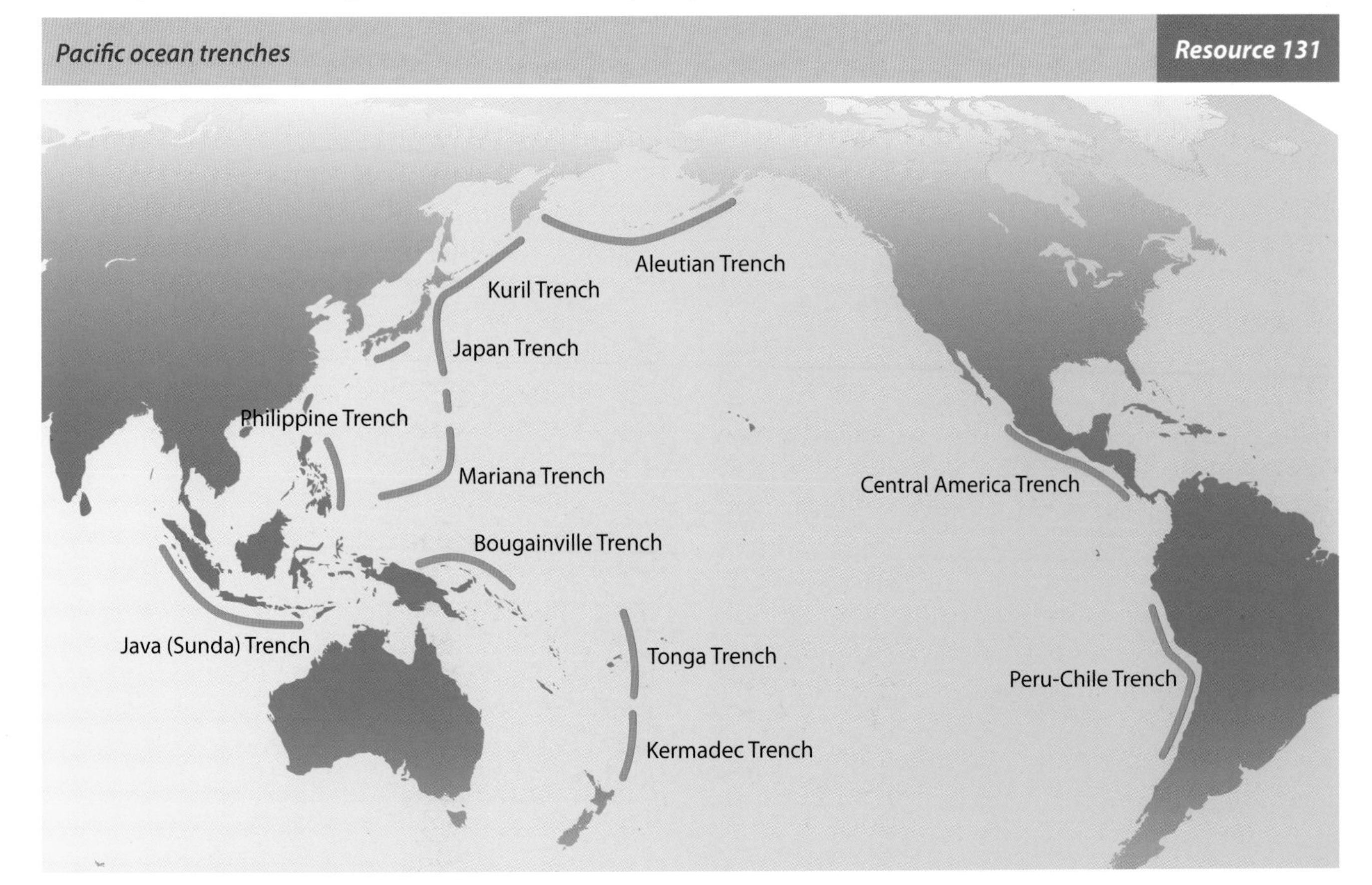

While debate continues about the precise nature of the forces operating within the mantle, the evidence that continents are mobile is now conclusive. Measurements using radio signals from 21 GPS satellites orbiting the Earth show that while the North Atlantic Ocean expands at an average rate of 2 cm per year, sea-floor spreading in the Pacific basin averages 6 cm and even 10 cm per year near Easter Island. Wegener's theory, dismissed in 1924 by some as lunacy, had 50 years later become accepted fact.

When Plates meet – Plate Margins

The plates that form the lithosphere are driven by slow flows of molten magma in the asthenosphere beneath them. These movements are termed **convection currents** (**Resource 132**) and represent material rising in the mantle from deep locations of excessive heat, in much the same way as warm air rises in the atmosphere. These currents reach the underside of the lithosphere, about 80 km below the surface, where they slowly migrate laterally, dragging the plates above. Alternatively, in places these currents break through into the crust or onto the surface as volcanic activity (**Resource 133**).

Under this process the continuously jostling plates meet at three distinct types of margin or boundary:

- **Constructive** – pulling or tension forces plates apart allowing new material to be formed, most commonly at the ocean ridges.
- **Destructive** – compression forces drive plates towards each other, causing one to be gradually subducted and destroyed or both to crumple (Collision Margin).
- **Conservative** – plates slide past each other without either forming or destroying plate material.

Resource 132 *Convection currents in the Upper Mantle (Asthenosphere)*

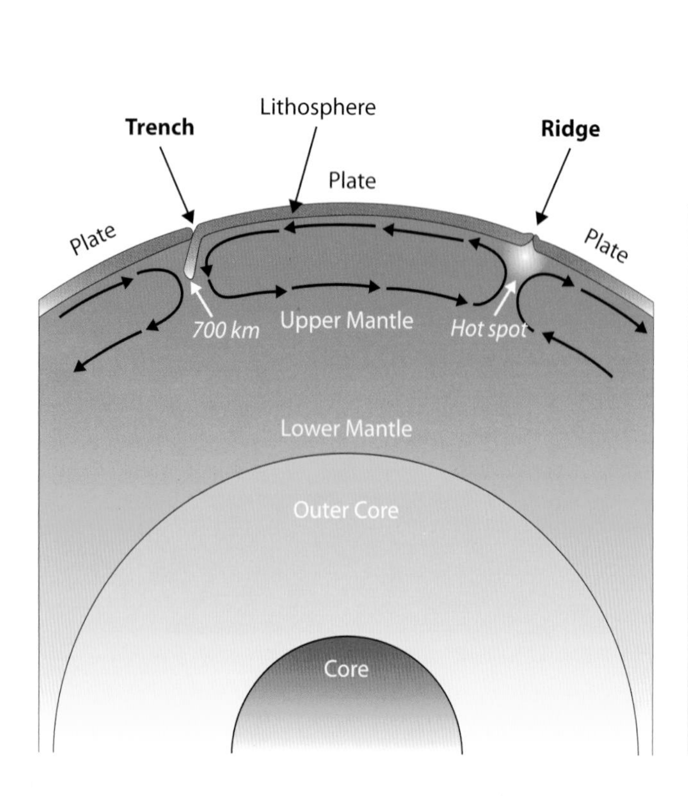

Resource 133 *The conveyor system linking sea floor spreading and subduction*

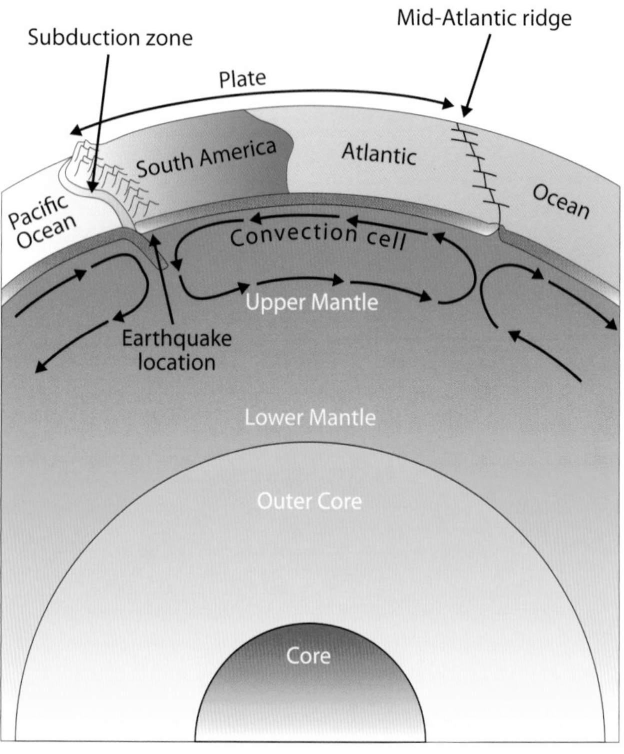

Stages in the development of a constructive plate margin — *Resource 134*

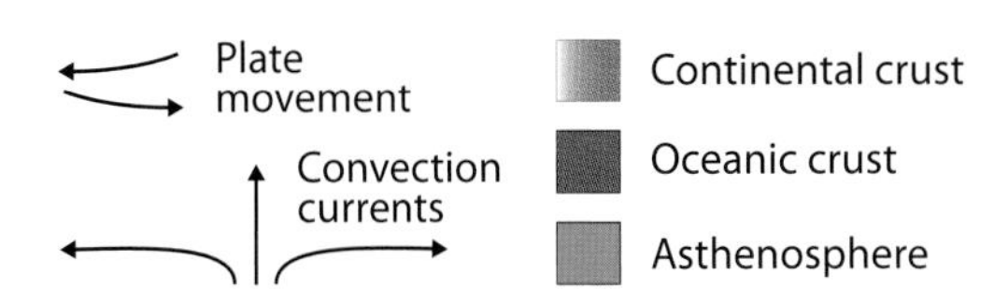

Warping, stretching of continental plate

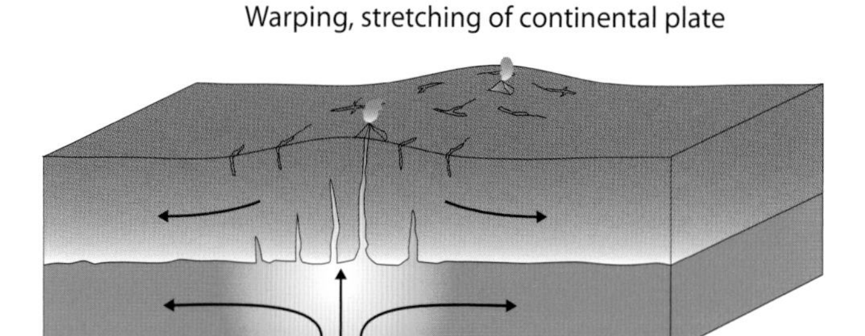

Formation of rift valley

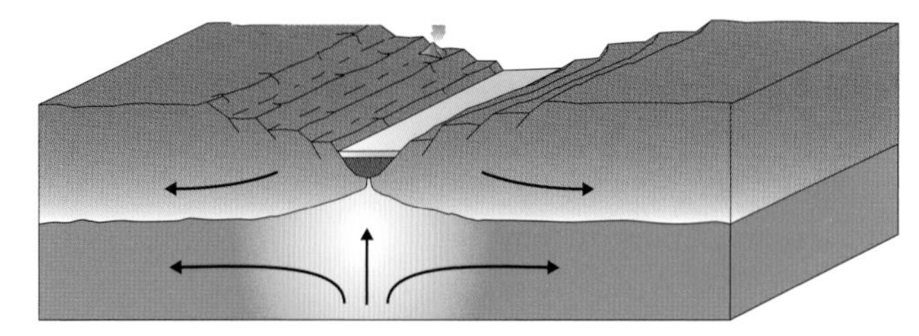

Linear sea

Mid-ocean ridge

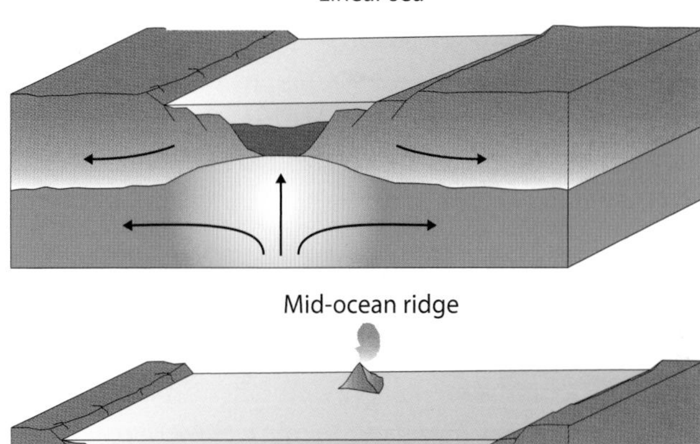

Constructive plate margins

As we have seen, the sub-marine mountain chains of the central Atlantic, Indian and Pacific oceans are the products of the process of sea floor spreading. The sequence of events that has created the world's ocean basins is as follows. Hot spots deep in the mantle cause magma to rise, forcing the solid plates above to stretch and break along a fault line. The line of weakness is marked by slumping blocks, forming a rift valley and the magma then solidifies to create new plate material (**Resource 134**).

As this divergence process continues, the stretching plate and rift valley may allow a nearby ocean to spill in and water to flow into the valley, initiating the formation of a new ocean basin. The North Atlantic is one of the most recent of these formations, as Europe and North America where firstly separated and then slowly forced apart. This process continues today. The island of Iceland is a summit of the vast mid-Atlantic mountain chain ridge that runs the entire length of the ocean. Along this line, which includes the central valley of Iceland itself, fresh eruptions pour out lava, forming new plate material and crustal rocks (**Resource 135**). Shallow earthquakes are also associated with constructive margins, caused by the movement of magma rising towards the surface.

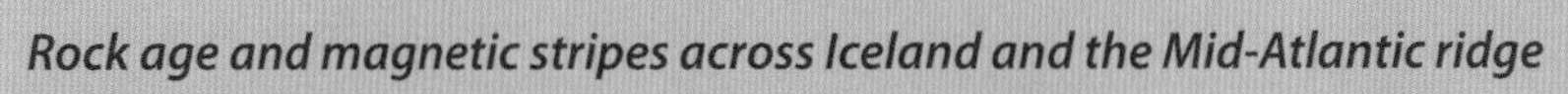

Rock age and magnetic stripes across Iceland and the Mid-Atlantic ridge — *Resource 135*

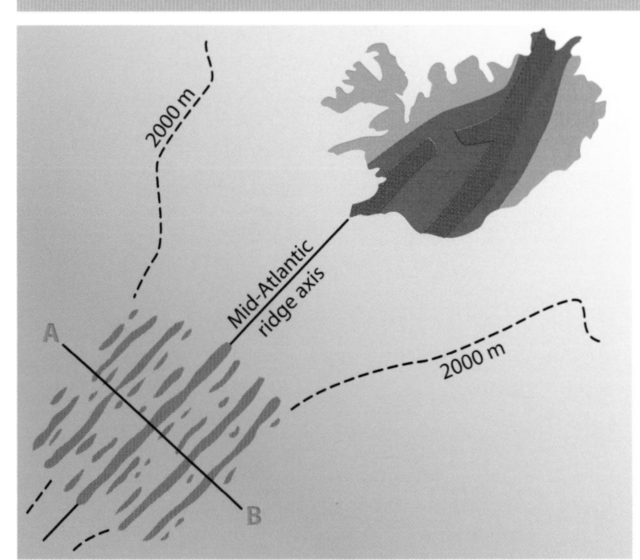

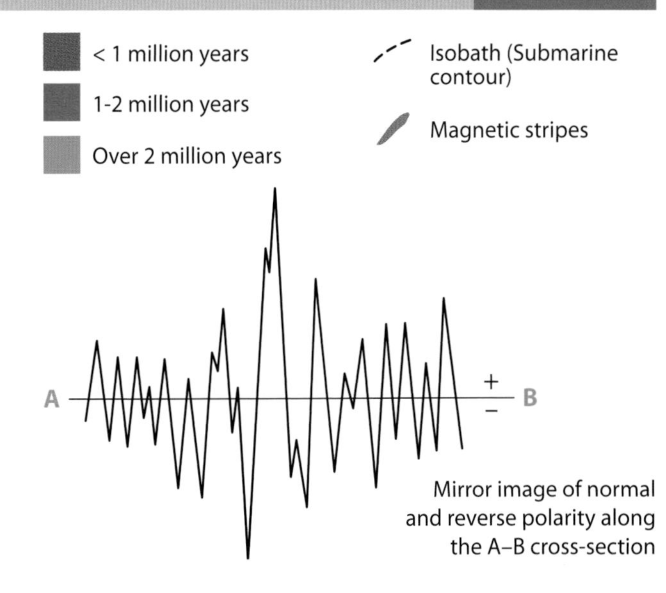

Mirror image of normal and reverse polarity along the A–B cross-section

Resource 136 *The East African rift valley*

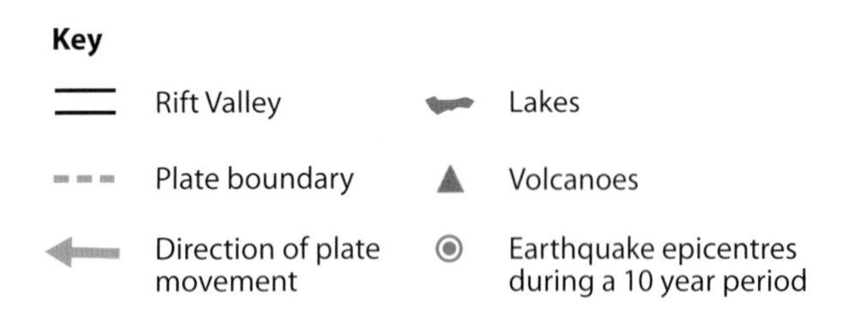

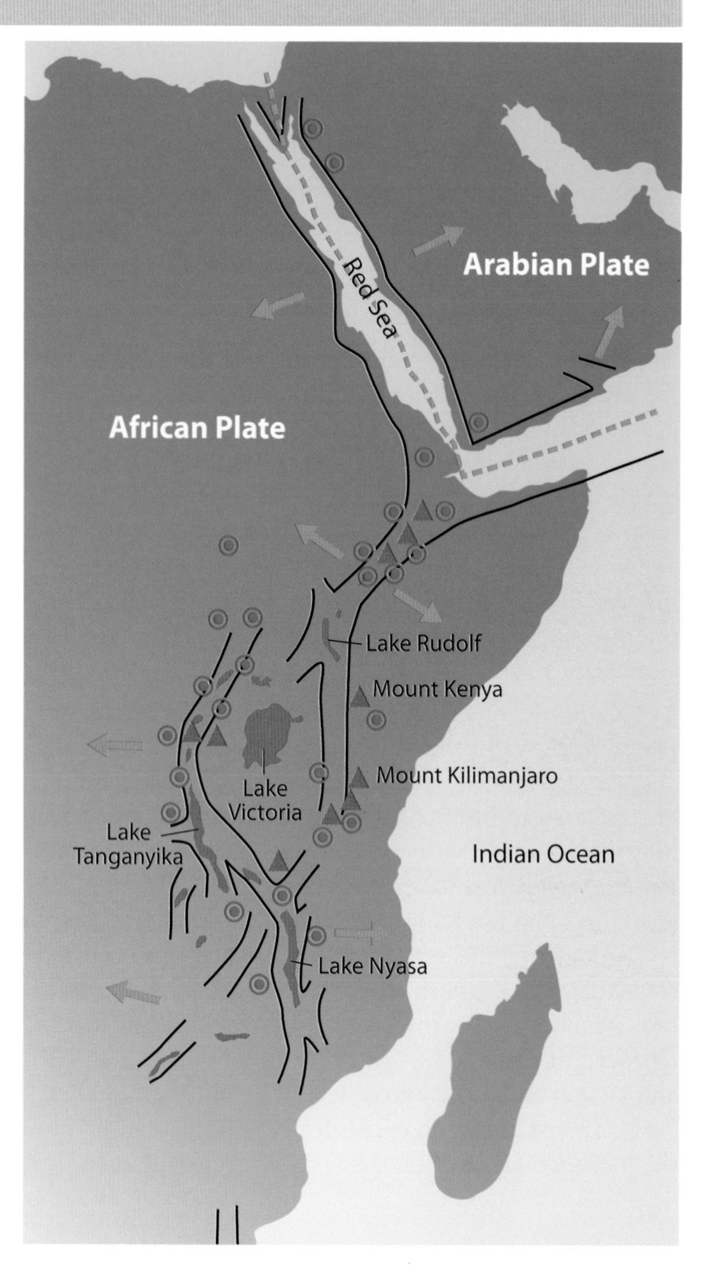

The mirror image of rock age and magnetic polarity around the central ridge reveals the sea floor spreading process.

There is one other location on land where a constructive margin may be studied. The Great Rift valley of East Africa is regarded as an initial stage in the formation of a new ocean, as the land stretches under the rising convection currents of magma from the mantle below (**Resource 136**). Such processes have already pulled Saudi Arabia away from the rest of the African continent and formed the Red Sea. Along the East African Rift the continental crust has been stretched and tension cracks have appeared on the surface. Magma rises and squeezes through the widening cracks, sometimes to erupt and form volcanoes such as Mt Nyiragorgo and Kilimanjaro. This may be the site of the Earth's next major ocean. These plate movements provide scientists with the chance to study at first hand the processes that started the birth of the Atlantic Ocean about 200 million years ago. Geologists suggest that if the spreading continues for another 10 million years, the plates will separate completely, allowing the Indian Ocean to flood the area through the Afar lowlands, leaving the region known as the Horn of Africa as a large island.

Exercise

1. Using an internet search engine, find references to the following terms and write a description, with an appropriate sketch diagram, to show the operation of a triple plate boundary at the Red Sea and Afar junction.

   Triple Junction **Afar Lowlands** **Red Sea**

2. On a copy of **Resource 134** select and write the correct paragraph from those below alongside the appropriate diagram.

   A – Plates begin to separate and a shallow sea forms above the new oceanic crust.

   B – A broad ridge develops within the ocean and widening continues. There is both submarine and occasional surface volcanic activity.

   C – The sea widens and sediment from the continent covers the sea bed at its edge. A mid-oceanic ridge develops.

   D – Convectional uplift from magma in the upper mantle leads to arching of the crust.

The destructive margin of Western South America **Resource 137**

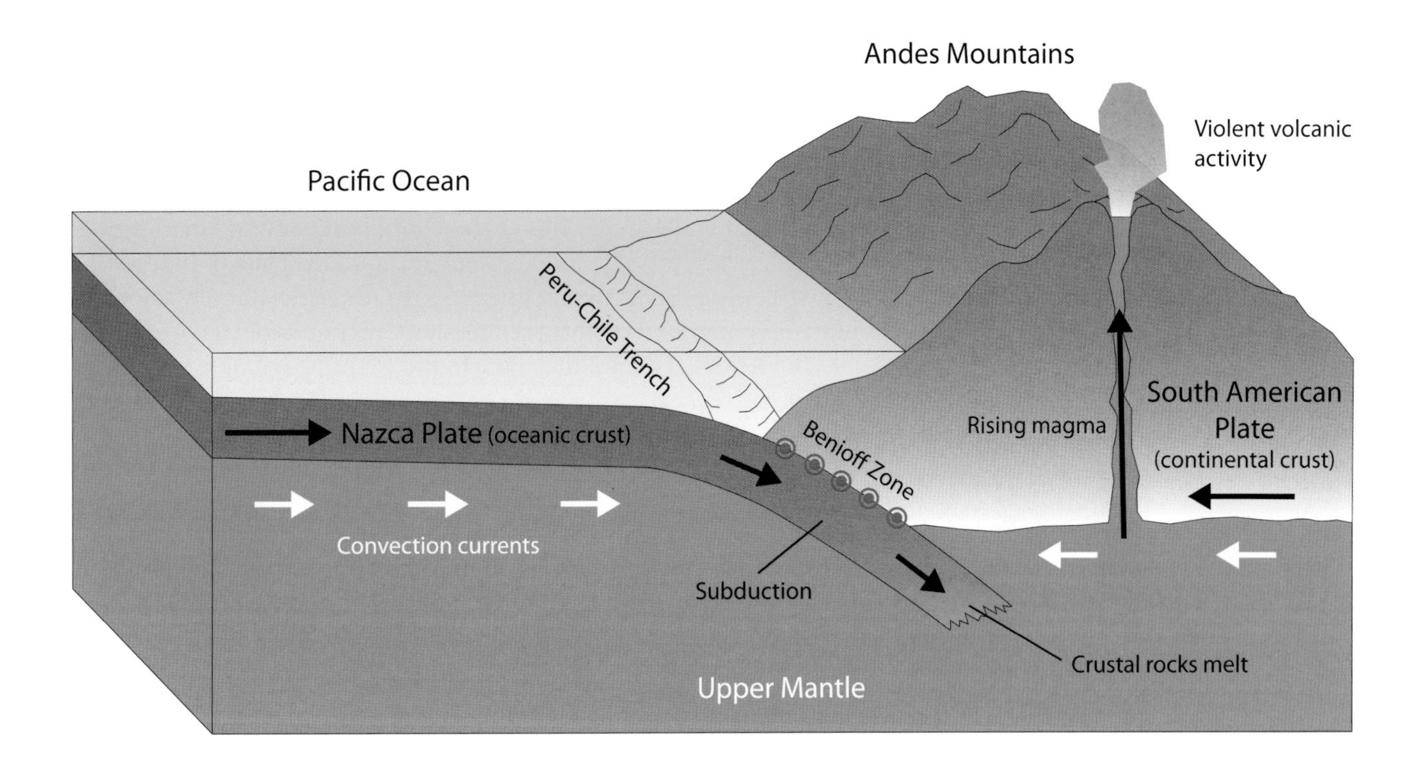

Destructive plate margins

The form of margin where plates are forced towards each other (convergence) by convection currents produces two possible variations:

A – the meeting of an ocean plate with a continental plate

B – the meeting of two oceanic plates

A – Ocean and Continental

The best known example of this lies in the Eastern Pacific Basin, where the relatively small, Nazca plate, formed by the constructive margin of the East Pacific rise, moves west to meet the South America Plate (**Resource 137** and **133**).

The South America plate not only carries the continent of South America but also the floor of the western section of the South Atlantic Ocean. The eastern edge of the plate is at the Mid-Atlantic Ridge, a constructive margin, but the western edge of the plate marks a destructive boundary. Where these two plates meet is marked by a distinctive series of landforms and patterns of tectonic activity. On the ocean floor, close to and parallel with the western coast of South America, lies a long, narrow, deep ocean feature – the Peru-Chile Trench. This marks the point at which the dense Nazca plate, pushing eastwards, meets the South America plate and is forced downwards into the asthenosphere beneath. This process is termed subduction. At the trench sea floor sediments are scraped up against the continent's coast. Beneath the surface, as the huge plates slowly grind past each other, earthquakes and tremors are frequent. Seismologists can plot an earthquake's focus with precision and in these regions a clear pattern of shallow to deeper foci is recorded. These mark the contact point between the plates as the oceanic plate subducts into the mantle. The region of these seismic events is known as the Benioff Zone (**Resources 137** and **138**).

On 9 June 1994, an earthquake measuring 8.3 on the Richter Scale struck north-east of La Paz, Bolivia, at a depth of 636 km. This quake, in the subduction zone between the Nazca and the South American plates, was one of deepest and largest ever recorded in South America. Fortunately, despite being felt as far away as Toronto (Canada), it caused no major damage due to great depth of the focus.

As the oceanic plate moves into the upper mantle its rocks are subject to increasing temperatures and start to melt. The new magma material is lighter than the surrounding rocks and starts to move upwards towards the underside of the continental South America plate. This molten material may force its way through lines of weakness into the plate or indeed right through it to erupt on the surface. The Western coast line of South America is closely associated with the high Andes Mountains, composed partly of sedimentary rocks pushed upwards by the collision of the two plates. The Andes also owe their size to the eruptions of numerous active volcanoes, including many of the highest in the world eg Mt Tacora (Chile) and Nevado del Ruiz (Colombia).

Ocean Trenches

If the world's ocean basins were drained, the topography revealed would more than rival the variation seen on land. Along with 9 km high mountains rising from the ocean floor, as at Big Island Hawaii, and the 50,000km long mountain chains of the mid-ocean ridges, there are also narrow chasms plunging down 10 km – the deep ocean trenches. The deepest of all lies in the Marianas Trench, south of Japan and is 10,923 m or nearly 11 km deep. Another trench, the Challenger Deep, was named after the British research vessel that first mapped it in 1951.

Ocean trenches are a sure sign of the process of subduction of an ocean plate at a destructive margin. They are commonly associated with earthquake patterns, increasing in depth with lateral distance from the trench and parallel lines of volcanic activity often hundreds of kilometres away.

Resource 138 *The pattern of earthquake foci at Benioff zone*

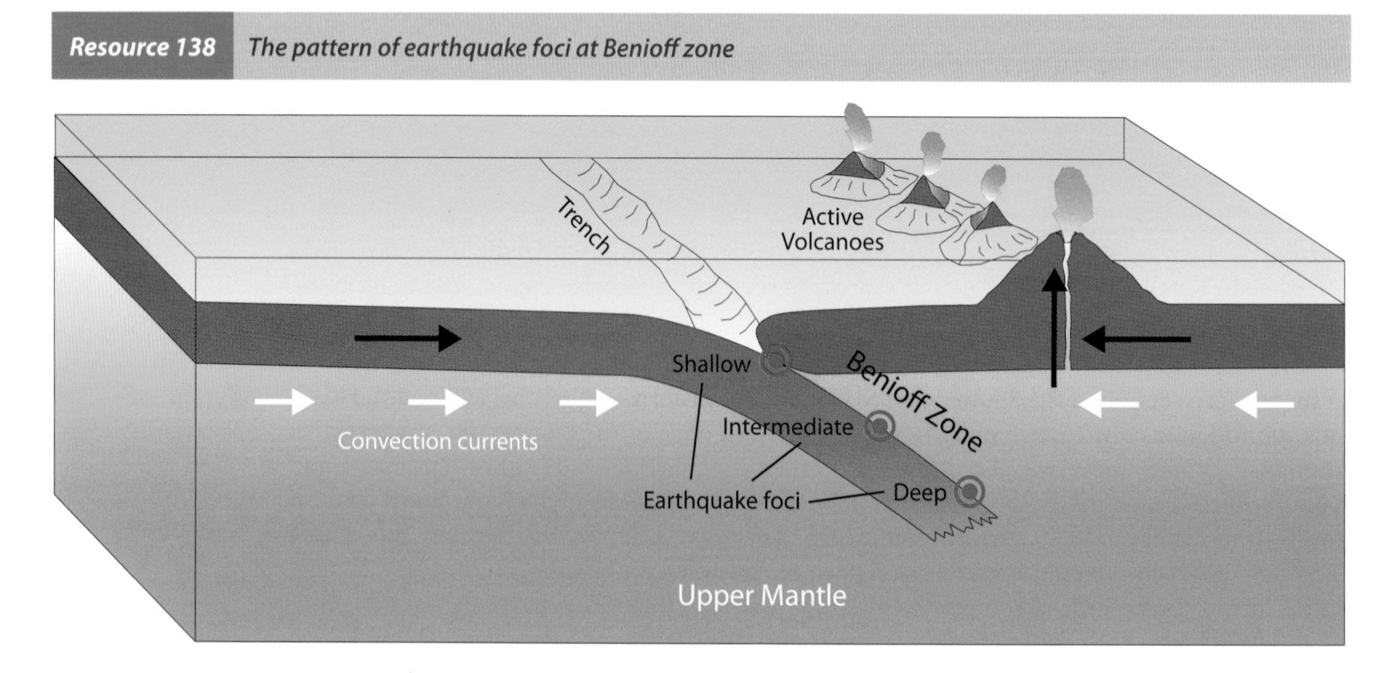

B – Ocean to Ocean Plates

Where convection forces in the mantle cause oceanic plates to collide, a line of volcanoes (submarine or as islands) is often found parallel to a deep ocean trench (**Resource 138**). These features, along with a linear pattern of earthquakes, indicate subduction. Similar to the previous destructive margin, one oceanic plate, probably the denser, is forced down into the upper mantle, creating friction earthquakes and eventually melting at depths of up to 600 km. Such

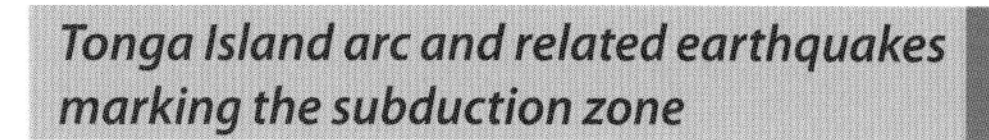

margins are common in the western region of the Pacific basin. These include the islands of New Zealand in the south, through those of Tonga, Mariana, Indonesia, the Philippines and Japan, to the Aleutians in the north. Long curving ocean trenches are paralleled by island arcs of volcanoes. **Resource 139** illustrates the Tonga islands and the associated Tonga trench. The cross section shows the location of earthquake foci beneath the region. Shallow earthquakes occur near the Tonga trench itself and with increasing distance away the quakes foci are deeper. The line formed is interpreted as the contact zone of the two plates along the subduction area or Benioff zone. The islands themselves are the result of molten plate material erupting onto the ocean floor, eventually building to reach the surface. Over a longer time period the build up and reworking of rock material produces more substantial landmasses and islands, such as those of Japan and the Philippines. These are termed mature island arc systems.

Tonga Island arc and related earthquakes marking the subduction zone — ***Resource 139***

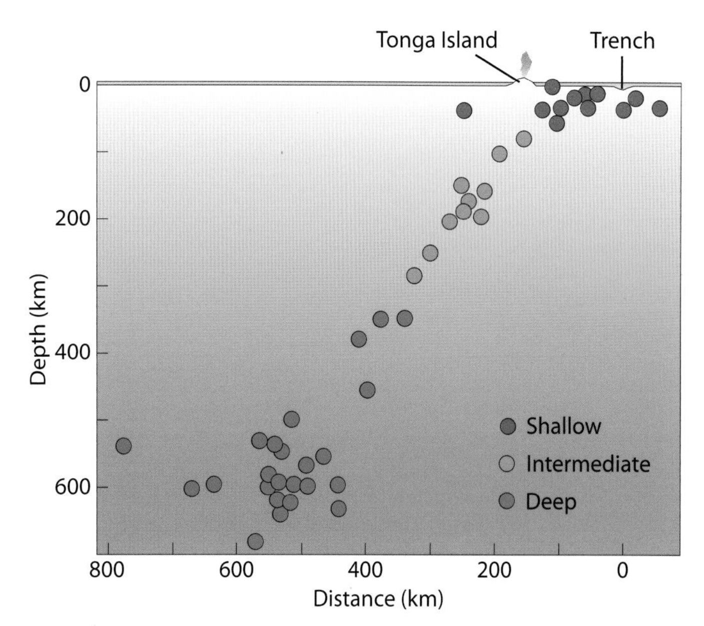

Exercise

Exercise

A sample examination question, based on the summer 2004 A2 1 CCEA paper is given.

For the first part of this question the mark scheme, a candidate's attempt with marker's comment and a model answer are provided.

The question

Question adapted from CCEA May 2004

1. Study **Figure 1** which shows volcanic and earthquake activity in the north-west Pacific.

   (i) Describe the distribution pattern of tectonic activity shown. (5)

   (ii) With the aid of a diagram explain the processes operating at the plate boundary. (12)

Figure 1

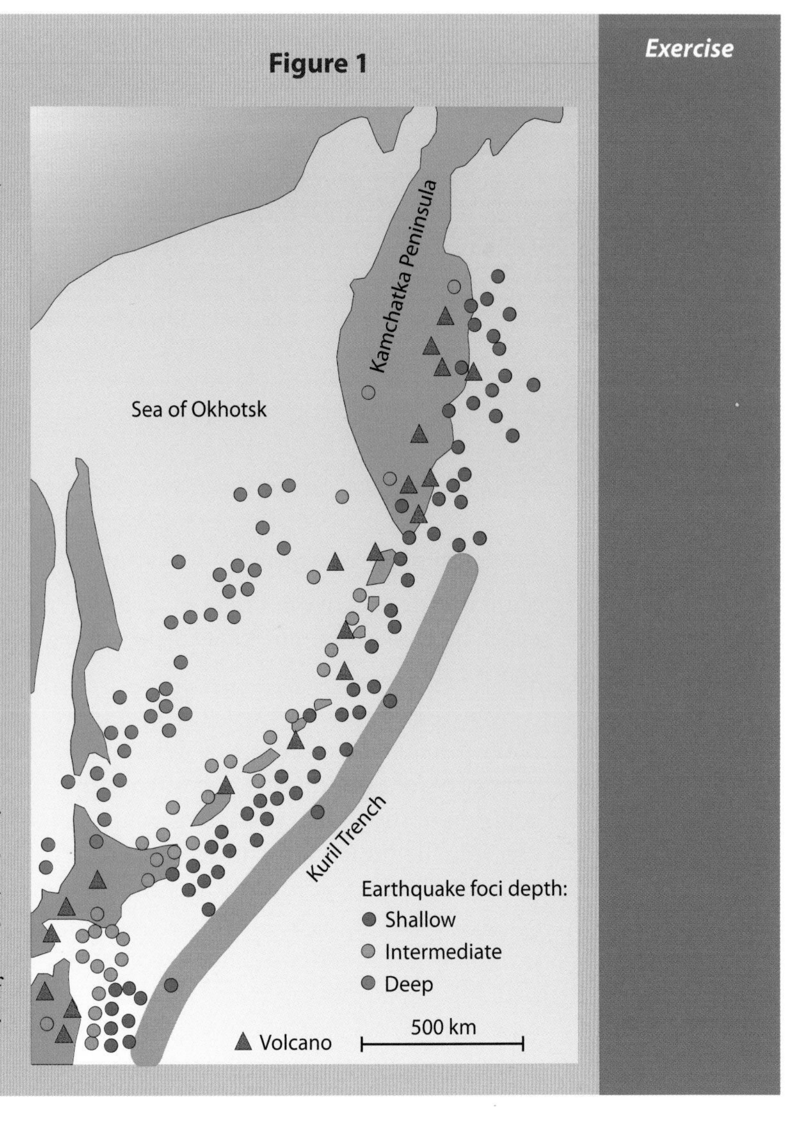

The mark scheme for (i)

There is essentially a linear pattern of over 20 volcanoes and numerous earthquakes running NE–SW parallel to the Kuril Trench. The depth of earthquakes increases with distance north-west from the trench. The linear patterns, the different depth of earthquakes and some figures of scale or numbers are required.

Exercise

One candidate's answer

"Earthquakes with a shallow focus are distributed evenly, along a **linear** stretch of **2,500 km**. These earthquakes are situated closer to the Kuril Trench, than any other earthquakes or volcanoes.

Earthquakes with intermediate depth foci are also situated in a linear strip but slightly further **west** of the shallow foci earthquakes. They are found further from the Kuril Trench. The distribution of these is more **uneven** and the amount in the area varies widely. In the **south** they are more **clumped** together. The deepest foci earthquakes have a more **clumped** distribution. They are found in a **linear** formation furthest from the Kuril Trench. These earthquakes only stretch across about **1,500 km**. The volcanoes are also distributed in a **linear** fashion but it is an **uneven** distribution in the **north** and **south**." (129 words)

Mark = 3 out of 5.

Marker's comment

"The candidate correctly addresses the distribution of all the tectonic activity shown, volcanoes and earthquakes in three depth categories. Some compass directions, distances and terms of pattern are used (**in bold** in the text). On the other hand, the candidate only names one location, the Kuril Trench and no reference is made to the numbers of each type of activity. The distance of each type of tectonic activity is also not noted and oddly despite the use of linear the term parallel is not employed."

A 'model' answer

"The tectonic activity is confined to a 750 km wide zone stretching 2,500 km from the Kamchatka Peninsula in the north-east to Japan in the south-east. The volcanoes and earthquakes at various depths lie to the northwest and parallel to the Kuril Trench in narrow linear belts. The sixty shallow focus quakes lie within 200 km of the trench while around 35 intermediate depth earthquakes are located between 100 and 400 km from the trench. The deepest earthquakes, over thirty in total, are located furthest from the trench at a distance between 500 and 750 km, mainly in the Sea of Okhotsk. Finally, the twenty volcanoes also lie north-west off and parallel to the ocean trench. They form a line over 2,500 km long with most between 100 and 400 km from the trench."

(127 words)

Collision plate margins

Similar to destructive boundaries, collision margins form where plates are moved towards each other by convection currents in the asthenosphere. However, in this case both plates carry continents.

Where two continental plates meet there is no subduction of plate material, rather the edges of the plates and any sediments deposited between the two continents are crushed upwards into a range of **fold mountains** (**Resource 140**). The Himalayas are one example, resulting from the collision of the Indian sub-continent plate into the huge Eurasian plate. In reality, as the plate carrying the Indian sub-continent sped across what is now the Indian Ocean, towards Eurasia, its leading edge was oceanic and subduction occurred. As the two continents drew near, the ocean drained as the sediments on its floor were forced upwards. These sediments continue to rise today as the series of huge ridges that form the mountain kingdom of Nepal and the vast high plateau of Tibet. It is said that the top of Mt Everest (Sagarmatha), at 8,850 m, is made of limestone, a rock formed under shallow tropical seas. Closer to home is another example of a collision boundary, where mountain building, earthquake and volcanic activity continue.

Himalayan mountain formation **Resource 140**

India drifts towards Eurasian Plate

Cross-section sequence of meeting of Indian and Eurasian plates

60 million years ago

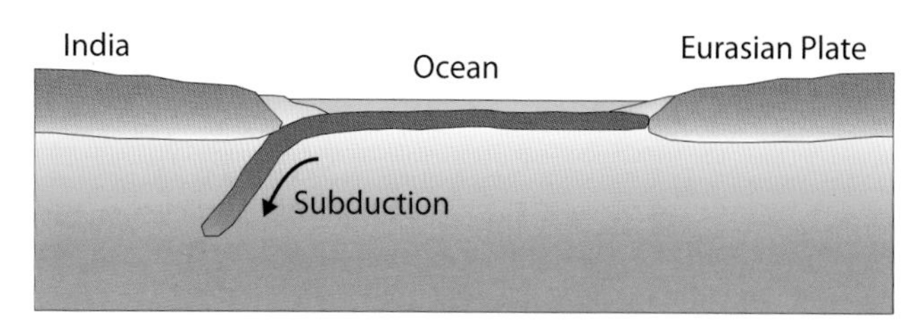

20 million years ago

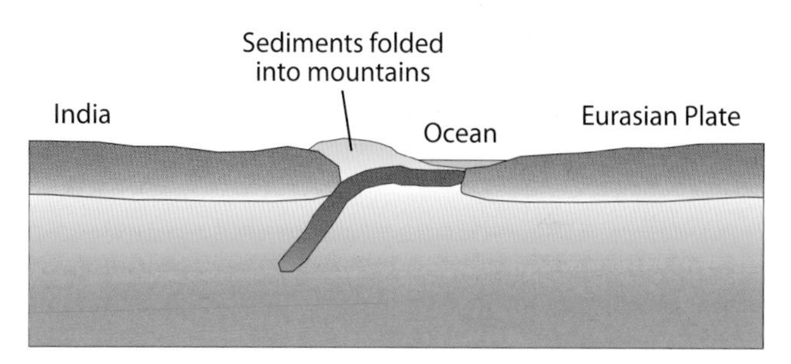

Present

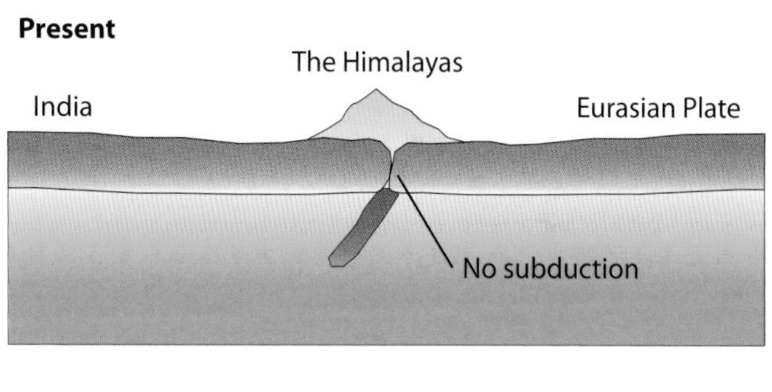

Continental crust
Oceanic crust
Lithosphere
Folded sediments

Africa meets Europe

The Alps are merely one part of a long and complex fold mountain chain that runs across the region. It includes numerous mountain ranges such as the Atlas (NW Africa); the Pyrenees, Apennines, Carpathian (in Europe); Taurus and Zagros Mountains (in Asia) (**Resource 141**).

A cross-section of the Alps would reveal that tremendous tectonic forces have been at work to squeeze and contort the rocks into a series of huge waves or **folds**, with older rocks turned over on top of younger ones, a reversal of the normal pattern. Only the clash of tectonic plates has the power to so comprehensively rewrite the geological landscape. The suggested sequence of events in this region is:

- As the two continents approached each other there was subduction of the oceanic plate.
- The continents crushed the sedimentary rocks of the sea bed upwards forming folded mountains, at this stage subduction no longer occured.
- Finally today, there are volcanoes and shallow earthquakes in the Mediterranean Sea region but no deep ocean trench or deep earthquakes that would suggest a subduction zone.

The term used for such a margin is a **collision zone**, an appropriate name given the degree of change to the sediments, the rocks and landscape of the continental masses.

Resource 141 *European fold mountains*

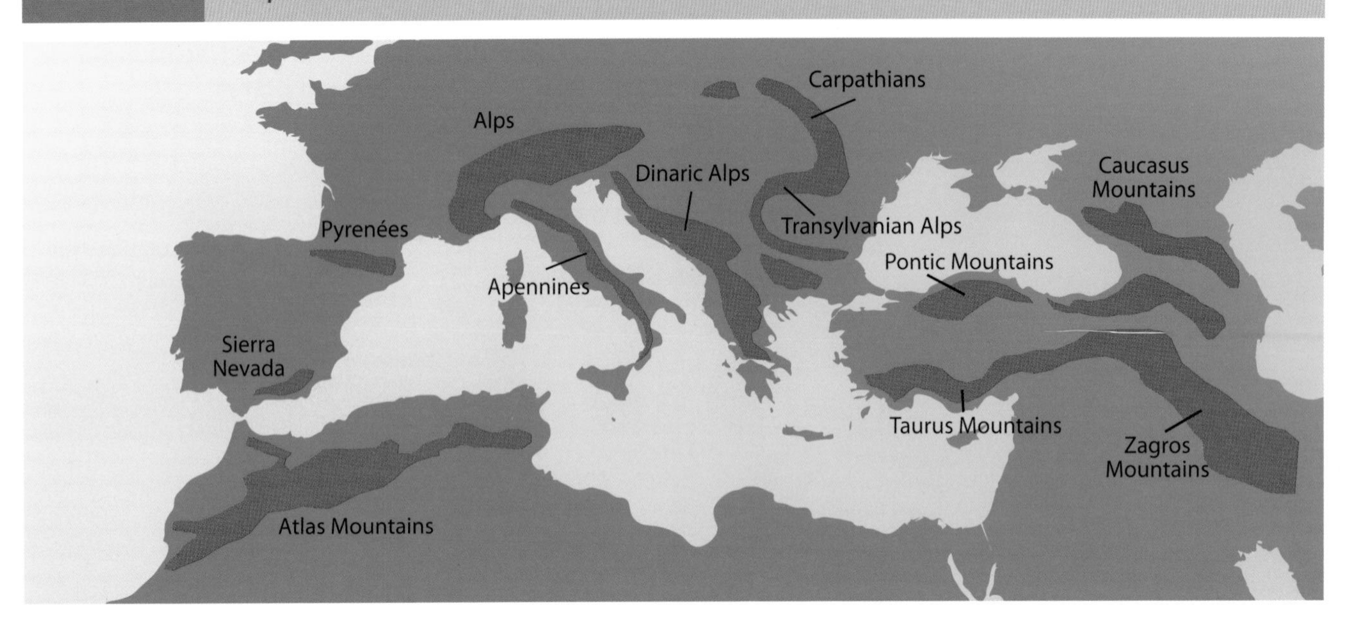

Fold Mountains

During mountain building phases, compression forces horizontal beds of sedimentary and volcanic rock to bend into a series of wavelike forms or folds. Rock folds may be microscopically small or they may involve thousands of metres of rock. Folds may be simple symmetrical waves or, as in the Alps, they may be overturned or recumbent. From the distant geological past there is evidence of several global mountain building periods (orogeny). One, named after the ancient mountains of Scotland, is the Caledonian. It is believed that Ben Nevis, at 1,344 m the highest mountain on these islands, is the remnant stump of its 9,000 m original height. In the current geological era, across the globe the formation of fold mountains continues. This is the Alpine-Himalayan orogeny and it includes the development of the Rockies and Andes chains, as well as those of Europe and Asia. The formation of Fold Mountains is closely related to the location of destructive/converging plate margins.

Conservative plate margins (also known as Transform Faults)

Margins where plates slide past each other are extremely common on the Earth's surface. Most are under the sea and run at angles across constructive margins. **Resource 142** shows that this is necessary to allow an even spread during sea floor spreading. Conservative margins are so called because they do not involve the creation or destruction of plate material and therefore no significant volcanic activity. They are, however, frequently the cause of earthquakes. One conservative margin that appears on land runs through the state of California. This margin is marked by a series of faults the most famous being the San Andreas (St Andrews) fault. Since 1906, when a powerful earthquake along the fault line destroyed the city of San Francisco, the San Andreas has been the focus of intensive study into the causes and possible prediction of earthquakes. It is expected that at conservation margins plates are moving in opposite directions but in this case the plates are both moving in the same north-west direction but at different speeds. The two plates involved are the North America Plate and the Pacific Plate. The first is moving at an average rate of 6 cm per year, the second at 2 cm per year, giving a relative difference of 4 cm per year (**Resource 143).** In the short-term, the people of California, especially around San Francisco, fear the 'Big One', a quake of the scale experienced in 1906 (8.3 on the Richter Scale). It is estimated that this would cause in the region of 10,000 deaths and over 50,000 injuries. In the longer term, if the plates continue on their present course, Los Angeles will move past San Francisco and south California will become an island off the west coast, in around 8 million years!

Transform fault **Resource 142**

Problem of uneven spreading at ridge

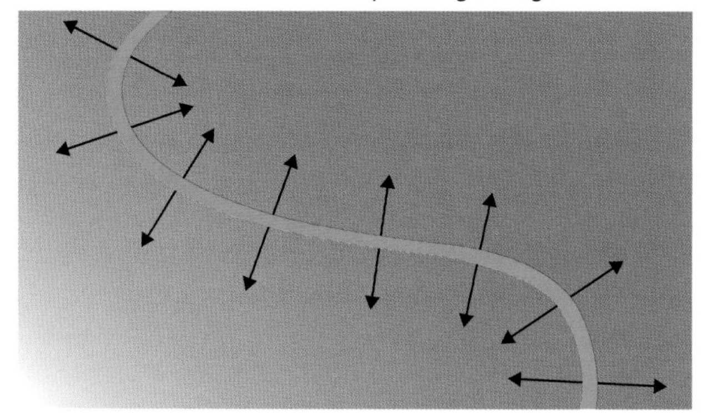

Transform faults allow even spreading

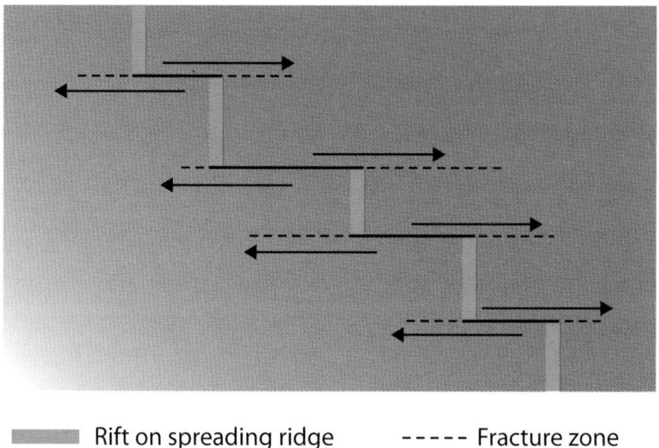

San Andreas map and relative motion **Resource 143**

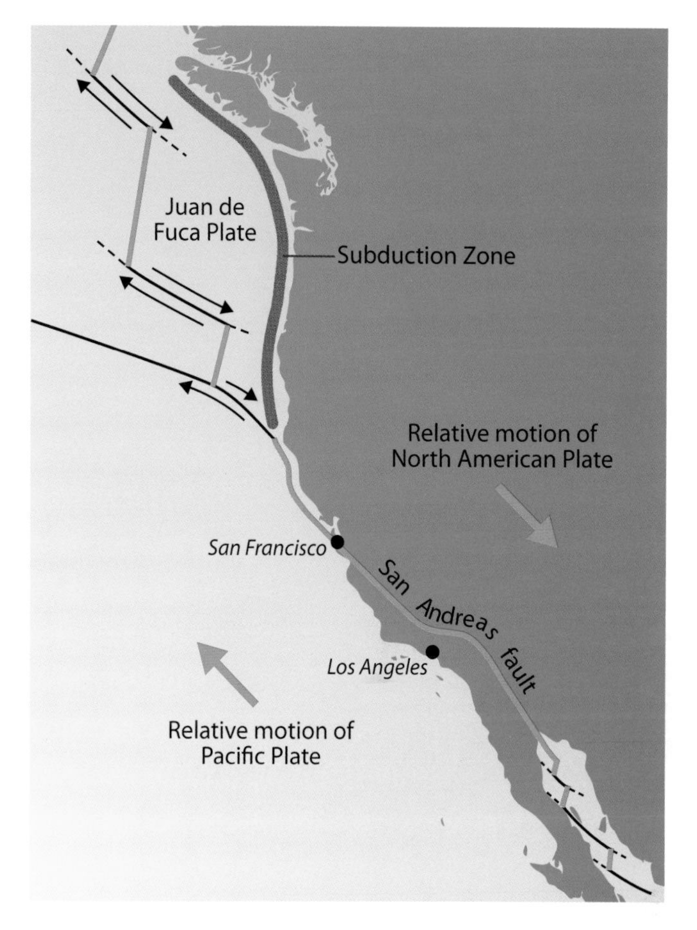

Convection currents in the Mantle

While most scientists are in agreement over the reality of plate tectonics, there remains much debate about the precise role of convection flows in the mantle. The two classic views are:

1) Huge convection currents rise from the border of the core and mantle to drag the plates along at the base of the lithosphere.

2) Convection is confined to the asthenosphere in the upper mantle, with separate layers of convection beneath.

More recently, some researchers suggest that the imbalances in the crust itself are behind the movement, in other words that plate movement drives flows in the mantle and not the other way round at all. Whichever theory or refinement is eventually accepted, the fundamentals on the nature of the Earth's crust, and its creation and destruction according to plate tectonic theory is already widely agreed.

The distribution of tectonic activity

The mapping of the worldwide distribution of earthquakes and volcanoes played a key role in the development of the Plate Tectonic theory. By identifying the linear zones of these activities, the boundaries of the lithosphere's plates were marked out. The presence of both earthquakes and volcanic activity at both destructive and constructive zones, though different in nature, helped shape the concepts. At conservative margins the tension that caused earthquakes but not volcanic action confirmed their nature. Plate margins and related fault lines account for the vast majority of tectonic activity but there are some processes found well away from these boundaries. Among these are the highly active and huge volcanoes of the Hawaiian Islands. Located in the centre of the Pacific Ocean these islands are about as far from an active plate boundary as it is possible to be – so why all the activity?

Resource 144 *An illustration of the Hot Spot effect on a moving plate*

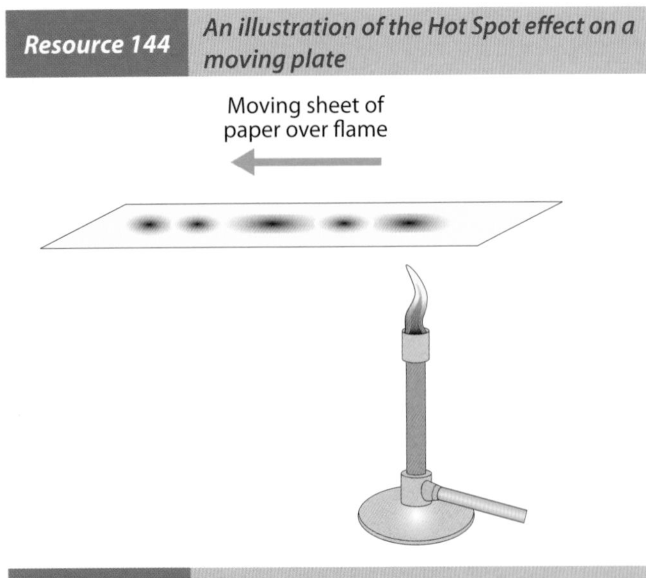

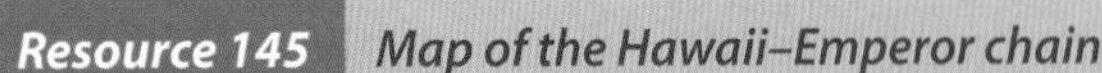

Resource 145 *Map of the Hawaii–Emperor chain*

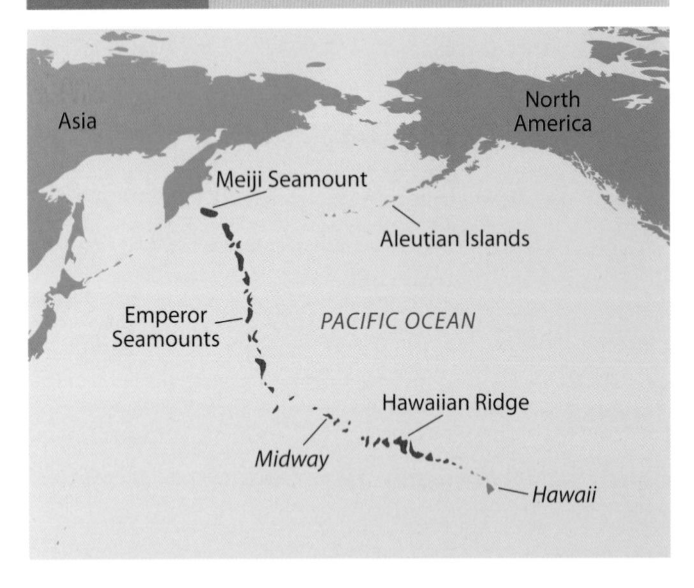

Resource 146 *Distance/rock age graph*

Graph of age of Hawaii–Emperor islands and sea-mounts against distance from active volcano (Kilauea)

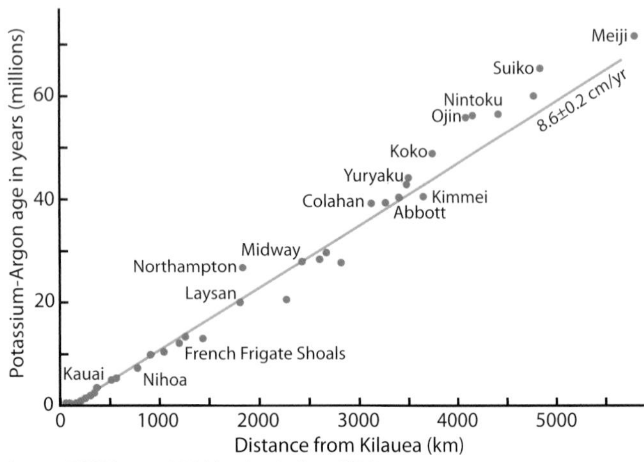

Source: USGS Paper 1350 Volcanism in Hawaii Vol1

Hot spots

Sub-lithosphere thermal anomalies or Hot Spots are seen as the driving force of convection currents and the creation of lines of construction and destruction at plate margins, but isolated Hot Spots beneath unbroken plates may also cause local volcanic and earthquake activity. A common picture used is the idea of a piece of paper being moved across the tip of a Bunsen burner flame. The paper would show a scorched or burn line. The paper represents an oceanic plate being pushed across a fixed rising plume of magma from a hot spot in the mantle. The magma rises through the plate to form a submarine volcano that might just grow to reach the surface as a volcanic island. The outcome is a conveyor-belt sequence of volcanoes that pass from active, over the hot spot, to dormant and eventually extinct as they move away (**Resource 144**).

CASE STUDY: The Hawaiian Islands/ Emperor Seamounts

In the central Pacific, a chain of fifty volcanic islands, coral atolls and submarine mountains (seamounts) stretches over 6,000 km from Hawaii to the Aleutian trench (**Resource 145**). Starting with the Hawaiian island chain itself, this merges with a series of atolls (coral reefs on the remains of islands), including Midway and then a string of mountains on the ocean floor – the Emperor seamounts. It is believed that all these features are the result of magma rising to the ocean floor above a fixed hot spot beneath the Pacific plate. **Resource 146** is a graph showing the strong, direct relationship between the ages of the rocks in these features against distance from Hawaii.

As the volcanic islands are moved away from the rising magma plume they become extinct. Weathering and erosion gradually reduces their size until they are worn down to below sea-level, firstly forming platforms for coral reefs to grow on and finally becoming mere stumps of their former size on the sea floor. The only active volcanoes today are found on the main and most southerly island of Hawaii, although offshore, there is already evidence of volcanic activity starting to build a new Hawaiian island. It appears that the Pacific plate has moved at an average rate of 8.2cm per year for the past 70 million years. About 43 million years ago, the direction of plate movement changed from northerly to north-westerly, as shown by the dog-leg in the line near the Yuryaku seamount. If you trace the map in **Resource 145**, then place the Meiji seamount over the hotspot at Hawaii, you can re-create the pattern of movement of the Pacific plate over the past 70 million years.

Exercise

1. Describe the processes of both subduction and seafloor spreading and explain their role in the movement of crustal plates according to the theory of Plate Tectonics. (10)
2. With the aid of a diagram describe the process which causes plate movement. (6)
3. Study **Figure 1** of the Juan de Fuca plate. Attempt to draw the view along the cross section X–Y and explain the active tectonic processes shown. (10)

Figure 1

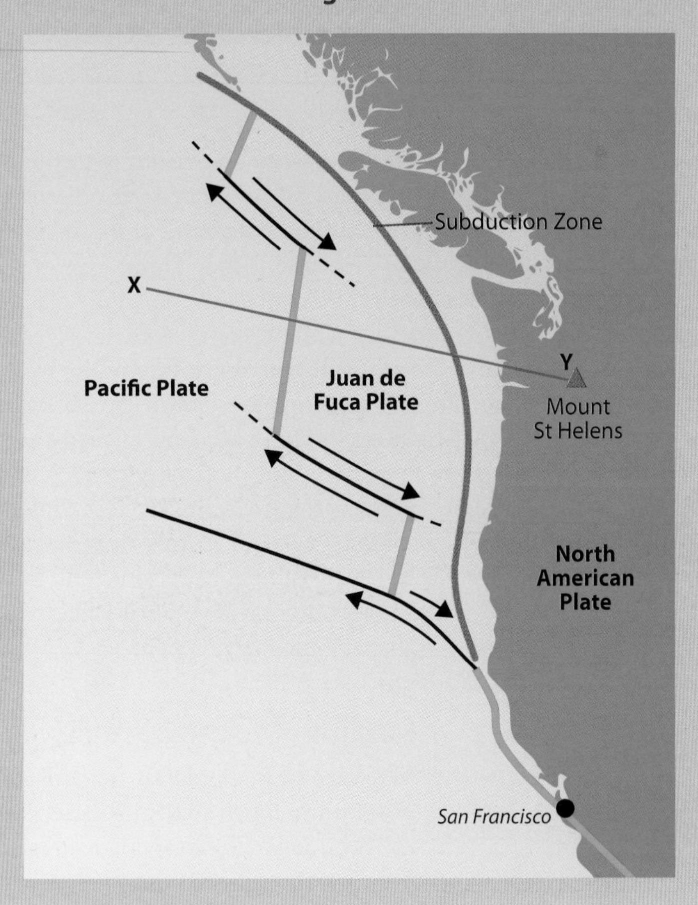

C2 VOLCANIC ACTIVITY AND ITS MANAGEMENT

Volcanic activity

The term volcanic is used to describe all the activity associated with the extrusion of magma onto the surface of the crust as lava. A volcano is formed at a rift or vent in the crust through which molten rock and gas erupts and solidifies. Volcanoes come in many shapes and sizes and the type of eruption is equally varied. Eruptions may come from a central single vent or along a line of weakness known as a fissure. Volcanoes are normally classified as being active, dormant or extinct. Dormant suggests that while there is no historic record of eruption the volcano cannot yet be regarded as extinct. Each year about fifty of the world's active volcanoes actually erupt. For some this is for the first time in many centuries (Mt Pinatubo in 1991) while for others it is a regular event (Mt Etna on the Italian island of Sicily every few years, 2001, 2002 and 2006). Some volcanoes are in almost continual activity such as Kilauea on Hawaii. In general, volcanic eruptions along constructive margins are less violent and extrude very hot freely flowing basaltic (low silica content) lavas to form volcanoes with gentle slopes. At destructive margins, including the Pacific 'Ring of Fire', eruptions tend to be more violent and the less fluid acidic, silica rich lavas form steeper cone shaped volcanoes.

Resource 147 *Potential hazards of volcanic activity*

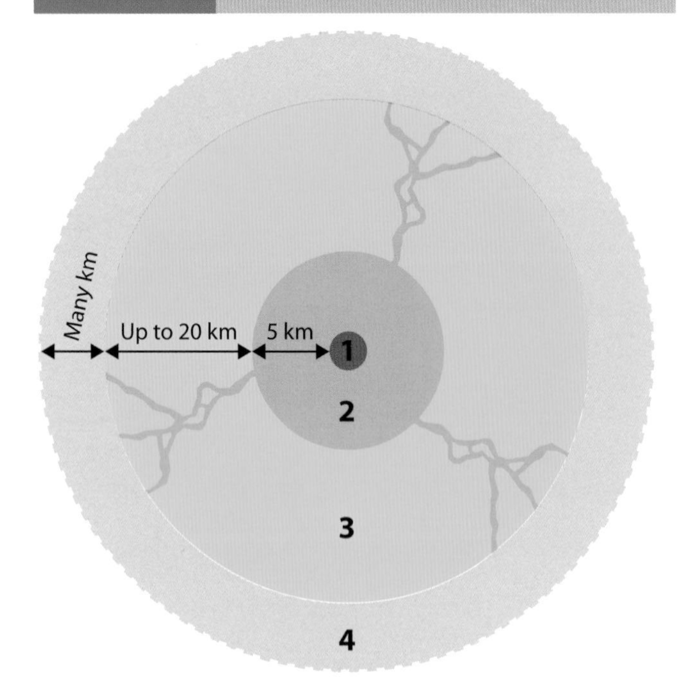

Hazards of volcanic activity

The variety of potential hazards following a volcanic eruption is illustrated in **Resource 147**. Some hazards are confined to the immediate area, including lava flows, others, such as lahars, may travel many kilometres from the source, while ash falls can settle over 100s of square kilometres or enter the upper troposphere and circle the globe.

Explosion

Some volcanoes erupt without significant violence, such as the volcanoes of Hawaii, but elsewhere the force of a volcanic eruption can be enormous. When Krakatoa erupted in Indonesia, in 1883, it was heard 4,000 km away in Australia. The blast destroyed the island itself and 36,000 people drowned in the 40 m tsunami that swept the coasts of the neighbouring islands. On one island a ship was washed 20 km inland along a river valley. Tsunamis are huge waves generated by either volcanic eruptions or earthquakes which can travel across oceans at great speed resulting in the devastation of coastal regions. The 2004 Boxing Day tsunami was the result of a submarine earthquake off Sumatra, rather than a volcanic eruption.

Types of hazards from volcanic explosions

Resource 148

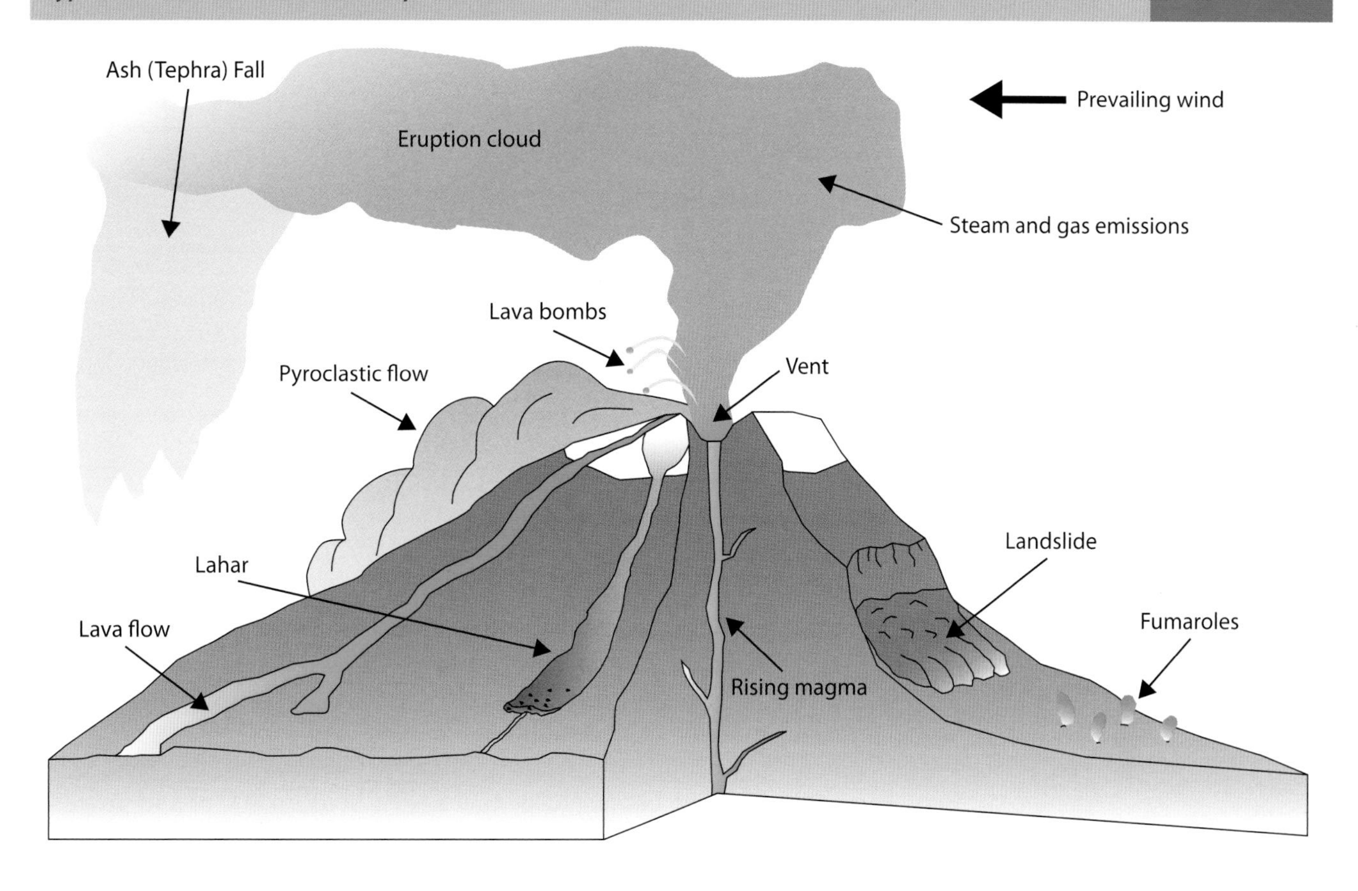

Krakatoa before and after the eruption of 1883

Resource 149

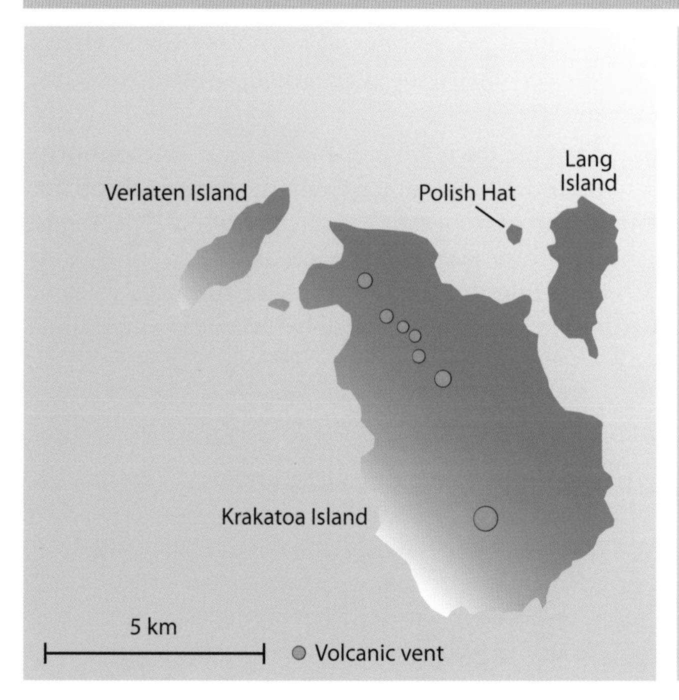

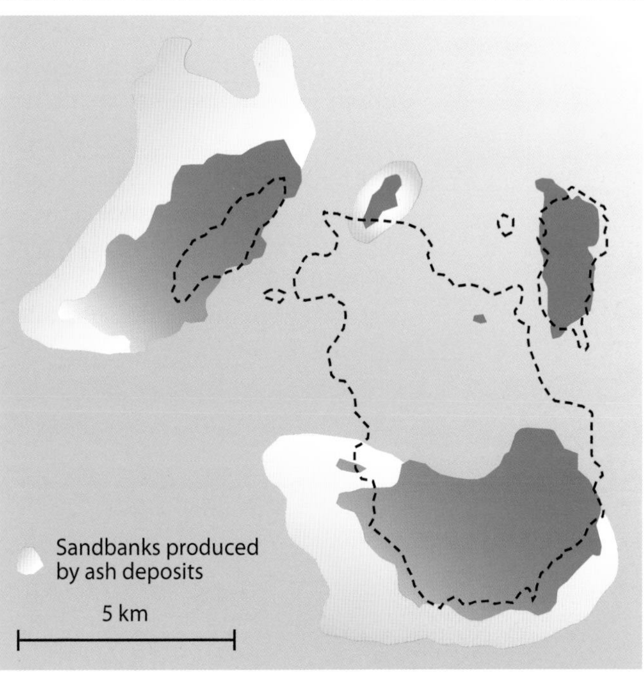

Dotted lines show the pre-eruption islands

Resource 150 *Materials ejected by volcanic activity*

LAVA (erupted magma)	PYROCLASTIC MATERIALS (ejected fragments)	GASES
Acid (viscous, silica rich) eg Andesitic Basic (free flowing) eg Aa (Ah Ah) or Blocky lava Pahoehoe or Ropy lava	Volcanic bombs Stones (lapilli) Hot ash and fine dust Pumice Cinders Nuée ardente (glowing avalanche)	Steam Sulphur dioxide Carbon dioxide Cyanide (These are often issued from small vents called fumaroles)

Materials

Numerous types of material are ejected by volcanoes such as lava, pyroclastic material and gases (**Resources 148** and **150**). The people of Hawaii and Iceland have several terms for lava, describing its flow and appearance.

Lava rarely threatens life as its flow is predictable but it does destroy property by swamping buildings or starting fires. The frequent lava that flows down the slopes of Mt Etna, Italy, in recent decades have destroyed cable car stations and overwhelmed houses, hotels and restaurants. The same events buried rich farmland burning vines and orchards. In 1990, a lava flow from Kilauea in Hawaii gradually burned houses and buried the village of Kalapana. Over a three year period the flow gradually covered 181 houses, much local arable farmland and crossed the main coast road. People would stand and helplessly watch their homes, gardens and property succumb to a creeping tide of lava.

Pyroclastic material is the term used to describe a wide variety of solid material ejected by volcanic activity other than lava. Nuée ardentes, (literally 'glowing cloud') are spectacular, potentially lethal mixtures of superheated gases, hot ash and rock fragments that flow at enormous speed down the side of some volcanoes. One of the best documented examples is the death of over 29,000 inhabitants in the town of St Pierre, on the Caribbean island of Martinique in 1902 (see box below). More recently, over the USA volcanic ash from the Mt St Helens eruption of 1980 entered the upper atmosphere and circled the globe helping create spectacular sunsets for months (**Resource 151** and **152**).

Volcanic gases are often hot and toxic. When the town of Pompeii was uncovered centuries after it had been buried by an eruption of Mt Vesuvius in southern Italy, the buried inhabitants were found with their hands at their mouths or throats suggesting mass suffocation. One August night in 1986 at Lake Nyos, a crater lake in Cameroon, over 1,700 people died of carbon dioxide poisoning. A heavier than air cloud, rich in carbon dioxide, was expelled from the volcanic lake and swept down adjacent valleys. Up to 23 km away people died in their sleep as the cloud replaced the air.

Resource 151 *Ash cloud and ash falls from Mt St Helens, May 1980*

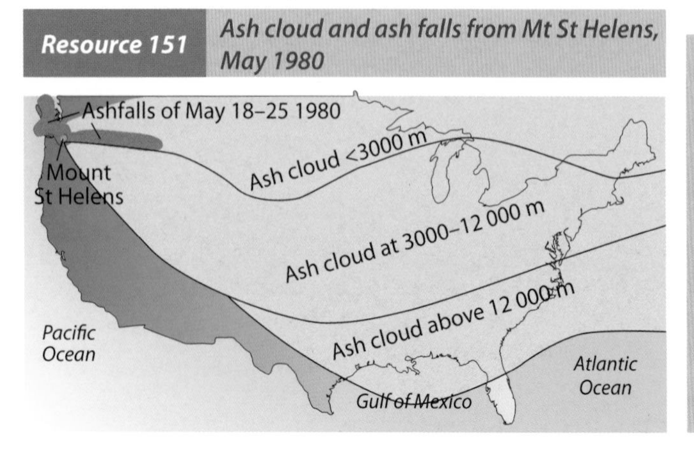

Mt Pelee on the island of Martinique erupted violently in 1902. Several nuée ardentes swept down the slopes and one reached the island's main port of St Pierre. All but two of the town's 29,000 inhabitants were killed by the heat and choking gases, while several large sailing ships anchored in the bay were burned and sunk. The nature of volcanoes was so poorly understood that despite activity in the weeks before the *nuee ardente*, the town was not evacuated. This event provides the name for a violent form of volcanic activity – a Pelean eruption.

Map of the impact zone of the 18 May 1980 eruption of Mount St Helens **Resource 152**

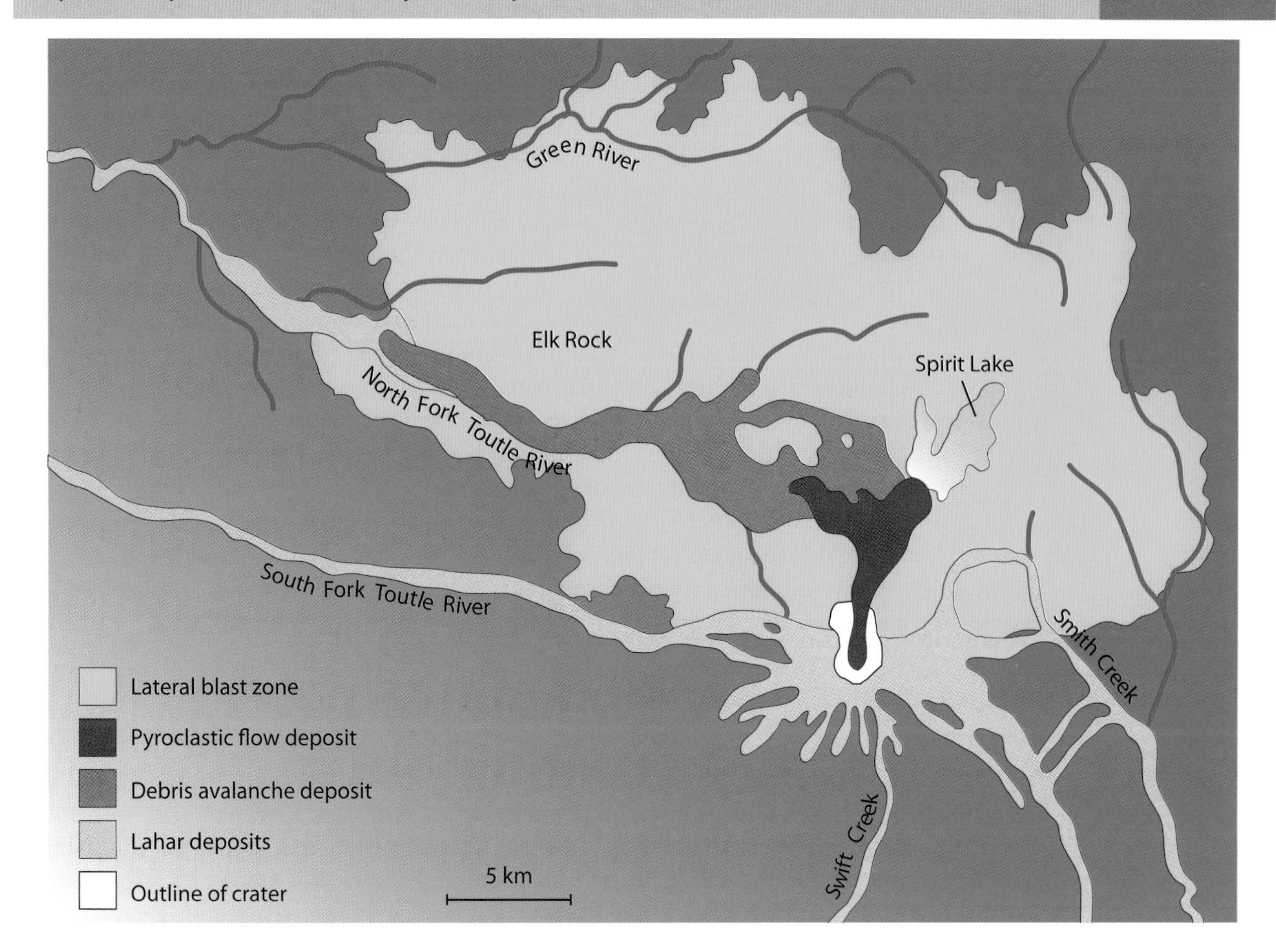

Landslides

Volcanoes often bulge as magmatic pressure builds up beneath them. This deformation of steep slopes may cause landslides. The devastating eruption of Mt St Helens in 1980 followed the collapse of the north side of the mountain, in the largest landslide ever recorded on film. Currently it is feared that volcanic activity in the Canary Islands might cause a huge landslide to generate an enormous tsunami, with devastating consequences especially on the densely populated eastern seaboard of the USA.

Lahars

These are volcanic mud flows. When hot ash mixes with river water or with heavy rain, which can be triggered by eruptions, it can flow as a thick hot mixture at great speed, flooding valleys, burying the environment and drowning people. In 1985, the eruption of Nevado del Ruiz in Colombia resulted in a lahar flowing at 100 km per hour through the town of Armero, some 50 km from the volcano. In one night over 20,000 of the town's 23,000 inhabitants perished, buried by hot mud.

Jokulhlaups

These are floods caused by volcanic eruptions beneath ice sheets or glaciers. In 1996 the Grimsvotn volcano in Iceland erupted beneath the Vatnajokull icefield. Just hours after emerging from the ice sheet, the jokulhlaup had a discharge of 5,000 cumecs, which increased to 15,000 within 90 minutes. Two large bridges – 380 m and 900 m long – were destroyed, along with a section of the main coastal highway. On the glacier itself, the collapse and subsidence associated with the event left an ice canyon 6 kms long with an average depth of 100 m.

The Impacts of volcanic hazards

Social – individuals, families and communities

Volcanic eruptions are often fatal but the estimated total of 200,000 deaths in the last 500 years is much lower than other natural (earthquakes and floods) or human (wars and traffic accidents) disasters. Sometimes signs or precursor events can allow prediction and evacuation of an area, however, this is not always the case. It has been possible to divert or steer some small lava flows but more often the red hot lava will destroy anything in its path regardless of planning. The preceding section identifies a number of examples of fatal volcanic hazards: lahars, gas emissions, tsunamis, pyroclastic flows and floods. Fatalities may be caused by secondary impacts such as the Icelandic famine after the Skaftar Fires eruption of 1783, in which one quarter of the island's population died. Other social impacts include homelessness and refugee movements. The 1991 Mt Pinatubo eruption displaced over 100,000 people, many of whom could not return to their homes for years, if at all. This was the result of a huge ashfall that collapsed their houses and buried their farmland. Repeated lahars swept the region's river valleys in the months and years after the eruption had died away. The aboriginal, Aeta tribal people had to abandon their mountain forest homes on the slopes of Pinatubo and in lowland refugee camps hundreds of their young children and elderly died of illness. This was a result of overcrowding and inadequate supplies of water and medicine. Any traumatic event caused by volcanic activity will have a huge psychological impact on the communities involved and people may simply refuse to return to the region even when it is possible to do so.

Economic – infrastructure damage and costs to agriculture, industry and government

Closely linked to social impacts are the negative effects on a region's economy. While lava flows can destroy any built structure, such as houses, factories, roads, bridges or farms, lahars, ash falls and jokulhlaups can extend this destruction over a much wider area. The damage caused to farmland, commercial forestry or tourist amenity may take decades of restoration to re-establish the economy. The blast of the 1980 Mt St Helens eruption flattened several million trees over an area of 600 km^2. Between 1995 and 1997, the Caribbean island of Montserrat, a British dependency, suffered because of an erupting volcano called Soufriere Hills. The net outcome was that most of the island was uninhabitable and over 7,000 of its 11,000 population had be to be evacuated and resettled for several years at least. Dealing with the impacts and this mass relocation program cost the British government over £100 million. Even in cases where the nature of the activity is less destructive, any disruption to people and their employment will be expensive in economic terms.

Environmental – landscape, ecosystem and climate

Volcanoes are capable of re-writing landscapes. People frequently describe the scene of recent eruptions as lunar – barren and desolate. In 1883 the enormous eruption on the island of Krakatoa replaced a 300 m high mountain with a 300 m deep submarine crater (**Resource 149**). At Mt St Helens the landslide and explosive eruption on its northern flank eventually reduced the near 3,000 m summit by 400 m. Such explosions and movements of lava and ash often kill all vegetation and animal life in the region. We know, for example, that over one million farm animals died at Pinatubo in 1991 but no accurate figure is known for its impact of the natural ecosystem (**Resource 159**).

Major volcanic events, or a series of them, can impact the global climate. In 1815, the cold summer and consequent worldwide crop failures and famine, in which millions died, has been linked to the eruption of Mt Tambora in Indonesia. Scientists speculate that worldwide mass extinction of species in the past may be the outcome of a series of volcanic eruptions. These could fill the upper atmosphere with dust and reduce the level of insolation entering the Earth's energy system.

Benefits of volcanic activity – social, economic and environmental

Despite their destructive image, volcanic activity is not only hazardous, it can prove beneficial to both people and the environment. Indeed, volcanoes may be the seed bed of all life on planet Earth, where the necessary physical and chemical conditions combine.

Land creation

While ash and lava may bury useful land, the same activity can create new land. In 1963, a fishing fleet off the south coast of Iceland saw a column of smoke rise from the sea. They immediately shipped their nets and made way to what they assumed was another boat in distress. On arrival at the scene they witnessed the summit of an underwater volcano breach the surface to form a new island, later named Surtsey. The new island has provided a golden opportunity for scientists to study not only volcanic processes but also the development of a prisere and ecological succession. On another Icelandic island, Heimaey, the eruption of Eldfell destroyed hundreds of houses buried by ash fall or burnt by lava. However, the lava flows that had threatened to block off the harbour entrance were stopped and actually enhanced the shelter provided for the local fishing fleet (**Resource 153**). To paraphrase a proverb, "It's an ill eruption that does no-one good".

Impacts of the Heimaey eruption in 1973 **Resource 153**

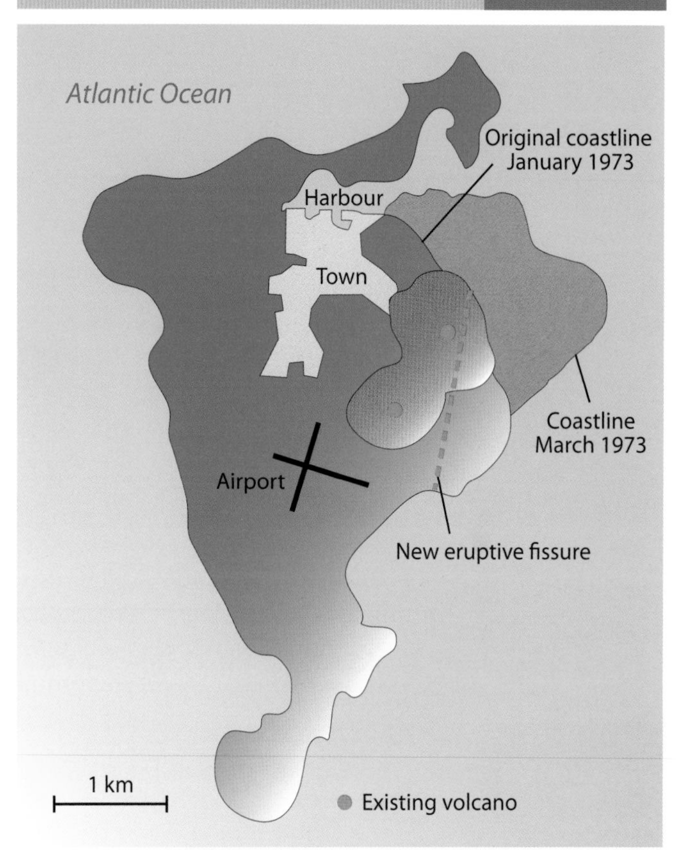

Fertile soils

Benefits from volcanic activity include the fact that some, but not all, lava flows and ash falls can be weathered into rich, fertile soils. Soils based on basic lavas or ash deposits rich in potassium or phosphorus are highly valued. It is not coincidence that over 20% of the population of Sicily lives and depends on the fertile slopes of Mt Etna, an active volcano. Here the high yield from olive and orange groves, and wine produced from local vineyards, supports a thriving agricultural community. This is at once both an economic and a social benefit. The natural environment benefits in a similar way. In the three years following an eruption of Katmai, Alaska, in 1912, the ash fall resulted in the tallest grass and largest berry production ever known.

Miners carrying sulphur blocks from Ijen volcano in Indonesia **Resource 154**

Mineral deposits – industrial resources

Volcanic deposits provide a wide variety of industrial materials and chemicals including sulphur, pumice, arsenic and boric acid. Beneath the surface in active volcanic areas, mineral-rich gas from lava cools, forming veins of minerals and metal ores. Examples include the copper and tin deposits in old volcanic rocks of Cornwall. In Indonesia, at the Ijen volcano, local workers climb into the 200 m deep crater at the top of the mountain to mine and carry out blocks of sulphur that is deposited around the perimeter of the crater lake. They undertake this back-breaking task on alternate days as the conditions within the crater are hazardous to their respiration (**Resource 154**). Diamonds are formed deep in volcanic zones along narrow channels called kimberlite pipes.

Resource 155 *60 MW Krafla geothermal power station in Iceland*

Energy

In Iceland, New Zealand, Italy and the USA naturally produced volcanic steam is harnessed to generate electricity (**Resource 155**). The largest such plant is The Geysers in California, generating 1,000 MW of electricity, said to be enough energy to supply the needs of San Francisco, a city of 800,000 people.

Reykjavik, Iceland's capital also gets most of its heating from geothermal water derived from volcanic springs. Over 50,000 homes receive water heated naturally to 87 ^{0}C from this environmentally friendly system. As a natural and renewable energy source, geothermal energy is both economically and environmentally beneficial.

Resource 156 *Cooking instructions at the Sankampaeng natural hot springs tourist resort, Northern Thailand*

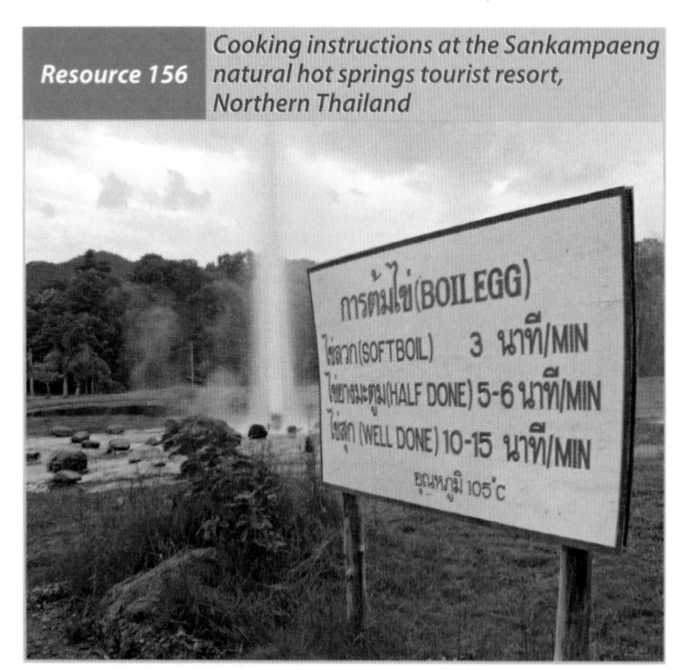

Tourism

Volcanoes, especially those that are currently or recently active, are strong magnets for adventurers and tourists alike. The 2001 eruption of Mt Etna in Sicily coincided with the holiday season and companies flew, coached and sailed thousands of visitors in to witness the event, which was particularly spectacular at night. The mud pools and geysers of Yellowstone National Park, Wyoming USA are the key attraction for tens of thousands of visitors annually. The most famous feature being Old Faithful, a geyser that regularly (around every 95 minutes) sends a column of hot water and steam into the air. In the Canary Islands or the volcanic islands in the Caribbean, a volcanic barbeque is often part of the tourist itinerary. The sheer beauty of volcanoes such as Mt Fuji in Japan is a priceless asset and Crater Lake in Oregon is regarded as one of the world's most beautiful landscapes. Even ancient volcanic activity can be of economic benefit. Northern Ireland's leading tourist attraction is the remnant of the outpouring of millions of tonnes of lava during the Tertiary era, that solidified into the regularly shaped columns of the Giant's Causeway. The economic spin-off from volcanic attractions is common to all tourism: jobs and income from guides, accommodation, catering, transport, ancillary services and the selling of souvenirs (**Resource 156**).

With respect to volcanic activity describe, with examples, its potential benefits under the following headings:
1) Social 2) Economic 3) Environmental

Exercise

Predicting volcanic activity

Volcano prediction

Some volcanoes are highly predictable, such as the huge crater of Hawaii's Mauna Loa or Mt Etna in Sicily – Europe's most active volcano in recent years. Others are much less readily anticipated. Of the 700 active (as opposed to dormant or extinct) volcanoes, only a fraction are continuously monitored and as few as 70 have detailed surveying maintained. Not surprisingly, volcanoes in the developed nations are studied more intensely and here prediction is achieved most readily. Prediction has several aspects; in the case of volcanic activity it is necessary to predict not only the time and length of an eruption but also its scale and the nature of its impacts. Inaccuracy on any one of these factors could prove even more disastrous than no prediction at all.

Warning signs

Warning signs or precursors for volcanic eruptions include local seismic events, the tilting of ground and gas release. Other observations that might be made are the melting of snow caps, disappearance of crater lakes or the death of local vegetation. Volcanoes by definition involve the release of magma or gas, so beneath them material must be moving upwards, causing earth tremors and bulging of the surface. Seismic activity does not guarantee eruption. For example, Vesuvius in south Italy has shown strong activity several times without a subsequent volcanic event. It is not uncommon for prediction to be accurate in terms of timing but inaccurate in terms of scale and even direction. The 1980, Mt St Helens eruption was well monitored and predicted. A 5 km wide exclusion zone was set up and if the volcano had erupted vertically then it is possible no lives would have been lost. In the event, an earthquake beneath Mt St Helens triggered a huge landslide on the mountain's northern flank, creating an outlet for the pressure from which an enormous blast of ash, debris and superheated gas erupted laterally devastating the landscape well beyond the 5 km zone in that direction (**Resource 152**).

Sometimes it all goes wrong. In 1985, a Colombian volcano, Nevado del Ruiz, was monitored by scientists following signs of activity. After several weeks they declared that a major eruption was not imminent. The next day it erupted and as mentioned earlier a lahar swept down an adjacent valley burying the town of Armero. It was of little comfort to the scientists that they had accurately predicted the path of such lahars – only their timing was wrong. By contrast, in 1980, scientists did evacuate many people from a threatening volcano at Mammoth Lake in California. No eruption occurred and the scientists faced the anger of residents over the inconvenience and their economic losses.

Bernard Chouet of the United States Geological Service (USGS) believes that the identification of a seismic pattern known as a long-period event is a reliable indicator of volcanic activity. A long-period event is a

Methods of moitoring volcanic activity **Resource 157**

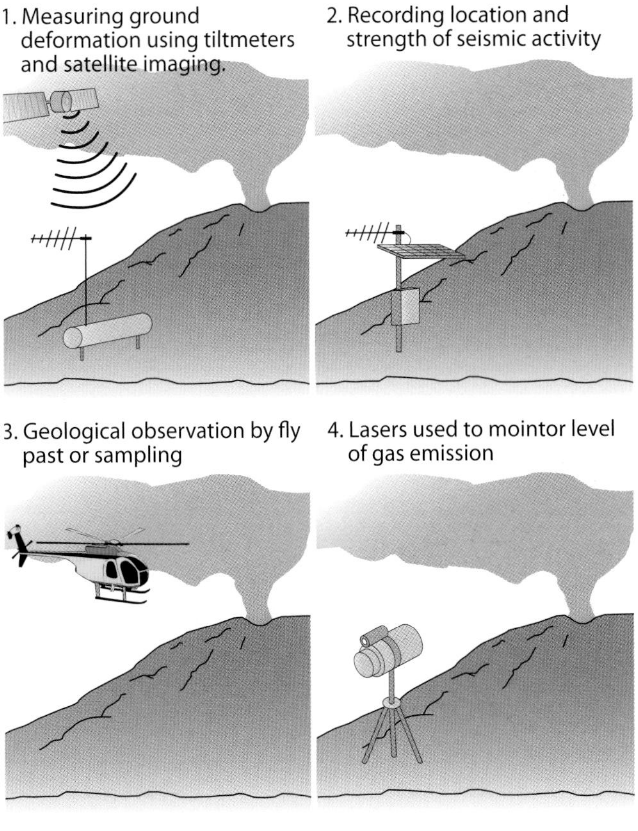

1. Measuring ground deformation using tiltmeters and satellite imaging.
2. Recording location and strength of seismic activity
3. Geological observation by fly past or sampling
4. Lasers used to mointor level of gas emission

particular frequency of movement that he suggests links to magma rising towards the surface. Models are now being designed to test these theories under laboratory conditions. Tiltmeters are used on the slopes and on the edge of volcano craters to monitor rises, falls or bulges in surface levels that reflect underground movements of magma. Kilauea's 1959 eruption was accurately predicted on the basis of seismic and tiltmeter recordings. Other physical changes that have been monitored to aid prediction are the temperature of crater lakes and springs, gravity and magnetism. The latter two are based on the idea that new magma moving below a volcano will subtlety alter these values. Vulcanologists also study gas emitted by volcanoes. New hi-technology, laser monitoring can be used to detect small changes in gases across the surface or crater of a volcano. Any changes in the chemical nature or quantity of these may help to forecast the timing, scale or nature of future events **(Resource 157).** Since 1995, the volcano of Soufriere Hills, on the island of Monserrat, has kept scientists busy assessing the nature and the future of its on-going activity. In this case, remote sensing from satellites has been used to detect heat changes, and to plot lava flows and gas emissions using ultra violet filters on camera shots. Another example is the work done in the months before the massive eruption of Mount Pinatubo in 1991 which is detailed below.

CASE STUDY: Predicting the 1991 eruption of Pinatubo, Luzon, Philippines

First signs

In July 1990, a 7.7 magnitude earthquake struck the Philippine Islands in South-East Asia killing about 1,600 people. A natural disaster itself, it was possibly the first indication of another major event less than a year later. Unknown to anyone in the months following the earthquake, deep beneath the surface the subducted Philippine plate was melting forming magma. This molten rock rose from the upper mantle or asthenosphere into a vast magma chamber beneath a 1,759 m peak on the island of Luzon. The hot intrusion reactivated material in the chamber creating a mass of gas-charged magma. This magma continued to rise up through the crust of the Eurasian plate towards the summit of the long dormant volcano known as Pinatubo. Local Aeta villagers began to notice changes in their neighbouring mountain that had not shown any life in 600 years. On 2 April 1991, steam started to issue from small side vents on its flanks. This was reported to local officials and scientists from the Philippine Institute of Volcanology and Seismology (PHIVOLCS) in Manila were brought in. Their leader, Dr Ray Punongbayan ordered an aerial survey of the area and initially the report suggested the mountain was merely 'letting off steam'. A portable seismometer was installed and over 400 earthquakes were recorded in two days. Punongbayan contacted the United States Geological Survey who were not only interested in the volcanic activity but also in protecting two large US military facilities then in the region, the naval base at Subic Bay and the Clark air force base. By the last week of May, American scientists led by Dr Dave Harlow, including some with experience from Mt St Helens in 1980, were working with the Philippine team. They set up their headquarters in Clark air force base (PVO – Pinatubo Volcano Observatory).

Watching and waiting – the methods used

The next seven weeks was an intense period of study and debate. Initial recordings quickly dismissed the less dangerous possibilities of a simple steam release by the volcano or purely tectonic activity beneath it. Magma was rising. The questions were how much and how far would it rise?

Previous history

One of the best guides for vulcanologists is the history of the volcano. Pinatubo had last erupted in the fourteenth century but no written record existed. A field study of the deposits and flows of pyroclastic material on Pinatubo's slopes showed it had only erupted 4 or 5 times in the last two millennia. Such infrequent events are usually violent eruptions and the ash fall and other flow deposits confirmed this large scale, explosive nature. Based on these observations a hazard map was published to help guide evacuation and identify safety zones (**Resource 159**).

Seismic monitoring

The USGS immediately established a network of seven seismometers around the mountain to maintain a continuous 3-D view of what was happening below the surface. Earthquakes at depths of 8 km continued at a rate of between 40 and 150 a day. This was not an unusually high rate but their spread over 5 or 6 km indicated magma rising over a broad area.

Visual observation

In addition to the continuous monitoring of the seismic net, daily flights by plane and helicopter were made. On these, the number and scale of steam emissions and surface changes were recorded.

Gas emissions

The helicopter flights also took gas samples using a correlation spectrometer (cospec). In particular the sulphur dioxide (SO_2) levels were studied, as rising magma forces this gas upwards. The first record of 500 tonnes per day was significant but over the next five weeks this rose to 5,000 tonnes daily.

Making the prediction

On the 3 June the largest earth tremors yet recorded occurred and the team decided to issue their first alert at level 2 (**Resource 158**). 20,000 people living within 10 km of the mountain were evacuated and the 15,000 personnel at Clark base were told to prepare to leave at short notice.

Table of levels of eruption alert ***Resource 158***

Alert Level	Nature of Warning
Level 1	Activity detected. Eruption NOT imminent
Level 2	Activity more intense. Eruption probable
Level 3	Eruption now likely within two weeks
Level 4	Eruption possible within 24 hours
Level 5	Eruption in progress

On the 5 June the earthquakes were more concentrated beneath the central zone of the mountain and the sulphur dioxide levels were falling. This second factor was a significant one, suggesting that the magma was now retaining its gas content, making it potentially explosive in nature. The team were very concerned about getting the timing right. On 7 June increasing seismic activity prompted the scientists to declare a level 4 alert and 120,000 people living within 18 km of Pinatubo were moved to temporary evacuation centres. The air force base personnel remained but on alert to move.

At this point reports arrived that Mt Unsen, a Japanese volcano which was also being carefully monitored, had erupted but with much greater violence than predicted. While 6,000 locals had been evacuated and saved, 34 individuals including two scientific observers were killed by an avalanche of hot gas, ash and rocks. It was a timely reminder for the team at PVO.

Between the 8 and 9 June a dome of lava was spotted from the air. The material matched the deposits from previous eruptions and confirmed the likely explosive nature of any eruption. The next day a level 5 alert was declared and the US air force base was evacuated, 14,000 people moved to a safe distance. A 60 km wide danger zone (not evacuation area) was declared that included the 300,000 people living in the city of Angeles. Only 48 hours later the first major eruption occurred.

Resource 159 *Hazard prediction and actual impact maps of Mt Pinutubo, August 1991*

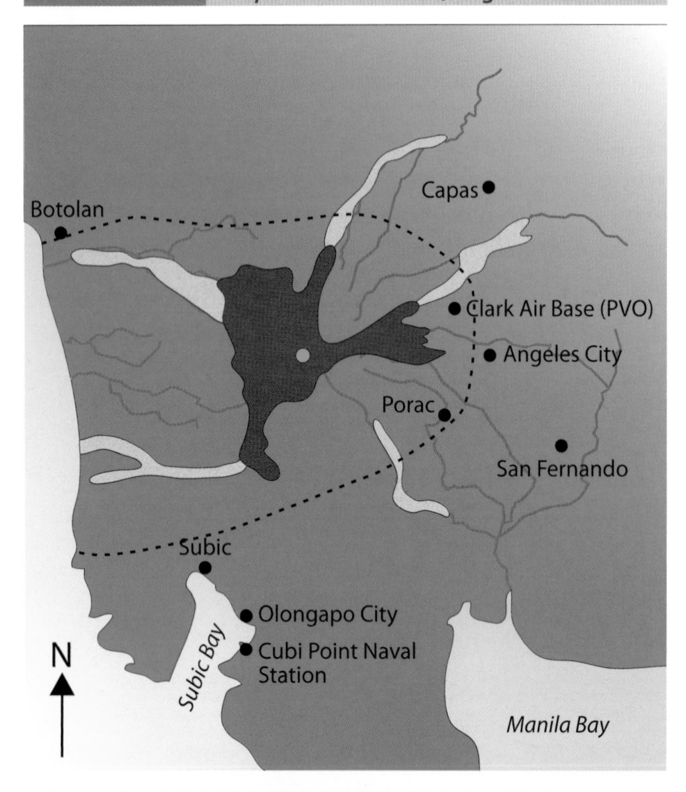

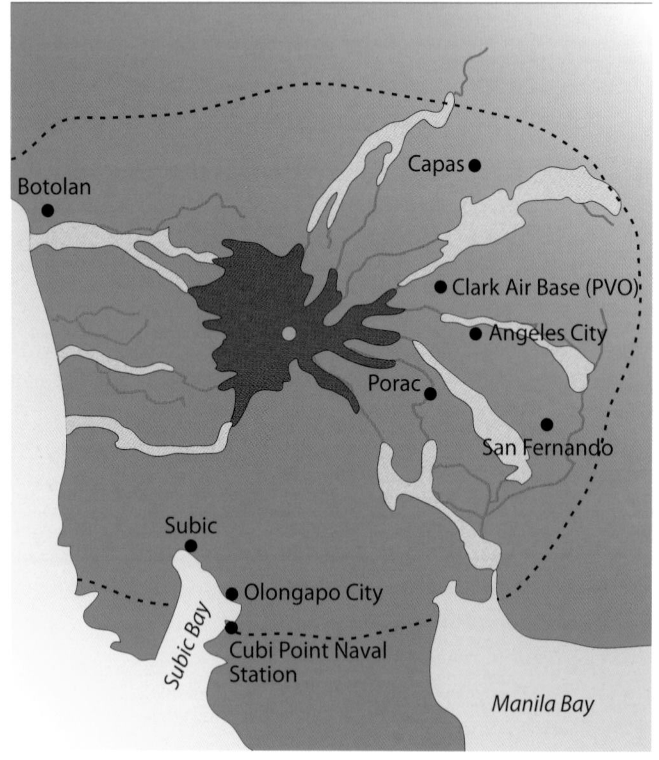

Extent of significant/damaging ash falls

Pyroclastic flow deposit

Lahar deposits

Outline of crater

Rivers

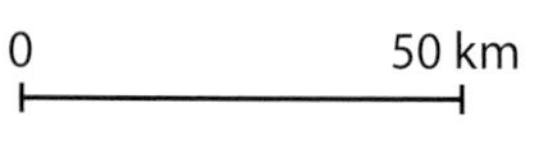

Impacts

The eruption covered the dense forest around Pinatubo with a thick layer of grey ash. Large eruptions continued with ash scattered up to 80 km away. At 2 am on the 15 June the first of a series of five massive overnight explosions occurred. A vast cloud of debris stretched over 16 km across and up over 30,000 m into the atmosphere. Volcanic ash was scattered in all directions and well beyond the exclusion zone – ash fall depths of 10 cm or more covering a 60 km radius. The eruptions released more material, a total of over 20 million tonnes, into the atmosphere, than any other twentieth century eruption. To compound the problem, the eruption coincided with a typhoon, with hurricane force winds and intense rainfall. The mixture of rain and ashfall buried thousands of hectares of farmland and killed over 1 million head of livestock. The sheer weight of debris caused thousands of buildings to collapse, including schools, hospitals, children's homes and thousands of houses in the city of Olongapo, 56 km south west of Pinatubo, where many evacuated groups had moved (**Resource 159**). The final death toll was around 900 and costs were estimated at £10 billion. Mount Pinatubo continued to erupt sporadically during 1992 and 1993 before finally settling, perhaps for another 500 or 600 years of dormancy.

Conclusion

The prediction work of the scientists at PVO was over and their accurate prediction undoubtedly saved thousands of lives. A positive aspect of the incident was that good communication between the team and local government meant evacuation had been undertaken in an efficient way. The hazard map also proved largely accurate, although while the area under threat of pyroclastic flows (nuée ardentes) had been identified, the scale and spread of the ashfall was greater than expected. Also, in the months after the eruption the wet monsoon generated numerous lahars of fast flowing water and hot ash. Some of the local vulcanologists turned their prediction skills to address the problems of where and when these events would occur. Most of the final death toll of 900 was the result of disease in refugee camps, with some 70 caused by lahars.

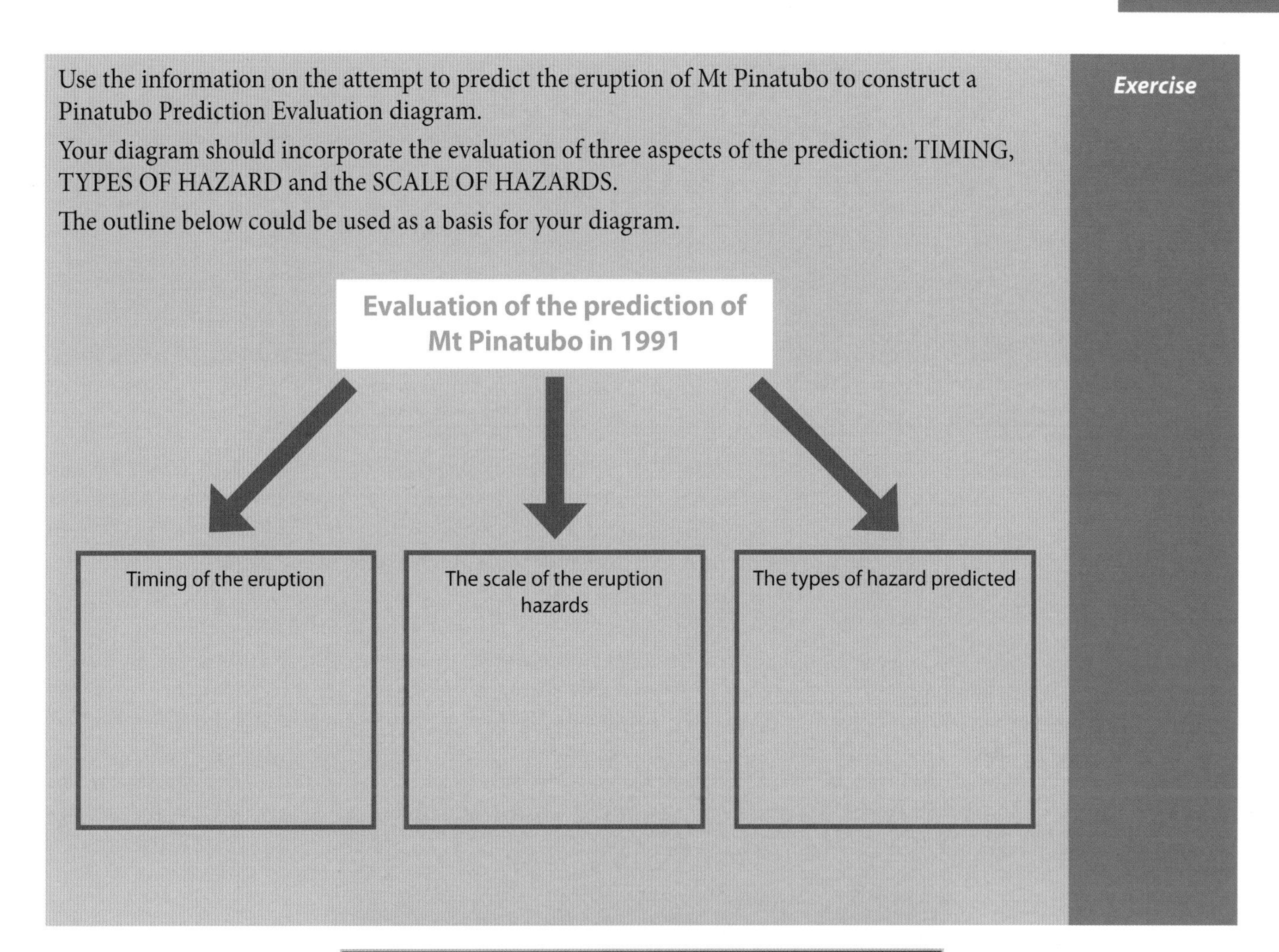

Use the information on the attempt to predict the eruption of Mt Pinatubo to construct a Pinatubo Prediction Evaluation diagram.

Your diagram should incorporate the evaluation of three aspects of the prediction: TIMING, TYPES OF HAZARD and the SCALE OF HAZARDS.

The outline below could be used as a basis for your diagram.

The eruption of Mt Pinatubo viewed from Clark Air Base.

Source: D Harlow, USGS

C3 EARTHQUAKE ACTIVITY AND ITS MANAGEMENT

Earthquake activity

Contrary to most people's experience, Earth is not an inactive planet. Seismic events are continuous, occurring every few minutes, with frequent significant hazardous quakes. On average, earthquakes are responsible for up to 10,000 deaths a year. When rocks in the crust are placed under increased stress they deform. Eventually the pressure is released in a sudden movement along a line of weakness or **fault**. This is called **elastic rebound** but the movement and the energy released is an earthquake. The location where the earthquake occurs is termed its **focus** and **seismic waves** radiate away from here. The point on the surface immediately above the focus is called the **epicentre** (**Resource 160**). Most earthquakes (75%) are shallow, no deeper than 70 km from the Earth's surface, with deep quakes occurring between 300–700 km below the surface, within the upper mantle. The depth of the focus is one important consideration in the impact of earthquakes, as deeper quakes are less damaging. Earthquakes have two common causes:

On-line textbook reference:
www.digitalgeology.net/page1.html

1. The release of stress between rocks moving at plate boundaries.
2. The movement of magma within the crust beneath active volcanoes.

As a consequence of this, around 95% of all earthquakes are located at plate boundaries and their global distribution is largely confined to the linear zones of destructive, constructive and

Resource 160 *Relationship between faultline, focus and epicentre*

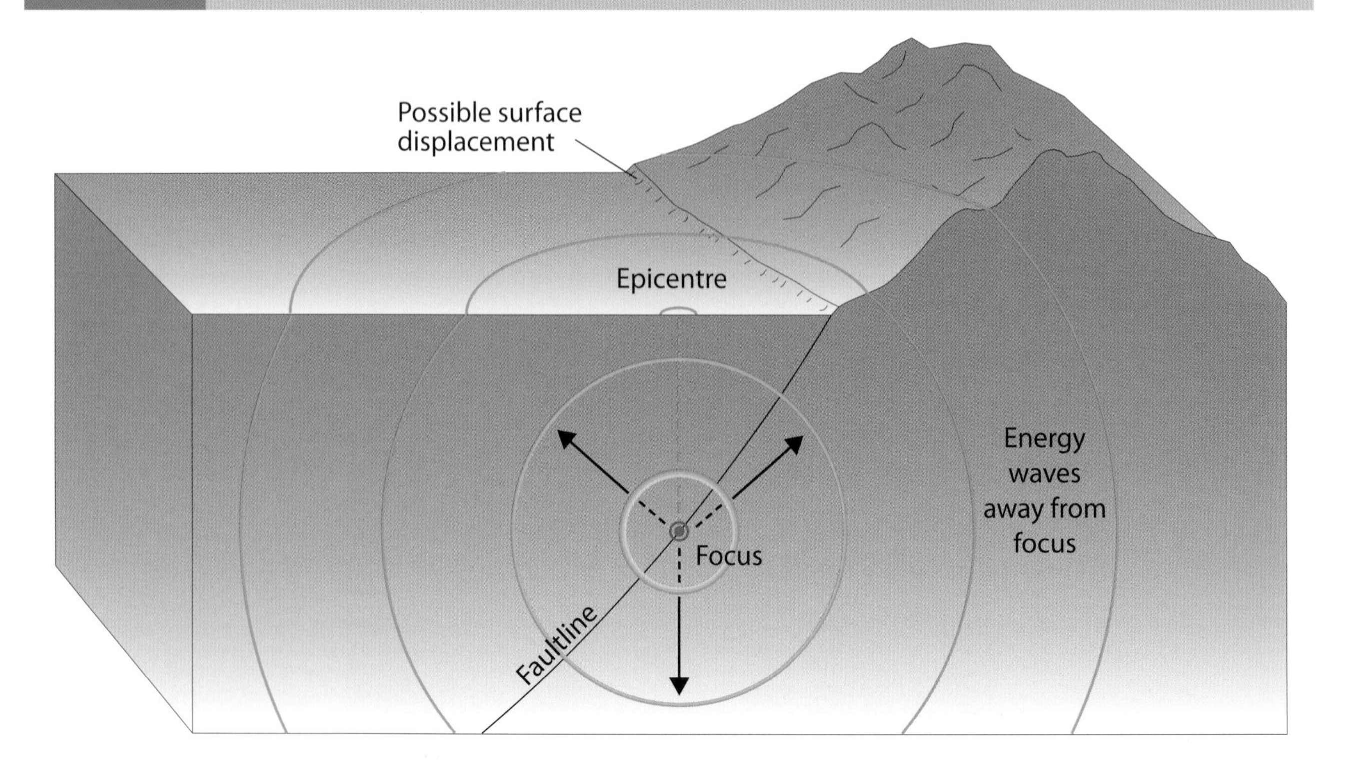

conservative margins (**Resource 128**).

The magnitude of earthquakes is commonly recorded by two different scales: the first is the Modified Mercalli scale, a 12 level system based on the impact upon built structures (**Resource 161**). The second is the Richter Scale, which records the energy release and wave size (**Resource 162**). The Richter scale is open ended and logarithmic in nature. On the Richter scale a magnitude 7 event will have a ten-fold increase in wave size, compared to a magnitude 6 and a thirty-fold increase in energy release. In turn, compared to a magnitude 5 event, the 7 has 100 times the wave motion and 900 times the energy! The 2004 Indian Ocean tsunami was the result of an earthquake registered at 9.1 on the Richter scale. This is one of the highest values ever recorded and in energy terms equivalent to 23,000 Hiroshima atomic bombs. Earthquakes normally last for seconds or minutes at most and the main event is often followed by aftershocks, which may cause additional damage.

The effects of earthquake activity

Apart from the climatic hazards of tropical cyclones, floods and droughts, earthquakes are responsible for more death and destruction than any other natural hazard. They are also a dramatic event that can modify the landscape in seconds whereas the slow processes of weathering and erosion may take millennia. There are several direct and indirect consequences of an earthquake. On the surface these include the following.

Ground deformation

Ground deformation is when the ground surface above an earthquake is distorted or displaced. The ground can be moved vertically, horizontally or a combination of these elements. Earthquakes along the transform San Andreas Fault in California often cause lateral deformation as seen by the offsetting of roads, walls, fences and even furrows in ploughed fields (**Resources 163** and **164**). In other cases, vertical movements can leave cliff-like steps running across the countryside from a few centimeters to several metres in height. A major earthquake in Alaska, USA, 1964, vertically lifted the land surface by an average of two metres and in some places by up to 12 m over a 400,000 km^2 area. Such ground deformation is normally confined to areas close to the epicentre but may run along the fault line for several kilometres. Study of seismic regions has shown that land may be warped upwards as stress builds before an earthquake and that subsidence of the surface may follow after the stress is released by a quake. However, in many cases earthquakes do not leave any

The Modified Mercalli scale based on observed impacts **Resource 161**

Level	Nature of structure damage
I	Felt by very few under special circumstances.
II	Felt by some at rest, especially on upper floors of buildings.
III	Felt noticeably indoors but not often recognised as an earthquake.
IV	During the day most indoors will feel it, like a vehicle striking the building.
V	Felt by nearly all, many wakened. Tall objects moved – trees, poles.
VI	Felt by all, some run outside, furniture moved but slight damage.
VII	Everyone runs out. Damage to ordinary buildings, little to those specially designed.
VIII	Considerable damage and collapse of structures – chimneys, some walls.
IX	Damage even to well designed buildings – some ground cracking.
X	Most masonry and frame buildings destroyed – badly cracked ground.
XI	Few masonry structures standing – bridges collapse. Wide fissures in ground.
XII	Damage total. Objects thrown up – waves seen on ground surface.

The Richter magnitude scale based on amplitude **Resource 162**

Richter magnitude	Effects of earthquake	Expected annual frequency
Less than 2.5	Recorded but not felt	900,000
2.5–5.4	Felt but only minor damage	30,000
5.5–6.0	Slight structural damage	500
6.1–6.9	Can be destructive in populous area	100
7.0–7.9	Major event – serious damage	20
8.0 and above	Total destruction to local region	One every 5–10 years

Resource 163 *Fence moved by fault displacement – 1906 San Francisco earthquake*

Source: GK Gilbert, USGS

Resource 164 *Driveway destroyed by fault displacement – 1989 Loma Prieta earthquake*

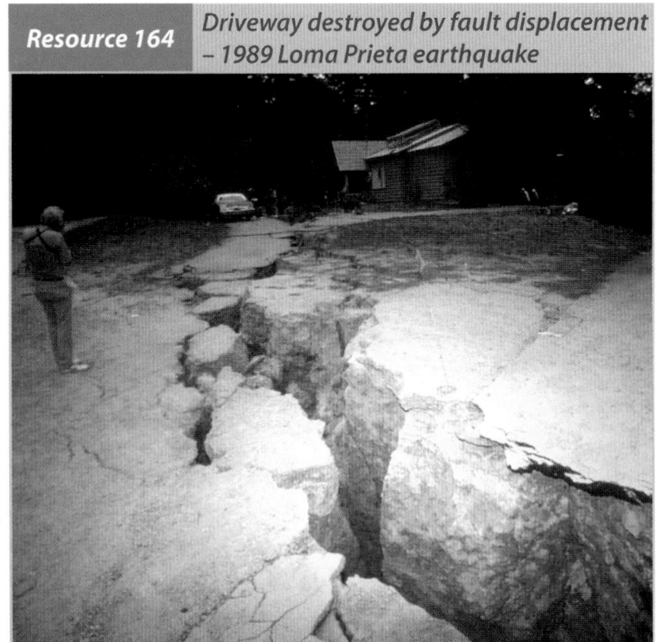

Source: JK Nakata, USGS

visible evidence of displacement at the surface. This may be because the surface line of the fault is covered by sediment or other rock material.

Ground deformation is the only direct impact of earthquakes on the surface. The impacts that follow are a consequence of the energy radiating from the focus of an earthquake in the form of seismic waves.

Seismic shaking

The energy released by an earthquake radiates out from its focus in all directions, like the ripples on a pond. These seismic waves shake the crust as they pass through it, and when they reach the Earth's surface they shake the ground and anything built on it. There are different wave forms but most cause a lateral side-to-side motion. This is known as a shear motion, bending structures at right angles. This is why building designs based on triangles are more earthquake resistant than rectangular forms (**Resource 166**).

Shaking of only 20–30 cm is potentially devastating for buildings made from weak materials and the longer the shaking persists the greater the damage caused. Design is another factor, in the 1995 Kobe earthquake many traditional homes collapsed as they had heavy tiled roofs supported by vertical wooden columns. On the other hand, ancient pagoda buildings have survived many quakes as they appear to flex with the seismic waves. Many modern buildings in Kobe were subject to a phenomenon known as 'pancaking'. In this case, shaking causes one floor of a building to crumble bringing the structure above that point collapsing down. Often the missing floor had less support, such as the ground floor shopping area in an office block.

As well as horizontal shaking, earthquakes may also cause violent vertical motion. It has been reported that during some earthquakes objects and people have been thrown repeatedly into the air. In one case a three tonne Californian fire truck bounced and damaged a wall over a metre above its parked position.

Walls made of weak material, such as mud brick (adobe) and poorly mortared brickwork, offer little resistance to shaking and such structures are often the cause of a large proportion of the deaths and injuries sustained. Even in well constructed buildings it appears that they may have a natural resonance that matches that of the earthquake and this increases the impact of shaking. In 1985, seismic waves from a distant earthquake shook Mexico City and several medium sized tower blocks collapsed with great loss of life. Later scientists showed that the tremors matched

Retrofitting of the Golden Gate Bridge, San Francisco **Resource 165**

Source: Professor Steve Royle

the natural resonance of these buildings, causing their destruction, while nearby smaller and taller buildings survived without significant damage.

Shaking buildings do not have to fall to create hazards. Glass from skyscrapers, overhanging balconies, parapets and even advertising hoardings may fall onto people and property nearby. Even inside buildings seismic shaking creates hazards; fixtures such as machinery in factories, filing cabinets in offices and large fridges in homes become potential threats to life and limb.

Structures other than buildings, including bridges and flyovers, may also suffer damage from shaking. The 1989, Loma Prieta earthquake, near San Francisco lasted only fifteen seconds but in that time dozens of concrete columns supporting a one kilometre long section of the upper tier of the Interstate 880 highway, known as the Nimitz structure, sheared away causing it to fall onto the roadway below (**Resource 167**). Dozens of vehicles were crushed and around 50 lives were lost at this site alone.

Studies show that shaking has significantly less impact on built structures constructed on solid rock foundations. In studies of the major earthquake that helped destroy San Francisco in 1906, the buildings on loose, often reclaimed land where subject to four times as much damage as those founded on bedrock (**Resource 168**).

Earthquake proofing for buildings **Resource 166**

Identification number visible to helicopters assessing damage after earthquake

Automatic shutters over windows to prevent pedestrians below being showered with glass

Rolling weights on roof to counteract shockwaves

12

Panels of glass flexibly anchored to steel super-structure

Rubber shock-absorbers in foundations

Interlocking steel frame construction with cross-bracing

Reinforced foundations deep in bedrock

Collapse of Interstate 880 highway, 1989 San Francisco **Resource 167**

Source: HG Wilshire, USGS

Resource 168 *The relationship between geology and impact of the 1906 quake in San Francisco*

Alluvium, sands, clays and mud

Solid rock

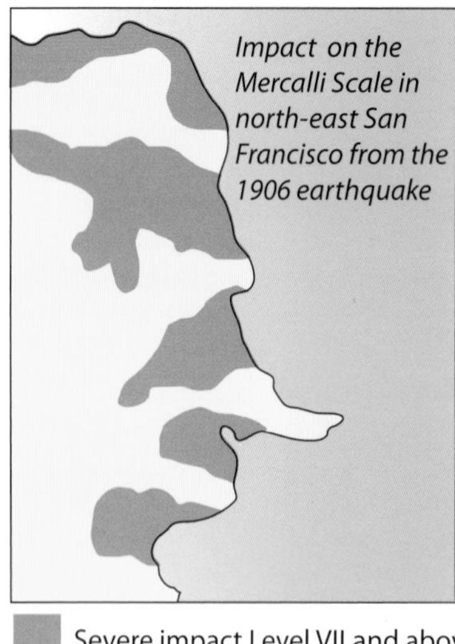

Severe impact Level VII and above

Impact less than Level VII

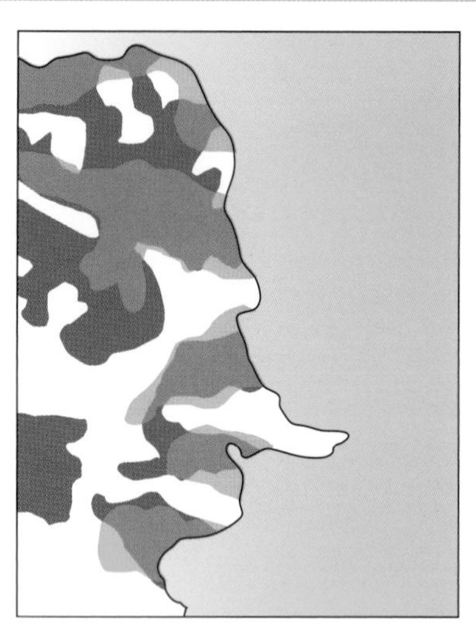

The correlation between areas of more severe earthquake impact and those with weak unconsolidated deposits

Landslides

The term landslide covers a range of material movement down slopes including rock falls, avalanches and earth slumps. In many cases earthquakes act as the trigger mechanism starting the movement down steep slopes. A disastrous earthquake in central China in 1976 is known to have killed at least 250,000 people. In the mountainous region near the epicentre, most deaths were caused by hundreds of landslides that carried away or buried rural settlements. One of the best documented cases of an earthquake induced avalanche was in 1970, in the mountains of Peru. A quake measuring 7.8 on the Richter scale triggered the movement of 50 million cubic metres of ice, rock and mud. Within minutes the debris fell over 3,000 m and traveled 11 km, burying two towns including Yungay, killing 18,000 residents.

An additional role that earthquakes play in landslides concerns the process of liquefaction (discussed below). It appears that on even gentle slopes this may cause slips and slumps that are unlikely to happen under normal slope processes.

Liquefaction

This is the process by which soft or unconsolidated sediments amplify the effect of shaking ground. The effect can occur with either dry or wet sediments but is most clearly seen where there is significant water content. Liquefaction is similar to the effect of standing on sand and wiggling your toes. The sand that supported your weight when standing still, allows you to sink down into it when you move. Liquefaction is when shaken loose sediment starts to act as a liquid, often causing building foundations to sink or subside (**Resource 169**). Beach or lake bed sediments, along with reclaimed land, are highly susceptible to liquefaction and it is wisest not to build on such material in seismically active areas. Not only will liquefaction cause land to fail to support buildings but underground service pipes may bend and fracture. In 1906, in the Marina District of east San Francisco the water mains were broken, preventing the fire department from dealing with the fires that eventually destroyed the city. In 1989 in the same area, the Loma Prieta quake induced liquefaction that caused the collapse of buildings and ruptured gas and water pipelines (**Resource 170**). The resultant fires were eventually brought under control by pumping saltwater from the nearby bay.

Liquefaction may also cause land and anything built upon it to spread laterally so that roads or airport runways can crack open. In 1995, the Japanese port city of Kobe was struck by a magnitude 7.2 quake (CASE STUDY: A MEDC earthquake event, page 276). The authorities

Liquefaction effect in saturated sediment **Resource 169**

WATER-SATURATED SEDIMENT

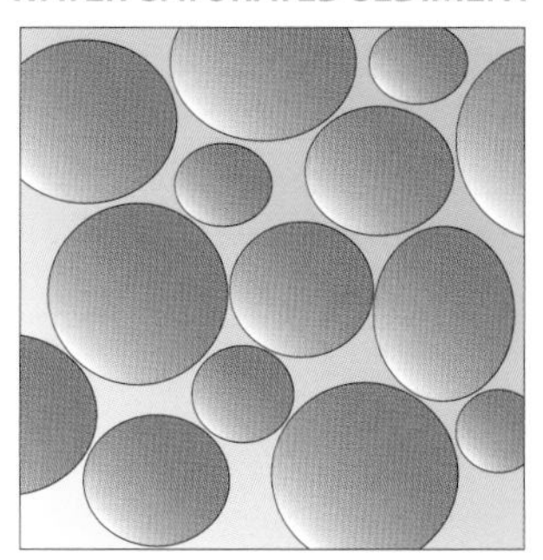

Water fills in the pore space between grains.
Friction between grains holds sediment together.

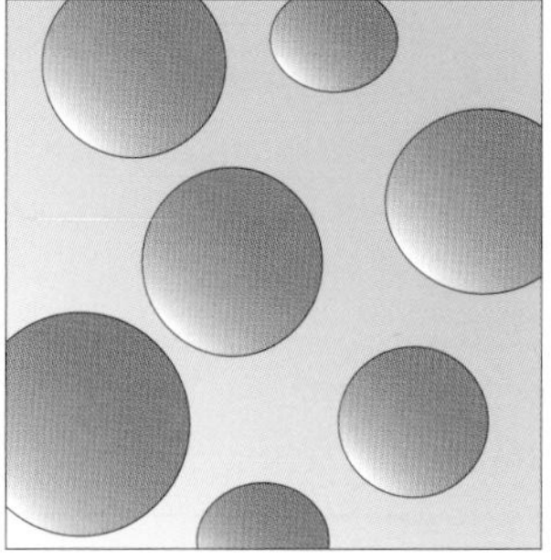

Water completely surrounds all grains and eliminates all grain to grain contact.
Sediment flows like a fluid.

Damage from liquefaction in the Marina District of San Francisco, 1989 **Resource 170**

Source: JK Nakata, USGS

had recently completed building the world's largest container port terminal on two artificially reclaimed islands in the bay. The loose infill material was water saturated, and during the 20 second quake it suffered widespread liquefaction and lateral settlement. Most of the port was damaged beyond use for many months and worldwide shipping was significantly disrupted (**Resource 176**).

Another phenomenon associated with liquefaction is that water-laden sand can rise to the surface as sand boils. These areas are rarely more than 3–5 m across and while not particularly hazardous, they indicate the presence of liquefaction.

Fire

The citizens of California and in particular those in San Francisco live in fear of, what they term 'The Big One', an earthquake event to rival that of 1906. In that year the city contained mainly wooden structures and unreinforced brick buildings. While many of these were badly damaged by seismic shaking, the greatest cause of destruction was fire. Initiated by broken gas pipelines and severed electrical cables, the fire raged out of control for three days, burning down 500 city blocks. The problem was compounded by the fact that liquefaction had also destroyed the city's underground water supply network, leaving fire fighters without their key weapon in the fight.

In Japan too, the city of Tokyo awaits the next great quake to match the Great Kanto quake of 1923. Here again, hundreds of fires started where traditional wooden homes were set ablaze, often by cooking stoves and open fires. Over 50,000 survivors took refuge in city parks and squares only to be later burnt to death. The numerous fires combined to produce a feature called a fire storm, which even swept across the open grass area. All this initiated by a few minutes of ground shaking.

Flood

Earthquakes cause flooding in several indirect ways. One fear during earthquakes is that the earth or concrete walls of dams may be weakened or destroyed releasing the water in the related reservoir to sweep downstream. River levées are another feature that may suffer during an earthquake, with the risk that rivers may flow onto adjacent floodplains. Another possibility is that landslides may block river channels causing water to back-up and flood the valleys. This natural dam may later break or overflow creating another flood risk. These examples relate to river valley flooding but the more common and probably more deadly risk of coastal flooding is associated with the tsunami.

Tsunamis

It is probably true to say that as a result of the events of 26 December 2004, the knowledge of the Japanese word 'tsunami' and the perception of its potential threat have become global. Technically known as seismic sea waves, tsunamis are fast moving high waves that radiate away from some large undersea earthquakes. When a section of oceanic crust rises or falls, a major earthquake follows, displacing a large amount of water and transferring a huge amount of energy. Tsunamis travel across the oceans at an amazing rate of between 500 and 950 km/hr. At the surface tsunamis spread out like ripples from a splash in a pond. In deep water the transfer of energy is as a low wave, often less than one metre high and with a wavelength of between 100 and 700 km. In the deep ocean these may go undetected and unnoticed by shipping. However, a tsunami changes its nature when entering shallower water. As waves feel the seabed, friction slows them down and causes water to pile up. Some can reach heights of 30 m – as high as a 10 storey building. Perhaps surprisingly, the first sign of an approaching tsunami is the withdrawal of water from the shore. At which point people should quickly move to higher ground. Between 5 and 30 minutes later the first great wave arrives as a surge of water, which may extend hundreds of metres inland, depending on the nature of the shore. Several waves may arrive sometimes with many minutes between. Common in the Pacific, a good tsunami warning system, based in Honolulu, Hawaiian Islands, USA, has existed for many years. The Indian Ocean has not had this warning system and many of the people who live along its coastline had little or no experience of the phenomenon (**Resource 171).**

Resource 171 *The Boxing Day 2004 tsunami on the coast of Thailand*

Source: David Rydevik

The 2004 Boxing Day tsunami was the direct consequence of one of the largest earthquakes ever recorded. Off the north coast of the island of Sumatra, Indonesia, a section of the seabed over 1,600 kilometres long dropped by 15 m, releasing a magnitude 9.1 undersea quake. The earthquake itself was felt over a huge region but the tsunami that was generated was the principal cause of the estimated death toll of 245,000, spread over eleven countries around the Indian Ocean basin.

The 30 m high tsunami wave impact was indiscriminate, destroying both luxury tourist resorts and poor fishing settlements. The destruction was most severe in the Indonesian province of Aceh, the island of Phuket in Thailand and along the southern shores of Sri Lanka and the south Indian state of Tamil Nadu. In places the tsunami wave swept up to three kilometres inland, destroying over 140,000 homes. Even twelve hours after the quake the tsunami still had the power to kill, as two died in South Africa over 5,000 km from the epicentre. A warning system is now being established for the Indian Ocean to replicate the one that exists in the Pacific Ocean.

Managing and responding to earthquakes

"Earthquakes do not kill people, falling structures do." This statement while not entirely true does stress that on many occasions it is the human built environment that contributes to the impact of these seismic events. The social and environmental impacts of earthquake activity are numerous:

Social impacts

- Death and injury.
- Human fear, anxiety and bereavement.
- Buildings collapse, wholly or in part, burying or trapping people.

- Other structures collapsing – bridges, flyovers or elevated route ways.
- Phone, road, rail and other communication links disrupted.
- Fracture of underground services – water, gas and sewage pipelines.
- Fires may be started or made worse by gas leaks.
- Homelessness, lack of adequate shelter, refugee camps and out-migration.
- The huge cost or debt in rebuilding infrastructure.
- Loss of jobs, closure of businesses and factories.

Environmental impacts

- Landslides moving or overwhelming buildings or whole settlements. Alternatively they may disrupt drainage causing flooding.
- Liquefaction and ground failure causing building foundations to sink or subside.
- Tsunamis have a devastating impact on coastlines and coastal settlement.

Any or all of these impacts may follow an earthquake but their intensity and severity may have less to do with the magnitude or nature of the earthquake than with the country or region involved. In general terms, nations that are more scientifically and economically advanced are better placed to prepare for and respond to an earthquake episode. **Knowledge** and **perception** are critical aspects concerning earthquake response. Knowledge relates to the scientific understanding of the nature and location of potential earthquake hazards, whereas perception is the broader awareness of these hazards and the degree to which awareness leads to action in preparation and planning.

Earthquake prediction

Despite years of research we can not yet make accurate predictions of earthquakes. Even our knowledge of the world-wide distribution of these phenomena is incomplete. In 1993, an earthquake of magnitude 6.4 struck Maharashtra in Western India. India has major earthquake events, as in 1935 and 2001, but unusually the 1993 quake was in a region regarded as tectonically stable. No preparation existed as it was believed that none was needed and 25,000 people perished as fifty villages and towns were destroyed. Most died as they slept, when the quake struck at 4 am. Despite soldiers and policemen being drafted in from all over the nation, devastated road and rail links, along with hordes of homeless refugees hindered the rescue operation. The region's poverty, especially in rural areas, meant that many injured were not adequately treated and disease broke out.

Even in more advanced nations surprises occur: the 1995 Northridge earthquake near Los Angeles, California, was on a previously unknown fault line running lateral to the San Andreas, the world's most intensely studied fault.

Methods of earthquake prediction and their limitations

Currently, it is possible to determine the regions in which the vast majority of earthquakes are likely to occur but we cannot yet predict when they will happen or their magnitude.

It could be argued that anything less that an accurate prediction in terms of location, time and scale would be a waste of time and effort. Why?

The Japanese spend over £80 million each year on earthquake prediction studies, yet they have never successfully predicted a quake and currently say that they will have less that one minute to warn the population of Toyko-Yokahama of an imminent event.

Precursors: The harbingers of doom

What would a class of A2 students think if their teacher went through the following steps at the beginning of their Geography class?

1. Tells them to leave their books at the front of the class.
2. Directs them to sit at separate desks.
3. Gives each one a sheet of lined paper.
4. Guides them to write down their name and the numbers 1 to 10 down the left margin.
5. Instructs them that no communication, verbal or written will be allowed.

Most will be expecting a test or assessment of some sort to follow. Why?

Because all these events point towards one course of action and perhaps they have experienced the same sequence before. This is an illustration of one of the main concepts behind earthquake prediction – the precursor: an event or action that signifies that another event, in this case an earthquake, will happen. Many suggestions have been made about things that may happen before an earthquake. Some, such as strange animal behaviour and 'earthquake weather', may be based on less than scientific observations; other signs are more measurable and therefore potentially reliable. If we accept the idea that earthquakes are a sudden release of energy along a fault line, after stress has built up over time – the elastic rebound theory – then all that is needed is to find and measure characteristics that indicate growing levels of stress. These would be precursors. Examples include ground level change, uplift, subsidence or tilting. After several Japanese quakes, scientists studying records have shown that nearby surface changes have occurred. Sadly, after the event is clearly too late. One example of a precursor event is the study of foreshocks– minor seismic events that precede a major event. One researcher has identified that foreshocks can form a ring of small events surrounding a major epicentre. Unfortunately this has never been used with success.

Examples of earthquake warnings noticed after the event!

Well water at Kobe

An article in New Scientist in 1995 reported that a well 30 km from the epicentre of the Kobe earthquake had been studied for months before the quake. Researchers had continuously monitored the level of radon gas in the water of the well and on the 7 January 1993 the level surged to very high levels and dropped to very low levels by the 10 January. The earthquake struck one week later. Had the rapidly changing radon level been a precursor? Could a warning system be developed?

Ground level changes in Japan

Also in Japan, before a major earthquake at Niigata in 1964, the nearby coastline had been rising out of the sea. After the quake the surface rapidly subsided back by 20 cm. Again the analysis came after the event but could surface measurements be used as a predictive tool for earthquakes as they often are in volcanoes?

The search for the precursor is linked to what is known as **Dilation Theory**. This states that as the rocks along fault lines become stressed, numerous microscopic cracks open up in the surrounding rocks. In turn, such microcracks may change some characteristics of the rocks which, if measured, can warn of an impending quake. A host of such characteristics have been proposed including: changing water levels in wells, increasing release of gases such as radon, changes in the electrical resistivity, temperature increases caused by friction, local gravity or magnetic changes and the decrease in speed of seismic waves.

Some researchers have gone as far as suggesting a five stage sequence of events based on precursor events (**Resource 172**). This is no more than a theoretical model, which at best will need much testing and refinement or at worst, may prove to be entirely worthless.

A second theory of earthquake prediction was based on work by American and Russian scientists and is known as the **seismic gap theory**. In brief, the concept suggests that in areas where earthquakes are known to happen regularly, but recent records show little activity, then

Resource 172 *Precursors suggested sequence table*

Stage	Description
Stage I	Strain builds up along a fault due to plate movement; all characteristics are at their normal state – no uplift, no radon increase, etc.
Stage II	Cracks begin to develop in underground rocks in the area. The build up begins to be visible as ground uplift of the area and seismic waves move more slowly through the cracked rocks. Radon gas can escape through the newly formed cracks and electrical resitivity decreases. The newly forming cracks and increasing stress may also result in a tiny increase in local seismicity.
Stage III	Groundwater flows into the new cracks, the ground's uplift stops and radon gas emission decreases. Electrical resistivity is still decreasing.
Stage IV	THE EARTHQUAKE
Stage V	This begins as soon as the main shock stops and consists of all the aftershocks.

stress must be building and a quake becomes more and more likely. One good example was that of the 1989 Loma Prieta earthquake along the San Andreas Fault (**Resource 173**). Before this quake the seismic activity of the previous 20 years showed that three sections of the fault had shown little activity – one around San Francisco in the north, a second to the south near Parkfield and the third around the Santa Cruz Mountains south of San Francisco. The Loma Prieta quake and its aftershocks effectively filled in the Santa Cruz Gap as **Resource 173** shows. Ominously the San Francisco Gap remains.

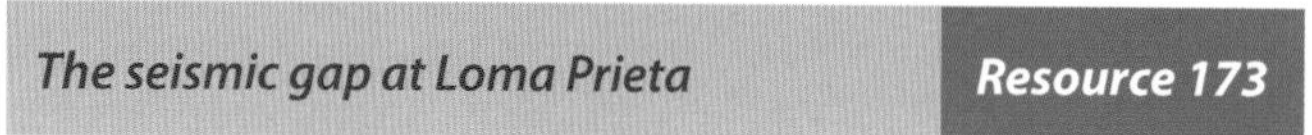

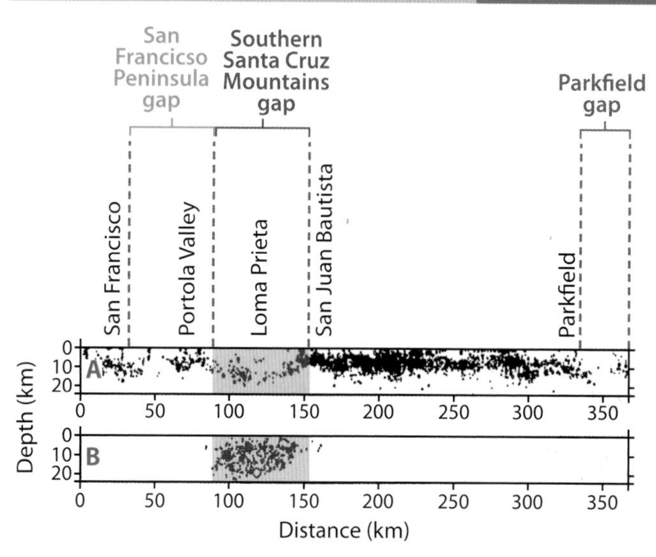

A – Earthquake foci between 1969–89 along San Andreas Fault, San Francisco to Parkfield. Three gaps are identified.

B – The 1989 Loma Prieta earthquake and aftershocks 'fill in' the gap.

The Parkfield Experiment

After the 1989 Loma Prieta earthquake researchers in California decided to catch a quake. Ironically the greatest difficulty of studying an earthquake to predict is to know when and where it will happen! What Californian scientists knew was that medium size earthquakes seemed to occur with regularity in and around Parkfield on the San Andreas Fault (**Resource 174**).

At Parkfield medium sized earthquakes have been recorded at similar intervals – in 1857, 1881, 1901, 1922, 1934, and 1966. Based on this, Californian seismologists invested heavily in monitoring the San Andreas Fault in and around Parkfield. Laser ranging devices, tiltmeters and seismographs where deployed across the area. Ground deformation, electrical resistivity, magnetism, gravity and temperature were continuously monitored. The experts waited not for the expected 5 years but for 15. Then in 2004 the medium strength earthquake happened. Scientists spent the next year analysing all their collected data. The conclusion was long and technical in its language but essentially they failed to identify any pattern or precursors. One scientist said that in effect, "…it just happened, one moment nothing – the next an earthquake."

Video camera looking along the San Andreas fault at Parkfield **Resource 174**

Source: J Adieman, USGS

Some researchers suggested that the data needed to be gathered much nearer the focus and so a borehole has now been drilled several kilometres deep down to the San Andreas Fault and instruments are being installed, ready for the next event in twenty or thirty years time.

Management of earthquake impact

The impact of an earthquake does not solely depend on its magnitude and duration but also on the degree to which the region is prepared for such a hazard. Preparation involves:

- Knowledge – a scientific understanding of the geological threat and of current technology.
- Perception – the level of awareness of the threat among decision makers and the public.
- Stage of development – the financial resources to create as safe an environment as possible.

CASE STUDY: A MEDC earthquake event

Kobe, Japan 1995 – The Great Hanshin Quake

On Tuesday 17 January 1995 at 5.46 am, an earthquake measuring 7.2 on the Richter scale occurred along a 50 km section of a complex plate margin off the coast of south central Japan. Here an ocean trench marks a subduction zone between the Pacific, Philippine and Eurasian plates. The focus of the earthquake was very shallow at less than 20 km deep and above it the epicentre, on Awaji Island, lay just 32 km from Japan's second largest concentration of population. Over 10 million people in the cities of Kobe and Osaka were impacted by the 20 seconds of ground shaking (**Resource 175**).

Resource 175 The location of Kobe, Japan

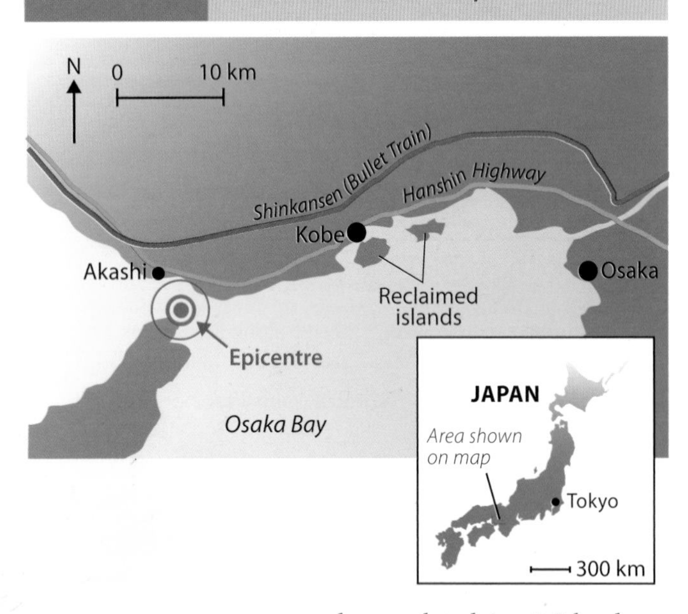

The impacts

The final death toll came to 6,400, with around 35,000 people injured. In the first day 180,000 buildings, including houses, were destroyed or badly damaged. Several highways collapsed, including a 500 m stretch of the Hanshin Expressway. The track of Japan's iconic bullet train, the Shinkansen, was twisted and services halted. Over 150 fires initiated by tumbling paraffin stoves and fed by gas leaks swept through traditional wooden homes, many of which had collapsed in the first minute of the event. Kobe's newly opened port – the largest in Japan – was devastated. Of its 170 quays, 140 were destroyed, many on two reclaimed islands, where liquefaction of the soft sediments amplified the impact of the shaking. Along the fault the crust shifted horizontally by 1.7 m and vertically by up to 1.4 m. On the surface this movement triggered 30 coastal landslides but the only ground displacement was on the sparsely populated Awaji Island near the epicentre (**Resource 176**).

The number of homeless rose to 310,000 in the aftermath of the fires. This figure included 30% of Kobe's resident population who were moved to temporary shelter in camps. Rebuilding costs were estimated at £70 billion, while the total cost of damages, including lost business, was set at over £120 billion. As only 3% of the population had earthquake insurance, the financial loss for individuals was enormous. Gas and other supplies remained off for up to three months due to severe underground damage. Local medical services reported continuing emotional stress amongst survivors and the bereaved in the months following the earthquake. Eventually 96,000 people moved away from Kobe reducing its population to 1.4 million.

Management – knowledge, perception and stage of development

Japan has a worldwide reputation as a nation that is acutely aware of the threat of earthquake damage and that has taken steps to prepare for such an event. The Kobe earthquake provided a test of these measures and highlighted their limitations. As with many quakes, it was the built structures that created the high death toll. Traditional homes, with heavy tiled roofs supported by wooden frames, collapsed quickly, burying their inhabitants. Some buildings fell or suffered from 'pancaking'. This is when poorly supported upper storeys fall onto those below. In the centre of Kobe nearly all of the modern steel framed office blocks survived, though some innovative designs did not perform so well. Research shows that structures, including bridges and elevated highways, built in the 1960s and 70s were subject to high levels of damage compared to those constructed after 1981, when new building standards were introduced and, more significantly, enforced. These new regulations implemented the use of stronger materials and more flexible structures that could sway and bend with seismic waves. Two earthquake resistant, modern constructions that survived the quake without damage were the Akushi Bridge and the Kansai International Airport. Also although 15 km of the bullet train track was unusable, a built in fail-safe system – that detects seismic motion and automatically shuts off power to the line – prevented any train derailments.

Earthquake damage at Kobe's port **Resource 176**

Source: USGS

In reviewing the immediate response to the earthquake, it was found that while both the emergency response and the search and rescue operations had saved many lives, they were less than satisfactory. Civil awareness of risk is maintained through annual disaster practice days on 1 September, the anniversary of Tokyo's devastating 1923 quake. Emergency earthquake kits were routinely available in supermarkets in the city and published advice on the need to secure heavy domestic appliances was distributed regularly. The preparations covering school buildings and street signs marking escape routes had performed well. Less successful was the investment of £80 million each year on earthquake prediction. While it was known that Kobe lay near a tectonically active zone most scientists had been convinced that the next major quake would be in another part of Japan. No warning signs were recognised, although:

- the area has had a lack of events over the previous 50 years hinting at the build up of stress;
- on 7 January research on groundwater near Kobe recorded unusual levels of radon gas;
- in another study high levels of electro-magnetic emissions were noted;
- seismic records showed a cluster of four minor foreshocks just hours before the main event.

Unfortunately such information was only highlighted months after the incident. The Kobe quake has heightened the awareness of the authorities and the public alike that the Tokyo region is not the only region of the country threatened by severe earthquakes.

Perhaps where Japan's knowledge and high level of development was most significant was in the recovery after the event. On the day following the earthquake apparently many shop keepers opened for business on the pavements and a year later 70% of Kobe's businesses were fully functioning again (some had relocated). Within four months of the event, utilities (gas, electricity, water and sewage) had been restored with some pipelines fitted with 'smart meters' that will isolate leaks automatically after a quake. By October 1996 the Hanshin highway was fully rebuilt and the port was 80% operational and completely restored by 1997. In conclusion, the earthquake has encouraged new resolve and urgency on a program of strengthening older structures, termed retrofitting, and maintaining tight building controls. However, while Japan still invests in earthquake prediction it also continues to develop reclaimed land, despite the threat of liquefaction.

Exercise

Read the notes on the impacts and management of the Kobe quake of 1995 then either:

- Make bullet point notes under the headings:
  Knowledge
  Perception
  Stage of development

or:

- Make structured notes on management, by time, under these three headings:
  Preparation before the quake
  Response during the event
  The follow-up management

Online resources

www.seismo.unr.edu/ftp/pub/louie/class/100/effects-kobe.html

CASE STUDY: A LEDC earthquake event

Gujarat, India 2001

On 26 January 2001 at 8.46 am, an earthquake registering 7.6 on the Richter scale occurred along a fault line in an area known as the Rann of Kutch, which lies in northwestern India, near the Pakistan border (**Resource 177**). The focus was about 17 km below the ground surface and the epicentre was near the town of Bhuj, 200 km northwest of the region's largest city, Ahmadabad. The 90 second long quake was felt in the Indian cities of Delhi and Mumbai, and as far away as Afghanistan and Nepal. Significant aftershocks continued for a month after the initial event. The region is not immediately adjacent to a plate boundary but it has a long history of earthquakes along a series of crustal faults.

Resource 177 *The location of Gujarat, India*

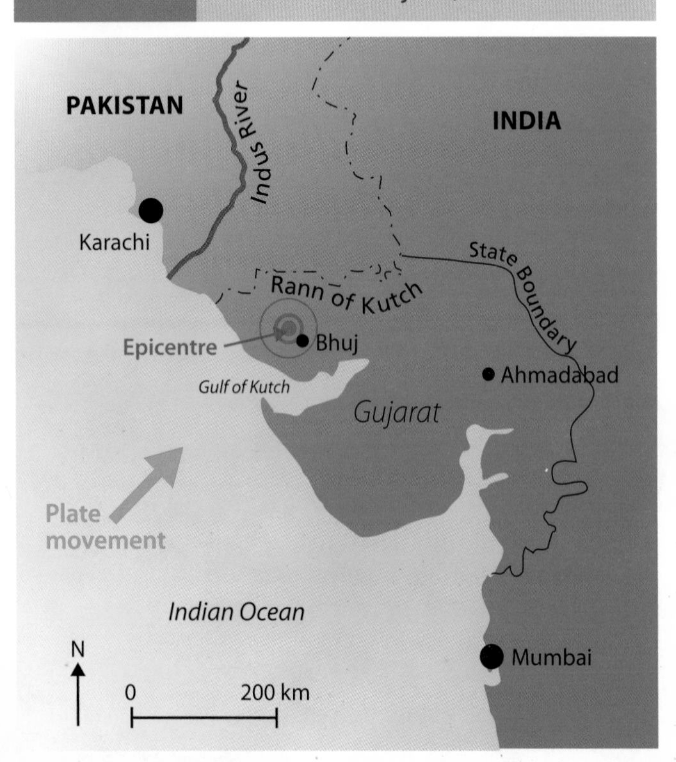

The impacts

Death tolls in earthquakes are notoriously inaccurate and initial reports varied from 10,000 to 100,000. A month after the event the official figure was 19,727 but this was later revised down to around 13,000 as both bogus and double recordings were eliminated. There were 166,000 injuries and over 600,000 people left homeless. A third of a million houses were destroyed and nearly a million more badly damaged. Transport was severely disrupted with the key Surajbari Bridge linking Kutch and the rest of Gujarat destroyed. Fibre-optic cabling and the telecom building in Buhj were destroyed, further isolating regions and hindering the rescue operation. The direct economic toll was stated by government sources as $1.3 billion, though others suggest a higher real impact in the order of $5.5 billion. The quake struck on India's national holiday, Republic Day, celebrating the establishment of their republic in 1950. As a result schools and government offices were closed and this may have contributed to the high casualty figures. Most victims were women and children and the vast majority died as the result of building collapse. Villages and towns were wiped out as houses were turned to rubble. Bhuj and Ahmadabad recorded thousands of deaths as buildings up to ten storeys high pancaked. Many state built structures fared badly, the central Bhuj civil hospital was flattened and of the 1359 primary schools in the region 992 were destroyed.

One town may illustrate the problems which faced numerous similar settlements. Bachao, population 42,000, was a prosperous town with around 10,000 buildings. It lay about 100 km from the epicentre. Nearly all its buildings collapsed, including six salt factories and their worker hostel accommodation. A small 20 bed hospital full of patients and staff fell within seconds of the tremor. Bridges, petrol stations and roadways were destroyed as the ground heaved and fissures opened. No outside help came for days after the event and locals used their bare hands in a desperate search and rescue effort. When rescue teams finally reached Bachao, numerous funerals pyres (cremation) were burning across the town.

The response and management

The rescue operation was hampered by many factors, including the continuing after-shocks and the disrupted transport and communication networks. The Indian Army, including six engineer regiments, Navy and Air Force, were mobilised and many international teams came to help. These included a Swiss team with trained sniffer dogs. Medical charities set up field hospitals using mobile generators and in the week after the event over 10,000 surgical operations were performed. Being January, cold winter nights were a real problem for the vast number of homeless. Blankets and tents were urgently required and frequently the number supplied was a fraction of what was needed. The Red Cross found many villages still awaiting emergency relief supplies a week after the quake. Meanwhile such supplies had been piled up for days on airport runways waiting distribution. Medical experts feared outbreaks of disease, as bodies decomposed and water supplies became contaminated. Reports came in from doctors of rising illness including diarrhea, especially among young children. A feared epidemic of cholera did not occur. Thousands of refugees left the Kutch region due to the fear of aftershocks and chronic food and water shortages.

The region contains numerous salt workings and significant rises in groundwater levels were recorded within these several days after the quake. In one case mine workings flooded so rapidly that the labour force had to run to escape. Satellites recorded the emergence of underground water at the surface and an 80 m wide, 100 km long river ran through Bhuj – an outcome of the shaking of the ground sediments.

The rebuilding of housing and compensation for victims is an ongoing problem in India with delays and complications. In one area the relocation of villages has been hindered both by the debate over the epicentre's precise location and by the conflict between the upper and lower ranks of the caste system (a social structure which divides people according to inherited social status). Inevitably, many local people believed that their government had failed them, before, during and after the event.

Knowledge of the threat

Management failures in the Gujarat quake are not the result of a lack of knowledge – at least in the academic sense. The region had experienced previous seismic events, including one in 1956, and academics had a working knowledge of the many faults underlying the region. The Indian government commissioned and had completed a comprehensive survey of the national earthquake risk. In 1998, the detailed Vulnerability Atlas of India was published. In Gujarat the existence of the Kutch Rift and other weaknesses were mapped and recognised – the area was classified as a Zone 5, the highest risk level (**Resource 178**). The Indian Building Code, issued in 1983, was based on extensive worldwide research – it identified the need for good structural design in earthquake prone zones. However, in 2001 the code and its regulations remained advisory only and were not supported by the necessary legislation. It is estimated that meeting the code adds between 20–30% to the cost of a building. In an LEDC such additional costs that are not required by law are unlikely to be paid. Within a week of the disaster many

Resource 178 *Earthquake vulnerability level across India*

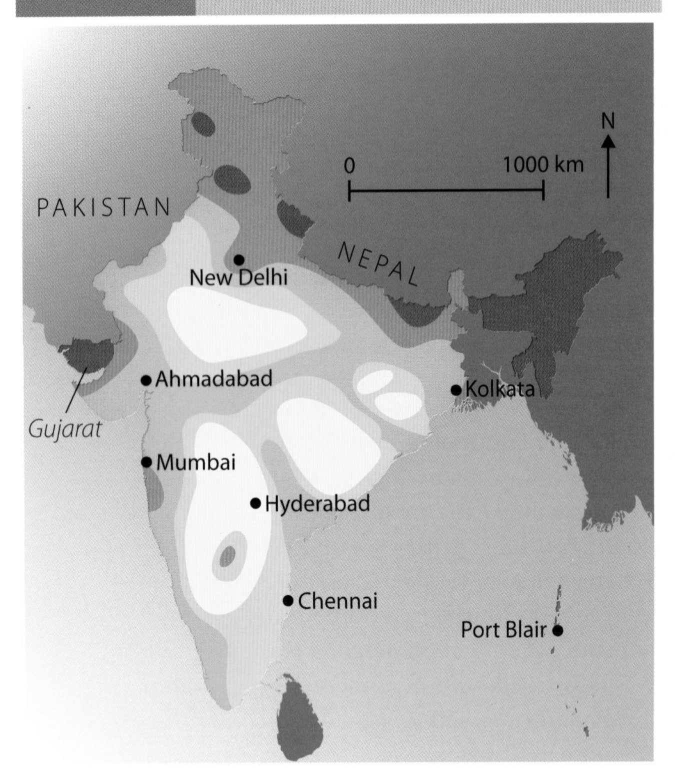

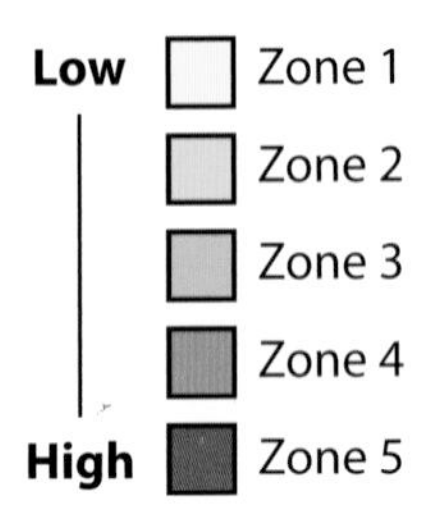

local builders were under investigation by the police following allegations of criminal negligence. In Bhuj it was admitted that buildings up to eight storeys high had been built in the two years before the event without any checks or inspections. Many public buildings did not meet earthquake standards and while the local nuclear power plants and dams survived, the Buhj state hospital and many schools were destroyed. A press report from Ahmadabad reflects findings, with echoes in many recent earthquakes affecting LEDCs such as Kashmir (Pakistan) 2005 and China 2008:

"Bribing officials to overlook poor workmanship or code violations is not uncommon, and officials are often unqualified to carry out inspections".

If the local authorities do not heed their own regulations on earthquake proofing are others likely to?

Perception and awareness

The low level of risk perception is an important factor in the region's poor response to the event. Locals under 50 years of age had no direct experience of a major quake and the threat was not a regular theme in government communication or the education system. The Indian Prime Minister, Vajpayee, admitted in the aftermath of the quake that the country was not ready to face such a disaster. The local Gujarat government took two days to set up a control room in Gandhinagar and even longer to move appropriate heavy earthmoving equipment into the region. Officials faced a barrage of criticism; some suggesting they were ignoring the region by not visiting problem areas, while others pointed out that the Prime Minister's visit entailed the closure of routes needed by rescue workers and the suspension of emergency flights. Newspaper articles highlighted local government failings as many rescue workers wasted time waiting to be allocated to problem sites. A lack of coordination was widespread.

There is little evidence that preparation was attempted in any systematic way prior to 2001. Schools did not practice emergency earthquake drills in the way that is routine in Japan or California. There was no equivalent to Japan's annual emergency day or Southern California's November 2008 'Great Shake Out' – an online practice to which over 5 million people registered. Most homes (70%) were self-built using a limited range of poor quality materials and traditional, rather than sound earth-proof designs. One of the priorities a year after the event was to educate people through staging drama productions highlighting the best techniques for rebuilding. The dominant local religion, Hinduism, may play a role in perception as some have a fatalistic attitude to such events, suggesting that any attempt to avoid fate is pointless. In short, the paper knowledge of earthquake risk in this region had not been translated into practice in either preparation or response for such an event. Short-term progress had prevailed over long-term safety. As journalist Deepal Jayasekera wrote after the quake, "it is the profit requirement of business – not the social need of the people – that determine government priorities before, during and after such calamities".

Stage of development

If a single, root cause of the management failure was to be identified, it would be the serious shortage of money and technology available to the region. India is an LEDC with a rapidly expanding rural and urban population. Gujarat is a region that faces a number of natural hazards, including the failure or over abundance of the annual summer monsoon rains causing drought or flood. It also has serious social divisions, including ethnic conflict between Hindus and Muslims. The disaster cost over $5 billion in damage and the repair and rebuilding has only been possible with the help of numerous NGOs, some Indian in origin but many funded by foreign aid. A year after the quake one charity reported that some people in rural areas had seen their communities rebuilt with the help of international agencies and money from all over the world. However, many in urban areas were still living in tents and shelters, in primitive conditions and there is no sign yet of damaged houses being redeveloped. The limited planning response to the quake reflects the inability of a poor nation to invest in reducing future hazards when its immediate needs are so demanding. Beyond research and knowledge little had been done in Gujarat to offset the impacts – immediate and long-term – of such earthquakes.

Selected textbooks and articles

Publications

EA Bryant, *Natural Hazards*, Cambridge University Press, 1991

EA Keller and N Pinter, *Active Tectonics: Earthquakes, Uplift and Landscape*, Prentice Hall, 2002

A Robinson, *Earth Shock*, Thames and Hudson, 1995

S Ross, *Natural Hazards*, Stanley Thornes, 1998

P Francis, *Volcanoes*, Oxford University Press, 1993

On-line text

http://wps.prenhall.com/esm_tarbuck_escience_9/

***Geofile* articles**

401 'Montserrat Volcanic eruptions 1995–98'

492 'Island Arcs'

510 'Tsunami 2004'

526 'Hot Spots in Plate Tectonics – Evolution of a Theory'

554 'Two Plate Boundaries: The Himalayas and Pacific USA'

Geo Factsheet

133 'Earthquakes: Why do some places suffer more than others?'

164 'Volcanoes: Why are some more hazardous than others?'

EXAMINATION TECHNIQUE

Maximising your potential

As you approach your GCE A2 examinations there are those who would say that they are the most important examinations you will take. Your GCE A Level results may indeed determine which course you take at which university. However, whether they are the most important exams you will ever take in your life is to some extent debateable. Nonetheless, the truth remains that your GCE A level examinations are very important.

To ensure that you maximise your potential and achieve a good grade in the A2 Geography examinations you need to develop, and put into practice, good examination technique. You may well have read the section on Examination Technique in the *AS Geography for CCEA* (Colourpoint, 2008) textbook. If so then this chapter will serve to remind you of the basics as well as looking at examination techniques specific to the A2 examination papers you will be taking.

What is examination technique?

So let's start at the beginning – what exactly is examination technique? Examination technique refers to the skills involved in taking an examination and includes:

- Paying attention to time
- Following instructions
- Understanding the demands of the question
- Recognising the scope of the question
- Making full use of the resource materials provided
- Developing answers to achieve higher marks

The Basics

Requirements

It may seem obvious but you need to know the requirements for each examination paper you will sit. The following summarises the main requirements for CCEA's A2 Geography.

Assessment Unit	Length of examination	Structure of examination paper	
		Section A	Section B
Assessment Unit A2 1 Human Geography and Global Issues	1 hour 30 min	Examines the Human Geography options listed in the specification. There will be three subsections corresponding to each of the optional units: • Impact of Population Change • Planning for Sustainable Settlements • Issues in Ethnic Diversity Each subsection comprises two structured questions. You must answer **two** questions: **one from each of your chosen subsections**. Each question has a total allocation of 30 marks. These questions have at least one extended element with a minimum mark allocation of 10 marks.	Examines the Global Issues listed in the specification. There will be four questions corresponding to Section B of the specification: • Air Pollution • Nuclear Energy • Agricultural Change and Its Impact • Issues in Tourism You must answer **one** question corresponding to your chosen Global Issue. Each question has a total of 30 marks. Each question will have at least one extended element with a minimum mark allocation of 10 marks. This section contributes to synoptic assessment.

Assessment Unit	Length of examination	Structure of examination paper	
		Section A	Section B
Assessment Unit A2 2 Physical Geography and Decision Making	2 hour 30 min	Examines the Physical Geography options listed in the specification. There will be three subsections corresponding to each of the optional units: • Fluvial and Coastal Environments • The Nature and Sustainability of Tropical Ecosystems • The Dynamic Earth Each subsection comprises two structured questions. You must answer **two** questions: **one from each of your chosen subsections**. Each question has a total allocation of 30 marks. These questions have at least one extended element with a minimum mark allocation of 10 marks.	Involves a decision making exercise which will take the form of a case study. The decision making exercise will have a total allocation of 50 marks. You will be presented with a variety of resources which you will be required to analyse and evaluate. You will be asked to adopt a specific role for answering part of the exercise. You may be asked to examine conflicting values that may be apparent in the case study. You must consider alternative choices and make and justify recommendations. This section contributes to synoptic assessment. This paper includes a detailed section titled Information for Candidates. Here you are given guidance on how long to spend on each section. You are strongly recommended to spend one hour answering Section A. When answering Section B, the Decision Making exercise, you are advised to spend at least 30 minutes reading the questions and selecting appropriate information before you start to write your answer.

Terminology

It is not the intention here to look at study skills in detail; there are many excellent books already on the market which will help you to develop good study skills. Neither will we look at the Decision Making Exercise; for that we would refer you to *Skills, Techniques and Decision Making* (Colourpoint, second edition, 2008) by Stephen Roulston and Mary Reid, which looks at the Decision Making exercise in detail.

Before you even begin thinking about examination technique there are two important points to remember. Firstly, you have a choice of questions on both assessment units at A2. You need to read carefully the **Instructions to Candidates** that are printed on the cover of the exam. The instructions will state how many questions you should answer and how they relate to the optional units you have studied. It is important that you take a few moments at the start of the exam to choose your questions carefully. Remember that the questions are structured and you should read all sub-sections of a question before you decide whether or not to answer it. The summary tables on pages 284 and 285 deal with the structure of the assessment units. You will find the specimen paper or past papers useful in providing a guide to the layout and structure of the examination paper. The specimen paper and past papers, where available, can be downloaded from www.ccea.org.uk/geography.

Secondly, you will be expected to know, understand and use appropriate geographical terminology. There is a clear link between marks awarded and the use of appropriate terminology – here's what the Chief Examiner has to say: *"Answers written in the correct terminology in good depth and detail will get high marks"*.

Hot Tip!
Use a copy of the current specification to identify key terms and concepts, then draw up your own glossary/ definition (you can download your own copy of the specification from www.ccea.org.uk/geography).

Checklist

Terms and concepts used on the Geography specimen exam papers for assessment unit A2 1 (Section A only)		
Epidemiological transition	Sustainable Development	Fertility
Local Agenda 21	Total fertility rate	Ethnicity
Ageing population	Ethnic Diversity	Economic migrants
Location Quotient	Out-migration	Multi-culturalism
In-migration	Ethnic conflict	Carbon footprint
Plural societies		

Terms and concepts used on the Geography specimen exam papers for assessment unit A2 2 (Section A only)		
Channelisation	Salinisation	Hard engineering
Oxisol	Soft engineering	Nutrient cycle
Depositional coastal landform	Tsunami	Erosional coastal landform
Plate boundary	Biomes	Environmental hazard
ITCZ		

Questions

Many students seem to think that when the moment comes to turn over the page and start the exam there's nothing more that can be done. Wrong! This is exactly when you need to have really sharp examination technique.

Let's start with the question – you need to have a clear understanding of what is required and what the scope of the question is. The best way to do that is to systematically deconstruct the question. Start by identifying the command word, for example, are you being asked to 'describe' or 'explain'? It is useful to circle, highlight or underline the command word and other key phrases.

Let's take an example.

With reference to case study material from **a MEDC and a LEDC**, **contrast** how knowledge, perception and stage of development have affected the **management of earthquake activity**. [15 marks]

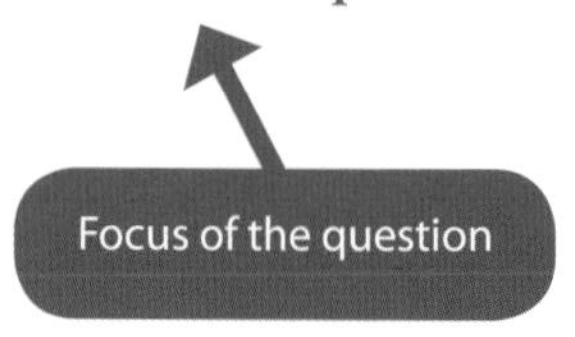

Source: Assessment Unit A2 2, Specimen Paper, Question 6 (c)

Plan of attack:

- Identify the command word: contrast. Make sure you understand what is meant by commonly used command words
- What is the subject or focus of the question, i.e. what are you being asked to describe? In this case the focus is the management of earthquake activity.
- The main focus or topic is often qualified, that is it is often narrowed down by specifying elements or aspects. In this case you are being asked to focus on how knowledge, perception and stage of development have affected the management of earthquake activity.
- The question often includes a spatial context. In this case it is with reference to case study material from a MEDC **and** a LEDC.
- The number of marks available, in this case [15 marks], will give you a guide to how much you need to write as your answer.

This may seem like it will take a long time. In reality, with practice, you will find that it takes only a few seconds and as the Chief Examiner says: "*The few seconds it takes to reflect on precisely what the question requires are worth spending*".

Hot Tip!

The question will never require you to simply 'write all you know about' a topic or a case study. Examination questions always require you to select from your knowledge.

In short – ***answer the question exactly as it appears on the paper!***

Commonly used command words in A2 Geography

Command Word	Meaning
Annotate	Add labels to summarise main features and/or processes as required.
Assess	This requires you to estimate the importance of something.
Compare	What are the main differences and similarities?
Contrast	What are the main differences?
Define	State the meaning of the term.
Describe	Give a detailed account; if a resource has been provided make sure you include details from the resource.
Discuss	In relation to a topic – this means both describe and explain. This command word may also be used in relation to a statement, in which case you should put forward arguments for and against (agree and disagree). A balanced answer is required.
Examine	A general instruction: both describe and explain.
Explain	Give reasons why.
Evaluate	This requires you to show the relative importance of something.
Identify	This means choose or select.
Justify	This requires you to present an argument.
Outline	This requires description and some interpretation but not in any detail.
State	Requires you to write a short answer presenting a fact or facts without further explanation.

Using resources provided with the exam paper

A feature of Section A of the CCEA A2 Geography examination papers is that you will be provided with resources for use with the questions. You should make full use of the material provided; it may contain enough information to provide a decent answer. You might be asked to:

- Extract information from a text source;
- Describe and/or explain trends on a graph;
- Describe and/or explain patterns on a map;
- Make use of photographs to identify processes or landforms.

However, before you turn to the resources make sure that you have read the question carefully as this will indicate what exactly it is that you need to focus on in the resources provided. Let's look at an example.

> Study **Resource 3B** (page 72 of the Resource Booklet) which is an account of the global issue of salinisation.
>
> (i) With the aid of **Resource 3B**, discuss the causes of salinisation. [5]
>
> (ii) With reference to your own regional case study material **and** Resource 3B, assess the impacts of salinisation on both the environment and people. [15]

Source: Assessment Unit A2 2, Specimen Paper, Question 3 (b)

Resource 3B
Global Salinisation

Is history repeating itself?

Historians now agree that the decline of several of the world's oldest civilisations was, at least in part, the result of salinisation of their irrigated farmland. Mineral salts occur naturally in the rain, rivers and groundwater as well as being bound up with soil particles. They include chlorides, sulphates and carbonates of sodium, calcium, magnesium and potassium. Even good-quality water has salt concentrations between 200-500 parts per million (ppm) and it is commonly used in irrigation of farmland. If a farmer applies 10,000 tonnes of irrigation water to a hectare of cropland annually then between two and five tonnes of salts will be added to the soil. Unless these are flushed out, enormous quantities can build up over the years.

Worldwide, one in five hectare of irrigated farmland suffers from build-up of salts in the soil. Soil salinisation costs the world's farmers an estimated £7 billion a year in reduced income, and the figure is growing. Spreading at a rate of up to two billion hectares a year, salinity is offsetting a significant proportion of the increased productivity achieved by expanding irrigation. Salt may well present as great a risk to modern society as it did to the ancients.

S Postal, 'Pillar of Sand: Can the Irrigation Miracle Last?' Worldwatch Institute, Worldwatch, www.worldwatch.org

Firstly, make sure that you read the question fully and carefully. In doing so you will be guided as to the focus you should take when studying the resource. This subsection of Q3 clearly focuses on *"the global issue of salinisation"*. Part (i) opens with the phrase *"with the aid of **Resource 3B**"*. It might seem obvious but it is essential that you make clear reference to Resource 3B in your answer. The focus of the question is the "*causes*" of salinisation so you can now read the resource highlighting or underlining any relevant reference to causes.

When using a map resource remember to quote place names and to use the main points of the compass – avoid descriptions such as *"in the bottom right hand corner ..."*.

If the resource is a graph then use the axes to quote figures to support your points as well as, if appropriate, to identify anomalies.

Text sources, such as that used in the example above, are frequently used at A2 Level; if you are describing issues from a text source it is a good idea to make use of carefully selected, short quotations.

Hot Tip!
Make full use of the resource materials provided otherwise you may lose marks.

Use of case study material

Throughout the CCEA A2 Level Geography you will be expected to draw on case studies to illustrate your answer. It is important that you use a case study at the correct scale (global, national, regional and small-scale). In some cases the case study must be drawn from a MEDC or a LEDC.

Such questions are usually marked using a levels mark scheme and you will need to provide specific place related information including facts, figures and dates as appropriate to ensure that you are awarded a Level 3 mark.

Let's look at an example.

> With reference to your case study material, explain how one national fertility policy attempted to achieve a balance between resources and population. [15]

Level 3 ([11]-[15])

Candidate provides a detailed and thorough explanation of how one national fertility policy has attempted to achieve a balance between resources and population. There is detailed and accurate case study material.

Level 2 ([6]-[10])

Candidate provides a general but accurate explanation of how one national fertility policy has attempted to achieve a balance between resources and population. The candidate draws on an appropriate case study but the depth and detail may be limited.

Level 1 ([1]-[5])

Candidate provides a limited answer which may focus on a description of a national fertility policy or explains the impacts of the policy rather than focusing on explaining how the policy attempted to achieve a balance between resources and population.

Source: Assessment Unit A2 1, Specimen Paper and Mark Scheme, Question 1 (c)

In order to be awarded a Level 3 mark for this question you will need to provide accurate facts and figures from your national fertility case study. It is important that the case study is at the correct scale – in this case a national scale case study is required. If you are in any doubt about your case study you should refer to your teacher or the specification for guidance.

Hot Tip!
Case studies have to be detailed, with facts and figures.

Synoptic assessment

In Section B of both A2 assessment units there is an element of synoptic assessment. Synoptic assessment requires you to draw on your understanding of the connections between different aspects of the subject represented in the specification. In short it assesses your ability to 'think as a geographer'.

Planning

You may think that planning your answer just takes up valuable time but the few minutes it takes to jot down a plan will be worthwhile and may result in your answer being awarded high marks. For both sections on A2 1 and for Section A on A2 2, there will be at least one extended element with a minimum mark allocation of 10 marks. Planning your answer will help you to:

- focus on the question exactly as it appears on the examination paper
- recall and select the material required; this will help you to avoid the tendency to write all you know about the topic
- ensure your case study (if applicable) is appropriate and includes detailed facts and figures
- give your answer a logical sequence

Getting help

There is no doubt that candidates do best when they know what to expect. In the first instance you should seek advice, help and guidance from your teacher. You may also find useful information within the Geography microsite on the CCEA website www.ccea.org.uk/geography where you will find:

- The current GCE geography specification
- Specimen papers and mark schemes
- GCE Geography Student Guide
- Chief Examiner's reports

Past papers and mark schemes will also be useful but they come with a warning – they were written for the previous specification and you need to use them carefully taking the time to check that the question relates to the current specification.

GLOSSARY

Human Geography

Age Specific Fertility Rate: the number of live births per thousand women within specific age bands per year. In some LEDCs women have children at an early age and this makes the **Age Specific Fertility Rate** a reliable indicator of the status of women in society.

Age Specific Mortality Rate: the average number of deaths per thousand of the population within specific age bands per year.

Annexation: taking political control of a neighbouring country.

Asylum seekers: people who have come to a new country without the required legal documentation to gain entry. They ask permission to remain on the basis that they will face torture or death if they return home.

Autonomy: a region is given some degree of political control while still remaining an integral part of the ruling country.

Barriers to migration: real and perceived obstacles that a potential migrant must overcome a number of before the move is made.

Brownfield sites: land, often in inner cities, that had been developed but is now derelict and ready for re-use.

Carbon Footprint: a sub set of the ecological footprint. It measures the total amount of carbon dioxide emissions that enters the atmosphere as a result of the electricity and fuel we use in everyday life as well as the amount of CO_2 emissions generated in making the products we buy.

Civil Disobedience: the active refusal to obey certain laws or commands of a government. It is a non-violent protest where the protesting group withdraws its participation in the working of the country.

Civil War: a situation where there are clearly identified armed forces within the country actively engaged in armed conflict with each other.

Colonisation: setting up settlements in a new colony, usually associated with the creation of empires.

Crude Birth Rate (CBR): measures the total number of live births per thousand of the population per year.

Crude Death Rate (CDR): measures the total number of deaths per thousand of the population per year.

Defensible Space: the territory that a resident will claim ownership of and take responsibility for, and which can be clearly demarcated by a physical boundary such as a wall, hedge or fence.

Deindustrialisation: large scale decline in industry usually affecting inner city industrial areas.

Demographic Transition Model: shows how the components of natural population change have operated through time.

Doubling Time: the number of years it will take a population to double if the current rates of natural increase are maintained.

Ecological Footprint: the total number of hectares (global hectares) required to provide an area with all of its needs, including farmland, fuel and water resources as well as the amount of land required to absorb its carbon dioxide and other waste.

Economic migrants: people who move to another country simply to obtain work and earn money.

Ethnic Group: a group of people with a long shared history and a distinct culture sharing some of the following characteristics: a common geographic origin or descent, a common language/literature, a common religion and being a minority within a larger community.

Ethnicity: the outward manifestation of belonging to an ethnic group.

Ethnic Cleansing: the whole scale violent removal of an ethnic group from an area.

Epidemiological Transition: shows how the causes of death change with time and levels of development.

General Fertility Rate: records the total number of live births per thousand women in the normal reproductive age groups (15–44 years) per year.

Illegal migrants: people who enter a country without the required legal documents, usually looking for work.

Infant Mortality Rate (IMR): the number of deaths per thousand children in the first year of life. This is a variation of the **Age Specific Mortality Rate** but only records the number of deaths of children who die within the first year of life. It excludes stillbirths. This is a useful indicator to use when comparing levels of development between countries.

Integrated Transport Network: coordinates several forms of public transport in the one location. This means that passengers on one form of transport can connect with another transport mode without changing location.

Life Expectancy: the number of years a person is expected to live assuming that the current mortality levels are maintained.

Local Agenda 21: sustainable development strategies formulated by local authorities following the Earth Summit in Rio 1992.

Maternal Mortality Rates (MMR): records the number of maternal deaths per hundred thousand live births.

Migration: the permanent change of place of residence of a person/persons for at least one year.

Migration Streams: groups of people moving from a common source region to a similar destination. Migration Streams can be either internal or international.

Multiculturalism: a political ideology/policy aimed at recognising, celebrating and maintaining the different cultural identities within society.

Natural Change: the percentage net gain or loss to a population each year based on the difference between the birth rate and the death rate. A natural increase occurs where the birth rate exceeds the death rate. A natural decrease occurs where the death rate is the greater figure.

Neighbourhood Unit: a subset of the wider community with some unifying characteristics.

Net Reproduction Rate: the average number of daughters born per woman. A NNR of 1 means that a population is replacing itself.

Primary factors: main characteristics used to identify ethnic groups including-race, nationality, language, religion and perceived ethnic identity.

Pluralism: a country or society with several ethnic groupings is referred to as a pluralist society.

Pull factors: the perceived attractions of the new destination.

Push factors: the negative aspects of the potential migrant's current place of residence.

Redevelopment: an entire area is demolished and redesigned, such as the old terraced houses in much of inner Belfast.

Refugees: defined by the United Nations as a group of people unable to live safely in their home country.

Regeneration: refers to the practice of upgrading the area, such as Titanic Quarter in Belfast.

Replacement Rate: the number of new births needed to maintain current numbers in a population assuming there is no migration. A Total Fertility Rate of 2.1 is the most commonly used figure.

Restoration: the original character of the building can not be altered but it may be restored to its original state.

Secondary factors: factors that may affect the expression of ethnicity, including social status, residential concentration, age, gender and caste.

Segregation: the physical separation of ethnic groups (when applied to ethnic diversity)

Sustainable Development: development 'that meets the needs of the present without compromising the ability of future generations to meet their needs' (Bruntland Report 1987).

Terrorism: armed conflict when the terrorist is a member of an illegal guerrilla organisation which operates within the community. Terrorism operates in pursuit of some ideological goal, such as a united Ireland for the IRA or a Tamil homeland for the Tamil Tigers in Sri Lanka.

Territorial division: the division or partition of a former country into two or more separate political entities, such as the division of Ireland into Northern Ireland and the Republic of Ireland.

Total Fertility Rate (TFR): records the average number of children a woman will have during her reproductive years, assuming she will live to the end of her reproductive life.

Traffic Cell: a self contained zone within a town with limited entry and exit points for all motor vehicles. Through traffic must use distributor roads that surround the cells.

Urban Conservation: protecting old buildings of historic or architectural value through one or a combination of the processes of restoration or regeneration.

Physical Geography

Afforestation: the planting of trees on land that is not currently forested.

Agroforestry: the use of land for a combination of agricultural and forestry.

Arch: a curved opening in a rock headland.

Aridisol: the zonal soil for tropical semi-arid and deserts regions.

Asthenosphere: the plastic layer of the upper mantle that lies below the solid lithosphere in which material flows, as convection currents, moving the plates above.

Autotrophs: self-feeding organisms such as plants.

Backwash: the return flow of a wave under gravity, after its breaks on the shore.

Bankfull: describes a river channel flowing at its maximum discharge.

Beach: an accumulation of loose material such as sand, shingle or pebbles, on a lake or sea shore.

Benioff Zone: a seismically active area below an ocean trench where subduction takes place.

Biomass: the total weight of living organisms in the area or ecosystem concerned. It is one of the three stores in the nutrient cycle model.

Biome: an ecosystem at a global scale, such as the tundra or mid-latitude grassland biomes.

Carnivores: meat eating organisms.

Channelisation: the process of artificially modifying the natural channel of a river by changing to shape, profile or course.

Cliff: a steep or perpendicular slope commonly associated with high energy coastlines.

Climate: the normal or average annual weather conditions for any given location.

Coast or **Coastline:** refers to the zone along a shore where the land meets the sea.

Conservation: is the act of protecting and maintaining an area or environment.

Constructive Waves: have a stronger swash than backwash and they often lead to the accumulation (aggradation) of sediment on the shore.

Continental Crust: the less dense rock material that forms the land masses carried by tectonic plates.

Continental Drift: a theory proposed by Alfred Wegener that the world's continents have changed their location over geological time. The theory is a forerunner of the modern concept of Plate Tectonics.

Continental Shelf: a gently sloping and shallow underwater plain that surrounds many continents.

Convection: the vertical movement of warm air.

Core: the central part of the Earth's structure. It consists of an inner solid core and a liquid outer core.

Collision Margin: a plate boundary where two continental plates meet forming fold mountains, such as the Himalayas formed by the collision of the Indo-Australian and the Eurasian plates.

Conservative Margin (Transform): a plate boundary where two plates move past each other without the creation of destruction of plate material, such as the San Andreas fault line in California.

Constructive Margin (Divergence): a plate boundary where two plates are forced apart by convection currents in the plastic upper mantle (asthenosphere). Magma rises at the margin to form new, normally ocean crust.

Convection Current: the exchange of energy in the form of heat by flows of liquid. In the mantle deep hot spots cause upward flows of magma towards the crust where they move the oceanic and continental plates of the lithosphere.

Crust: the outermost shell of the Earth's structure. It is composed of solid rocks and varies in thickness from thin ocean floor (average 7 km) to the continents (average 35 km).

Decomposers: organisms that breakdown waste or dead organic material into simpler compounds.

Destructive Margin (Convergence): a plate boundary where one of two plates moving towards each other is forced downwards, subducted, into the upper mantle and subsequently destroyed.

Destructive Waves: high energy features in which the backwash is stronger than the swash, causing sediment to be removed or combed down from the shore into deeper water.

Dilation Theory: the concept that under tectonic stress, rocks strain and open up microscopic cracks in their structure.

Diversion Channel: is an artificial course along which a river can be wholly or partly diverted during a flood episode.

Domestic: refers to use in the home. In the case of water this would include cleaning, washing, cooking and sanitation.

Dredging: is the process of removing material from the bed of a river, lake or sea. It is a common process used to increase the carrying capacity or discharge of rivers.

Dynamic Equilibrium: describes a situation where a balance is maintained despite continuous change. For example the removal of material from a beach by longshore drift is balanced by new material carried in from the erosion of nearby cliffs.

Ecology: the study of the inter-relationships between living organisms and their environment.

Ecotourism: tourism based on the natural attraction of an area and designed to safeguard the environment. It is a form of sustainable development.

Elastic Rebound: the return of rocks to near to their original position when they have been stressed, for example, by an earthquake.

Epicentre: the point on the Earth's surface directly above the origin or focus of an individual earthquake event in the crust.

Equator: is an imaginary line that marks a plane at right angles to the Earth's axis. It divides the globe into the northern and southern hemispheres and it is the base line for latitude (0°).

Erosion: is the wearing away and transport of the land surface by natural agents, including running water, wind, moving ice and wave action.

Estuary: this feature is the tidal mouth of a river where salt seawater and fresh river water meet.

Eustatic Change (Eustasy): the worldwide change in sea levels.

Fault: a line of weakness in rocks along which vertical or lateral dislocation of the rocks has occurred.

Fetch: the distance of open sea over which a wind can blow to create waves.

Flood Control: attempts to moderate the scale or frequency of flood episodes in rivers and river valleys.

Fluvial: means of or pertaining to rivers.

Focus: the point of origin of an earthquake event in the Earth's crust.

Fold and **Folding:** the bending of rocks caused by pressures from the Earth's crust.

Fold Mountains: a range of mountains resulting from tectonic forces crushing rocks upwards into folded forms, for example, the Alps of southern Europe.

Gabion: a device used to protect river banks or shorelines from erosion. They consist of pebbles or rocks contained in a wire cage.

Geographic Information Systems (GIS): digitally stored and assessable geographic data, commonly as layers of mapped information.

Ground Deformation: changes in the shape of the ground surface, for example, as a consequence of an earthquake.

Hadley Cell: this is the model for the atmosphere's circulation in low latitudes (between 35° north and south of the Equator.

Hard Engineering: is defined as the controlled disruption of natural processes by the use of artificial structures.

Herbivores: plant eating organisms.

Heterotrophs: organisms that depend on other organisms for their energy. They include herbivores, carnivores and omnivores.

Hot Spot: technically a sub-lithospheric thermal anomaly – a point deep in the earth's mantle where thermo-nuclear activity creates a hotter than average location. It is from these points that active plumes of magma (convection currents) rise to power the processes of plate tectonics.

Hydroelectric Power (HEP): electric power generated by falling water.

Indigenous: originating in or native to an area. The term is applied to plants, animals and people.

Interdependence: the concept that places are mutually linked to each other through complex physical and social links. It suggests that any change in one part of a system inevitably has consequences, positive or negative, for other parts of that system.

Interplanting: a system of farming where different crops are mixed in rows within one field or plot. This may include tree crops and annual plants.

Inter-Tropical Convergence Zone (ITCZ): this describes the area of the Earth's atmosphere where the north-east and south east trade winds converge and it marks an area of low pressure (Doldrums) near the Equator associated with convectional uplift and heavy rainfall. Its location follows the annual migration of the overhead sun.

Irrigation: is the artificial and deliberate addition of water to the land to improve soil conditions for plant growth.

Island Arc: a curved line of islands marked by volcanic activity associated with a destructive margin between two oceanic plates.

Isostatic Change: the alteration of the relationship between land and sea levels. For example, the gradual rise of land following an Ice Age.

Land Zoning: when planning designates how areas may be used. Examples include zoning to prevent building in an earthquake prone area or allocating an area of floodplain to be available to store water during a flood episode.

Laterite: a layer of hardened sub-soil composed of iron and aluminium oxides found under certain conditions under tropical forests. It causes drainage problems and may limit the agricultural use of the soil.

Levée: a raised bank on a river, while these can be natural features they can be reinforced or raised higher as a flood control measure.

Liquefaction: is the process by which loose and/or wet sediments lose their cohesion and strength when subjected to intense shaking, such as occurs in earthquakes.

Lithosphere: the solid outer layer of rocks of the Earth's structure. It includes the crust and the solid upper mantle which rests on the plastic material of the astehenosphere.

Litter: the layer of organic material that gathers on the soil surface. It includes both waste products and dead plant and animal material. It is one of the three stores in the nutrient cycle model.

Long Shore Drift (LSD): the process whereby waves approaching the coast at an angle move sediment laterally in a zig-zag motion.

Magnetic stripping: the pattern of normal and reversed polarity magnetism recorded by rocks across the mid-ocean ridges of constructive plate margins.

Mantle: the bulk of the earth's mass is formed by this layer, or sphere that surrounds the core and lies beneath the crust.

Mid-Ocean Ridge: a series of narrow, parallel ridges that mark the creation zone of new oceanic plates along a constructive plate margin. They often contain a deep central rift valley. For example the Mid-atlantic ridge runs at the centre of the ocean only rarely seen above sea-level in places like Iceland.

Modified Mercalli Scale: an earthquake intensity scale based on earthquakes' effects on buildings and structures. It has now largely been replaced by the Richter scale.

Mohorovičić discontinuity (Moho): the line of change in the transfer speed of earthquake waves that marks the lower boundary of the crust where it meets the mantle.

Municipal: of or pertaining to local authorities, especially in a town or city. An example would be municipal water use for public facilities such as schools, hospitals and leisure centres.

Non-Government Organisation (NGO): a voluntary body often with international membership. The term often refers to charities, especially in development issues.

Nutrients: chemical 'foods' for plants.

Oceanic crust: the thinner but more dense plate material that forms the seafloor.

Ocean trench: a narrow but very deep section of the ocean floor, marking the point of subduction of one oceanic plate at a destructive plate margin.

Omnivores: organisms whose normal diet consists of both plant and animal material.

Orogeny: a period of geological history marked by the formation of folded mountains. For example, the current period is termed the Alpine orogeny and it is associated with the present formation of mountain ranges, including the Andes, Rockies, Atlas and Himalayas.

Oxisol: the term for the zonal soil found under tropical forests.

Respiration: technically this means the taking in, use and release of any gas material by an organism. In ecosystems it refers to the loss of energy by organisms due to any and all of their life processes.

Pancaking: a process in which parts of tall buildings collapse on top of themselves as a result of earthquake events.

Palaemagnetism: the fossilized record of past magnetic patterns 'captured' as molten volcanic rocks harden and form, for example, along ocean ridges.

Parent material: the underlying geology beneath a soil from which much of its inorganic material may be derived by weathering proceses.

Plate: a section of rigid rock that forms part of the Earth's crust.

Plate tectonics: a theory that suggests that the Earth's crust is composed of irregularly shaped sections or plates, some of which carry continents, while others form the ocean floor. These plates are moved slowly by convection currents in the asthenosphere.

Precursor: an event or pattern of change that comes before an active earthquake episode.

Primary Productivity Index: this is a measure of the rate at which an area of vegetation produces new plant material. It can be measured in tonnes/hectare/year or kg/m^2/year.

Productivity (Gross and Net): is the growth rate of new plant material in a given area over time. While gross productivity is the total rate, the net rate allows for the energy used by plants during their life processes.

Realignment: changing the course of a river channel, often to make it straighter by removing meanders.

Resectioning: changing the cross-section of a river channel to enlarge it and/or to make a more efficient shape.

Revetments: a coastal defence strategy composed of concrete walls, sheet piling, rip-rap or gabions.

Richter Scale: a scale measuring earthquake magnitude. It is based on the impact on a standard seismograph 100 km from the epicentre of the quake. It is an open-ended scale with a magnitude 9 event the highest yet recorded (the Boxing Day 2004 Indian Ocean submarine earthquake).

Riffles and **Pools:** the sequence of shallows and deep sections found along a river channel and associated with the formation of meanders.

River (Drainage) Basin: all the land area drained by a river and its tributaries.

River Navigation: the use of the river for the transport of people and goods.

River Restoration: the process of returning a river that has undergone engineering to a more natural form.

River Training: attempts to modify the shape of a river channel and its flow characteristics.

Savanna: the term used to describe the tropical grassland ecosystem of Africa. It is often used as a synonym for tropical grasslands.

Sea-floor Spreading: the process by which new lithospheric plate material is formed at mid-ocean ridges.

Seamount: an isolated topographic feature rising from the sea floor, usually a submarine volcano.

Seismic: related to or characteristic of movement within the Earth.

Seismic Gap Theory: the concept that active seismic regions, that have had a long period without activity, are increasingly likely to be the location of a future earthquake event.

Selva: the South American term for tropical rainforest. It refers to the dry land forests as opposed to the flooded varzea forests found near rivers that are regularly inundated.

Shifting Cultivation ('slash and burn'): this is the traditional form of agriculture in the tropical forests across the world. It consists of the clearance and short-term use of small plots of forest for crop production followed by an extended period of abandonment for soil fertility regeneration.

Shore: technically the land between the low water mark and the point where storm waves can reach – the area where the land reaches the sea.

Sial: the term to describe the less dense granitic that form the bulk of the continents. They are dominated by the elements silica and aluminium.

Silviculture: the cultivation of trees, both forests grown for timber products, and groves and orchards for plant products, such as fruit, nuts and seeds.

Sima: the term to describe the more dense basaltic that form the ocean floors. They are dominated by the elements silica and magnesium.

Soft Engineering: the use of ecological practices to reduce erosion and stabilise shorelines and river edges, while enhancing local habitats.

Soil Profile: a vertical section of a soil from the surface to the parent material, showing the pattern of horizons and characteristics.

Spillway: an overflow channel for water, often from a reservoir.

Stacks and **Stumps Stacks:** isolated masses of rock near coastal cliffs, usually the remnant of a former arch. Stumps are worn stacks that may be covered at high tide.

Storm Surge: an unusual rise in sea level above normal, caused by low pressure conditions in the atmosphere.

Stratum Specificity: in tropical forests the layered structure of the vegetation is matched by an assemblage of animal species that are associated with each layer.

Sub-aerial Processes: weathering and erosion processes caused by the atmosphere.

Subduction: the process by which plate material, generally oceanic, is forced down into the mantle and gradually destroyed by melting in a deep sea trench at a destructive plate margin.

Sustainability: the degree to which the use of a resource or resources impacts on its long-term use or availability.

Swash: the run of water onto a shore after a wave breaks.

Terre Firme: refers to the dry land forests in the Amazon Basin as opposed to the flooded varzea forests found near rivers that are regularly inundated.

Tide: the regular rise and fall of sea level resulting from the gravitational influence of the moon and sun.

Trade Winds: the constant winds found around the equatorial region. They form the surface element of the Hadley Cell and their name reflects their importance in the era of sailing ships.

Transverse Fault: a line of weakness in rocks where the two sides slide past each other, in different directions or at different rates. These are very common along constructive plate margins on the ocean floor.

Trophic: a term used in ecosystems to describe the transfer of energy between organism through feeding.

Tropics: the lines at 23½°N (Tropic of Cancer) and 23½°S (Tropic of Capricorn) of the equator that mark the latitude to which the overhead summer moves by mid-summer.

Tropical: strictly refers to the area between the tropics but more commonly to the whole region between 30°N and 30°S of the Equator.

Tropical Desert: an arid biome associated with the high pressure zone around 30°N and 30°S of the Equator.

Tropical Grassland: a biome associated with the wet and dry tropics between the equatorial forests and the tropical deserts.

Tropical Forest (TRF): a biome associated with the continuously hot and wet climate of the equatorial region of low pressure.

Tropopause: the line marking the upper boundary of the lowest layer of the atmosphere. It lies around 6 km above the surface at the poles to a maximum of around 16 km at the equator.

Troposphere: the lowest layer of the atmosphere in which most weather conditions are confined.

Tsunami: the Japanese term for a large sea wave created by earthquake or volcanic activity on the sea bed.

Varzeas: tropical forest areas in the Amazon Basin that are subject to regular river floods. These tend to have more fertile soils than the rest of the basin.

Wave: the transfer of energy by moving water in the ocean generated by winds.

Wave-cut platform (bench): a gently sloping erosion surface extending seaward from the base of coastal cliffs.

Wing Dykes (River groynes): walls or barriers built part-way across river channels from one bank. They are designed to either: (a) create a deeper river channel for navigation; or (b) encourage erosion of opposing banks to establish new meanders in river restoration schemes.